IMPROVING MATHEMATICS PROGRAMS

IMPROVING MATHEMATICS PROGRAMS:

TRENDS AND ISSUES IN THE ELEMENTARY SCHOOL

Edited by M. VERE DEVAULT
The University of Texas

CHARLES E. MERRILL BOOKS, INC., COLUMBUS, OHIO

Library of Congress Catalog Card Number: 61-10796

Printed in the United States of America

To Barbara

PREFACE

Improving Mathematics Programs provides a basic collection of readings related to the improvement of elementary school mathematics education. Such a collection is timely because of the substantial number of experimental and demonstration programs under way in our schools. If these programs survive, they will do so because classroom teachers and instructional leaders understand the research, theory, and practice which give direction to mathematics curriculum planning.

Four groups will find *Improving Mathematics Programs* useful in the study of trends represented by these new programs. First, the book will be valuable for individual or group study by in-service teachers. Second, the book has been planned specifically for use in graduate courses in the teaching of elementary school mathematics. It has not been designed as a methods text, but will serve effectively as a supplement to such a text in undergraduate courses. Third, many graduate students will find the readings and comprehensive bibliographies of value as they pursue advanced work in elementary school curriculum problems. Finally, the lay person interested in understanding current problems in the development of effective mathematics programs will find the text helpful.

The task of preparing such a volume required a considerable expenditure of time and effort on the part of many people. Several educational leaders were contacted to assist the editor in the identification of the major issues in the teaching of elementary school mathematics. These persons assisted in the identification of issues to be finally included in the text; they made suggestions as to persons who could be contacted to serve as editors of individual chapters; and they identified problems related to each of the issues under consideration. The selection of readings to be included in specific chapters was done by chapter editors. Because of the great amount of material available, the number of original items suggested for inclusion was great enough to fill two or three volumes. One of the tasks of the editor was that of making suggestions relative to the reorganization of many of the chapters so that materials would meet space limitations and would provide continuity of readings throughout the text.

Chapter editors have approached the task of selecting appropriate readings in a variety of ways. Some have chosen only a few complete reports; others have collected smaller portions of many articles or chapters. Some editors have presented their materials in a chronological order so that the reader might understand better the changing nature of the problem presented. This is particularly apparent in the chapter on content. Some editors have organized the material in two or more sections to show particular points of view. Still others, as in the case of the chapter on textbook use, have presented a large portion of the total amount of material available on the subject. Each chapter has been organized along those lines to which the material of the given chapter most readily lends itself. A comprehensive view of the trends and issues which face those who plan effective mathematics programs for today's schools results from the combined efforts of these editors.

In addition to the authors and publishers who have granted permission for the use of their materials, grateful appreciation is due several people. To Kenneth E. Brown, William T. Guy, Lowry W. Harding, Phillip Peak, Esther Swenson, and Ralph Ward appreciation is expressed for help during the early stages in the selection of issues to be included as chapters in this text. Appreciation is also expressed to all chapter editors for their co-operation in the development of their respective chapters. Deletions, revisions, and substitutions were frequently suggested to maintain consistency and continuity throughout. The co-operative manner in which each person responded to these changes with suggestions and ideas of his own made the task of editing this volume a pleasurable educational experience. Finally, appreciation is due Harriet McMeans and Nell Mays for assistance in the preparation of the manuscript and with the correspondence involved in obtaining permissions to reprint from authors and publishers.

M. VERE DeVAULT

CONTENTS

ix

Contents

Contents xxi

I OBJECTIVES OF ELEMENTARY SCHOOL MATHEMATICS

M. Vere DeVault, Claude C. Boyd, The University of Texas

INTRODUCTION

BIBLIOGRAPHY

INTRODUCTION

Recent technological and cultural developments have forced a re-examination of the objectives of our educational institutions from the primary grades through graduate schools. This re-examination is not new to the American educational scene. Since the beginning of the experiment with the great American dream of universal public education, there has been much debate relative to the function of the school in our society. The first schools in this country were established for the purpose of teaching children to read so that they might know the scriptures. Later, the common school, organized on the principle of separation of church and state, took its objectives from the society of which it was a part.

Historically, a number of issues relative to objectives of the arithmetic program have been debated. Arithmetic was first introduced as a part of the curriculum in the schools of this country because of its usefulness in business. During much of the nineteenth century, arithmetic was accepted by many thoughtful persons because of the contribution it made to the

1

development of mental powers. Early in the present century objectives were determined largely by studies which reported the uses made of arithmetic by businessmen and adults. This was followed by the child-centered movement which looked to the interests of children in determining the objectives of the arithmetic curriculum. More recently, the effective mathematics curriculum has been viewed as a program with a two-fold objective: a mathematical phase and a social phase.

Since World War II more emphasis has been given to the purely mathematical objective. Arithmetic is seen as a part of mathematics. In co-operation with educators in colleges, universities, and public schools, many mathematicians have turned their interest and attention to public school mathematics programs. Through such co-operative action, efforts are being made in the re-examination of objectives, content, and methods of teaching mathematics in the public schools. The National Council of Teachers of Mathematics, the School Mathematics Study Group, and the University of Illinois Committee on School Mathematics have made substantial contributions to the re-examination of the secondary school mathematics program. Under the auspices of these organizations some beginnings in the re-examination of the elementary school mathematics program are under way.

More has been written about what to teach and how to teach in the elementary school than has been written about the problem of identifying objectives toward which the efforts of teachers and students should be directed. Apparently, objectives of instruction in mathematics either have been taken for granted or have been thought to be adequately presented in the brief mention they have been given. Have we been satisfied to express mathematical objectives largely in terms of content?

The student may well consider the following questions as he reads this opening chapter: What is the role of mathematics in the liberal education of the student? To what extent should utility be the function of the American public school? What objectives are of primary importance? Do we have the same objectives for all pupils?

AIMS AND PURPOSES OF ARITHMETIC

Guy M. Wilson

Purposeful teaching is directed by clearly perceived aims. Without the guidance of aims, teaching is apt to be routine and formal; frequently such teaching means that time is practically wasted; often it leads to results that are definitely detrimental, for example, confusion and unfavorable attitudes.

Many statements of the aim of the subject are too greatly extended; too much is claimed. If all possible values are claimed for a subject, the teacher is left without guidance that is definite enough to be of value. On the other hand, a discriminating and critical view of aims in a subject aids immediately in (1) choosing the right subject matter, (2) selecting right teaching methods, and (3) deciding on right conditions for effective teaching. Usually there are a few dominating aims or objectives in a subject, and clear perception of these aims will help most in placing the work of the subject on a functional basis.

Is There Any One Major Aim in Arithmetic?

There is no doubt that, historically, arithmetic was introduced into the schools of America because of its practical value as a tool in business. One of the first records of the teaching of arithmetic in the schools is that of the New Amsterdam Colony.[1] The Dutch West India Company, as the controlling factor in the New Amsterdam Colony, wanted men trained in figuring to act as "keepers and assistants." Schools for the teaching of arithmetic were accordingly organized.

However, arithmetic came into the schools of America very slowly. It was half a century after the establishment of the Massachusetts Bay Colony before arithmetic was admitted into the schools of Boston.[2] There

[From *Teaching the New Arithmetic* (New York: McGraw-Hill Book Co., Inc., 1951), pp. 8-13. Reprinted by permission of the author and the McGraw-Hill Book Co., Inc.]

---

[1] W. H. Kilpatrick, "The Dutch Schools of New Netherlands and Colonial New York," *U.S. Bureau of Education, Bulletin* 12, 1912.

[2] F. A. Fitzpatrick, "The Development of the Course of Study in American Schools," *Educational Review*, XLIX (January, 1915), 1-19. In 1682, two schools were set up in Boston, "to teach writing and ciphering."

it was accepted as a subject against the protests of the teachers; its general introduction into the schools was delayed another half century. It was not until fairly well along in the last century that a knowledge of arithmetic was required even for entrance to Harvard, Yale, or Princeton.[3] The explanation is that in those early days the schools were centered upon teaching reading in order that the Bible and hymns might be read and in teaching Latin in order that the one great requirement for college entrance might be met.

It was inevitable, however, that a subject so valuable as arithmetic should sooner or later make for itself a place of major importance in our schools, particularly in a country where every man was more or less his own business manager and where business on some scale was the concern of everyone. Gradually, therefore, we have arithmetic being introduced into the schools on the basis of its "practical values in business."

However, when once accepted as a school subject, arithmetic ran the usual course of all school subjects. In the first place, it was in the hands of teachers who knew very little about business. In the second place, content began to be supplied by academic-minded people, such as college professors and schoolmasters; they wrote the texts. In the third place, it may be noted that arithmetic had a very ancient history independent of business usage. That is to say, among the cultured non-business classes of the Greeks, arithmetic was recognized as "the science of number," and this was quite separate and apart from the practical arithmetic used in commerce. Commerce, for the most part, was engaged in only by slaves or by merchants who were not accepted as equal to the cultured, leisure classes of Athens. Since class distinctions continued to be emphasized down through the ages, it is but natural that this science of number should have survived among the intellectual groups. During the Middle Ages,[4] it was the monks in the monasteries who kept alive and further developed this science of number; it gave them something to do on long winter evenings; they cultivated the puzzle-type of problem, magic squares, manipulation for its own sake.

In view of the above history, it is an easy matter to understand how arithmetic, although introduced into the schools because of its practical values, became gradually changed by teachers, by textbook writers, and by the general fact of having a venerable background based upon considerations other than the practical.

_____

[3] Elmer E. Brown, *The Making of Our Middle Schools* (New York: Longmans, Green & Co., Inc., 1902), pp. 128-29.

[4] Paul Monroe, Lecture notes at Teachers College, Columbia University, New York, 1911.

It is undoubtedly true, although direct evidence is not at hand, that the discussion of aims in other subjects, particularly the subject of Latin, carried over and influenced the consideration of aims in arithmetic. In general, all subjects when first introduced into the schools are useful, or at least are looked upon as serving a useful purpose. Latin in Sturm's School,[5] in 1537, was the chief subject, and the most useful considering the purpose of the school. The few bright boys in the school were all planning to enter universities where the lectures and class discussions were in Latin and where most of the books in the library were in Latin.

But three hundred years later, the classical languages were still the core of the secondary-school curriculum, although the picture had greatly changed in many of its essential features. In the first place, literature in the vernacular had developed in all modern nations, and lectures in the universities with few exceptions were no longer delivered in Latin. In the second place, the enrollment in secondary schools had greatly increased. It included girls as well as boys; it included many boys who did not expect to go to college. In the third place, mathematics and science, as well as national literatures, had developed.

Yet, notwithstanding these and other significant changes, the defense of Latin became more radical and more vocal. In England, Spencer and Huxley were roundly scored as "uncultured Philistines" for their attempts to find a place for mathematics, science, and health in the schools. In America, Horace Mann was equally beset by the defenders of the classical culture.

The story of Latin, at first useful and later merely formal and relatively useless, is, in large measure, the story of every subject in the schools, because, even if conditions have not changed outside in society, the subject in the schools will have changed, owing to the forces noted in the preceding paragraphs.

The attempts to justify arithmetic in the schools on bases other than that of usefulness in the practical affairs of life are developed more fully in other sections; but it may be said here that, in general, they run the usual course. Educators, finding themselves interested in the development of the subject and lacking the practical business basis for its proper development, take the easy way out. That is, they cease to worry about the practical and justify themselves on the basis of mental discipline. In time, however, mental discipline became discredited as an argument. Under these circumstances, the argument is shifted slightly, although remaining essentially the same. For disciplinary values are substituted transfer values,

---

[5] Paul Monroe, *Text-book in the History of Education* (New York: The Macmillan Company, 1915), pp. 391-92.

cultural values, preparatory values, conventional values, sentimental values, social values, or other general "arguments."

It is interesting to note that in the history of arithmetic in this country such extra values came to dominate practically all the thinking, with the result that arithmetic was greatly extended until all its possibilities from the standpoint of the science of number were developed in textbooks and became part of the drill program of the schools. Procedures other than drill were not thought of in connection with arithmetic until recently.

Naturally, there were protests by forward-looking men.[6] Thoughtful teachers naturally saw that legitimate aims were being exceeded. Pupils of course were discouraged and defeated. Yet protests and criticisms were met by increased insistence that arithmetic was the great mind developer of the schools. The argument was extended to the high school. Mathematics develops the mind, it develops powers, it broadens the mind, it makes one an accurate thinker; in fact, all possible claims were made for arithmetic and mathematics exactly as similar claims had been made a century earlier to keep Latin in the schools after it had ceased to serve practical usefulness.[7]

It was in 1911 [8] that a slightly different attack was made on how to determine what is really useful in arithmetic. Businessmen were asked to indicate the topics usually taught in arithmetic for which they had no use.[9] Later this same type of study was extended the country over. It was a beginning toward more specific thinking in terms of actual usage.

In 1919 there began to appear a series of studies based directly upon the figuring done by adults.[10] These studies revealed such a simple story of actual usage that they naturally led to vehement protests on the part of those who had been justifying arithmetic and mathematics in the

---

[6] Such, for example, as Frank M. McMurray, "Desirable Omissions from the Course of Study," *Annual Report of the National Educational Association*, 1904, p. 194.

[7] J. W. A. Young (chairman), *et al.*, *National Committee's Report on the Reorganization of Mathematics in Secondary Education*. Aims, 1923, Chapter 11.

[8] Guy M. Wilson, and co-operating teachers. *Course of Study in Elementary Mathematics*, Questionnaire to Businessmen, Connersville, Ind., 1911; republished by Warwick and York, Baltimore, 1922, p. 9.

[9] The statement of the purpose of arithmetic in the Connersville *Course of Study in Elementary Mathematics* has been widely quoted. That statement was as follows:

"*Purpose:*—While not denying the cultural and disciplinary value of arithmetic (in common with any subject systematically studied), this course of study is dominated by the idea that the chief purpose of arithmetic in the course of study is its utility in the common affairs of life. We learn the multiplication table not primarily to sharpen the wits or comprehend a beautiful system, but in order to figure our salaries, our taxes, or the interest on a note."

[10] By Wilson, Wise, Woody, Charters, Thorndike, Schorling, Bobbitt, and others. For summaries of these various studies, see Guy M. Wilson, *What Arithmetic Shall We Teach?* (Boston: Houghton Mifflin Company, 1926).

schools on the basis of mental discipline or similar bases. That group, being the older and better organized group, seized the advantages of national publication,[11] thus prolonging, at least for a time,[12] the influence of those who would retain many useless topics, on a drill basis, in the program of arithmetic in the schools.

This discussion of aims in arithmetic has attempted to set forth briefly, in an impartial manner, the story of the various aims that have been urged in justification of arithmetic in the schools. The present tendency is strongly toward the restoration of the original purpose, i.e., the organization of arithmetic around its use as a simple tool in business. If this aim is finally established as the one dominant and justifiable aim, it will mean that we shall need not only to study arithmetic as drill, but *also to become acquainted with business.* It is the connection with business that gives arithmetic its real significance. Business units should precede, accompany, and follow the development and mastery of useful drill. These simple business units, developed as functional problem units and closely connected with the pupil's experience and his community, will replace the present useless, isolated written problem as it appears in textbooks.

Limiting grade work in arithmetic to the mastery of the socially useful not only will remove a great burden from the backs of children but will contribute to better teaching and a better mental-hygiene program in the schoolroom. Thus other values of good teaching, such as favorable attitudes toward learning, more fundamental thinking, and a more integrated and purposeful personality, will be served.

It should be noted, in fairness to the total picture on aims in arithmetic at the present time, that there are many good thinkers of today who would limit arithmetic as taught to children to the needs of children [13] and who urge that the needs of adults are too far removed from childhood. Much favorable reference will be made to these writers throughout the pages of the present volume, because the present authors are much more nearly in accord with the child-usage viewpoint than with the viewpoint of those who would urge abstruse mathematics as mental discipline.

The viewpoint of the authors, if set forth more fully, would involve the following:

1. The basic and dominating aim of arithmetic in the schools is to equip the child with the useful skills for business.[14] Business calls for

---

[11] *Twenty-ninth Yearbook of the National Society for the Study of Education,* 1930.

[12] See *Educational Method,* January, 1937. Throughout this number, progressive viewpoints in arithmetic are developed.

[13] Henry Harap, and Charlotte E. Mapes, "The Learning of Fundamentals in an Activity Program," *The Elementary School Journal,* XXXIV (March, 1934), 515-25.

[14] Josephine L. Driscoll, "The Purpose of Arithmetic," *Educational Method,* XVI (January, 1937), 208-10.

decisions in terms of money. It calls for estimating and comparisons. Figuring, much of it simple but some very complicated, is the regular accompaniment of business; arithmetic is "the tool of business." Yet 90 per cent of adult figuring is covered by the four fundamental processes: addition, subtraction, multiplication, and division. Simple fractions and reading of decimals, if added to the four fundamental processes, will raise the percentage to over 95. Mastery of these essentials becomes the drill load in arithmetic for the grades. Beyond that, the work is functional problem work or appreciation units, adjusted to child interests.

2. In any case, the start on any work and its further progress can by good teachers be made to rest on child interests. Thus, there are always understanding and motivation in terms of childhood. The start is on the child level; the work is carried forward on the child level; common adult usage comes in to set the limits on drill-mastery requirements. The number needs of adults in the more common affairs of life do not go so far beyond child needs as to prevent cordial co-operation between progressives and ultraprogressives.

In practice, children can be easily motivated to go into arithmetic the necessary distance to cover common adult usage, for in the average American home the problems of the home and the father's business are discussed enough so that children early acquire an interest in adult problems.

3. There will remain many optional recreational or free-activity opportunities beyond the mastery of the useful. These are always encouraged in any subject by inspiring teachers. But they are not in the nature of fundamentals for tool mastery.

Many readers may be disappointed that the authors have not claimed more for arithmetic, that they are satisfied to accomplish the three simple aims noted above. However, it should be observed that these three aims are very significant for arithmetic and that they *all relate to arithmetic,* not to life in general. As noted above, it is common for authors writing on their favorite subjects to claim all possible values. But it is obviously impossible for all subjects to contain all values, so there must be much of error in such claims. The authors believe that we are more likely to accomplish correct aims in a subject if our aims are set up with discretion and with an eye to distinctive and characteristic aims. There is no advantage in claiming the whole world for a subject. It leaves us just where we started. The discriminating view points to definite programs of work. Good teachers may be expected to accomplish right general aims in all subjects, through good teaching. Curiously enough, right general aims are best realized through the accomplishment of specific subject aims.

THE SOCIAL CONTRIBUTIONS OF ARITHMETIC

Leo J. Brueckner

In the modern arithmetic program two major objectives are recognized: (1) the development of the ability of the learner to perform the various number operations intelligently and skillfully, and (2) the development of the ability of the learner to apply quantitative procedures effectively in the social situations encountered in life outside the school.

The first of these objectives relates to what is commonly referred to as the *mathematical* phase of arithmetic, the second to the *social* phase of arithmetic. In any well-organized instructional program both phases should be dealt with in a balanced, well-integrated way so that neither phase is neglected or over-emphasized. It is an unfortunate fact that in the past so much stress has been placed on repetitive drill to assure skill in computation that the social phase of arithmetic has often been almost overlooked. An analysis of the contents of recent courses of study shows that in many schools this condition is being corrected.

In dealing with the mathematical phase of arithmetic the teacher stresses such points as the meaning and structure of our number system, the meaning of the various number operations and their skillful manipulation, the perception of relations between quantitative ideas, and the ability to arrange numerical data systematically and to interpret information presented in graphic or tabular form. However, these abilities cannot be effectively developed in isolation or apart from the social situations in which they normally function.

The social phase of arithmetic deals with such items as the use of instruments of precision, the importance and the significance of social institutions such as money, insurance, and standard time, the kinds and sources of information essential for intelligent buying and selling, that is, consumer education, the quantitative vocabulary involved in business practices and social relations, and methods of securing reliable information needed to deal with emerging personal and community problems.

[From "The Social Contributions of Arithmetic," *The National Elementary Principal*, XXX, pp. 7-10. Reprinted by the permission of the author and *The National Elementary Principal*.]

A TEACHER'S VIEW OF MATHEMATICS

Bruce E. Meserve

What are we trying to do when we teach arithmetic in the primary grades? Simply condition a few unthinking responses as Pavlov did for his dog? I assume that most of you have read of Pavlov's work in regularly serving food to his dog immediately after ringing a bell, until the dog's salivary glands were stimulated simply by the ringing of the bell even though no food was brought in. Are we looking for such automatic responses in arithmetic? Although there are times when a few automatic responses would be welcome, I do not think that such are our goal. Our use of numerous pictures in which groups of girls are compared with groups of doll carriages, groups of children with groups of chairs at a table, and so forth, are intended to develop the child's recognition of a common number property of sets which can be matched in a one-to-one manner—students with chairs, husbands with wives, automobiles on a highway with drivers, and so forth. First a child recognizes when one set is the same, more, or less than another. Later he abstracts a number property of a set of elements and identifies this property by a word or symbol as in the case of five fingers on his right hand or 75 people in a room.

Children start their number concepts by abstracting properties of sets of objects. We must stimulate them to continue thinking of mathematics as a study of properties abstracted from the world in which we live. Mathematics as a mass of memorized facts is deadly; mathematics as a study of systems of symbols capable of representing important properties of the physical universe can be a vibrant and living subject.

Many elementary school teachers do an excellent job of emphasizing the ways in which positive integers and arithmetic operations represent physical situations. In secondary school we tend to cut away this dependence upon sets of physical objects and leave things suspended in mid air. Unfortunately many students feel very soon that they are simply drifting in a dense cloud with no sense of up or down and no particular goals in sight except to get out of this mess. When an infant's umbilical cord is cut, other sources of nourishment must be found. When we cut

[From "A Teacher's View of Mathematics," *School Science and Mathematics*, LVI (December, 1956), pp. 716-18. Reprinted by permission of the author and *School Science and Mathematics*.]

away the pupil's reliance upon manipulations of sets of objects, we must produce other foundations for his work. These new foundations are composed of definitions and assumptions (postulates) based upon the arithmetic experiences in elementary school. We are taking another step in our abstraction of number properties. We are developing systems of number symbols and procedures for combining number symbols. The development and use of such systems is one of the major aims of mathematics. Consider as examples of such systems:

the set of positive integers
the set of positive rational numbers
the set of all rational numbers (positive, negative, and zero)
the set of real numbers
the set of complex numbers
the algebra of real variables and numbers
the geometry of points and lines on a plane
the geometry of points, lines and planes in space

Each of these sets of elements and the operations with them have many very practical interpretations in our physical universe. There are also other mathematical systems including some that are so abstract that no applications for them have been found to date.

Mathematical systems are obtained by abstracting properties of sets of elements, by extending and generalizing other systems as in the gradual expansion of the student's concept of number from positive integers to positive rational numbers, to rational numbers (positive, negative, and zero) to real numbers, and, near the end of his high school career, to complex numbers. These systems are abstract systems because of their removal from a strict dependence upon sets of objects and yet it is only in this way that they gain their usefulness. It is bad enough to have different types of units for measures of distances, areas, volumes, angles, weights, time, and so forth. Thank goodness we can use the same arithmetic in each of these cases. Our arithmetic is useful because of the many interpretations and representations that may be used.

Not long ago I visualized our task as teachers of mathematics to be the development of mathematical systems that may be used to represent the various quantitative aspects of our physical universe. I still think that such a goal is a very noble one and a useful guide in seeing beyond a dismal day drilling on fractions to a reasonable understanding of "What is the use of it all?" Fractions represent rational numbers. Rational numbers and operations upon rational numbers may be interpreted in a very wide variety of ways including the basic problems of sharing equally at the primary grade level, the measurements for recipes and also for druggists, prescriptions, and simple ratios. These and many other interpretations can only be understood by understanding fractions. The same understanding is a part of the training of the pilot of a jet airplane and the engineers who design the plane. The range of applications of many topics of secondary school mathematics is unbounded. As teachers of mathematics we need to look up from our preoccupation with details to glimpse the immensity and the brilliance of the superstructure which rests upon our work, and to find in this superstructure the courage and the inspiration for renewing the vigor of our attack upon our daily problems.

This requires us to develop a perspective for appraising the significance of various aspects of our work. We need to see how the future of mathematics and the future of our pupils in this scientific world depends upon the concepts that we are teaching. We need to see how nearly all mathematical concepts arise as abstractions, generalizations, and applications of arithmetic concepts similar to those underlying our work. We need to seek points of view which will help our better students develop creative methods of thinking in mathematics.

Certainly these goals would keep any of us from becoming complacent and yet another aspect of mathematics is needed to complete the picture. Mathematics is changing. During the life-time of the youngest person here there has been more new mathematics than in all previous recorded history. Modern mathematics is now concerned with all patterns of action, all regularities, all patterns making predictions possible. Some of the predictions such as the number of traffic fatalities on a holiday weekend or the fluctuations of our economy appear far removed from the abstractions of number properties of sets of objects in primary grades. Yet, even though some patterns are currently understood better than others, all of them (whether quantitative or not) are becoming recognized as within the domain of mathematics, within the possible area of application of the methods of study, attack upon problems, and creative thinking that you develop in your classroom.

I hope that these comments will help you to see the significance of your work and the importance of developing in your students a concept of mathematics as a growing body of knowledge composed of numerous systems (including the systems that you are teaching) and having great importance because of the variety of possible interpretations of these systems. Your pupil's future in a steadily increasing number of areas depends upon his understanding of the mathematical concepts of elementary and secondary school. In a very real sense you hold the key to an important part of the future of each of your pupils.

ARITHMETIC AS A FIELD OF MATHEMATICS

Elva Anderson, Harriet Grant, John D. Hancock, Dorothe Nelson, and Marie Renaud

In the American "ladder of education" the elementary and secondary programs developed independently, and their articulation has always been rather casual. Arithmetic is the primary responsibility of the elementary school, and what is done there has not been a major concern of secondary teachers. This is unfortunate, in view of the fact that, in several important areas, both levels are seeking the same outcomes. The secondary teachers depend for what they can do upon what has been started in arithmetic.

Among the widely divergent opinions as to the direction reforms in the secondary mathematics curriculum should take, for example, there is general acceptance of the importance of developing such abilities and understandings as the following:

1. Understanding of the fundamental laws of operations which underlie all manipulations of elementary algebra;

2. Understanding the primitive concept of number, as distinct from the symbolic expression;

3. Ability to use the concepts and principles of mathematics to explore a new situation and improvise new procedures for solving a problem;

4. Understanding the relationship of mathematics to the social and scientific aspects of the culture.

It is interesting to find these also accepted as major outcomes in arithmetic. Apparently the secondary schools and elementary schools, in seeking the same outcomes independently, are each operating in ignorance of what the other is doing.

This fact is of special importance in view of the nature of the outcomes. Abstract understandings and concepts such as these are developed over a long period, from innumerable concrete experiences. What can be achieved in a year of algebra, by itself, for example, is sharply limited. But if a year of algebra is the culmination of a series of experiences running through the grades, the outcomes may be planned on a more ambi-

[From "Arithmetic as a Field of Mathematics." Prepared as a committee project in the course Education 391, Modern Developments in Secondary Mathematics, The Shell Merit Fellowship Program, Stanford University, 1958, pp. 428-36. Reprinted by permission of the authors and The Shell Merit Fellowship Program.]

tious basis. This articulation requires a common understanding of the elementary and secondary programs with mutually defined expectations and obligations for each level. As a step in that direction, it is proposed here to call attention to what is being done in the grades to achieve each of the above outcomes. The literature on arithmetic methods has been reviewed to find what is recommended, and recent texts have been examined to identify current practices. From this it is possible to describe, with reasonable confidence:

1. The typical activities, at various levels, directed to the outcome;

2. The level to which the understanding or ability is commonly developed;

3. Some suggestions as to modifications in practice that might be useful to promote articulation of the secondary and elementary programs in achieving the outcome.

The Associative, Commutative, and Distributive Laws

The three basic laws of number, although applied by school children throughout the grades, are rarely formalized and consequently seldom thoroughly understood. Except where they have been carefully taught, they are not grasped even by high school graduates. The associative, commutative, and distributive laws in algebraic form, with arithmetic examples, are as follows:

Associative Law	*Algebraic Form*	*Arithmetic Example*
For addition	$a + (b + c) = (a + b) + c$	$3 + (5 + 8) = (3 + 5) + 8$
For multiplication	$a\,(bc) = (ab)\,c$	$2\,(3 \times 5) = (2 \times 3)\,5$

Commutative Law

For addition	$a + b = b + a$	$6 + 9 = 9 + 6$
For multiplication	$ab = ba$	$7 \times 5 = 5 \times 7$

Distributive Law

For multiplication	$a\,(b + c) = ab + ac$	$4 \times 27 = 4\,(20 + 7)$
		$= (4 \times 20) + (4 \times 7)$
For division	$(a + b) \div c = \dfrac{a}{c} + \dfrac{b}{c}$	$168 \div 3 = \dfrac{150}{3} + \dfrac{18}{3}$

Although at first the laws may seem obvious, note that none of them applies to all four fundamental processes. Indeed some examination is necessary occasionally (i.e., the distributive law for division) to determine that the law really does hold. Even though a pupil realizes that

$$3 + 4 = 4 + 3,$$

what happens to him when he first encounters a + b or a − b? Unless he has a clear understanding of the law, his first intuitive guess may be that the first is equal to b + a (true) and that the second is equal to b − a (untrue).

As Boyer points out:

> If we should now plan to venture into an application of mathematics to fields we cannot connect with our experience, it is obvious that we must plan to pay greatly increased attention to the fundamental laws of operations. For in the correct application of these laws, and in this only, can we find confidence that the conclusions we establish will be valid.[1]

Applications of the laws are encountered in the early grades. The pupil is taught explicitly, with concrete examples, that 5 + 2 and 2 + 5 are both equal to 7. He learns that in multiplication either factor may be used as the multiplier. This fact facilitates multiplication, since $\frac{189}{\times 3}$ is simpler than $\frac{\times 3}{189}$. The distributive law is applied in multiplying 8 × 29 :

$$(8\times9) + (8\times20) = 72 + 160.$$

In division, the dividend is broken up into appropriate addends, each of which is divisible by the divisor:

$$168 \div 3 = (150 \div 3) + (18 \div 3).$$

Observe how this comes about in the algorism:

$$
\begin{array}{r}
56 \\
3\overline{)\,168} \\
15 \\
\hline
18 \\
18 \\
\end{array}
$$

While applications of the laws are found in grade-school textbooks, they are never explicitly formalized. Even methods books on the teaching of arithmetic and on the teaching of secondary school mathematics, are remarkably devoid of direct attention to these laws. Spencer and Brydegaard generalize the commutative law for addition: "The order of the addends may be changed without changing the value of the sum."[2]

---

[1] L. E. Boyer, *An Introduction to Mathematics for Teachers* (New York: Holt, Rinehart & Winston, Inc., 1945), p. 158.

[2] P. L. Spencer, and M. Brydegaard. *Building Mathematical Concepts in the Elementary School* (New York: Holt, Rinehart & Winston, Inc., 1952), p. 120.

This is accompanied by examples. Note, however, that they do not *name* the laws even in a book for teachers. Marks, Purdy, and Kinney [3] go further in naming the laws and giving examples.

Since the applications have been developed intuitively before grade seven, the laws could profitably be formalized by the end of the eighth grade. Such formalization would consist in recapitulating examples to show what each law is and how it has been used. The pupil would learn why the associative and commutative laws are applicable in multiplication and addition, but not in division or subtraction. He knows this intuitively; it is time to make it explicit. He should be able to explain how the distributive law operates in multi-place multiplication and long division. It could be extended to devising procedures for multiplication with Roman numerals, and to explaining the rationals for the "lattice" algorism for 379×875:

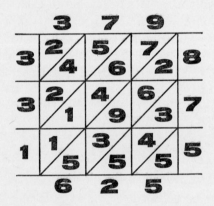

If the fundamental laws have been learned as they apply in the fundamental operations of arithmetic, their applications can readily be generalized in algebra. If not, it is doubtful if a year is sufficient time to accomplish this outcome. Algebra should be a generalization of what has been previously learned in arithmetic.

Primitive Ideas of Number, as Distinct from Symbols for Number

Some recommendations [4] for content in ninth-grade algebra place considerable importance on learning the differences between number

---

[3] J. L. Marks, C. R. Purdy, and L. B. Kinney. *Teaching Arithmetic for Understanding* (New York: McGraw-Hill, 1958), pp. 153, 187, 215.

[4] University of Illinois, Commitee on School Mathematics, "Algebra for Grade Nine" (Urbana, Illinois: 1955).

and the symbolism of number. While this is an important distinction, the possibility should be considered that continued re-emphasis on these differences in the later grades would make further teaching at the secondary level unnecessary.

Every child comes to school with some concepts of number. He may not grasp the idea of a year of time as such, but certainly when he learns to count out as many fingers as candles, as an answer to the oft-repeated question, "How many years old are you?" or "How old are you?" he is beginning to develop the concept of number.

An inspection of methods books in the teaching of arithmetic shows that they stress in varying degrees the development of the primitive idea of number before the pupil learns to use the symbols. The purpose of this distinction is to make the symbols a tool for use in thinking and in problem-solving, avoiding the verbalism that results from premature use of the symbol before the concept is developed. Combinations of groups, place value, and grouping to ten and one hundred, are developed first through concrete materials, then tallies, and finally symbols. By the third grade, according to some authors, children should be using symbols in handling money values, telling time by clock and calendar, and counting by groups of two, ten, five, and three.[5]

Clark and Eads [6] devote the entire first chapter to progressing from "things to concepts." These authors begin with experiences, progress beyond experiences to having ideas about arithmetic, then to expressing arithmetical relationships concretely through handling representative materials, thence to seeing mathematical relationships, and finally to symbolic representation of concepts.

These procedures are recommended also in teachers' manuals for the newer elementary arithmetic texts.[7,8,9] They carefully point out the development of concepts of number and how the teacher may best accomplish it in using the books.

After the early years, however, this distinction tends to be lost. Introduction of Roman numerals in grade four or grade five could well afford another opportunity to distinguish between the number and the symbol, since the pupil now sees the same number represented by two different symbols. If, in grades seven and eight, the pupils studied number sys-

---

[5] J. Marks, C. Purdy, L. Kinney, *op. cit.*

[6] Clark and Eads. *Guiding Arithmetic Learning* (New York: World Book Company, 1954).

[7] *Discovering Numbers.* California State Series (New York: Holt, Rinehart & Winston, Inc., 1956).

[8] McSwain, Ulrich, Cooke. *Understanding Arithmetic* (Palo Alto: Laidlaw, 1956).

[9] Buswell, Brownell, Sauble. *Arithmetic We Need* (Boston: Ginn and Co., 1955).

tems with bases other than ten, the meaning of numbers, as well as of place-value, might be strengthened to the point where little re-emphasis on the distinction of number and symbol in grade nine would be necessary.

Developing Concepts and Principles through Analysis and Exploration

The ability to analyze a new situation and symbolize existing relationships in order to improvise a tentative solution is fundamental to success in algebra. What is frequently overlooked by secondary teachers is that this is an ability toward which "meaningful" procedures in arithmetic are directed. In learning new concepts in the grades, pupils are encouraged to explore and test new ideas that might lead them to discovery and generalization. In this the teacher is concerned with achieving two outcomes: (*a*) teaching the pupil the rationale of the concept or process; and (*b*) teaching the pupil the general method of discovering a tentative generalization, and testing its validity, that is typical of mathematical reasoning.

The "meaningful teaching" of arithmetic, which is basic to the procedures encouraged in all modern arithmetic texts, emphasizes the utilization of such reasoning and understanding in the early grades.

> The goal in all meaningful learning is for the pupil to organize what he learns from specific experiences into broader, more generally applicable principles. . . . Such principles, developed progressively from active and concrete experiences in increasingly complex arithmetic situations, tend to organize and systematize learning.

Consider an example of how a third-grade teacher introduces multiplication by four. It is near Valentine's Day. The teacher suggests they have a post office in the corner of the room so they can post their valentines. The pupils choose a postmaster, who must deal with the selling of four-cent stamps. It may be hard for him at first to figure out how much three four-cent stamps will cost. The class helps him find the answer, probably in several different ways including counting and addition.

A variety of situations are provided for, each calling for the same process, such as having the pupils arrange strips of colored paper in groups of four. The teacher may ask, "How many strips of paper do you have?" The students will probably count them. She then asks how many there are in one group, and writes on the blackboard $1 \times 4 = 4$. She then does this for two groups: $2 \times 4 = 8$. After experiences with these and other concrete materials for exploration and improvising, the pupils are ready to generalize and discover the more economical process of multiplication.

The teacher will then show them how this new process saves time in selling four-cent stamps. Putting on the board $1 \times 4 = 4$, $2 \times 4 = 8$, and $3 \times 4 = 12$, she will ask the students to generalize: $4 \times 4 =$ what? Many of the students will follow the line of logical reasoning and be ready to answer. The teacher will ask $5 \times 4 = ?$ She can have them make another group to prove the validity of the generalization. In this way the use and value of the multiplication tables are "discovered" and the pupils proceed to master the combinations for use in practical situations.

This detailed description illustrates at an elementary level the general approach used in the grades. In learning a new process the pupils are expected to explore, improvise, and discover the relationship underlying the operation. It takes longer than demonstration and explanation, it will often be trial and error, but each pupil becomes an active participant in the learning process. Generalizations or rules thus appear late in the instructional process, for they are an end rather than a beginning. The pupil gains his rules as generalizations resulting from experimentation, rather than words to be learned and applied by rote.

This elementary type of exploration, generalization and validation is carried through the multiplication process and into division. It is not emphasized, as it might be, however, in grades seven and eight. The secondary program would be strengthened if the "meaningful" approach were extended at this more mature level to the process of problem solving.

While there are innumerable problems, there is only a limited number of types of problems as defined by the relationship between the elements in the problem. Many problem situations, such as a trip in a plane, a car, a boat, hiking, bicycle riding, or a foot race, afford examples of travel at a constant speed for a specified time. Once the pupil has sensed the similarity of the problem and ignores the extraneous details, he sees the common elements of d, r, and t with their constant relationships. This similarity can be high-lighted in the *post-solution analysis*. Thus consider the problem:

A plane is traveling 350 miles an hour. How long will it take to travel from San Francisco to New York if the distance is 2800 miles?

Once the problem has been solved, the numbers can be changed, and attention directed toward the procedure for solving the problem. The next step is to substitute letters for numbers:

If a plane is traveling r miles per hour, what is the time required to travel the distance of d miles?

Handling the relationships as letters rather than as numbers focuses attention on the elements common to all problems of this type.

Once the relationships between time, rate, and distance have been recognized, they can be applied to a variety of similar situations. The same relationship is valid whether for rowboat or rocket. Eventually, when the pupil expresses the relationship as a formula, $d = rt$, he has a compact and meaningful tool which applies to an identifiable type of problem situation.

Continued experience in post-solution analysis leads to still broader generalizations in identifying types of problems:

The total cost $c =$ number of items $n \times$ cost of each item p.

This same relationship applies also to the total amount earned, given a number of hours and wages per hour; the total number of gallons of gasoline consumed by a plane given the number of hours traveled and the number of gallons consumed per hour; and so on.

As experiences with these relationships accumulate, the pupil eventually generalizes that in each case one number is the product of two others, and that one formula, $A = BC$, expresses the relationship common to all.

Such a logical and systematic study of arithmetic can lead the pupils to look for common relationships, to state the relationship as a general principle, then verify and refine the principle. This is a mature method of thinking on which a more effective secondary program could be built.

Mathematics in its Social Setting

Arithmetic is an essential part of the everyday life of every pupil. Throughout the grades this everyday setting is continually utilized. We have seen how in teaching the multiplication tables, for example, the process is introduced to the pupil in a situation that is familiar to him, in buying stamps at four cents each. After he has systematically mastered the process, he must learn to recognize situations that call for multiplication. These are also found in his everyday experience and the experience gives him practice not only in applying the process he has learned, but also in recognizing situations that call for multiplication as distinct from addition.

The problem setting, then, should serve two purposes: to illustrate the type of situation to which the process (in this case, multiplication) applies; and to provide opportunity to study the important applications of arithmetic in the environment. For most pupils, this is to be accomplished in the grades, since there is no further study of arithmetic after grade eight.

To a limited extent, arithmetic can be used to broaden the experiences of the pupil. Applications new to him can be made interesting and meaningful through special procedures. The bulletin board can be of material assistance in this stage, with contributions both from the teacher and from the pupils. Many successful teachers make this a central part of the class activity under direction of a designated committee. Films, film strips, and resource persons are also utilized with good effect, when the planning is carefully done, to make problem situations real.

The older textbooks included extended treatment of interest, insurance, investments, property taxes, and installment buying. It was discovered, however, that there is a limit to the extent that problem situations outside the pupil's experiences can become meaningful. It is doubtful if these important applications can be made sufficiently meaningful to be profitably studied by a fourteen-year-old pupil. A junior or senior in high school will be in a group where buying a car, for example, will make many of these problems significant. The present secondary curriculum is not organized, however, so that study of these topics can parallel the experiences of the pupil. While a few schools have a twelfth-grade mathematics course that includes these topics, such courses are an exception rather than the rule.

If we are serious in maintaining that mathematics is to be imbedded in the scientific and social structure of our environment, it is important that this neglected area be recognized as such and taken into account as the secondary curriculum is revised. This will come about only when the problems studied in the curriculum can be related to the everyday experiences of the pupil.

Summary

From these illustrations the following conclusions may reasonably be drawn:

1. The elementary and secondary schools are working independently toward common outcomes, each of which requires joint planning to secure sequential treatment.

2. Some outcomes (such as primitive concepts of number as distinct from symbolization) could probably be achieved in the elementary school.

3. Others (as social applications) cannot be completed in the elementary school, but require systematic attention at the secondary level as well.

4. Others are so comprehensive and important that they call for joint planning, and a clear understanding as to the desired level to be reached

in the elementary school. This is true of the fundamental laws, and
ability to explore and generalize. Here it is necessary for grades seven
and eight to assume new and important responsibilities in the teaching
of mathematics.

It is clear that an effective program will not be possible, either in elementary arithmetic or secondary mathematics, until an articulated program has been planned for grades one through twelve. Mathematics is a
highly sequential field. It cannot be effectively taught unless each teacher
can build on what the pupil has learned, and knows what the next
teacher is doing. Only when program articulation has reached this stage
of development, can important outcomes such as those discussed here
be adequately achieved.

THE FUNCTION OF SUBJECT MATTER
IN RELATION TO PERSONALITY

Guy T. Buswell

The teaching of arithmetic has commonly been evaluated in terms
of the development of mathematical skills, the ability to think quantitatively, and the ability to apply arithmetic in social situations. Few would
deny that these are significant ways of measuring the value of an arithmetic program. On the other hand, the outcomes of arithmetic may also
be evaluated in terms of their contribution to the development of personality. This latter basis for evaluating arithmetic has become prominent
in the literature only during the last decade, although, in essence, it is
not a new criterion since it is only a particular illustration of one of the
aspects of transfer of training. Furthermore, not only arithmetic but
all subject matter is equally open to examination in terms of its contribution to the development of a child's personality.

Positive and Negative Views

One does not need to search far in the educational periodicals to find
statements, both positive and negative, relative to the effect of subject matter on personality. For example, in *Childhood Education* Nina

[From "The Function of Subject Matter in Relation to Personality,"
National Council of Teachers of Mathematics, Sixteenth Yearbook
(1941), pp. 8-18. Reprinted by permission of the author and the National
Council of Teachers of Mathematics.]

Jacobs [1] defends the proposal that arithmetic has important and positive values for the development of personality. She gives numerous concrete illustrations from her own classwork to show how an understanding of number contributes to the development of a sense of security, of the idea of responsibility, and of the feeling of necessity for cooperating with others. She defends the position that no subject gives a greater sense of security than does mathematics.

Quite in contrast with the position defended by Miss Jacobs is that expressed in an article by Professor Lane [2] published in a later issue of the same journal. Professor Lane blames the "three R's" for much of the personality maladjustment found in young children. He takes the position that

> It seems absolutely essential that reading, writing, and arithmetic shall cease to occupy the center of the attention of primary teachers. These skills are learned through a relatively small number of flashes of insight rather than through careful learning of all the elemental processes involved in them. The good teacher of the skills is one who can help children live well and richly regardless of skill equipment and who is able to detect in individual children the need for assistance in attaining insight. The good teacher never induces labor leading to the delivery of ideas or insight. . . . To primary teachers I would suggest a few marked changes in procedure: De-emphasize the three R's. From the remotest corner of the subconscious drive out the concept of respectability as related to achievement in the three R's. Make certain that every child is experiencing worthwhile attitudes and meanings regardless of his skills. Under no circumstances cause a child to lose caste or status, nor to gain it, with you or with his associates, through the skills.

It is obvious from the two preceding illustrations that in this same subject of arithmetic Miss Jacobs sees positive values which can make a marked contribution to personality whereas Professor Lane so fears negative outcomes that he would like to see arithmetic subordinated and "de-emphasized" in the school's program. Other illustrations could be cited showing such opposing points of view related to the arithmetic of the intermediate and upper grades.

Apparently, here is an issue of major importance since the nature of the arithmetic program will depend very much upon which of these two positions is taken. Furthermore, as has been said, the issue is far larger than simply the subject of arithmetic since, in essence, the prob-

---

[1] Nina Jacobs, "Personality Development and Adjustment through Number," *Childhood Education*, XIII (February, 1937), 258-61.

[2] Howard A. Lane, "Child Development and the Three R's," *Childhood Education*, XVI (November, 1939), 101-4.

lem is the extent to which organized subject matter contributes to or inhibits the development of personality. There is also involved the question whether personality is a direct or an indirect outcome of education and whether the concept of personality is adequate to cover all the desirable objectives of education.

The assertion that arithmetic as taught during the past twenty years produces some undesirable outcomes is not open to dispute. Certainly, the application of the drill theory has produced a meaningless outcome which no one can adequately defend. Furthermore, the attempts to introduce the subject by teaching abstract number combinations, without first building up a background of concrete understandings, has separated the arithmetic of the schools from the vivid and genuine number experiences which the child builds up in his out-of-school quantitative experiences. In the middle and upper grades the situation has been little better as the work of the pupils is all too often characterized by a formal manipulation of arithmetical processes devoid of either mathematical meaning or social significance. The need for reform in arithmetic is freely admitted. The question is: What shall be the nature of this reform?

Proposals for Reform

Those who have attacked arithmetic from the standpoint of its bad effects on personality development have made three proposals. The first of these, made by only a small minority of the group, is that there be a complete abandonment of systematic school subjects, a proposal which affects not only arithmetic but all organized subject matter. No one has yet worked out a complete program to substitute for organized subject matter and the proposal is often expressed in such loose terms as Professor Lane has used when he urges teachers to "study childhood, have faith in children, provide a wealth of worthwhile child-like experiences and watch 'em grow!" This trustful faith in "watching 'em grow" (like Topsy!) is worthy of serious consideration only as it is modified by the phrase, "provide a wealth of worthwhile child-like experiences." The whole issue hinges on what should be the nature of these "worthwhile experiences." If they are to be nothing more than the incidental and extemporaneous experiences proposed by teachers and pupils from day to day there is little to look forward to except chaos. On the other hand, if these "worthwhile experiences" are the product of intelligent and serious study they are bound to eventuate in some kind of organized content which will be available for all teachers. This will still be some sort of organized subject matter and it is quite immaterial whether it is called "arithmetic," or "a school subject," or whether it goes by such names as "activities" or "projects." Abandonment of organized subject matter cannot be defended.

A second proposal for the reform of arithmetic is that the subject be postponed or that some of the content be deferred until children are more mature. There is a great deal of sense to this proposal, provided the school does not simply postpone the subject as it is now taught but rather makes a careful study of the relationship between maturity of children at different ages and the arithmetical concepts and experiences which can be made meaningful to them. The various proposals which have been made for deferring arithmetic have fallen considerably short of this criterion. For example, the widely known proposal of Benezet as described in the N. E. A. *Journal* ³ was a postponement in name only. Benezet did not postpone arithmetic to the seventh grade as a reader might infer from his statement, "If I had my way, I would omit arithmetic from the first six grades." Rather he eliminated many of the formal aspects of the subject and substituted in their place some very desirable learning experiences which simply made a different kind of arithmetic.

Certainly, few teachers are so naïve as to believe that number experiences can be postponed completely until the seventh grade or, for that matter, until the third grade. Consequently, the proposal to postpone arithmetic until children are more mature is very misleading. What the proposal really calls for is an abandonment of *formal* teaching, with which anyone will agree, and the rearrangement of number experiences to fit the developing maturity of a child, to which, also, no one can take exception. The shallow argument that pupils can learn more arithmetic in the same amount of time if the subject is postponed scarcely needs consideration since, by the same argument, everything could equally well be postponed. It is difficult to name any type of learning which cannot be accomplished more readily by an eighteen-year-old person than by one six or nine years of age, but the implication is not that all education be postponed and presented as a lump as soon as maturity is reached.

A third proposal of those who admit the deficiencies of arithmetic as it has been taught, and who are interested in much more than just a school subject and are, consequently, concerned with the effect of arithmetic on personality, is that a major reorganization of subject matter and methods is needed, but that the outcome must be an organized body of number experiences from which both mathematical insight and social significance may be derived. Furthermore, they maintain that in this

---

³ L. P. Benezet, "The Story of an Experiment," *Journal of the National Education Association,* XXIV (November, 1935), 241-44.

type of number experience positive contributions to the development of desirable personality traits can be found. Before analyzing this proposal a brief consideration should be given to the nature of personality development.

The Nature of Personality Development

A personality characteristic is always a generalized rather than a specific form of behavior. For example, being courteous is not a matter of stereotyping specific responses, such as saying "Thank you" or "Excuse me," but is, rather, a generalized form of response which expresses itself in various forms of speech and behavior, and always arises from the recognition of a set of values relating to other people and reflecting attitudes of respect and consideration for them. Personality characteristics grow out of experiences.

A commonly accepted hypothesis holds that personality develops through adjustment to frustrations in experience. The way a person adjusts to being thwarted in obtaining the things which he craves either by nature or by habit makes his personality what it is. If frustrations become too numerous or too severe the individual may develop a feeling of inferiority and a defeatist attitude. If life becomes full of fear the individual may adjust by cringing and hiding or by adopting bullying attitudes to conceal his fear. If life becomes altogether too easy and the child is able to satisfy his cravings with no effort on his own part, there is no basis for developing strength of personality and the individual takes on attitudes of smugness and arrogance which are as socially undesirable as are some of the attitudes which develop frustrations, the individual develops feelings of poise, assurance, and confidence. Education can contribute to these modes of control.

Mathematics and Quantitative Relationships

One of the large areas of human experience has to do with quantity and with quantitative relationships. It is the function of mathematics to contribute to one's ability to meet situations of this kind. Children who cannot read the clock are frustrated in making adjustments to social practices. Once they learn to read the clock they can avoid many frustrations by arranging their activities in accordance with the necessities of a time schedule. Children who have not learned to count are excluded from participation in many activities in which other children find much pleasure. Number plays a large part in the activities of even primary grade children. Because of the very basic and permeating character of mathematics it becomes a mode of control of increasing importance as children mature and the frustrations requiring control are as numerous in their thought experiences as in their overt behavior.

The advantages mentioned in the preceding paragraph are seldom pointed out when arithmetic is criticized on the ground that it damages personality. When this criticism is made it is asserted that arithmetic is dull, that it is abstract at too early a level, that it destroys interest, that it produces an aversion for school, and that it sets up habits of intellectual formality instead of vigorous mental responses. There is no doubt that all of these faults may be witnessed in some arithmetic classes. There is also no doubt that they may be found in some classes in any subject. The cause of these undesirable modes of response cannot be laid to arithmetic or to any other particular subject; they are the result of poor selection and organization of content, poor methods of teaching, and poor personality of the teacher. Formality is an attitude of mind; it has no place in any proper scheme of education. Arithmetic, or any other subject, may be taught formally and the outcomes may be damaging or undesirable. On the other hand, arithmetic, or any other subject, may be taught with complete lack of formality when content and method are so planned that understandings are vivid throughout and so that the later abstractions are always the products of earlier concrete experiences.

In considering the relationship between arithmetic and the development of personality, some specific charges should be considered.

Faults Attributed to Arithmetic

One of the chief objections to arithmetic has been that it is too difficult, that the percentage of failures in the subject is too high, and that because of its difficulty it causes children to dislike school in general. It is true that arithmetic is more difficult than some other more concrete forms of experience. In the very nature of the case arithmetic deals with abstract symbols, and dealing with abstractions is always more difficult than dealing with concrete experiences. On the other hand, no thinking person would deny that the special values of arithmetic reside in the fact that it does deal with abstract relationships. Quantitative relationships can be handled effectively by using arithmetical processes simply because so handling them makes it possible to abstract the essential quantitative relationships from the great mass of concrete accompaniments and to save much time, effort, and confusion in arriving at the solution. Any good education leads toward abstract concepts no matter what is the field of activity.

It is, of course, more difficult to learn to divide by a fraction than to work out the same problem concretely through the use of sticks or counters, but the reason we develop abstract processes from concrete experiences is simply because, once they are learned, the abstractions furnish a much more economical method of dealing with experience. However, there is no denying the fact that some difficulty is involved in learning any abstraction. Nevertheless, to eliminate anything that is difficult on the ground of such statements as that quoted from Professor Lane, namely, "The good teacher never induces labor leading to the delivery of ideas or insight," is open to direct challenge, and to challenge on the very grounds that a complete elimination of labor from the process of learning would be damaging in the extreme to personality development.

One of the commonest adjustments which must be made in all kinds of life experience is the adjustment to work. The necessity of work frustrates individuals in every conceivable kind of experience. A personality that has never learned to adjust to a work situation leaves much to be desired. When arithmetic is handled by good teachers, and there are many of them, it furnishes an exceptionally good opportunity to develop personality characteristics of persistence, industry, and concentration, because in the very nature of arithmetical operations the results of such activities are so clearly verifiable. The previous sentence is not a revival of a doctrine of formal discipline. The writer is not talking about the development of any hypothetical abilities or "faculties of the mind," but simply about the establishment of generalized habits of reacting to frustrations of difficulty in the ways described. As has been previously pointed out, personality is merely the sum of these generalized habits which are the outcome of experience.

The organization and grade placement of arithmetic may be so poorly managed that the pupil is frustrated by work assignments entirely beyond his stage of maturity; but, on the other hand, number experiences may be properly related to the developing maturity of children in such a manner that the difficulties imposed are stimulating rather than depressing, and the child may learn the exhilaration of mastering a series of meaningful experiences. It is because arithmetic has often been presented through barren drills rather than through meaningful experiences that criticisms of this type have appeared; but to throw out arithmetic because it is sometimes presented in too difficult a fashion is like "throwing out the baby with the bath."

Another criticism of arithmetic is that it often produces formal, meaningless responses from children, leaving them confused and with a feeling of dullness in the face of quantitative situations. There is little doubt that an overemphasis on speed in computation, with the attendant large amounts of drill, may produce such outcomes. This is no particular charge against arithmetic since it is doubtful whether any kind of content could have succeeded under such methods of teaching. The outcome, however, is by no means universal and there are many persons, the products of our schools, for whom number operations are clear and meaningful. Since the year 1930 there has been a most marked improvement in this particular respect and, as noted in the introductory chapter of this Yearbook, the position of this Committee is completely in accord with emphasis on meaning and understanding, rather than on speed in computation. There are ample grounds for this kind of criticism of arithmetic but certainly the alternative for the schools is not an abandonment of the teaching of the subject. Rather, it is the development of a much superior kind of teaching of arithmetic. It is the improvement of teaching, rather than the criticism of poor teaching, which should receive the attention of school people.

The position taken in this chapter is that arithmetic has decidedly positive values to offer to the school's program of personality development. It can help children adjust to those types of frustrations which defeat all too many adults. Some illustrations may serve to make this point clearer.

Some Illustrations

In the writer's dealings with graduate students in education numerous cases have been encountered in which students have deliberately sidestepped worth-while problems because these problems involved some understanding of statistical concepts. They were frightened by any suggestion of the need for statistical understandings. These cases have exhibited a great range of forms of adjustment, even to some students who have paid sizable sums of money to secure assistance on operations so simple that a few hours of intelligent study would enable any individual to understand them. Yet they expressed a feeling of utter inadequacy in the face of any mathematical situation. They go through life with feelings of inferiority and dread simply because they have not learned enough mathematics to enable them to behave intelligently in quantitative situations. The damaging results of a lack of arithmetic in these cases are far more obvious than any damaging results which might accompany a serious attempt to understand the subject.

There are in this country a large number of women who, when they find it necessary to triple a recipe, measure out two-thirds of a cup of flour three times rather than hazard the mental operation of "How much is three times two-thirds?" Everyone knows persons who are afraid to display their lack of ability at adding scores in a card game and are much embarrassed by the fact that they are afraid to do so. Many otherwise intelligent citizens throw up their hands in surrender in the face of trying to understand the financial operations of even local government. Innumerable people are caught in the trap of installment buying because they do not know how to work out the simple arithmetic of the situation. Short-term loan agencies flourish on the patronage of people who never realize the exorbitant rates of interest they are paying until they are trapped by the impossibility of keeping pace with the rapidly accumulating size of their loans.

As Professor Wheat has pointed out,

> One can remain so ignorant of number as to be very complacent in the face of the problems and frustrations of modern life. Many people are fairly well-integrated personalities merely because they know so little about the demands which number relations make in a complex world. These are the "Ham-and-Eggers" and "Thirty-Dollars-Every-Thursday" people. On a low level of thinking, they may be very well integrated; with some understanding they are less so on a higher level; and with more understanding they may become integrated on a higher level.

Thus, one can see in every direction examples of frustrations caused by a lack of genuine understanding of the arithmetic of quantitative experiences. The arithmetic of the elementary schools has been inadequate for these purposes. It must be improved, not eliminated.

Although the development of personality is an important obligation of the school, it is not an outcome which can be produced by direct attack such, for example, as offering courses in personality, or teaching a person how to be self-reliant, or self-confident, or "how to make friends." This kind of direct teaching involves the danger of producing introverted prigs. It may result in changes in personality, but changes of an extremely undesirable kind.

BIBLIOGRAPHY

Adams, A. S. "Civic Values in the Study of Mathematics," *Mathematics Teacher,* XXI (1928), 37-41.

Anderson, Elva, Harriet Grant, John Hancock, Dorothe Nelson, and Marie Renaud. "Arithmetic as a Field of Mathematics," *California Journal of Secondary Education,* XXXIII (November, 1958), 428-36.

Bloom, Benjamin S. *Taxonomy of Educational Objectives.* New York: Longmans, Green and Co., 1956, 44-50.

Breslich, E. R. "Mastery of the Fundamentals of High School Mathematics: A Graduation Requirement," *School Science and Mathematics,* XLV (November, 1945), 743-56.

Brueckner, Leo J. "The Social Contributions of Arithmetic," *The National Elementary Principal,* XXX (October, 1950), 7-10.

Buswell, Guy T. "The Function of Subject Matter in Relation to Personality," *Arithmetic in General Education,* National Council of Teachers of Mathematics, Sixteenth Yearbook (1941). Washington, D.C.: The Council, 8-19.

Deans, Edwina. "Arithmetic in the Primary Grades," *The National Elementary School Principal,* XXXIX (October, 1959), 22.

Educational Policies Commission. *The Unique Function of Education in American Democracy.* Washington, D.C.: National Education Association, 1937.

————. *The Purposes of Education in American Democracy.* Washington, D.C.: National Education Association, 1938.

Fehr, Howard F. "Teaching for Appreciation," *School Science and Mathematics,* LII (January, 1952), 19-24.

Flournoy, Frances. "Relating Arithmetic to Everyday Life," *The National Elementary School Principal,* XXXIX (October, 1959), 29-32.

Hickerson, J. Allen. "Teaching the Number System Inductively," *The Arithmetic Teacher,* V (October, 1958), 178-84.

Jacob, Nina. "Personality Development and Adjustment Through Number," *Childhood Education,* XIII (February, 1937), 258-61.

Kearney, Nolan C. *Elementary School Objectives.* New York: Russell Sage Foundation, 1953, 43-51, 113-20.

Lane, Howard A. "Child Development and the Three R's," *Childhood Education,* XVI (November, 1939), 101-4.

Marks, John L., C. Richard Purdy, and Lucian B. Kinney. *Teaching Arithmetic for Understanding.* New York: McGraw-Hill Book Co., Inc., 1958.

Meserve, Bruce E. "A Teacher's View of Mathematics," *School Science and Mathematics,* LVI (December, 1956), 716-18.

McSwain, E. T. "A Functional Program in Arithmetic," *Elementary School Journal,* XLVII (March, 1947), 380-84.

————, and Ralph J. Cooke. "Essential Mathematical Meanings in Arithmetic in Quantitative Thinking, Computation, and Problem Solving," *The Arithmetic Teacher,* V (October, 1958), 185-92.

Progressive Education Association, Commission on the Secondary School Curriculum. *Mathematics in General Education.* New York: Appleton-Century-Crofts, Inc., 1940, 241-68.

Shane, Harold G. "Aims of Elementary Education," *Review of Educational Research,* XXIX (April, 1959), 137-45.

Stern, Catherine. *Children Discover Arithmetic.* New York: Harper & Brothers, 1949.

Thompson, Mathew R. *Objectives of a Twelve-Year Mathematics Program for Elementary and Secondary Schools,* Doctoral Dissertation. Oregon State College, 1955.

Wheat, Harry. "Changes and Trends in Arithmetic since 1910," *The Elementary School Journal,* XLVII (November, 1946), 134-44.

Wilson, Guy M. "Aims and Purposes of Arithmetic," *Teaching the New Arithmetic.* New York: McGraw-Hill Book Co., Inc., 1951, 8-19.

II IMPROVING THE CURRICULUM CONTENT IN MATHEMATICS

D. Richard Bowles, Assistant Director of Curriculum,
Austin Public Schools

INTRODUCTION

BIBLIOGRAPHY

INTRODUCTION

The Spanish philosopher Ortega y Gasset, writing of the ancient world and the Middle Ages, speaks of "earlier days, before mathematics had laid waste the spirit of life." [1] Several observers have suggested that this dim view of the "queen of the sciences" apparently has been shared by many school children and some teachers. Developing a more wholesome attitude toward elementary mathematics and greater success in learning and using it have been objectives of curriculum workers for almost half a century. Efforts to improve content have paralleled clarification of objectives and reforms in methods and materials.

The teaching of mathematics in the elementary grades has been influenced by several of the major forces operating generally on the public schools during this time. One of the first major content break-throughs came in connection with the Economy of Time Studies of the Department of Superintendence early in this century. As new subjects found places in the public school curriculum, the older subjects had to justify their status and the time given to them. Investigations soon led to the removal of material not socially useful. Accompanying studies sought to find the time in the child's experience when given content could be learned with least effort. The result was that many topics were eliminated from lower grades. Added impetus to the trend was given by child development studies seeking to find the most appropriate experiences for children at each stage of development.

These forces reached their height with the publication of the Thirty-eighth Yearbook of the National Society for the Study of Education. Despite numerous attacks on the methods used by the investigators and on some of their conclusions, textbooks for the next generation reflected their influence. Even then, however, some observers were calling for an emphasis on understanding the basic meanings of the number system and for application of the principles of learn-

---

[1] José Ortega y Gasset, *Man and Crisis* (New York: W. W. Norton and Company, Inc., 1958), p. 47.

ing. This point-of-view blended with the social utility philosophy to find expression in the Fiftieth Yearbook of the National Society for the Study of Education.

The search for understandings leads inevitably to greater emphasis on the truly mathematical aspects of arithmetic instruction. The fifties were marked by accelerating efforts to "put more mathematics" into the curriculum. Indeed, the title of this present volume reflects a more sophisticated attitude toward the subject earlier thought of only as "numbers" or "arithmetic" in the lower grades.

In their search for the mathematical content of arithmetic, curriculum workers have enlisted the help of secondary and college mathematics teachers. In their concern with strengthening the mathematics program all along the line, teachers of advanced mathematics have become interested in the concepts taught in the elementary grades. Significantly, the Twenty-fourth Yearbook of the National Council of Teachers of Mathematics describes *The Growth of Mathematical Ideas, Grades 1-12*. Preliminary reports of various individual experimenters, study groups, and commissions evidence similar concerns. Many of these are working most intensively on the mathematics of the junior high school, but their efforts are also being felt in the lower grades. The immediate task of curriculum workers and teachers is to make sure that the content suggestions made by the subject specialists find a sound rationale of teaching method.

APPROACHING THE MODERN ERA

Ben A. Sueltz

During the period 1850 to 1890, educational thinking was dominated by a "faculty psychology" which extolled "training the mind" in such aspects as memory and reasoning. It was generally considered that one who learned to reason in arithmetic would be a good reasoner in other areas. One textbook served grades one through eight. These books did not break

[From "Arithmetic in Historical Perspective," *The National Elementary Principal*, XXXIX (October, 1959), pp. 12-16. Reprinted by permission of the author and *The National Elementary Principal*.]

a process into sub-parts. Long division was presented as a whole unit operation. Exercises were not restricted to simple easy numbers and problems which may have had a close bearing on the contemporary scene were frequently unreal. This was the era of the cistern problem: If pipe A can fill a cistern in 3 hours and pipe B can fill it in 5 hours and if pipe C will drain the cistern in 6 hours, how long will it take to fill the cistern if all three pipes are operating to capacity?

In the late nineteen hundreds, educational psychology became important to school people and by 1920 principles of learning were established. Such terms as motivation, readiness, exercise, effect, threshold of learning, and overlearning entered into discussion. Two or three textbooks for the first eight grades became standard, drill exercises were greatly multiplied, and the more fanciful problems were dropped. Processes were developed in steps but the stage of minute step mastery came later.

In the interim, roughly 1920 to 1935, the psychology of "readiness-exercise-effect" was supreme and educational practice featured drill. Processes were analyzed into many subskills to be memorized, several researchers found the relative difficulty of subskills such as addition combinations, and then textbook writers used these studies to provide practice exercises in quantity to match the difficulty of the skills. "Transfer" was denied. To accommodate the necessary drill, one book was provided for each grade. Long division could be learned if the thirteen substeps were mastered. Column addition required 1090 skills. Teachers drilled and drilled their pupils and still they couldn't remember arithmetic. Learning was mechanical memorization and forgetting was rapid. Understanding was not a prime goal of the arithmetic of the period. The psychologists and researchers of the era did much to lower the esteem of thoughtful teachers for psychology and research. Many schools found it necessary to use workbooks to supplement the textbooks.

In the 1930 period, one heard of "progressive education" and psychology was replaced by child development. The terminology of the period included "satisfyingness," "peer group," and "educate the whole child." In arithmetic, the concept of social utility was revered. What arithmetic do children and adults actually use? Why teach something that no one will normally encounter? There were researches which showed that no one ever used a decimal fraction of more than three figures and that common fractions of halves, fourths, and eighths were about the only ones necessary to learn. During this period, a committee published many articles showing the mental age necessary to learn a process such as division. Thoughtful people at that time made such remarks as "the halt leading the blind," and "you can't hit it if you can't see it." The dominant method of learning was still drill and memorization and forgetting was a concern.

But during this period, a few people began to insist that pupils should understand what they were learning and should see the sense of it and of its usefulness in society.

Topics such as fractions were spread over a range of several school years with the easier concepts and operations coming early and the mastery stage of more difficult computations delayed one or two years beyond former practice. In general, the mastery stage was reached from one-half to one year later than in the early 1920's.

CONTRIBUTIONS OF RESEARCH TO THE SOLUTION OF CURRICULUM PROBLEMS IN ARITHMETIC

Zenos E. Scott

While the available data relative to the question, when shall formal arithmetic begin, are incomplete, they point to the desirability of more careful attention to reading ability and the entire omission of formal number work, except for counting, from the first grade. In other words, from the small amount of available data, one would draw the tentative conclusion that the time usually spent on formal number work in the first grade might, perhaps, better be spent in developing comprehension—ability in silent reading, and an experience basis for number work. The inference is that with this ability developed, children who do not begin formal arithmetic until sometime in the second or at the beginning of the third grade will at the end of the third grade not be handicapped in competition with children who have had formal number work regularly during the first and second grades.

.   .   .   .

What are the socially useful processes? The actual analysis of usage has become the basis for inclusion of processes found useful, or the exclusion of processes not used.

As to what should take the place of this material in the arithmetic course of study for which there seems to be little use at present, there has

[From "Arithmetic," *The Nation at Work on the Public School Curriculum*, American Association of School Administrators, Fourth Yearbook (1926), pp. 173-220. Reprinted by the permission of the American Association of School Administrators.]

not been sufficient research to give a definite answer, but the present tendency is toward the use of motivated "life situations" for building up the child's number concepts.

For this work teachers are using such life situations as the school grocery store, buying a lot and building a residence, planning a savings scheme for a college education, organizing a stock company and selling stocks and bonds, budgeting the family money, the annual cost of an automobile in upkeep and depreciation, taking out life insurance, the marks of a sound investment, and many others, simple or complex according to grade and ability of group. The purpose of this work is to give the child a working understanding of useful applications of number concepts in modern life. This work within the schoolroom should be supplemented by actual experience outside the schools, such as shopping for mother, managing a vegetable garden project for profit, handling the business of a paper route, working for wages, keeping books on money received and spent, maintaining a savings account, and conducting a school-community fair.

REPLACE DRILL WITH INFORMATIONAL WORK IN LOWER GRADES

Guy M. Wilson

This entire report is merely a brief summary. The data reported speak for themselves. They do suggest tremendous possibilities of improvement over present practice. They suggest replacing time on drill in grades one and two by a broader and more fundamental preparation for life's real problems through understanding and experience. They indicate the possibility of letter perfect results in the fundamentals for most children. These results are accompanied by a happier childhood through co-operation, understanding, and success. Arithmetic has been the tyrant of the schools. It has caused more failure and grief than any other subject in the grades, and the final results have been poor.

The results of this experiment are so strikingly in contrast with the usual results as to place the burden of proof upon those who oppose the plan of

[From "New Standards in Arithmetic: A Controlled Experiment in Supervision," *Journal of Educational Research*, XXII (December, 1930), pp. 351-60. Reprinted by the permission of the author and the *Journal of Educational Research*.]

replacing formal drill with informational work in grades one and two, followed by a systematic attack for 100 per cent mastery of the fundamentals beginning with grade three, as recommended in the Fourth Yearbook of the Department of Superintendence.

GRADE PLACEMENT OF TOPICS ACCORDING TO MENTAL GROWTH

Carleton B. Washburne

There is a point in a child's mental growth before which it is not effective to teach a given process in arithmetic and after which that process can be taught reasonably effectively. The child's preceding grasp of those facts and processes that enter into the new topic he is going to study is even more important than the mental level he has reached. Through mental testing and achievement testing, a teacher can and should determine when the children in her class are ready to undertake a new process, and either through ability grouping or individual work should see that each child gets the arithmetic for which he is ready at a time when he is ready for it.

Being faced with the necessity of establishing a criterion as to what constitutes adequate mastery of an arithmetic topic, the Committee of Seven has adopted the following standard:

Adequate mastery shall be considered as that degree of mastery which enables a child to pass a retention test with adequate time limits covering all the important phases of a topic, six weeks after the conclusion of his study of that topic, with a score of 80 per cent or better. A topic should not be taught to children until they have reached a mental age and a degree of mastery of prerequisite facts and processes sufficient to enable at least three-fourths of them to achieve this mastery.

.   .   .   .

To attempt to teach a topic before either the minimum or optimum stage of mental growth is reached is not merely to waste much time and effort

[From "Mental Age and the Arithmetic Curriculum: A Summary of the Committee of Seven Grade Placement Investigations to Date," *Journal of Educational Research*, XXIII (March, 1931), pp. 210-31. Reprinted by permission of the *Journal of Educational Research*.]

on the part of teacher and pupil, but to doom a considerable number of children to failure, and a much larger number to that hazy half knowledge, so characteristic of children's grasp of arithmetic and so inimical to the clear thinking and sure-footed progress that should characterize the study of mathematics.

EMPHASIS ON SIGNIFICANCE, MEANING, AND INSIGHT

B. R. Buckingham

I have used the terms *significance, meaning,* and *insight* in the title of this paper. By the *significance* of number I mean its value, its importance, its necessity in the modern social order. I mean the role it has played in science, the instrument it has proved to be in ordering the life and environment of man. The idea of significance is therefore functional.

On the other hand, the *meaning* of number, as I understand it, is mathematical. In pursuit of it we conceive of a closely knit, quantitative system. It has broader aspects than those which we teach to children. The domain of number transcends the field of arithmetic and has become so diverse that mathematicians no longer give us a definition of number. Its domain lies beyond whole numbers and fractions, positives and negatives, irrationals and imaginaries, etc., each classification being infinite in its members. Even in the realm of so-called natural numbers the series is infinite. "There is no last number."

Under the heading of meaning I include, of course, the rationale of our number system. The teacher who emphasizes the social aspects of arithmetic may say that she is giving meaning to numbers. I prefer to say that she is giving them significance. In my view the only way to give numbers meaning is to treat them mathematically. I am suggesting, therefore, that we distinguish these two terms by allowing, broadly speaking, significance to be social and meaning to be mathematical. I hasten to say, however, that each idea supports the other.

By making this distinction between significance and meaning I think we shall gain greatly. We shall perhaps begin to do two things, namely, to teach arithmetic as a social study and to teach it as mathematics. The one

[From "Significance, Meaning, Insight—These Three," *The Mathematics Teacher*, XXXI (January, 1938), pp. 24-30. Reprinted by permission of the author and *The Mathematics Teacher*.]

emphasis will exalt arithmetic as a great and beneficent human institution, the supporter of a fine humanistic tradition. The other emphasis, the mathematical one, will lift arithmetic, even in the primary grades, from a formalized symbolism to the dignity of a quantitative system. In short, when arithmetic is taught with meaning it ceases to be a bag of tricks and becomes, as it should be, a recognized branch of mathematics.

It seems to me entirely possible to offer real arithmetic successfully in the primary grades, provided it is concrete. This arithmetic can meet the most exacting mathematical demands. It can be a type of arithmetic which does not have to be done over, which necessitates no new moves designed to correct errors or misconceptions. Concrete arithmetic is, or can be, true arithmetic. It is the true and proper support of abstract and generalized arithmetic. The trouble is that in the primary grades we do not give enough concrete arithmetic. We begin with counting objects. This is admirable so far as concreteness is concerned, though it is generally unnecessary, because most children can count objects before they receive instruction in school. Usually the child is then expected to take up the number facts as abstractions. This he is not ready to do. We show too great haste in arriving at a goal which we see clearly, but to which the child has not been led by steps that conform to the way he grows.

When I speak of *insight* I am talking no longer about arithmetic, no longer about the curriculum, but about the learner himself. Insight implies a person. When significance and meaning are given to arithmetic in the presence of a class, the pupils gain insight. They do so simply because that is the way man, the human animal, is made. He is essentially an experiencing organism. Bagehot in one of his literary essays explains Shakespeare as the product of a first-rate experience operating on a first-rate experiencing nature. This is the distinction I want to make. The school should offer a first-rate experience. The child brings to it, by the very nature of his organism, an experiencing nature.

When we confront children with a significant and meaningful experience, and when they make this experience theirs, they acquire insight, each to the degree that he is able. More specifically, and in particular relation to number, they gain in two ways: they understand number as such, and they also understand when and how to use it to serve their purposes. It is obvious that significance and meaning are nothing without an experiencing nature.

USE OF UNITS IN ARITHMETIC TEACHING

Leo J. Brueckner

First, the arithmetic curriculum should place much greater emphasis on social arithmetic than has been the practice in the past. The acceptance of this position should result in a radical change in the character of the arithmetic work in the primary grades, a recognition of stages one and two in the development of arithmetic. Here it is essential that stress be placed on the development of number meanings and an appreciation of the functional uses of number in the affairs of children. This readiness program should have as its major purpose the development of readiness on the part of pupils for the more formal number work to be begun at the third stage of instruction.

Second, the core of the curriculum should consist of a series of carefully selected units of social arithmetic of demonstrated value adapted to the needs, interests, and level of progress of the pupils. The purpose of these units should be to give the pupils a rich social insight and an understanding of the functions of number in daily life and to enable them to participate more effectively in the affairs of a changing industrial democratic society. The units should vary from locality to locality, but the basic principles underlying their selection should be the same in all places. Emphasis is placed by the Yearbook Committee on the planned approach to be made to this work, since it is held that an unplanned, incidental approach to the subject will not produce the desired results. Much experimental work must be done before we can be sure that the elements of a planned program of arithmetic that gives due consideration to child development are validly established.

Third, through these units of work the pupil should also be led to see the functional value of the various number processes and be given ample opportunity to apply them in a meaningful way. It is essential that the work in social and computational arithmetic be carefully integrated. This can be accomplished by selecting units of work for the different grade levels that will give the best opportunity to present the number processes most suitably taught at each level.

[From "The Development of Ability in Arithmetic," *Child Development and the Curriculum*, National Society for the Study of Education, Thirty-eighth Yearbook (1939), Part I, pp. 294-95. Reprinted by permission of the author and the National Society for the Study of Education.]

THE UNIFIED OPERATION OF THE THREE CRITERIA

Robert L. Morton

No one of the three criteria which have been discussed can operate successfully in isolation from the other two. This point has already been made but is repeated here for emphasis.

The teacher will begin the consideration of new topics in arithmetic by basing them upon situations which normally occur. She will also see to it that much of the arithmetic which the pupils experience is closely related to interesting activities. Thus, full account is taken of the operation of the social criterion. *At the same time,* however, the resourceful teacher will respect and take proper account of the organization of arithmetic as a science. This means that the teacher will choose from the many and varied situations in which arithmetic is used those which permit the building of a program in accordance with the logical criterion as well as the social criterion. It is not true that attention can be given to the social criterion on one day and to the logical criterion on another day. Rather, attention must be given simultaneously to both of these criteria every day.

The emphasis accorded to the psychological criterion will indicate its relative importance. The greatest hope for improvement in the teaching of arithmetic lies in the utilization of the psychological criterion to help children learn. Very properly, much has been said in recent years about making arithmetic meaningful. Making arithmetic meaningful, however, is more than explaining the rationale of the number system and the processes with numbers. In the discussion of the psychological criterion meaning has been stressed, to be sure. But emphasis has also been placed upon relating new experiences to old experiences, upon a gradual step-by-step development of the processes, upon the importance of having pupils discover new truths for themselves, upon the futility of mechanical tricks and devices, upon the need for telescoped reteaching rather than the traditional "test and drill" kind of review, and upon other important matters related to the all-important objective of helping pupils to learn.

All three of these fundamental criteria must operate simultaneously. Although the teacher's major concern will be the implications of the

[From *Teaching Children Arithmetic* (New York: Silver Burdett Company, 1953), pp. 60-61. Reprinted by permission of the author and the Silver Burdett Company.]

psychological criterion, at no time can she afford to neglect the requirements which are imposed by the logical criterion and the social criterion. To plan and put into operation a program which is simultaneously based upon the implications of these three criteria is not an easy task. However, the teacher will soon discover that it is not an impossible task.

LOGICAL ANALYSIS AND
SOCIAL UTILITY THEORIES COMBINED

Herbert F. Spitzer

. . . It is reasonable to conclude that the research studies based on the theory of social utility have not yet produced acceptable data for selecting the content of a satisfactory arithmetic program. In the absence of complete data on the uses of number, a logical analysis of the mathematical system as it applies to life situations is perhaps the best guide for the selection of arithmetic content. Both the narrow "utilitarians" and those who have made a logical analysis of the uses of number have reached the conclusion that number is a valuable tool for those who know how to employ it. The utilitarians have seized upon one of the most obvious of these uses, the computation involved in the solution of life problems, as the thing to teach. The logical "analysts" have decided that the problem-solving use as well as other number uses can be taught by teaching the outstanding features of the number system and the various number procedures. By one scheme, facts and processes are taught in order that children may learn to solve problems. In the other, problems are used to illustrate the mathematical facts, processes, and relations that form the framework of the number system. To the utilitarians no educational value, other than the provision of a useful tool, results from the teaching of arithmetic. To the logical analysts, as interpreted in this book, there is educational value in the learning of the number system. In addition, the child acquires the possession of a valuable tool.

It does not require much imagination to see that if the logical-analysis method is used without any checks, the teaching of operations without much merit could easily become a part of the arithmetical content. For example, the teaching of the factor method of multiplying when a two-

[From *The Teaching of Arithmetic* (Boston: Houghton Mifflin Company, 1954), pp. 311-13. Reprinted by permission of the author and the Houghton Mifflin Company.]

figure multiplier is present ($35 \times 24 = 7 \times 24 \times 5$) could be justified on the basis of its contribution to the understanding of the multiplication process without reference to its value as a check of the accuracy of computation.

What is needed then is a combination of the logical analysis and the social utility theories in the selection of curriculum content. A broad interpretation of the theory of social utility would be essential in any attempt to combine the two methods. This combination should result in greater emphasis given in the arithmetic content to such items as (1) oral or unwritten arithmetic, (2) approximate computation, (3) development of the idea that tens, hundreds, and so on are handled just as ones are, (4) development of relations within the number system and the laws governing operations with numbers, (5) reference measures, (6) the making of judgments in situations where common measures are used, (7) procedures for showing how number and number operations make for simplicity of thought (e.g., the use of such ratios as 3 : 2 for two cities with populations of 223,476 and 140,871 people, respectively), and (8) material for the enrichment of arithmetic, including historical and recreational material.

THREE CRUCIAL QUESTIONS ABOUT THE PRIMARY GRADE PROGRAM

William A. Brownell

To the first of these questions, "Can primary-grade children learn arithmetic?" research gives the answer, "Yes." The evidence is of two kinds. The first kind of evidence is inferential: children, when they enter Grade I, already possess (that is, have learned) much arithmetic, and the assumption is that, properly taught, they can learn much more in the primary grades. This evidence comes from the extensive inventories, new and old, which have been conducted by personal interviews and by group testing. . . . The second kind of evidence is more direct: research shows unmistakably that if primary-grade children are taught arithmetic, they will learn it. . . . The only occasion for dispute with respect to this conclusion lies in the meaning assigned "learn." If "learn" is made to mean

[From *Arithmetic in Grades I and II* (Durham, North Carolina: Duke University Press, 1941), pp. 160-62. Reprinted by permission of the author and the Duke University Press.]

"attain mastery in," the conclusion does not hold. If, however, the word means "make substantial progress toward the outcomes set," then the conclusion is valid. It is in the latter sense that the word is here used. The former connotation involving "mastery" seems to the writer to be quite inapplicable when primary pupils are under discussion. "Mastery" . . . is best viewed as the end-product of long periods of experience and practice.

The second crucial question is not to be answered so definitely, "Should primary pupils be asked to learn arithmetic?" Insofar as school practice is determinable from the ability of children measurably to profit from teaching, the answer here is "Yes." But ability to learn is admittedly only one of the factors which affect policy. Other factors, sociological, philosophical, and psychological, are also involved. Indeed, according to some educational theories ability to learn is of slight importance as compared with "natural interests and needs." According to other theories, perhaps more "traditional," ability to learn is more important, especially when the thing to be learned is of demonstrable social significance. The answer to this second question is, then, largely a matter of theory and opinion. To the writer the facts argue for systematic arithmetic starting in Grade I. . . .

The third crucial question is, "Granted that primary pupils can and should learn arithmetic, how should the program be organized?" There is no final answer to this question. Research has not yet tested enough programs and collected enough facts. . . . As teachers and research workers continue to study the way children learn and to locate and remove the sources of their difficulty, we may confidently expect steadily improved programs.

There should be no occasion for surprise in the writer's frank statement that he favors systematic arithmetic from the outset of schooling. . . . The person who subscribes to this view is put at once on the defensive: he may be accused of being a "subject matter specialist," more interested in arithmetic than in children; he may be charged with "forcing" children to learn things they are not "ready" to learn. It may even be thought that he is indirectly (or directly) supporting the hammer-and-tongs tactics of an earlier decade.

The basic fallacy in these charges lies in failure to recognize that there are different kinds of arithmetic and different kinds of systematic instruction. The "drill" program of arithmetic . . . is formal and is open to the charges listed above, for it calls for a type of learning of which primary-grade children at the outset are incapable. But to speak in behalf of systematic instruction does not commit one to this program of arithmetic; there is another kind of arithmetic against which the objections named cannot properly be leveled.

INTERMEDIATE ARITHMETIC:
AN EMPHASIS ON PROCESS

John W. Dickey

An earlier statement of the content of these grades was in terms of the *products* to be learned. The focus of attention was primarily upon the subject matter rather than upon the learner. The fourth grade was concerned with the more difficult aspects of whole numbers; the fifth grade, with the beginnings of the systematic work in common fractions; and the sixth grade, with the more difficult common fractions and the serious study of decimal fractions. The emphasis was upon skills acquired; and much of the work in problem-solving was disguised drill. The results of standard tests were a valid measure of the learnings. Fortunately, in recent years these requirements have become less difficult and more purposeful for the pupil.

A more recent definition of middle-grade arithmetic is in terms of *concepts* to be learned, *skills* to be mastered, and *problem-solving ability* to be acquired. This definition seems more functional. The focus of attention is primarily upon the learner. This definition places the major emphasis upon the *process,* and somewhat less emphasis upon the product learned. The teacher must "see both sides of the coin"—the products and the processes. Our culture demands competency as well as interest in the personality of the pupil.

In the area of concepts with whole numbers, some fundamental learnings include the place-value idea as used in addition, in compound subtraction, in the handling of the partial products in multiplication, and in the regrouping with division. The relationships between counting, addition and subtraction, and multiplication and division are important insights to foster organized learning.

[From "Comments on Middle-Grade Arithmetic," *The Arithmetic Teacher,* V (February, 1958), pp. 37-8. Reprinted by permission of the author and *The Arithmetic Teacher.*]

PRINCIPLES OF CURRICULUM DEVELOPMENT
IN JUNIOR HIGH SCHOOL MATHEMATICS

Leo J. Brueckner, Foster E. Grossnickle, and John Reckzeh

The basic principles underlying the mathematics curriculum . . . may be summarized as follows:

1. The learning of arithmetic and other branches of mathematics is a gradual growth process that should be guided and directed at all stages by a systematic, planned program. It should begin early in the primary grades.

2. The mathematics program should include a well integrated treatment of the mathematical and social phases of the subject, dealing with topics and processes of undoubted social value and significance to the average individual. The more difficult computations such as are required in technical work should be deferred to levels beyond the elementary school.

3. The content of the curriculum should be based on personal and social needs emerging in current living both in and out of school. The evidence is clear that students at the junior high school level have many quantitative experiences that should be made mathematically meaningful and socially significant to them.

4. The student should be made intelligent about the development, status, and likely future trend of important social institutions through which number functions in the community.

5. Mathematics should be taught in close association with any and all school work in which the use of quantitative procedures will clarify the situation and help to make it meaningful.

6. A most fruitful approach to the enrichment of mathematics instruction is the consideration of significant problems that will illuminate the present social situation for the learner, particularly in the area of economic competence.

7. Growth in the ability to apply mathematical procedures effectively in social affairs is greatly facilitated by abundant experience in using number in a variety of purposeful activities.

8. Even though much arithmetic is learned incidentally through con-

[From *Developing Mathematical Understandings in the Upper Grades* (New York: Holt, Rinehart & Winston, Inc., 1957), p. 55. Reprinted by permission of the authors and Holt, Rinehart & Winston, Inc.]

tact with number in social experiences, such learning is neither systematic nor comprehensive. It is clear that direct instruction is necessary for mastery of the basic skills and efficient work methods.

9. Systematic provision should be made for adapting curriculum content and instructional procedures to differences in the interests, abilities, and needs of the pupils, as well as differences in the rates at which they learn.

10. The curriculum should be so arranged as to provide for continuity of pupil development, with a minimum of strain and tension, and it should be so organized that there is a reasonable likelihood of successful learning. The available evidence as to the learning difficulty of number processes should be carefully considered in the gradation of subject matter.

TOPICS IN MODERN JUNIOR HIGH MATHEMATICS

Veryl Schult

After examining the contents of . . . experiments with "modern" mathematics it was interesting to see that they all included topics in the following categories which underlie traditional arithmetic:

1. *Numeration.* The idea of one-to-one correspondence was studied in each experiment. Other systems of numeration besides the decimal were studied. The binary system was of particular interest, because of its use in electronic computers. Better students studied numeration systems with bases other than 2 and 10, learned to calculate in such systems, and discovered their advantages and disadvantages.

2. *The laws of our number system.* In order to have pupils understand better the meanings of the arithmetic they are studying, pupils are being led to discover the laws of the number system—associative, commutative, distributive. Pupils can then see how these laws explain the arithmetic processes that they have been doing by rote. For some gifted students, the work in computation in the decimal system was also made more meaningful by a study of modular arithmetics, a study of their properties, closure, identities, and inverses, and a look at the natural numbers and the whole numbers as mathematical systems.

[From "Whither Arithmetic in Grades Seven and Eight?" *Education*, LXXIX (January, 1959), pp. 280-86. Reprinted by permission of the publishers, The Bobbs-Merrill Co., Inc., Indianapolis.]

3. *Elementary number theory.* A natural extension of pupils' knowledge of computing is a study of fascinating facts about numbers from elementary number theory. Many pupils have "cast out nines." Why does this work? When doesn't it work? In base-8 arithmetic, can we cast out sevens? Which numbers are divisible by 2, 3, 4, 5, 8, 9, etc.?

4. *Deductive reasoning.* Since mathematics is the science of deductive reasoning, it is reasonable that pupils should get this idea before studying geometry in the tenth grade where this aspect of mathematics is emphasized particularly. For simple but exciting things, each of the experiments mentioned above included some work with logic and with postulates and simple theorems.

JUNIOR HIGH SCHOOL MATHEMATICS FOR THE COLLEGE-BOUND STUDENT

Commission on Mathematics

The Commission's program is necessarily predicated on certain learnings expected of students before they begin the program. There are in the United States a number of different arrangements of school organization, commonly known as 8-4, 6-3-3, 6-6, and 7-5, where the numbers indicate, respectively, years of study in each division of an elementary and secondary school system. Presumably, regardless of school organization, the mathematics studied year by year should be practically the same under all plans. This is not the case, however. Textbooks written for the seventh and eighth year of study in an eight-year elementary program (8-4) stress arithmetic more, and informal geometry much less, than books written explicitly for a junior high school program (6-3-3).

The Commission recognizes the need for a careful study of the mathematics program of grades 7 and 8 (and, indeed, of the earlier grades as well). But this is not the task of the Commission. To fill this gap, it must rely on other groups such as the School Mathematics Study Group, the University of Maryland Mathematics Project, and the Curriculum Committees of the National Council of Teachers of Mathematics.

This much can be said: regardless of the form of school organization, in order to give students in grades 7 and 8 the type of mathematics study

[From *Program for College-Preparatory Mathematics* (New York: College Entrance Examination Board, 1959), pp. 18-20. Reprinted by permission of the Commission on Mathematics.]

that will form a proper foundation for the Commission's program, the following subject matter is regarded as essential. The Commission is convinced that it can be mastered by all college-capable students during grades 7 and 8. The better students can cover this work in one to one-and-a-half years and move on to the Commission's program during the eighth school year.

Arithmetic

Fundamental operations and numeration—Mastery of the four fundamental operations with whole numbers and fractions, written in decimal notation and in the common notation used for fractions. This includes skill in the operations at adult level (i.e., adequate for ordinary life situations) and an understanding of the rationale of the computational processes. Understanding of a place system of writing numbers, with use of binary notation (and perhaps other bases) to reinforce decimal notation. Ability to handle very large numbers (greater than 1,000,000) and very small numbers (less than one ten-thousandth). The meaning and use of an arithmetic mean. In addition, a knowledge of square root and the ability to find approximate values of square roots of whole numbers is desirable. (The process of division and averaging the divisor and quotient —Newton's method—is suggested.)

Ratio—Understanding of ratio as used in comparing sizes of quantities of like kind, in proportions, and in making scale drawings. Per cent as an application of ratio. Understanding of the language of per cent (rate), percentage, and base. In particular the ability to find any one of these three designated numbers, given the other two. Ability to treat with confidence per cents less than 1 and greater than 100. Applications of per cent to business practices, interest, discount, and budgets should be given moderate treatment.

Geometry

Measurement—The ability to operate with and transform the several systems of measure, including the metric system of length, area, volume, and weight. Geometric measurements, including length of a line segment, perimeter of a polygon, and circumference of a circle, areas of regions enclosed by polygons and circles, surface areas of solids, volumes of solids, measure of angles (by degrees). The use of a ruler and protractor. The student should know the difference between the process of measuring and the measure of the quantity. Ability to apply measurement to practical situations. Use of measurement in drawing to scale and finding lengths indirectly.

Relationships among geometric elements—These include the concepts of parallel, perpendicular, intersecting, and oblique lines (in a plane and in a space); acute, right, obtuse, complementary, supplementary, and vertical angles; scalene, isosceles, and equilateral triangles; right triangles and the Pythagorean relation; sum of the interior angles of a triangle. The use of instruments in constructing figures; ideas of symmetry about a point and a line.

Algebra and Statistics

Graphs and Formulas—Use of line segments and areas to represent numbers. Reading and construction of bar graphs, line graphs, pictograms, circle graphs, and continuous line graphs. Meaning of scale. Formulas for perimeters, areas, volumes, and per cents—introduced as generalizations as these concepts are studied. Use of symbols in formulas as place-holders for numerals arising in measurement. Simple expressions and sentences involving "variables."

UNIVERSITY OF MARYLAND MATHEMATICS PROJECT FOR THE JUNIOR HIGH SCHOOL

M. L. Keedy

The content of both courses was chosen in such a way that several basic principles are followed. It was felt, for one thing, that the separation of algebra and arithmetic, which is usually made, is artificial and detrimental to learning. Therefore no distinction is ever made between the two subjects in the UMMaP [University of Maryland Mathematics Project] courses. The word *algebra* never appears, even though the equivalent of first-year algebra, as traditionally taught, is embodied in the two years' work. Rather, *properties of numbers* are studied, and those properties used to carry out calculations, solutions of equations, factoring and the like.

It is also known to be important to seek unifying concepts, in order that the total number of basic ideas may be reduced. Unifying concepts of several kinds have been used in the courses. Among the most important

[From "Mathematics in Junior High School," *Educational Leadership*, XVII (December, 1959), pp. 158-59. Reprinted by permission of the author and the Association for Supervision and Curriculum Development.]

of these is the concept of a *mathematical system*, which is introduced early and used again and again.

A third fundamental principle concerns the use of language. It soon becomes apparent to those concerned with the precise expression and communication of ideas that the language traditionally used in mathematics is heavily lacking in precision. Present vocabulary and habits of usage have been accumulated over thousands of years of mathematical activity, and one easily finds vague and contradictory notions, as well as a lack of words with which to express today's mathematical ideas clearly and briefly. Therefore the writers have spent considerable effort in clarifying ideas by altering language and using it precisely.

A fourth fundamental principle is that the student should *understand* mathematics, rather than simply learn by rote a variety of manipulative skills. Furthermore, motivation and retention should be far greater when students can be led to make discoveries themselves. For these reasons the course materials, including texts and teacher manuals, have been written so as strongly to encourage discovery on the part of students. The discovery is to be both inductive and deductive, in accordance with good mathematical method. The deductive reasoning on the part of students is first very informal, becoming gradually more and more formal.

THE ROLE OF UNIFYING CONCEPTS

Richard D. Crumley

One of the important contributions of modern curriculum theory has been the determination of the role of *unifying concepts*. This role has been described in some detail by Tyler.[1] Unifying concepts are those concepts that occur again and again in a variety of situations. For this reason many of them can be used effectively to produce a better curriculum and to bring about better learning. It is my purpose to call attention to a few of these unifying ideas in the area of arithmetic and to indicate how these concepts might be used to advantage.

[From "Unifying Ideas in the Arithmetic Curriculum," *School Science and Mathematics,* LVIII (May, 1958), pp. 341-46. Reprinted by permission of the author and *School Science and Mathematics.*]

---

[1] Ralph W. Tyler, *Basic Principles of Curriculum and Instruction* (Chicago, Illinois: The University of Chicago Press, 1950), p. 83.

The use of unifying concepts in arithmetic and mathematics would seem to be quite natural because of the interrelation of the various elements making up this branch of knowledge. Most of us are quite aware of the way that ideas and skills build upon other ideas and skills in arithmetic. What we need to do is to capitalize upon this stair-step arrangement of the concepts in arithmetic.

Let us now examine three concepts which serve well as unifying concepts in arithmetic. These three are not the only unifying concepts that we should use, but they seem to be very important ones.

The first example is the well-known concept that *our decimal system of symbolizing numbers is based upon grouping by tens.*

The second unifying concept that I would like to call attention to is the concept that *in measuring something we use a unit of measure.*

Let us now consider a third unifying concept—the concept of *rate.*

.   .   .   .

It is hoped that the three unifying concepts mentioned have illustrated how useful and important such concepts are. Good textbooks are organized in such a way as to take advantage of some unifying concepts, and textbooks will be better when more unifying concepts are used. Teachers, of course, are in a position to help the child unify his learning by calling attention to the ways in which the various concepts and skills of arithmetic are related. Teachers can often be more effective in doing this than textbooks. After we become aware of the great worth of the use of unifying concepts, we ought to make every effort to understand them and their use. A greatly improved arithmetic curriculum is sufficient reward for our efforts.

THE MATHEMATICS PROGRAM

Texas Curriculum Studies

More attention is being given to (1) the structure of the number system, (2) the meaning of the fundamental processes and their relationships, and (3) the general mathematical principles for operations with numbers.

[From the report of the Commission on Mathematics, *Texas Curriculum Studies* (Austin, Texas: Texas Education Agency, July, 1959), pp. 15-18. Reprinted by permission of the Texas Education Agency.]

1. An understanding of the decimal number system is basic to an understanding of the language of arithmetic. Knowing that numbers are regrouped on the base of ten and that the place of a digit in a numeral determines its value simplifies the interpretation and the manipulation of numbers. This helps pupils understand the need for a zero or an equivalent concept. It gives meaning to the algorisms (the way the figures are arranged in a computation) of the four fundamental processes. It simplifies work with decimal fractions as children become aware of the fact that the place-value principles of the number system operates with fractions whose denominators are powers of 10. It involves comprehending that in moving to the left from one's place, each successive digit has ten times the value it would have in the preceding place, and that in moving to the right from one's place, each successive digit has one-tenth the value it would have in the preceding place.

.   .   .   .

2. Careful teaching of the meanings and the interrelationships of the four fundamental processes is necessary if satisfactory problem solving ability is to be developed. Elementary school pupils should be guided in the discovery of such essential meanings and relationships as the following:

a) Addition is the process of combining two or more groups to form a single group. It is a short cut of counting and may be checked by counting.

b) When the sum of any two one-digit numbers is more than ten, the sum is found by making a group of ten and some ones.

c) Subtraction is the inverse of addition and may be checked by addition.

d) Multiplication is a short way of adding groups of equal magnitude.

e) Division is the inverse of multiplication and may be checked by multiplication.

3. A pupil grows in his ability to apply certain fundamental principles of operation with numbers as his understanding of the fundamental processes increases and as he gains insight into number relationships. The teacher should take advantage of every opportunity to emphasize the meaning, use, and importance of these principles. Some of the most important principles are:

a) *The closure law for addition*—The sum of any two natural numbers (counting numbers) always yields another natural number. That is, $4 + 5 = 9$; $a + b = c$; etc., when a, b, and c denote any numbers used in arithmetic.

b) *The closure law for multiplication*—The product of any two natural numbers always yields another natural number. That is $2 \times 4 = 8$; $a \times b = c$, etc., when a, b, and c denote any numbers used in arithmetic.

c) *The commutative law of addition*—Two numbers can be added in any order without affecting the sum. That is, $3 + 2 = 2 + 3$; $a + b = b + a$, etc. when a and b denote any numbers used in arithmetic.

This law is applied in teaching the basic addition facts and in checking column addition by adding in the opposite direction.

d) *The commutative law of multiplication*—The order in which two numbers are multiplied does not affect the product. That is, $3 \times 4 = 4 \times 3$; $a \times b = b \times a$, etc., when a and b denote any numbers used in arithmetic.

This law is applied in teaching the basic multiplication facts and in checking multiplication by interchanging the multiplier and the multiplicand.

e) *The associative law of addition*—Three addends [1] may be grouped in any order without affecting the sum. That is, in adding $9 + 3 + 7$, we may group the addends thus: $(9 + 3) + 7$; $9 + (3 + 7)$; $(9 + 7) + 3$. Generally stated, $a + b + c = (a + b) + c = a + (b + c) = (a + c) + b$ when a, b, and c denote any numbers used in arithmetic.

The application of this law leads to increased skill in mental computation. For example, in adding $9 + 2 + 6 + 7$, we regroup the addends to $(9 + 2 + 7) + 6$ and think "two 9's $+ 6 = 24$." Likewise, in adding $2\frac{1}{3} + 7\frac{1}{5} + 3\frac{2}{3}$, we regroup the addends to $(3\frac{2}{3} + 2\frac{1}{3}) + 7\frac{1}{5}$ and think, "$6 + 7\frac{1}{5} = 13\frac{1}{5}$."

f) *The associative law of multiplication*—Three factors [2] may be grouped in any order without affecting the product. That is, in multiplying $3 \times 4 \times 2$, we may group the factors thus: $(3 \times 4) \times 2$; $(3 \times 2) \times 4$; $(2 \times 4) \times 3$. Generally stated $a \times b \times c = (a \times b) \times c = a \times (b \times c) = (a \times c) \times b$ when a, b, and c denote any numbers used in arithmetic.

The application of this law leads to certain shortcuts in multiplication as the most convenient grouping is chosen. For example, in finding the

---

[1] This law should be extended to any number of addends.
[2] This law should be extended to any number of factors.

product of $2 \times 7 \times 5$, one views it as $2 \times 5 \times 7$ and thinks "$10 \times 7 = 70$." In finding the product of $67 \times 25 \times 4$, one thinks "$67 \times (25 \times 4) = 67 \times 100 = 6700$."

g) *The distributive law which links the process of multiplication with addition*—The sum of two numbers may be multiplied by a third number by adding the numbers and multiplying or by multiplying each of the numbers and then adding the products. Thus, $3(4 + 3) = 3 \times 7$ or $(3 \times 4) + (3 \times 3)$; $a(b \times c) = (a \times b) + (a \times c)$, etc., when *a*, *b*, and *c* denote any numbers used in arithmetic.

This idea is essential in deriving a rule for multiplying by a two-digit numeral. It is also essential for explaining the multiplication algorism. For example:

$$
\begin{aligned}
26 &= (20 + 6) \\
\times 42 &= (40 + 2) \\
\hline
52 &= (2 \times 6) + (2 \times 20) \\
104 \ &= (40 \times 6) + (40 \times 20) \\
\hline
1092 &= (2 \times 6) + (2 \times 20) + (40 \times 6) + (40 \times 20)
\end{aligned}
$$

This law can also be seen at work in finding the perimeter of a rectangle. In using the formula, $p = 2 (1 \times w)$, with $1 = 6$ and $w = 4$, the perimeter can be found in either of the following ways:

$$p = 2(6 + 4) = 12 + 8 = 20 \qquad p = 2(6 + 4) = 2 \times 10 = 20$$

h) *The product-factor relationship*—If two factors are known, the product can be found by multiplying; if the product of two numbers is not zero and one of the factors is known, the other factor can be found by dividing the product by the known factor. That is, if $4 \times 3 = n$, $n = 12$; if $n \times 4 = 12$, $n = 12 \div 4$. (This solution grows out of an understanding of the relationship between the multiplication and division processes. Pupils who see the relationship clearly come to think of the product as the dividend and the factors as the divisor and the quotient of that dividend.) The usual way to solve the equation "$n \times 4 = 12$" is to divide both members of the equation by the same number, thus: $\dfrac{n \times 4}{4} = \dfrac{12}{4}$. This method of solving such an equation can be used after pupils have been taught that both members of an equation may be divided by the same non-zero number without changing the value of the equation.

This principle has wide application in arithmetic since many problem situations involve finding a product when two factors are known or finding one factor when the product and one factor are known. For example:

Find the percentage when the base and rate are known.
Find the rate when the percentage and the base are known.
Find the commission when the amount of the sales and the rate are known.
Find the number of items when the price of one item and the total cost are known.
Find the rate when the distance and the time are known.
Find the length when the area and width are known.

i) *The fundamental principle of fractions*—The value of a fraction is not changed if both the numerator and the denominator are multiplied or divided by the same number, excepting zero. That is,

$$\frac{2}{3} = \frac{4}{6} = \frac{8}{12}; \frac{8}{16} = \frac{4}{8} = \frac{1}{2}; \text{etc.}$$

This principle is applied in changing fractions to lowest terms, raising fractions to higher terms, changing an integer or a mixed number to an improper fraction, and changing an improper fraction to a mixed number. Its application is necessary in the addition and subtraction of fractions and is useful in comparing the values of fractions. In fact, most of the work with fractions is simply an application of this principle and it is exceedingly important that children really understand it (not just know what it says).

CONTENT VARIATION

Casis School Faculty

If content variation is accepted as an operating principle, what does it imply? It means that some topics are not studied by some children, that some topics are studied to a greater depth by some pupils, and that some topics are studied earlier or later by some children than by others. Nine ways of content variation are discussed below:

[From *Meeting Individual Differences in Arithmetic,* Bureau of Laboratory Schools Publication No. 11 (Austin, Texas: The University of Texas, 1959), pp. 8-11. Reprinted by permission of the Bureau of Laboratory Schools.]

1. Certain topics might be omitted from the program for those who have difficulty in achieving proficiency in arithmetic. Roman numerals, short division and column addition involving more than four addends and addends containing more than three digits are examples of such omissions at the third and fourth grade levels. Three-step word problems, square measure, cubic measure, perimeter, and the area of rectangles and triangles are examples of such omissions at the fifth and sixth grade levels.

2. For certain topics studied by all some children would not be expected to undertake work on as high a level of difficulty as other pupils. Working with larger numbers and more addends in addition of whole numbers, larger minuends and subtrahends and more involved borrowing in the subtraction of whole numbers are examples of higher level performances not expected of slow learners of arithmetic. Confining the work in fractions in the third and fourth grades to halves, thirds, and fourths represents a lower level of expectation for these learners. In grades five and six the slow learners of arithmetic would not be urged to carry their level of performance to include dividing by decimals, dividing by a three-place number, multiplying by a three-place number, reading and writing decimal fractions smaller than thousandths, reading and writing whole numbers beyond hundred-thousands, addition and subtraction of unrelated fractions (e.g., $\frac{1}{4} + \frac{1}{3}$), multiplying a fraction by a fraction (an operation seldom required in daily life), and dividing a fraction by a fraction.

3. On some topics studied by all pupils the abler ones could be urged to attain higher levels of understanding and performance than their less able classmates. In a sense all the illustrations given in the preceding paragraph also illustrate the type of content variation discussed in this paragraph. But there are still other ways in which rapid learners of arithmetic can be helped to rise to higher levels of attainment on topics studied by all. In third and fourth grades above-average achievers may be introduced to unusual counting exercises such as counting forward or backward by unusual units (e.g., start at 27 and count by 4 to 80) or to become proficient in such exercises as "Follow the Leader" in mental arithmetic $(6 \times 3 + 4 + 8 \div 6 \times 8 - 7 =)$. Examples at fifth and sixth grade levels consist of duplation multiplication, lattice multiplication, two methods for deciding on the quotient figure when dividing by a two-place divisor, and the two ways of dividing common fractions.

4. Topics not found in the typical course of study could be added for rapid learners of arithmetic. Learning to count and to perform the four fundamental operations with whole numbers having a base other than 10, learning to use early ways of telling time or early measures, factoring, finding median and mode, finding square root, figuring longitude, study-

ing foreign money and rates of exchange, understanding unusual measures such as carat, horsepower, and acre-feet are examples that fall in this classification.

5. Rapid learners of arithmetic can be provided with horizontal enrichment consisting of social applications of the computational skills normally studied in a given grade. Examples at the third and fourth grade levels include such exercises as finding the elements of cost which must be covered in the price of a quart of milk, adjusting recipes in cooking, determining how club dues are used, and finding the cost of keeping a dog. In fifth and sixth grades some pupils can figure the cost of medical care for the family, study the reasons for and uses of a retail sales tax in states which collect such a tax, study time around the world, find the cost of an education, study the questions one must resolve regarding automobile insurance, learn about freight rates, measure air pressure, find the cost of advertising in the local paper, keep accounts in the school cafeteria, and find the cost of installment buying or the cost of mortgages.

6. Above-average achievers can be provided with types of horizontal enrichment which stimulate the mathematical appetite and foster an interest in mathematics as a hobby. Among the exercises suggested by Spitzer as useful for this purpose are a clock puzzle, constructing a sundial, measuring the angle of the sun, measuring a silk thread, and finding an unknown dividend and quotient.

7. Below-average achievers may also profit from experiences with simple materials of this kind to provide "fun with numbers." The program can be enriched for rapid learners of arithmetic by permitting them to study topics normally allocated to higher grades. This means that some pupils would move forward in the arithmetic program at a faster rate than others. Rapid learners in first and second grades might be permitted to complete the learning of all the basic addition and subtraction facts, to read and write numbers into the thousands, to add and subtract two-place numbers with carrying and borrowing. Third and fourth graders might move into the meaning of per cent and the adding and subtracting of unlike fractions. Fifth or sixth graders might tackle areas of parallelograms and circles; measuring angles, gas, and electricity; budgeting; square root; ratio; interest; and commissions. In a sense this type of adaptation results in time variation as well as in content variation, thus illustrating how these two avenues may intermingle.

8. The introduction of some topics is delayed for slow learners of arithmetic. If the rapid learners are permitted to advance through the common offering at a faster pace, it seems logical to make the opposite adjustment for the slow learners. In the first two grades familiarity with measures, the understanding of simple fractions, and reading and writing numbers

beyond 100 illustrate topics whose initial presentation might be postponed to a later grade. At the third and fourth grade levels slow learners might be given a reprieve on the multiplication and division facts and types of problems involving these operations. Understanding decimal fractions and multiplying and dividing common and decimal fractions could become topics for delayed introduction from grade five or six.

9. Extra practice exercises with different content can be provided for any pupil who needs more than the usual amount of practice to establish facility with a given process or operation.

HISTORICAL CONTENT

Carroll V. Newsom

A good teacher cannot afford to ignore the historical background of his subject. The biologists have their theory of recapitulation which states that to a great extent each individual in his early development reproduces in himself the early evolution of the race. I sincerely believe, more than we sometimes realize, that each student develops in his understanding of mathematics along much the same line that history reveals that man developed. This is especially true, I believe, of our students of arithmetic. It is apparent, of course, that too rigid an interpretation can be placed upon this statement, but I, as a teacher, must admit my own indebtedness to my study of man's historical struggle to build the remarkable system called mathematics. A knowledge of history is imperative for other reasons. The evolution of such a discipline as mathematics cannot be separated from the rest of the stream of history; mathematics has been a contributor and a recipient in terms of the other factors of civilization. The fact that mathematics is a living body should dominate the attitudes of the teacher and should be portrayed to our students.

[From "Some Observations on the Contemporary Mathematical Scene," *The Arithmetic Teacher*, VI (October, 1959), pp. 191-94. Reprinted by permission of the author and *The Arithmetic Teacher*.]

THE MAN-MADENESS OF MATHEMATICS

M. Vere DeVault

Three important routes through which teachers are approaching an understanding of the man-madeness of mathematics are: (1) an understanding of symbolism in mathematics, (2) an understanding of the systematic organization of quantitative symbols, (3) the story of man's creation and use of symbols and organization of symbols. Elementary classroom teachers contribute to each of these objectives in a variety of ways.

[From "Mathematics as a Man-Made Invention in the Elementary Classroom," *The Bulletin of the National Association of Secondary-School Principals,* XLIII (May, 1959), pp. 111-13. Reprinted by permission of the author and the National Association of Secondary School Principals.]

A PRESENT-DAY ELEMENTARY MATHEMATICS PROGRAM

E. Glenadine Gibb

Past experience should be a guiding star, not a hitching post. In teaching mathematics, perhaps more than in any other subject, we need to keep this epigram in mind. In mathematics, we have developed and maintained a traditional sequence of study. Yet, we have very little experimental evidence to support the belief that this sequence is better than other possible sequences.

The demands of the world today and the expected requirements of tomorrow have necessitated a re-examination of the traditional elementary-school, secondary-school, and college mathematics curriculums. As a result, there is now much activity and interest in the development of new programs in mathematics—programs which regard mathematics as a study and classification of possible structures and not as a study of tricks and rules.

[From "Some Approaches to Mathematics Concepts in the Elementary School," *Journal of the National Education Association,* XLVIII (November, 1959), pp. 65-6. Reprinted by permission of the author and the *Journal of the National Education Association.*]

In re-examining our present mathematics programs, we ask ourselves several questions:

1. Do elementary concepts from the newer fields of mathematics, such as set theory, game theory, topology, and symbolic logic, have a place in our school mathematics curriculum, and if so, what is that place?

2. Does our program place its heaviest emphasis on developing understanding of techniques or is it based on developing an understanding of mathematical ideas?

3. Do we find mathematics being taught as merely a set of rules explained by the teacher followed by the pupil's practice in using them, or is there also a spirit of inquiry and discovery in the classroom as experiences are selected for developing mathematical ideas?

4. Are we too concerned with isolated ideas at particular grade levels and in certain courses, or do we sense the unifying ideas which permeate the school mathematics program?

Number and Its Name

From early childhood, children learn to associate names with ideas. They learn that a whole class of animals may be given the name *dog*. Some of these animals are black and others are white. Others are red, brown, spotted, gray, big, little, short-haired, long-haired.

Children learn that certain characteristics enable them to distinguish which animals are dogs regardless of many differences. Furthermore, they learn that an ordered set of letters, *d-o-g*, spells the word they have learned to associate orally with that class of animal.

In a similar way, a child comes to learn about the nature of number. He learns that there is a name given to the number of a set of objects.

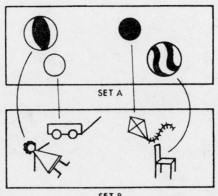

SET A

SET B

How can a child tell if the number name of one set is also the number name for another set? He may, for instance, learn that the number name of Set A (page 62) is four. He also learns that if he can match this set of four balls with a set of toys (Set B page 62), by means of one-to-one correspondence, and there is a ball for each toy and a toy for each ball, then the number of Set B is the same as that of Set A, or that four is the number common to both sets.

In guiding early number experiences of young children, the teacher should be familiar with the nature of those classroom experiences that help children in developing the concept of number and those experiences that are mere means of learning a set of number names.

Too often, "learning our numbers" has been a matter of learning to make symbols and learning to count. Thus, experiences are selected for developing the idea of number names and a process for determining those names.

Mathematical Systems

In the primary grades, children learn that putting a group of five objects with a group of three objects gives the same result as putting a group of three objects with a group of five objects. In symbols, they learn to write $5 + 3 = 8$ and $3 + 5 = 8$.

Later, they express this mathematical pattern in more general terms by saying if $a + b = c$, then $b + a = c$ and that $a + b = b + a$. They learn that the order in which they add numbers makes no difference in the result.

Likewise, when adding three or more numbers, they learn that only a pair of these numbers can be added at one time and that it makes no difference which pair is added first.

Similar relationships in multiplication are taught. Children learn that the order in adding or multiplying a pair of whole numbers not only makes no difference in the result, but also that the sum or product is another whole number.

However, if they change the order of a pair of numbers in subtraction, they are unable to come up with a whole number as their answer; that is, if $5 - 2$ is changed to $2 - 5$, one is unable to give a whole number as the result in both situations. A similar situation is encountered in division.

Clearly in these situations, children learn that there are no answers in the set of whole numbers. In later years, they learn that there are other number systems which have numbers that are answers to these examples; that is, $2 - 5 = -3$, and $2 \div 8 = \frac{2}{8}$ or $\frac{1}{4}$.

Understandings about the elements of a mathematical system have their beginnings in the elementary school. If we teach arithmetic merely as a collection of isolated skills, it becomes more difficult for the student to arrive at the idea of a mathematical system.

Different Names—Same Number

To help children to better understand the concept of number and our decimal system of numeration, a study of other systems of numeration may be found helpful. This approach is now being used experimentally in the junior high school, and also has been used effectively by fifth- and sixth-grade teachers.

The following illustrations may help to show what patterns children see in systems of numeration other than the decimal system:

Suppose we use different systems of numeration to name the number of the sets of dots below. Remember that the number remains the same. In

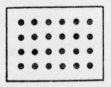

our decimal system of numeration, we group by tens. Our collection of dots appears as:

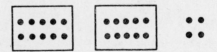

We name this number 24, or 2 groups of tens and 4 ones.

If we group by sixes, our collection of dots appears as:

We name the number 40, or 4 groups of sixes and no ones.

If we use a base of three, our collection of dots appears as:

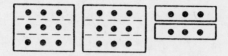

We name the number 220 or 2 nines, 2 threes, and no ones. Written another way it is $[2 \times (3 \times 3)] + [2 \times 3] + [0 \times 1]$.

Children come to see the general pattern of place value as:

	base X base	base	ones
For base of ten			
For base of six			
For base of three			
For any base	b^2	b^1	b^0

We can also interpret the meaning of a numeral in such a way as to explain different systems of numeration to children. We can use the idea of place value to explain that in the numeral 245, for example, the 5 means 5 ones, the 4 means 4 groups of the base, and the 2 means 2 groups of the base squared.

If the grouping is by tens, 245 means $[2 \times (10 \times 10)] + [4 \times 10] + [5 \times 1]$ or more simply, $(2 \times 100) + (4 \times 10) + 5$. If the grouping is by sixes, then 245 means $[2 \times (6 \times 6] + [4 \times 6] + [5 \times 1]$ or $(2 \times 36) + (4 \times 6) + 5$. These ideas of different systems of numeration may be further extended to operations of addition, subtraction, multiplication, and division.

The study of numeration systems using other bases also provides an opportunity for children to examine characteristics of certain properties of numbers. How do children learn to distinguish between even numbers and odd numbers? Do they recognize even numbers because they end in 0, 2, 4, 6, 8? Let us examine the number of dots in the sets below:

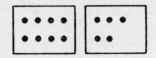

We say the number in the set at the left is even. The number in the set at right is odd. The name for the number of dots on the left, we say, is 8. We also name this number 11 (base seven), 12 (base six), 13 (base five), 20 (base four), 22 (base three).

Regardless of the names (11, 12, 13, 20, 22) the number still remains even—the elements can be separated into an exact number of pairs.

Similarly, we commonly say the number of dots on the right is five and that five is an odd or non-even number. Yet, other names for this set of dots are 10 (base five), 11 (base four), 12 (base three), and 101 (base two). 3, 7, 9, and 11 are also other odd numbers. If we know the base, is there some way of knowing whether the number is even or odd? Children are quick to see the pattern which helps them to make this decision.

Re-examining the Curriculum

Often trouble spots in teaching give us our only reasons to search for new approaches for developing arithmetical concepts. Perhaps all of our ideas about teaching mathematics need to be re-examined with an eye toward new and better means of developing them and with a question as to whether or not these particular concepts should properly be developed in the elementary school.

In all our curriculum considerations, may we provide opportunities for our students to study mathematics in terms of *structure* and *pattern* rather than in terms of *rules* and *tricks*.

COMING CHANGES

William A. Brownell

Important as have been the changes in the arithmetic programs in our elementary schools during the last half century, other equally far-reaching

[From "Arithmetic in 1970," *The National Elementary Principal,* XXXIX (October, 1959), pp. 42-5. Reprinted by permission of the author and *The National Elementary Principal.*]

changes are in the making. What some of them will be, it takes no gift of prophecy to predict. The directions of these changes, which will affect content, grade placement, and instructional emphasis, are already fore-shadowed in current happenings.

I shall deal here with only four kinds of change that will take place in the years to come. They are:

1. Much of the traditional content of arithmetic will be taught sooner.

2. Greater prominence will be given to the mathematical aspects of the subject.

3. Practicable means will be found to accommodate effectively differences in learning ability.

4. The program in the higher grades will include much that is new.

For each of these statements I should like to explain briefly what is meant and why arithmetic as a school subject will be altered in the manner indicated.

Traditional Content Taught Sooner

One important change is that much of the traditional content of arithmetic will be taught sooner. This change marks the reversal of an unfortunate trend that began some thirty years ago.

. . . .

With the return of arithmetic, and a better kind of arithmetic, to the primary grades, much that in the "stepped-up curriculum" had to be done in grade three is actually being done beforehand. And the process of shifting downward the concepts, skills, and mathematical principles and relationships until recently taught in later grades has already begun. In another ten years, the grade placement of topics may differ little from what it was thirty years ago, except possibly for the most difficult aspects of this content. These may be retained about where they are, in order to spread learning over a longer period of time. For the "stepped-up curriculum" a "stretched-out curriculum" will almost certainly be substituted.

Emphasis on Mathematical Aspects

Another change will give greater prominence to the mathematical aspects of the subject.

This is not the place to catalogue all the mathematical ideas, principles, relationships, and generalizations now a part of "meaningful arithmetic." But they are numerous and they will become more numerous. Groups of mathematicians at the University of Illinois, the University of Maryland, and Yale University, together with commissions and committees of national mathematical organizations, originally motivated by the desire to improve secondary mathematics, are now turning their attention to arithmetic. It is too early to predict the fruitfulness of their explorations concerning the place of such mathematical ideas as set, symbolism, and verification in arithmetic; but they are certain to influence the arithmetic program of the higher grades and will probably affect to some extent that in the lower grades as well. As a matter of fact, their influence *could be too great* if their activities should produce a sterile arithmetic. By this term, I mean arithmetic as the pure science of number, taught with little regard for the ability of children to learn it or for the social purposes to be served. This danger, however, is unlikely to become a reality, for forces are available within the schools to counteract it.

Accommodating Learning Differences

Practicable means will be found to accommodate effectively differences in learning ability. Attempts to adjust content and methods of teaching to individual differences in learning ability have been none too successful, and published instructional materials have been only moderately helpful.

New Content for Higher Grades

The program in the higher grades will include much that is new. Texts and courses of study for the higher grades still contain long sections on such topics as insurance, investments, and banking. These materials are taught because arithmetic is involved in each and because the study of such topics is supposed to "prepare for life." But children aged 12 or 14 do not themselves take out insurance policies or seek to obtain mortgages. It may be ten years or more before they do, and by that time much that they learned in school will have been forgotten. Furthermore, other more profitable ways of putting arithmetic to work through applications are available. As a consequence, much of the so-called "social arithmetic" (but not the major concepts) will disappear from the arithmetic of the higher grades.

One is less confident in stating what will take its place, but not because of a dearth of possibilities. For the average child in the higher grades some of the possibilities include more or new work on: statistics, approximation, mental computation with short cuts, the history and cultural contribution of arithmetic and of mathematics in general, number systems other than our own (with bases of 8, 5, and 2, for example), mathematical procedures like casting out 9's as a means of checking computations, very large and very small numbers, intuitive geometry, and algebraic concepts to assure readiness for a later grade.

The list is long but could easily be made longer. Choice among such topics as those mentioned will need to be made. A limiting circumstance is time. There may well be more time than we now foresee, particularly if (as we anticipated elsewhere in this article) much arithmetical content is moved downward, if the rearranged content is taught with greater emphasis on its mathematical aspects, and if non-functional social subject matter now in the program for the higher grades is removed.

So much for higher grade arithmetic for the learner of average ability. Now what about arithmetic for the slow learner and for the rapid learner? For the former, the present content for grades one through six would seem to be adequate, and the changes called for are related rather to instructional methods than to the addition of new topics. For the rapid learner, probably *all* of the content mentioned above for the average learner is appropriate, and the treatment in each instance can be extended. There can be added, too, the study of prime numbers, a rational approach to square root, elements of the calculus, and many other mathematical procedures and concepts now under consideration.

Changes Will Be Made

There is no question at all that, partly because of the nation's need for more scientists and mathematicians and partly because of the criticism of the present elementary curriculum as demanding less than it should, changes will have to be made. But the situation is far from desperate, for we know at least some of the changes that are called for. Whatever they may prove to be, one thing is certain: Arithmetic ten years hence will be quite different from what it is today.

BIBLIOGRAPHY

Brownell, William A. "A Critique of the Committee of Seven's Investigations on the Grade Placement of Arithmetic Topics," *Elementary School Journal,* XXXVIII (March, 1938), 495-508.

———. "Arithmetic in 1970," *The National Elementary Principal,* XXXIX (October, 1959), 42-5.

———. "Observations of Instruction in Lower Grade Arithmetic in English and Scottish Schools," *The Arithmetic Teacher,* VII (April, 1960), 165-77.

———. "Revolution in Arithmetic," *The Arithmetic Teacher,* I (February, 1954), 1-5.

Brueckner, Leo J. "The Development of Ability in Arithmetic," *Child Development and the Curriculum*, National Society for the Study of Education, Thirty-eighth Yearbook (1939), Part I, 275-98.

——. "Social Contributions of Arithmetic," *The National Elementary Principal*, XXX (October, 1950), 7-10.

——, Foster E. Grossnickle, and John Reckzeh. *Developing Mathematical Understandings in the Upper Grades*. New York: Holt, Rinehart & Winston, Inc., 1957, pp. 1-58.

Buckingham, B. R. "Significance, Meaning, Insight—These Three," *The Mathematics Teacher*, XXXI (January, 1938), 24-30.

——. "Social Point of View in Arithmetic," *The Teaching of Arithmetic*, National Society for the Study of Education, Fiftieth Yearbook (1951). Chicago: University of Chicago Press, Part II, 269-81.

Buswell, Guy T. "The Content and Organization of Arithmetic," *The Arithmetic Teacher*, VI (March, 1959), 77-83.

Casis School Faculty, eds. Frances Flournoy and Henry J. Otto. *Meeting Individual Differences in Arithmetic*, Bureau of Laboratory Schools Publication No. 11. Austin: The University of Texas, 1959, 8-11.

Commission on Mathematics. *The Mathematics of the Seventh and Eighth Grades*. New York: College Entrance Examination Board, 1957.

——. *Program for College-Preparatory Mathematics*. New York: College Entrance Examination Board, 1959.

Crumley, R. D. "Unifying Ideas in the Arithmetic Curriculum," *School Science and Mathematics*, LVIII (May, 1958), 341-46.

——. "Teaching Rate and Ratio in the Middle Grades," *School Science and Mathematics*, LX (February, 1960), 143-50.

Deans, Edwina. "Arithmetic in the Primary Grades," *The National Elementary Principal*, XXXIX (October, 1959), 22-8.

De Francis, J. "Elementary Math Program in Russia," *School Science and Mathematics*, LX (April, 1960), 301-13.

DeVault, M. Vere. "Mathematics as a Man-Made Invention in the Elementary Classroom," *The Bulletin of the National Association of Secondary-School Principals*, XLIII (May, 1959), 111-13.

Dickey, J. W. "Comments on Middle-Grade Arithmetic," *The Arithmetic Teacher*, V (February, 1958), 37-8.

Eads, Laura K. "A Mathematics Curriculum for the Elementary Schools," *Education*, LXXIX (January, 1959), 295-98.

Flournoy, Frances. "Relating Arithmetic to Everyday Life," *The National Elementary Principal*, XXXIX (October, 1959), 29-32.

Gager, W. A. "Functional Approach to Elementary and Secondary Mathematics," *The Mathematics Teacher*, L (January, 1957), 30-4.

Garstens, Helen L., M. L. Keedy, and John R. Mayor. "University of Maryland Mathematics Project," *The Arithmetic Teacher*, VII (February, 1960), 61-66.

Genise, L. R. "Impact of the Maryland and Yale Programs," *The Arithmetic Teacher,* VII (February, 1960), 66-70.

Gibb, E. Glenadine. "Some Approaches to Mathematics Concepts in the Elementary School," *Journal of the National Education Association,* XLVIII (November, 1959), 65-6.

Glennon, Vincent J. "Arithmetic for the Gifted Child," *Elementary School Journal,* LVIII (November, 1957), 91-6.

Grossnickle, Foster E. "Teaching Arithmetic in the Junior High School," *The Mathematics Teacher,* XLVII (December, 1954), 520-27.

Hartung, Maurice L. "Mathematics in the Total School Program," *The Mathematics Teacher,* LI (May, 1958), 336-43.

Horn, Ernest. "Arithmetic in the Elementary-School Curriculum," *The Teaching of Arithmetic,* National Society for the Study of Education, Fiftieth Yearbook. Chicago: University of Chicago Press, Part II, 6-21.

Jones, Phillip S. "The Growth of Mathematical Ideas," *Journal of the National Education Association,* XLVIII (December, 1959), 53-4.

Keedy, M. L. "Mathematics in Junior High School," *Educational Leadership,* XVII (December, 1959), 157-61.

Lerner, Norbert, and Max A. Sobel. "Sets and Elementary School Mathematics," *The Arithmetic Teacher,* V (November, 1958), 239-46.

Marks, John L., C. Richard Purdy, and Lucien B. Kinney. *Teaching Arithmetic for Understanding.* New York: McGraw-Hill Book Co., 1958, 43-60.

McSwain, E. T., and Ralph J. Cooke. *Understanding and Teaching Arithmetic in the Elementary School.* New York: Holt, Rinehart & Winston, Inc., 1958, 328-65.

Merriman, A. M. "Sets and Some Elementary Problems," *The Mathematics Teacher,* LIII (April, 1960), 266-69.

Mitchell, H. Edwin. "Some Social Demands on the Course of Study in Arithmetic," *Third Report of the Committee on Economy of Time in Education,* National Society for the Study of Education, Seventeenth Yearbook (1918). Chicago: University of Chicago Press, Part I, 7-17.

Morton, Robert Lee. *Teaching Children Arithmetic.* New York: Silver Burdett Co., 1953, 21-65.

Newsom, Carroll V. "Some Observations on the Contemporary Mathematical Scene," *The Arithmetic Teacher,* VI (October, 1959), 191-94.

National Council of Teachers of Mathematics. *The Growth of Mathematical Ideas, Grades K-12,* National Council of Teachers of Mathematics, Twenty-fourth Yearbook (1958). Washington, D.C.: The Council.

Parsons, Cynthia. "Algebra in the Fourth Year," *The Arithmetic Teacher,* VII (February, 1960), 77-80.

Peters, Ann C. "Articulating Geometry Between the Elementary and Secondary Schools," *The Bulletin of the National Association of Secondary-School Principals,* XLIII (May, 1959), 131-33.

Raths, Louis E. "The Grade-Placement of Addition and Subtraction of Fractions," *Educational Research Bulletin,* XI (January, 1932), 29-38.

Reeve, W. D. "What Should Be the Nature and Content of Junior High School Mathematics?" *The Mathematics Teacher,* XLVIII (October, 1955), 413-15.

Sawyer, W. W. "Algebra in Grade Five," *The Arithmetic Teacher,* VII (January, 1960), 25-8.

Scott, Zenos E., *et al.* "Arithmetic," *The Nation at Work on the Public School Curriculum,* Department of Superintendence, Fourth Yearbook (1926), 173-220.

Schult, Veryl. "Whither Arithmetic in Grades Seven and Eight?" *Education,* LXXIX (January, 1959), 280-86.

Spitzer, Herbert F. *The Teaching of Arithmetic.* Boston: Houghton Mifflin Co., 1954, 299-317.

Stone, Marshall H. "Fundamental Issues in the Teaching of Elementary School Mathematics," *The Arithmetic Teacher,* VI (October, 1959), 177-79.

Sueltz, Ben A. "Arithemtic in Historical Perspective," *The National Elementary Principal,* XXXIX (October, 1959), 12-16.

––––––. "Curriculum Problems– Grade Placement," *Arithmetic in General Education,* National Council of Teachers of Mathematics, Sixteenth Yearbook (1941). Washington, D.C.: The Council, 20-44.

Swain, Robert L. "Modern Mathematics and School Arithmetic," *Instruction in Arithmetic,* National Council of Teachers of Mathematics, Twenty-fifth Yearbook (1960). Washington, D.C.: The Council, 270-95.

Swenson, Esther J. "Arithmetic for Preschool and Primary-Grade Children," *The Teaching of Arithmetic,* National Society for the Study of Education, Fiftieth Yearbook (1951). Chicago: University of Chicago Press, Part II, 53-75.

Texas Curriculum Studies. *Report of the Commission on Mathematics,* Report No. 3. Austin: Texas Education Agency, July, 1959, 14-45.

Thiele, C. L. "Arithmetic in the Middle Grades," *The Teaching of Arithmetic,* National Society for the Study of Education, Fiftieth Yearbook (1951). Chicago: University of Chicago Press, Part II, 76-102.

––––––. "The Mathematical Viewpoint Applied to the Teaching of Elementary School Arithmetic," *The Teaching of Arithmetic,* National Council of Teachers of Mathematics, Tenth Yearbook (1935). Washington, D.C.: The Council, 212-32.

Ulrich, R. P. "Grade Placement of Computational Topics in Arithmetic," *Elementary School Journal,* XLII (September, 1941), 50-59.

Van Engen, H. "Arithmetic in the Junior High School," *The Teaching of Arithmetic,* National Society for the Study of Education, Fiftieth Yearbook (1951). Chicago: University of Chicago Press, Part II, 103-19.

––––––. "Concepts Pervading Elementary and Secondary Mathematics," *The Bulletin of the National Association of Secondary-School Principals,* XLIII (May, 1959), 116-18.

––––––. "Twentieth Century Mathematics for the Elementary Grades," *The Arithmetic Teacher,* VI (March, 1959), 71-76.

Washburne, Carleton W. "The Grade-Placement of Arithmetic Topics: A 'Committee of Seven' Investigation," *Report of the Society's Committee on Arithmetic,* National Society for the Study of Education, Twenty-ninth Yearbook (1930). Chicago: University of Chicago Press, Part II, 641-70.

———. "Mental Age and the Arithmetic Curriculum: A Summary of the Committee of Seven Grade-Placement Recommendations to Date," *Journal of Educational Research,* XXIII (March, 1931), 210-31.

———. "The Work of the Committee of Seven on Grade-Placement in Arithmetic," *Child Development and the Curriculum,* National Society for the Study of Education, Thirty-eighth Yearbook (1939). Chicago: University of Chicago Press, Part I, 299-324.

West, R. L., Charles E. Greene, and W. A. Brownell. "The Arithmetic Curriculum," *Report of the Society's Committee on Arithmetic,* National Society for the Study of Education, Twenty-ninth Yearbook (1930). Chicago: University of Chicago Press, Part II, 65-142.

Wheat, Harry G. "Unifying Ideas in Arithmetic," *The Arithmetic Teacher,* I (December, 1954), 1-8.

Wilson, Guy M. "Arithmetic," *Research in Constructing the Elementary School Curriculum,* Department of Superintendence, Third Yearbook (1925), 35-109.

———. "New Standards in Arithmetic: A Controlled Experiment in Supervision," *Journal of Educational Research,* XXXII (December, 1930), 351-60.

———, *et al. Teaching the New Arithmetic.* New York: McGraw-Hill Book Co., Inc., 1951, 25-28.

Wrightstone, J. Wayne. "Influence of Research on Instruction in Arithmetic," *The Mathematics Teacher,* XLV (March, 1952), 187-92.

III TEACHING FOR GREATER UNDERSTANDING

Marguerite Brydegaard, San Diego State College

INTRODUCTION

INTRODUCTION

The words *meaning* and *understanding* have been affixed
to most materials of recent vintage regarding the teaching
of mathematics. No word offers richer opportunity for *mis-*

74

understanding than the word *understanding*. To define the word is not difficult, but identifying concepts and skills underlying *understanding* and knowing how to teach so that a learner creates basic *understandings* are problems of great magnitude.

Understanding in mathematics, as is true in all subject areas, is created by the learner. Understanding, per se, cannot be taught. But, the teacher's success in teaching mathematics depends upon the extent to which he challenges a child to create understandings that are sharp, refined, applicable, and expanding. The teacher's power to release the learner to create understanding is unknown. It would be difficult to measure such power because there are no limits for understanding; understandings continuously expand and terminal points are undetermined. The greater the depth of understanding, the greater is the potential for expansion through which new meanings, rooted in preceding understandings, emerge.

As you read this chapter, consider how the following factors determine the teacher's power to challenge the learner to create understanding:

1. The teacher's identification, classification, and understanding of the system of concepts that underlie mathematics in the elementary school.

2. The teacher's ability to see the hierarchy of understandings and skills within the system so that he can challenge the learner to evolve given segments in logical sequence.

3. The teacher's knowledge of how children learn, and his ability to determine the readiness level of his learners with regard for the given understandings that are to be developed.

4. The teacher's science and art of teaching that lead him to challenge the learner to create understanding of and develop appreciation for mathematics.

What constitutes mathematics in the elementary school is an important consideration. In general, writers and educators agree that mathematics in the elementary school is much broader than numerical computation and the understandings related to computation. It includes concepts of quantity and of quantitative relationships concerning size, order, position, and amount. It includes basic procedures concerning how to measure, what to measure, and the many ideas regarding system, including number systems. Understanding of mathematics call for original thinking and the ability to generalize. It includes communicating ideas regarding quantitative relationships, estimating, sensing, and interpreting mathematical relationships, the formulation of problems, the imagination to hypothesize, etc., as well as efficiency with numerical computation. We need to evaluate our "price-tag" on numerical computation in its relationship to our "price-tag" on understanding.

As you read this chapter, consider the following questions:

1. What is the nature of mathematical understandings and the nature of teaching that facilitates understanding?

2. Are recent textbooks freighted with material designed to challenge the learner to ask why and to interpret topics such as the division of common fractions, multiplication of decimal fractions, etc.?

3. How can we teach so that the learner creates understandings that lead him continuously to appreciation for and conquest of mathematics?

PART I: THE NATURE OF UNDERSTANDING

A PHILOSOPHY OF ARITHMETIC INSTRUCTION

Howard F. Fehr

Needs

The concept of *need* pervades all modern theory with regard to learning. Parents and teachers are asked to discover and help the child satisfy his needs. The child's needs are to be at the center of all educational programs. However, there has been little or no suggestion that the child must also sense the need of understanding his parents and teachers, and

[From "A Philosophy of Arithmetic Instruction," *The Arithmetic Teacher*, II (April, 1955), pp. 27-32. By permission of the author and *The Arithmetic Teacher*.]

their guidance and counsel. The school has as its primary task not only to serve the child to satisfy his immediate needs, but also to equip him for service to society in his later life. Hence the child has need for that elementary mathematics which is demanded of all people in our free democratic society. Children will recognize some of these needs in their own daily experience, but other needs must be shown the pupils through experience supplied by the teacher.

In this connection it is well to note that in his experience alone a child will never meet all number situations called for in later life. Nor can he, from a large number of isolated arithmetic situations, ever come to have a basic knowledge for use in later life. Accordingly, we must teach the pupils a structure of arithmetic and sufficient applications of the structure, so that in new situations, in life problems, he can use the structure for the necessary solution of problems.

A need is a feeling for something which is absent, which if present, will *tend* to give satisfaction. These needs are biogenic, such as the need for food, shelter, survival, and so on. They are also social such as status, power, intellectual satisfaction, acceptance into society, and so on. It is these latter needs with which arithmetic learning is mostly concerned. The teacher can find these needs in a number of places. They are in our everyday cultural environment as indicated in the check list of the National Council of Teachers of Mathematics. The needs for intellectual, esthetic, and social activities may frequently arise simply and naturally from the nervous system and its interrelation with its environment. Not all children lack curiosity and not all children dislike arithmetic. The teacher is also well aware of the needs in the many, many social problems which the child will not encounter until he is much older, such as saving and spending the income, investment, insurance, loans, statistical interpretation, and so on. However, a beginning can be made by creating a make-believe adult situation for the child. (Playing store is one make-believe adult situation.)

Planning

In planning a program the teacher must at all times recall that arithmetic is a logical structure as well as a social instrument. Unless these two concepts are continually interrelated, we shall not succeed in reaching our objective of an adult who *knows, recognizes,* and *uses* arithmetic in his daily life problems. While different parts of arithmetic can be learned in various orders, the logical order cannot be violated. We must learn some addition of whole numbers before we learn some meaningful multiplication. We must know the operations with whole numbers before we can learn to operate reasonably with fractions. But we can learn some of all the operations, one after the other, in some logical order, rather than learn all of one operation before we proceed to the next. To see the structure of arithmetic as a whole, rather than as separate parts, appears to give better success in its study.

Pupils sense needs for arithmetic in the world about them, at home, on the radio, in the papers, in their games, and so on. They seldom sense a need for a complete understanding and mastery of a number system. Real problems, and problems to which reality can be given, may be used to show the pupils the need of knowing arithmetic. The experiences, however, must not produce emotional reactions which detract from the learning of arithmetic; the experience must create within the pupil a drive which makes the learning of the arithmetic obligatory to him.

All of this suggests that we plan our program of instruction with our classes. Of course it is impossible for a group of children in grades 3 to 5 to plan its own program. Children are totally incapable of reproducing what great minds operating through centuries of time have created. We can, however, from time to time, discuss with the children what we are going to do, what they think they need, and how they can best learn what thus becomes their objective as well as the teacher's objective. We can seize on all aspects of children's interest to motivate their learning. Instead of allowing outside interests to distract attention from arithmetic, a wise teacher uses them in promoting the study. Radio, television, the movies, the newspapers, even the comics are filled with arithmetic and a little search will reveal profitable examples. The resourceful teacher will adapt all these experiences to the level of maturity of her pupils. She will also look for causes of fear, defeat, and rejection among a few pupils and find ways to reassure and help them through their interests. However, in motivating the learning through interest in experience, we must take care that eventually it is the mastery and understanding of arithmetic that is achieved, as well as a fine personality.

Meaning

Granted the child sees the need for knowing how to multiply, how shall he learn it? Shall we show him how and drill, and expect that he will know? Shall we expect him to understand (have some meaning of) every particular algorism we use? The basic philosophy of meaning as a necessary concomitant of learning is now generally accepted. The degree to which meaning is necessary, how to obtain it, and what this does to drill, are still debated issues in arithmetic teaching.

A fact, concept, or operation is meaningful to a child when he relates it to his previous learning in such a manner that it becomes a working aspect of his behavior. How well it works depends upon the child's intelligence and the degree of practice he has in using the arithmetic. Drill (or practice) is the continued repetition of an act within limits of human variation. We should note that meanings may be correct or incorrect meanings or operations can interfere greatly with further learning. Suppose to a child a fraction has come to have the incorrect concept "2 out of 3 for $\frac{2}{3}$," "3 out of 5 for $\frac{3}{5}$," etc. Then if he is asked to add $\frac{2}{3} + \frac{3}{5}$, he says 5 out of 8 or $\frac{5}{8}$. Thus the whole thing has meaning to him, but not the meaning we desire. The more this child practices the more he is in trouble. In this case practice makes not perfect, but a perfect mess. So we must be very careful that the meaning the child puts into his arithmetic is the correct meaning.

Once a child has put meaning into an operation or a relationship, there must be practice or drill to secure facility and accuracy thereafter. This drill can be of a number of different types. The most common usage of drill is the repetition of the same isolated fact until it can be quickly recalled. This procedure usually depends on pure rote learning. An almost similar type of drill is the repetition of various isolated facts, such as 6×3, 8×7, 2×5, 7×8, etc. This process of securing retention of concepts is also one closely related to rote learning. The more modern concept of drill is the repetition of varied facts in varied situations. This process follows the field psychology point of view; the seeing of the relations of the parts to the whole structure of arithmetic in as many aspects as possible. We believe that it will give a more permanent and more useful learning. When a new operation has been related to some past experience or concrete situation so as to be of use in new situations, it has become meaningful. Depending on how it is learned the multiplication table can become a mere rote mechanism soon to be forgotten, or it can become a long-remembered meaningful relation of numbers in an arithmetic operation.

Practice

Once children have sensed the mathematical operation, have put meaning into it, and see where it is of value, they are ready to drill. Then and then only will drill be effective. Buckingham [1] has pointed out that drill is effective only when to the child it has *purpose*, he senses its *value*, he has *confidence* in his ability to perform because of some familiarity with the operation, so that he can *direct* himself toward the deepening and broadening of his understanding.

---

[1] Burdette R. Buckingham, "What Becomes of Drill," *Arithmetic in General Education*. National Council of Teachers of Mathematics Sixteenth Yearbook (1941), pp. 196-225.

John Dewey has expressed the place of drill in arithmetic, by two excellent statements. "Practice skills can be intelligently, non-mechanistically *used,* only when intelligence (meaning) has played a part in their learning" and "An erroneous conception widely held is that since traditional education rested upon a concept of organization of knowledge that was almost completely contemptuous of living (present experiences), therefore education based upon living experiences should be contemptuous of the organization of knowledge."

What then is the place of drill? It is present and must be present in our learning. The arithmetic used for solving quantitative problems demands *facility in computation which is obtained only through practice.* The learning of division and per cent, and other applications in later grades, demands facility in the use of the more elementary operations, so that the mind can give its attention to the newer concepts and relations. This faculty is gained only through practice. However, the practice comes after meaning; it comes in varied situations and problems, and because of meaning the learning is faster, more permanent, and less practice is needed than is necessary for rote learning.

Learning

The teacher may now well ask, how do we get the child to put meaning into his arithmetic? We can seek an answer to this question in asking ourselves how *we* do it. A newspaper article said the U.N. forces advanced 6 miles all along a 60 mile front. What meaning do you see in this? Do you see a soldier walking forward 6 miles, and others to his left and right doing this also? Do you see $6 \times 60 = 360$ square miles of territory has been covered? However or whatever you do, you usually go back to concrete experience and that is where learning of all type begins. So multiplication, division, fractions, and so on, always have the initial learning phases embedded in concrete situations. All learning begins in a concrete experiential problematic situation in which the organism is motivated to find a solution.

Motivation is goal-directed behavior. The motivation is entirely within the child, but it is brought about partly by the environment acting on the child, and partly by the child's own internal structure. These factors cause nervous tension of the energies within the body, and the release of these tensions in physical and mental activity is the drive that sends the pupil toward a solution, that is, to learn. Without this motivation and drive, no real learning takes place. So we try to develop the type of environment, the type of stimuli that help the child to motivate his learning. When this motivation is present, then self-instruction (and all real learning is ultimately self-instruction) takes place. This motivation has its first seeds in experience, concrete sensual experience. Here is where meaning begins. But it does not and should not end at this point. However, the uses of visual and mechanical aids for learning and re-learning through experimentation is a first step toward developing meaning.

The teacher must next encourage the child to abstract certain recurring properties in his experimentation and to generalize these relations into arithmetic rules and principles. These general principles must also be related to previous generalizations. Thus, the proper placement of partial products in multiplication must be related to previously learned generalizations. Thus, the proper placement of partial products in multiplication must be related to previously learned generalizations regarding multiplying by 1, 10, 100, etc. The adding of these partial products to get the total product must also be related to the general principle of distribution.[2] It is such generalizations that the meaning of multiplication deepens and the relationship of one operation to another takes on the aspect of a structure. This is not explicitly recognized by pupils in the beginning, but the implications will later develop into a broader understanding of the subject. It is quite evident that such learning demands more, and more carefully planned instruction on the part of the teacher. The learning may proceed more slowly, but in the end we shall get a better educational product.

Under such learning, there is a need for continuous evaluation of the patterns of thinking going on in the child's mind. Computation tests with pencil and paper are not sufficient for this. Frequent oral explanations by the pupil form a better testing device for evaluating understandings. But more important, from a point of view of learning, the children must by their own planning and teacher guidance, constantly measure their own progress, come to recognize their own weaknesses, as well as strength, and by the use of teacher-prepared tests discover where they stand, what they need, and seek advice on how to get it. We must have children more and more take on *responsibility* for their own progress in learning. This is a long-neglected aim in all school instruction.

Problem Solving

Along with this generalization and structuring of the knowledge of arithmetic is problem solving. In good instruction, problem solving is always present for problem solving is learning and learning is problem

---

[2] The distributive law is fundamental to all mathematics and is given symbolically by $a(b + c) = ab + ac$. Hence, 256×68 is $256(60 + 8)$ or $60 \times 256 + 8 \times 256$.

solving. To develop the ability to solve new problems by the use of arithmetic is the greatest objective of our instruction. It is in problem situations that arithmetic can best be seen as a whole—as a completed body of knowledge. At this point, many teachers will no doubt ask: "How do you teach problem solving?"

This is in large measure an unanswered question, but many valid suggestions to aid the developing of problem-solving ability are at hand. Perhaps most significant are (1) always look at the whole problem, the whole situation; (2) seek the relationship of the parts to the whole, and the whole to the part; (3) analyze, organize and reorganize the relationships until what is known is directly related to what is wanted, then insight will occur. Thus problem solving demands *ceaseless attention to the building of clear, well interrelated arithmetic concepts in all the areas of common experience.*

Preliminary to the solution of word problems are three characteristics of arithmetic instruction that have received all-too-little attention in the past. They all rely on active thinking as a mode to learning rather than on passive listening to instructions. The first is *estimation.* Of course, to make intelligent estimates one must have rather clear cut concepts of number, the number system, and the operations. To find the cost of three articles each priced at 48 cents, the second-grade child (since he knows the number system) says this price is a little less than 3 half dollars or $1.50. As he advances through the grades he continues this estimation in far more difficult situations. The second characteristic is *mental solutions* to both computations and problems. Using the knowledge he has of the structure of arithmetic, here the child reasons without the aid of pencil or paper. He does not do mental gymnastics or visualized computations, but he does secure the accurate answer. In the preceding problem he reasons each article is 2 cents less than a half dollar—3 times 2 is 6—the price is 6 cents less than $1.50 or $1.45 minus 1 cent or $1.44. This type of mental solution is to be practiced from grade 1 on up into high school, the problems increasing in complexity each year. Estimation and mental solutions are the great practices that business men use every day.

The third characteristic is the association of language with an *operation.* As subtraction is taught, such language as—*take away—how much more—what is the difference—what is left—how much less—minus—less than—lost*—and so on are used in connection with concrete objects, so that the child associates a manner of speaking with the operation of subtraction. In this way, he is able to recognize a phrase or sentence in a word problem as indicating the separating of a group from a larger group to the size of the remaining group, or the comparing two groups of unequal sizes to find their difference. Language and concepts are highly interdependent in arithmetic.

The foregoing philosophy of instruction can and should lead to an educational product that has a healthy attitude toward arithmetic. It should result in a person who has self-assurance in the field of arithmetic because of a genuine understanding of the mathematical implications as well as the ability and compunction to recognize and use arithmetic in all life's quantitative situations. What psychology of learning is this philosophy based upon? Upon all those principles which have been common and supported by research findings in the several psychologies. The psychology largely used is that of the gestalt school, but it is supported by connectionism under its modern interpretation. To go further here into any of these psychological theories would be of no great help to interpret the point of view expressed.

Summary

Learning arithmetic stems from the needs for arithmetic as perceived by the learner. The child and the teacher together discuss and plan these needs. Arithmetic can be learned only if it has meaning to the child. Meanings in arithmetic arise from thinking about things, from concrete experience, and from problem situations. However, meanings and experience are only the beginning. They must be organized into some sequential structure, and the facts must be made nearly automatic (that is easy to recall) through practice. Thus meaning and understanding—that is, concept building—precede practice or drill. The child learns to evaluate his own progress with the help and guidance of the teacher. All testing is for the purpose of learning and motivating learning. The final goal of all instruction is to develop within the mind of each child a problem solving ability in quantitative situations. This ability is best acquired through a problem solving approach to learning arithmetic operations as well as by practice in real problem situations.

FROM THINGS TO CONCEPTS

John R. Clark and Laura K. Eads

If concepts and generalizations are to be developed, it is necessary that mathematical *thinking* be encouraged at all levels of development. Chil-

[From *Guiding Arithmetic Learning* (Yonkers-on-Hudson, N.Y.: The World Book Company, 1954), p. 22. By permission of the authors and The World Book Company.]

dren *think* mathematically as they are helped to see the mathematics in their experiences. They *think* when they use concrete materials to represent experience situations. They *think* when they see mathematical relationships, when they discover relationships of their own, when they try out relationships discovered by others. They *think* when they become independent of concrete materials: as they approximate, as they test solutions derived by other children, and finally as they use shortcut, conventional methods of computing.

PART II: THE NATURE OF LEARNING IN A PROGRAM DESIGNED TO DEVELOP UNDERSTANDING

WHICH WAY ARITHMETIC?

Henry Van Engen

Like the American automobile, new models of the arithmetic program are coming out. The new arithmetic models have been coming out for the past few years. The underlying reasons for the new models in the arithmetic program is that teachers are slowly but surely changing their concept of how children learn arithmetic. This requires new ideas, new techniques, and new equipment. Furthermore, it requires some deep thought on the part of all of those who are responsible for any part of the program for educating the elementary school child.

Some teachers will say, "These new ideas are too hard. We can't teach them to kids." This may be true, but *it should be kept in mind that for adults to relearn is often more difficult than it is for the child to learn. To relearn requires the checking of reactions that may have been habituated for years and years, and what is more difficult to break than a well established habit? Children do not have these response patterns for arithmetic habituated. They don't have the same learning problem the teacher has. Hence, it does not necessarily follow that what is hard for the teacher is also hard for the child.* (Italics are editor's.)

[From "Which Way Arithmetic?" *The Arithmetic Teacher*, I (December, 1955), pp. 131-140. By permission of the author and *The Arithmetic Teacher*.]

THE LITTLEST MATHEMATICIAN

Margery Baumgartner

The object of teaching is not to go through processes but to understand principles. It is not only permissible but preferable to have non-verbal awareness before pinning down processes with labels. It is the teacher's job to supply the experience necessary to invest symbols with real meaning for the students.

The Littlest Mathematician has no prejudice against arithmetic—yet. He grapples with mathematical problems for the sheer joy of it. It is fun, just as stretching his muscles dancing to the music is fun. There would be no shortage of people wanting to go into science and mathematical fields if the natural delight of the child in these phenomena could be maintained. Some effort is made in the schools to convince children that music and Shakespeare can be fun. Mathematics is rarely taught in this way. The teacher's cue should be to keep alive the spirit of exploration—the scientific approach—and to preserve the concentrated interest and delight which children naturally bring to their learning. When this kind of teaching operates, mastery of number facts is accomplished with less "drill." Drill often means practicing errors and so does infinitely more harm than good.

The teacher who is himself in love with his subject has the best start in the world.

[From "The Littlest Mathematician—An Approach Applicable at All Levels," *The Arithmetic Teacher*, V (April, 1958), pp. 131-36. By permission of the author and *The Arithmetic Teacher*.]

MEANING IS THE KEY

Gladys Risden

Meaning is the key. The best preparation for the teacher of arithmetic in regular or remedial classes is understanding of the wonderful consisten-

[From "Meaning is the Key," *The Arithmetic Teacher*, III (November, 1956), pp. 183-86. By permission of the author and *The Arithmetic Teacher*.]

cies and relationships which make mathematics a discipline for handling quantities in life and in the classroom, effectively and economically. This teacher of arithmetic teaches her pupils for *knowing*, not merely for saying, if and when she grasps the basic ideas. The only thing we can do with quantities are take them apart and put them together again. We can put them together in unequal groups (addition) and equal groups (multiplication). We take them apart in unequal groups (subtraction) and equal groups (division). We must group—see groups as wholes, not aggregations of ones, if we are to learn for *knowing*, not merely for *saying*.

The well-prepared teacher will find experimenting with thinking groups together and apart, fun. She will say what she is thinking in common sense language, not technical words, until she has made the generalizations which bring the technical words and the ways of stating rules, popping into her head.

.   .   .   .

The test of *knowing* is using; *knowing* is more than *saying*.

DO THEY SEE THE POINT?

Peter L. Spencer

Do They See the Point? This question has a dual meaning. "The Point" refers both to the actual dot, i.e., the decimal point, and to the "point" or meaning of the expression wherein the decimal point is used. Likewise two forms of seeing are implied. The one has to do with the adequacy of the sense of *sight*. The other is concerned with ideological understanding and judgments of significance, i.e., *insight*. The one refers to visual sensitivity. The other to conceptual sensibility. Both are important and worthy of careful consideration.

The visibility of the decimal point in mathematical printing or writing is often given little regard. The symbol commonly corresponds in size with the dot of the *i* or the period dot used. However, both the dot and the period generally have configurational cues within the structure of the word or sentence which make them likely to be observed.

[From "Do They See the Point?" *The Arithmetic Teacher*, V (November, 1958), pp. 271-72. By permission of the author and *The Arithmetic Teacher*.]

In most decimal number expressions there is little of configurational cue as to the location of a decimal point. Its location is determined by the quantitative amount which the number is designed to express. The decimal point serves to "point out," i.e., to locate the units' place within the number expression. Consequently the decimal point needs to be as "readable" as the other aspects of the number symbol. Failure to see a decimal point or failure to "see" the implication of a decimal point can be a source of serious failure in communication.

An analysis of the incorrect responses produced by several hundreds of children in grades 7 and 8 of a city school discloses evidence of possible failure to see the decimal point. Some of these failures may well have been *sight* failures. The others are more properly classed as deficiencies with *vision*.

The omission of a necessary decimal point in the answer was one type of characteristic error. We have no way of determining whether the omissions were due mainly to *sight* deficiencies or to those of vision, i.e., intellectual deficiencies, but that sight may have been a significant factor is suggested by the following data:

1. When a decimal point occurred in the example in the dividend only, the decimal point was omitted in 22 per cent of the incorrect answers.

2. When no decimal point occurred in either the divisor or dividend, a necessary decimal point was omitted in 57 per cent of the incorrect answers.

3. When a decimal point occurred in both the dividend and divisor, the decimal point was omitted in only 8 per cent of the incorrect answers.

4. When a decimal point occurred in the divisor only, the decimal point was omitted in 33 per cent of the incorrect answers.

The omission of a decimal point where one is needed is, demonstrably, an important source of error. The wide variance between the proportion of omissions when no decimal points occurred in the statement of the example, 57 per cent, and the proportion of omissions when decimal points occurred in both the dividends and the divisors, 8 per cent, suggests that the visual sensing of the decimal point may tend to provoke one to use a decimal point when he might not otherwise do so. Hence, we recommend that serious attention be given to make the decimal points visually legible. As a purely arbitrary standard until a better basis for legibility can be determined, we recommend that the decimal point have double the diameter of the period or of the dot of the *i* used in printing or writing. Readers need to *see* the decimal point.

Visibility is a *prerequisite to* but it certainly is no *guarantee of* "seeing the point" in the intellectual sense of that expression. One may see the point in the sight awareness sense, but not "see the point" of it as a symbol of quantitative significance. Failure to see the point as a sign of quantitative value is a perceptual rather than a receptual deficiency.

If placing a decimal point in the answer can be accepted as evidence that the pupil had awareness of it, then misplacing the decimal point may comparably be interpreted as a failure to understand its meaning or significance. Let us examine how the children mentioned previously performed in this regard. The decimal points which they placed in answers to examples with decimal points in their dividends only were misplaced in 30 per cent of the incorrect answers. The decimal points were misplaced in 21 per cent of the incorrect answers when no decimal points occurred in either the dividend or the divisor.

Misplaced decimal points occurred in 42 per cent of the incorrect answers when decimal points appeared in both the dividend and divisor of the examples. And, decimal points were misplaced in 59 per cent of the incorrect answers when a decimal point occurred only in the divisor of the example.

The discrepancies of omitting the decimal point or misplacing it occurred in roughly 52 per cent of the incorrect answers when a decimal point occurred in the dividend only; in 78 per cent of the incorrect answers when no decimal point appeared in the example as given; in 50 per cent of the incorrect answers when a decimal point occurred in both the divisor and the dividend, and in 82 per cent of the incorrect answers when a decimal point was presented in only the divisor of the example. Failure on the part of the pupils to see the point merits the attention of teachers.

Compared with the errors with the decimal point errors the number aspects of division were much less numerous. With examples having a decimal point in the dividend only, approximately 18 per cent of the incorrect answers contained a number fact error. With examples having no decimal point, 9 per cent of the incorrect answers contained a number fact error. Examples with decimal points occurring in both the divisor and dividend produced 25 per cent of incorrect answers contained in the number facts. Examples with a decimal point in the divisor only produced answers of which 55 per cent were incorrect but only 9 per cent of the incorrect answers contained a number fact error. As reported above, 82 per cent of the incorrect answers contained a decimal point error. Approximately 9 per cent of the "incorrect" responses were instances of omission or failure to attempt a solution.

Summary

This paper attacks the problem of "seeing the point" as regards the decimal point from two points of view, viz., visual sensing and understanding. Omissions of decimal points were classed as possible sight deficiencies. Since this occurred with considerable frequency, it is proposed that care be taken to make decimal points clearly legible.

Misplacement of decimal points were classed as failures to "see the point" of the decimal symbol intellectually. More attention needs to be given to the development of meaning and judgments of significance. When a pupil writes a decimal point, he should be expressing an idea rather than performing a computational skill.

THE CHALLENGE OF PRACTICAL APPLICATIONS

Margaret F. Willerding

Let us consider first of all just when a practical application is a challenge to the student. It seems to me the first requirement must be that the application be a *real one*. Although there are many real practical applications in modern text books, problems are much more real to the student if the teacher supplements the text book treatment of an application with live data he has assembled or with information collected by the students.

Students should be made aware of the *World Almanac* and *The Annual Statistical Abstract of the United States* as sources of practical applications. Students should also be taught to read newspapers and magazines with an eye peeled for practical applications of mathematics in daily life. They should consult business and professional people, many of whom will be their own parents, as sources of practical applications of the mathematics they are studying or will need to study.

A second requirement of a practical application if it is to be challenging to the student is that it be within reasonable comprehension of the student. Many of the applications of mathematics arise out of situations which students of elementary mathematics have no basis for understanding. These applications come from the research laboratory or from the technical work of engineers. When the instructor tries to present such applications in mathematics classes it is often to confuse many of the students more than to stimulate them. Some instructors feel that it takes more time and effort to explain the setting of the applications and therefore

[From "The Challenge of Practical Applications," *School Science and Mathematics*, LVII (June, 1957), pp. 437-46. By permission of the author and *School Science and Mathematics*.]

their meanings than the values derived from them. These same instructors feel that the usual "age" problems, "clock" problems, "mixture" problems and "pursuit" problems that have been appearing in algebra texts for centuries would have disappeared long ago if equally easily understood real, modern applications could have been found as substitutes.

. . . .

Instructors should encourage individual pupils who have special interest in particular kinds of applications to pursue these interests independently of the rest of the class and bring the mathematics problems which arise from these interests to class for discussion. In this way the instructor will have data from a wide range of interests which he can use in creating real practical applications for his classes.

LANGUAGE IN MATHEMATICS

Irvin H. Brune

Through language man has shared his discoveries, widened his understandings, preserved his learnings, developed his civilizations, and educated his children. Thus language has benefited mankind. Yet, because at best it reveals meanings imperfectly, language has produced misunderstandings, bred dissensions, and even fomented wars. The power of language, like the force of fire, can effect good or ill in human affairs.

In the teaching of mathematics language has also both succeeded and failed. Whenever it has led pupils to enjoy the satisfactions of thinking through a mathematical situation, language has helped. Whenever it has engendered lack of clarity as pupils seek to solve problems, language has hindered.

. . . .

Teachers hunt words to relight the flame of curiosity which incited pupils before pat phrases and answers-in-alabaster smothered it. Teachers

[From "Language in Mathematics," *The Learning of Mathematics in Theory and Practice,* National Council of Teachers of Mathematics, Twenty-first Yearbook (1953), Washington, D.C., pp. 156-91. By permission of the author and the National Council of Teachers of Mathematics.]

plan daily to challenge, to ask why, to doubt, to interest, to evaluate, and to exploit numerous ways to further pupils' growth. Good language challenges; it does not bore; it does not frustrate. And teachers help pupils to handle words.

.   .   .   .

Verbalisms have abounded in mathematics—"Invert the divisor and multiply"; "Crossmultiply"; "Cancel"; "Transpose"; "Reduce"; "Bring down"; "Drop the per cent sign and move the decimal point two places to the left"; "Annex the per cent sign and move the decimal point two places to the right"; "Factor completely"; "Double the width, double the length, and add"; "Divide the number following *is* by the number following *of*"; "Add the number of decimal places in the multiplicand to the number of decimal places in the multiplier"; "Subtract the number of decimal places in the divisor from the number of decimal places in the dividend, adding zeros to the dividend if necessary"—such statements often lack meaning for the pupils who have learned to recite them. Teachers of mathematics can readily adduce more examples of verbalisms. They realize, too, that although a pupil's words may conceal his lack of understanding, yet his words may not substitute for the understanding. Sooner or later the parrot quits mathematics.

To help pupils to increase their mathematical understandings teachers plan experiences for the pupils. In arithmetic, for example, a program of extended, unhurried concept-building helps pupils discover relationships among numbers before the pupils learn technical words to express those relationships. John and Mary learn to recognize groups, to count, to measure, and to solve simple problems largely through discoveries they make with groups of people, toys, sticks, pictures, drawings, and marks.

**PART III: THE RELATIONSHIP BETWEEN THE LEARNER'S
UNDERSTANDING OF CONCEPTS AND HIS
SKILL WITH NUMERICAL COMPUTATION**

MEANING AND SKILL—MAINTAINING THE BALANCE

William A. Brownell

To sum up, the balance between meaning and skill has been upset, if
indeed it ever was properly established. The reasons are many, some of
them relating to educational theory in general, others to misconceptions
of psychological theories of learning, others to failure to teach arithmetical
meanings thoroughly, and still others to carry learning in the case of
computation to the level I have denoted meaningful habituation, and
then to fix learning at that level. I have discussed these matters at length,
perhaps at unwarranted extent in view of the fact that the remedy for the
situation can be stated briefly. The remedy I propose is as follows:

1. Accord to competence in computation its rightful place among the
outcomes to be achieved through arithmetic.

2. Continue to teach essential arithmetical meanings, but make sure
that these meanings are just that and that they contribute as they should
to greater computational skill.

3. Base instruction on as complete data as are reasonably possible
concerning the status of children as they progress toward meaningful
habituation.

4. Hold repetitive practice to a minimum until this ultimate stage has
been achieved; then provide it in sufficient amount to assure real mastery
of skills, real competence in computing accurately, quickly, and confidently.

[From "Meaning and Skill—Maintaining the Balance," *The Arithmetic
Teacher,* III (October, 1956), pp. 129-36. By permission of the author and
The Arithmetic Teacher.]

RELATIVE ROLES OF MEANING AND DRILL

J. Houston Banks

What are the relative roles of meaning and drill? One hundred per cent mastery of the facts and skills of arithmetic is wasted effort if attendant meanings and understandings are missing. Without meanings there can be no understanding and without understanding there can be no application. The ultimate objective of instruction in arithmetic is the development of problem-solving ability. The child may know what you mean when he is told to multiply ⅔ by ⅕. "Multiply numerators to get the numerator of the result and multiply denominators to get the denominator" may be a perfectly meaningful statement for the child. He may be capable of following the instructions and obtaining the correct result and still not understand why this gives the correct result. Unless he understands the significance of what he does he cannot apply his knowledge to the solution of a problem. Understanding furthermore lends permanence to acquired skills. A process that is understood is not easily forgotten, and if it is forgotten the understanding serves as a framework for re-establishing the skill.

There are differences of opinion as to whether drill (if drill is a bad word, read *practice* or *use*) should precede or follow understanding. Undoubtedly, drill on understood material is more efficient; the child is thus more easily motivated. Complete mastery is obtainable with less drill. But to require full understanding before any drill is to ignore the fact that use broadens and deepens understanding. The use of drill before understanding does not necessarily imply that a skill which is not understood has value. Although, ideally, understanding should come first, in practice development of skill and meaning proceed together. Yet neither occurs as a result of the other. No amount of skill can insure understanding, and understanding does not eliminate the need for drill to establish the skill.

[From *Learning and Teaching Arithmetic* (Boston: Allyn and Bacon, Inc., 1959), pp. 10-11. Reprinted by permission of Allyn and Bacon, Inc.]

TEACHING THE NUMBER SYSTEM INDUCTIVELY

J. Allen Hickerson

More Than One Way

Some teachers believe that children would be terribly confused if they were taught that there is more than one way of getting an answer. As it is, these teachers hold, many children can hardly learn even *one* technique of adding, subtracting, multiplying, or dividing.

This, too often, is true. It may be due, however, to certain remediable causes. Perhaps, first of all, the attitude of teachers from the kindergarten up can either encourage or discourage exploration and experimentation with numbers.

Over-emphasis upon accuracy and perfection in computation causes many children (and teachers) to hold on to *one* sure method, even if it is counting on fingers. Rewarding and praising accuracy and speed tend to stifle venturesomeness with numbers.

Children must have adequate intelligence as well as an experimental and inventive attitude to be capable of engaging in creative and original thinking with numbers. Some children would be mentally capable of experimenting with subtraction of 2-digit numbers, for example, if they only could wait another year before being taught the process.

Performing a computational process that is shown or demonstrated by the teacher or book and then drilled upon requires less mental ability than discovering or thinking it out for oneself and then drilling upon it. Since computational techniques *can be acquired without understanding* and *can be performed mechanically*, some teachers are tempted to teach a process before children are ready to understand it.

To be sure, some people may never be able to understand many of the intricacies of our number system. They require patient showing, telling, and demonstrating. *All* children, however, should not thus be taught deductively.

Those children who are potential mathematical thinkers should not be hindered from learning what creative mathematical thinking is. They should not be deprived of the opportunity to experience the joys of arithmetical discovery.

It is my opinion that basing computational understanding upon early systematic and deductive teaching of the place-value structure of our

[From "Teaching the Number System Inductively," *The Arithmetic Teacher*, V (October, 1958), pp. 178-84. By permission of the author and *The Arithmetic Teacher*.]

number system and that teaching children that there is a best way for all
to add, subtract, multiply, or divide tend to stifle creative thinking and
to instill in children the attitude that arithmetic is difficult to understand.
(This attitude is fostered when the teacher or the book is always telling
or showing or explaining—and correcting.)

It is also my opinion that mathematicians should learn more about how
children think; that elementary school teachers should learn more about
arithmetic and its possibilities in enriching the creative lives of their children; that teachers in teacher-preparation institutions should learn how
to help future teachers lose their arithmetical insecurities, dislikes, and
fears; and that parents acquire a more positive attitude toward the mathematical potentials of their children and the teaching potentials of teachers.

The aim of all of us, I submit, should be the production of more and
more people who are not afraid of mathematics, who have some understanding of and ability to use mathematics, and who think imaginatively
and creatively in mathematics. Such people should be the products of our
schools—not *in spite of* their teachers but *on account of* them.

MODERN METHODS AND CURRENT CRITICISMS OF MATHEMATICAL EDUCATION

Maurice L. Hartung

Methods that once worked well now often seem to fail us. Successful
teaching is much more difficult today than it used to be, and the use of
modern methods is more important than ever before. Let us, therefore,
briefly review some general features of these methods.

In the first place, modern teachers put much stress on meaningful learning. These teachers try to make sure that pupils see sense in what they
are doing and really understand it. Teachers use a variety of ways of
doing this. One popular way is to relate mathematics to situations in
which it may be applied—in short, to stress the applications. This works
in two directions. On the one hand, we can begin with problem situations
familiar to the pupils and help them see the mathematics in them—to
develop the new concepts by generalization and abstraction from familiar
concrete situations. On the other hand, we can show the pupils situations
—practical or even not very practical—new to them but in which familiar

[From "Modern Methods and Current Criticisms of Mathematical Education," *School Science and Mathematics*, LV (February, 1955), pp. 85-90.
By permission of the author and *School Science and Mathematics*.]

mathematical concepts can be applied. In either case, we hope that this process of relating mathematics to real and practical situations will make the concepts more meaningful.

If we examine the trends in the development of materials for children during the half-century just past, we can find clear and convincing evidence of progress toward this kind of meaningfulness. Arithmetic, of course, has always had a strong practical flavor. What we observe is that modern materials rely heavily upon problem situations chosen on the basis of the interests of children rather than those of adults. It is believed that these child-experience situations contribute more to the development of meaning with children than the more adult type of situation once prevalent. At the high school level the trend toward the use of more meaningful experiences is also evident. At this level, however, attention to more adult types of applications of mathematics is common and defensible.

There are, I believe, very few critics who will argue that this aspect of modern methods—that is, concern with the meaningfulness of experience—is not good. If there are some who do argue this way, their views run directly counter to the results of much substantial research by psychologists and others who have studied human learning. It is possible, however, to overdo this attention to the uses of mathematics, or the so-called "social meanings." This is particularly true when social or practical situations are used to introduce new concepts. We must be sure the mathematical aspects are brought clearly into focus and become objects of study. Sometimes this is not done, and although the children may arrive at a solution of a particular problem, they learn so little mathematics from it that they are unable to deal successfully with similar new situations.

A second popular way of helping pupils toward meaningful learning is to use visual or, more broadly, multi-sensory learning aids. The reasons for using these aids are well known to modern teachers, and we do not need to consider them here. The number and variety of such aids now described in the literature has increased much faster than the tendency to be critical about them. It is probably possible to devise a helpful model or aid of some kind to teach any topic you care to mention. Thus, we have aids available for teaching content that is of little or no value. When we examine an ingenious aid, we should ask: Why is it important for the pupil to learn what this aid is designed to teach? We sometimes waste time by skillfully teaching unimportant things.

Although the increased use of visual and mechanical aids is one of the characteristics of modern teaching, in most classrooms this kind of activity accounts for a relatively small part of the instructional time. It is difficult to see how this aspect of modern methodology can be blamed for the alleged deterioration of the schools.

A third and very modern way of helping pupils toward meaningful learning is to encourage them to participate in *planning* the learning experiences. This practice is, of course, in sharp contrast to the usual one in which "the assignment" is made by the teacher. Teacher-pupil planning and similar methods of encouraging interaction among members of the class are still seldom used in mathematics classes. Hence the alleged great deterioration in achievement can hardly be attributed to this as a cause. Similarly, the integration of mathematics with other subjects in a core curriculum is very infrequent. The core curriculum is a focus for attack by some vigorous critics of modern education, but teachers of mathematics are outside this line of fire.

BIBLIOGRAPHY

Alkire, E. Russell. *An Experimental Study of the Value of a Meaningful Approach to the Operation of Division with Common Fractions,* Master's thesis. Claremont, Calif.: Claremont College, 1949.

Anderson, G. Lester. "Quantitative Thinking as Developed Under Connectionist and Field Theories of Learning," *Learning Theory in School Situations,* University of Minnesota Studies in Education, No. 2. Minneapolis: University of Minnesota Press, 1949, 40-73.

Banks, J. Houston. *Learning and Teaching Arithmetic.* Boston: Allyn and Bacon, Inc., 1959, 10-11.

Baumgartner, Margery. "The Littlest Mathematician, An Approach Applicable at All Levels," *The Arithmetic Teacher,* V (April, 1958), 131-36.

Brownell, William A. "Meaning and Skill—Maintaining the Balance," *The Arithmetic Teacher,* III (October, 1956), 129-36.

——. "The Evaluation of Learning in Arithmetic," *Arithmetic in General Education,* National Council of Teachers of Mathematics, Sixteenth Yearbook (1941). Washington, D.C.: The Council, 225-67.

——, and Charlotte B. Chazal. "The Effects of Premature Drill in Third-Grade Arithmetic," *Journal of Educational Research,* XXIX (September, 1935), 17-28.

——, and Foster E. Grossnickle. "The Interpretation of Research," *Arithmetic in General Education,* National Council of Teachers of Mathematics, Sixteenth Yearbook (1941). Washington, D.C.: The Council, 316-17.

——, and Harold E. Moser. *Meaningful versus Mechanical Learning: A Study in Grade III Subtraction,* Duke University Research Studies in Education, No. 8. Durham, N.C.: Duke University Press, 1949, 207.

——, and Verner M. Sims. "The Nature of Understanding," *The Measurement of Understanding,* National Society for the Study of Education, Forty-fifth Yearbook (1946). Chicago: University of Chicago Press, Part I, 27-43.

Brueckner, Leo J. "Intercorrelations of Arithmetical Abilities," *Journal of Experimental Education,* III (September, 1934), 42-44.

Erune, Irvin H. "Language in Mathematics," *The Learning of Mathematics in Theory and Practice*, National Council of Teachers of Mathematics, Twenty-first Yearbook (1953). Washington, D.C.: The Council, 156-91.

Brydegaard, Marguerite. "The Insatiable Quest: Mathematicking," *The Arithmetic Teacher*, VII (January, 1960), 9-12.

Burch, Robert L., and Harold E. Moser. "The Teaching of Mathematics in Grades I Thru VIII," *Review of Educational Research*, XXI (October, 1951), 290-304.

Burchenal, Joyce M. "A Device for Measuring Understanding of the Meaning of Units of Measure," *School Science and Mathematics*, LVIII (November, 1958), 601-4.

Clark, John R., and Laura K. Eads. *Guiding Arithmetic Learning*. New York: World Book Company, 1954, 22-23.

Clark, John R. "Number, Numeral and Operation," *The Arithmetic Teacher*, VII (May, 1960), 222-25.

Collier, C. C. "Blocks to Arithmetical Understanding," *The Arithmetic Teacher*, VI (November, 1959), 262-68.

Corle, Clyde. "Thought Processes in Grade Six Problems," *The Arithmetic Teacher*, V (October, 1958), 193-203.

Dawson, D. T., and A. K. Ruddell. "The Case for the Meaning Theory in Teaching Arithmetic," *The Elementary School Journal*, LV (March, 1955), 393-99.

Deery, Ruth T. "Linda Learns the Hexal System," *The Arithmetic Teacher*, V (November, 1958), 251-55.

Eads, Laura K. "Learning Principles That Characterize Developmental Mathematics," *The Arithmetic Teacher*, IV (October, 1957), 179-82.

——. "Ten Years of Meaningful Arithmetic in New York City," *The Arithmetic Teacher*, II (December, 1955), 142-47.

Fehr, Howard F. "A Philosophy of Arithmetic Instruction," *The Arithmetic Teacher*, II (April, 1955), 27-32.

——. "Teaching for Appreciation of Mathematics," *School Science and Mathematics*, LII (January, 1952), 19-24.

Glennon, Vincent J. "Testing Meanings in Arithmetic," *Arithmetic 1949*, Supplementary Educational Monograph No. 70. Chicago: University of Chicago Press, 1949, 64-74.

Harding, Lowry R. "Evaluation of Mathematical Meanings and Understandings," *Emerging Practices in Mathematics Education*, National Council of Teachers of Mathematics, Twenty-second Yearbook (1954). Washington, D.C.: The Council, 355-64.

——, and Inez Bryant. "An Experimental Comparison of Drill and Direct Experience in Arithmetic Learning in a Fourth Grade," *Journal of Educational Research*, XXXVII (January, 1944), 321-37.

Hartung, Maurice L. "Distinguishing Between Basic and Superficial Ideas in Arithmetic Instruction," *The Arithmetic Teacher*, VI (March, 1959), 65-70.

Hartung, Maurice L. "Modern Methods and Current Criticisms of Mathematical Education," *School Science and Mathematics*, LV (February, 1955), 85-90.

Hickerson, J. Allen. "Teaching the Number System Inductively," *The Arithmetic Teacher*, V (October, 1958), 178-84.

Howard, Charles F. "Three Methods of Teaching Arithmetic," *California Journal of Educational Research*, I (January, 1950), 25-29.

Hull, C. L. "Quantitative Aspects of the Evolution of Concepts," *Psychological Monographs*, XXVIII (1920), 1-85.

Johnson, Donovan, and H. C. Trimble. "Evaluation of Mathematical Meanings and Understandings," *Emerging Practices in Mathematics Education*, National Council of Teachers of Mathematics, Twenty-second Yearbook (1954). Washington, D.C.: The Council, 343-55.

Kenney, Russell A., and Jesse D. Stockton. "An Experimental Study in Teaching Percentage," *The Arithmetic Teacher*, V (December, 1958), 294-303.

McConnell, T. R. *Discovery versus Authoritative Identification in the Learning of Children*, University of Iowa Studies in Education, IX (1934). Iowa City: University of Iowa, 13-62.

McCormick, Chester A. "Helping Children Discover Arithmetic," *School Science and Mathematics*, LII (May, 1952), 339-43.

McSwain, E. T., and Ralph J. Cooke. "Essential Mathematical Meanings in Arithmetic in Quantitative Thinking, Computation, and Problem Solving," *The Arithmetic Teacher*, V (October, 1958), 185-92.

Miller, G. H. "How Effective Is the Meaning Method?" *The Arithmetic Teacher*, IV (March, 1957), 45-49.

Moyer, Haverly O. "Testing the Attainment of the Broader Objectives of Arithmetic," *The Arithmetic Teacher*, III (March, 1956), 66-70.

Parker, Helen C. "Teaching Measurement in a Meaningful Way," *The Arithmetic Teacher*, VII (April, 1960), 194-98.

Piaget, Jean. *Judgment and Reasoning in the Child*. Translated by Marjorie Warden. New York: Harcourt, Brace and Company, 1928.

Pieters, Mary Ballard. "Utilizing the Strategic Moment in Teaching Arithmetic," *The Arithmetic Teacher*, V (December, 1958), 311-14.

Pikal, Frances. "Review of Research Related to the Teaching of Arithmetic in the Upper Elementary Grades," *School Science and Mathematics*, LVII (January, 1957), 41-47.

Rappaport, David. "Preparation of Teachers of Arithmetic," *School Science and Mathematics*, LVIII (November, 1958), 636-43.

———. "Units in Measurement Should be Meaningful," *School Science and Mathematics*, LX (March, 1960), 202-6.

———. "Testing for Meanings in Arithmetic," *The Arithmetic Teacher*, VI (April, 1959), 140-43.

———. "Understanding Meanings in Arithmetic," *The Arithmetic Teacher*, V (March, 1958), 96-99.

Reed, Calvin H. "Developing Creative Thinking in Arithmetic," *The Arithmetic Teacher*, IV (February, 1957), 10-12.

Risden, Gladys. "Meaning Is the Key," *The Arithmetic Teacher,* III (November, 1956), 183-86.

Spencer, Peter L. "Do They See the Point?" *The Arithmetic Teacher,* V (November, 1958), 271-72.

———, and Marguerite Brydegaard. *Building Mathematical Concepts in the Elementary School.* New York: Holt, Rinehart & Winston, Inc., 1952, 34-35.

Spitzer, Herbert F. "Testing Instruments and Practices in Relation to Present Concepts of Teaching Arithmetic," *The Teaching of Arithmetic,* National Society for the Study of Education, Fiftieth Yearbook (1951). Chicago: University of Chicago Press, Part II, 186-202.

Stokes, C. Newton. "80,000 Children's Reactions to Meanings in Arithmetic," *The Arithmetic Teacher,* V (December, 1958), 281-86.

Sueltz, Ben. "The Measurement of Understandings and Judgments in Elementary Mathematics," *Mathematics Teacher,* XL (October, 1947), 279.

———, Boynton Holmes, and Irene Sauble. "The Measurement of Understanding in Elementary School Mathematics," *The Measurement of Understanding,* National Society for the Study of Education, Forty-fifth Yearbook (1946). Chicago: University of Chicago Press, Part I, 138-56.

Swenson, Esther J. "Organization and Generalization as Factors in Learning, Transfer, and Retroactive Inhibition," *Learning Theory in School Situations,* University of Minnesota, Studies in Education, No. 2. Minnesota: University of Minnesota Press, 1949, pp. 9-39.

Thiele, C. Louis. *The Contribution of Generalization to the Learning of the Addition Facts,* Contributions to Education, No. 763. New York: Bureau of Publications, Teachers College, Columbia University, 1938.

Van Engen, H. "An Analysis of Meaning in Arithmetic," *The Elementary School Journal,* XLIX (February, 1949), 321-29; XLIX (March, 1949), 395-400.

———. "Which Way Arithmetic?" *The Arithmetic Teacher,* I (December, 1955), 131-40.

Weaver, J. Fred. "Developing Flexibility of Thinking and Performance," *The Arithmetic Teacher,* IV (October, 1957), 184-88.

———. "Some Areas of Misunderstanding About Meaning in Arithmetic," *Elementary School Journal,* LI (September, 1950), 35-41.

Willerding, Margaret F. "The Challenge of Practical Applications," *School Science and Mathematics,* LVII (June, 1957), 437-46.

———. "Dramatizing Mathematics," *School Science and Mathematics,* LX (February, 1960), 99-104.

———. "Take a Number and Build a Number System," *The Arithmetic Teacher,* VII (January, 1960), 35-37.

Williams, Catharine M. "Arithmetic Learning in an Experience Curriculum," *Educational Research Bulletin,* XXVIII (September, 1949), 154-68.

Wrightstone, J. Wayne. "Constructing Tests of Mathematical Concepts for Young Children," *The Arithmetic Teacher,* III (April, 1956), 81-84.

IV ACHIEVING MATHEMATICAL MATURITY

Laura K. Eads, Bureau of Curriculum Research,
New York City Public Schools

INTRODUCTION

Maturation implies growth and development. In elementary school mathematics particular periods in development toward maturity may be designated as levels of mathematical maturity, that is, levels of mathematical power, depth, reasoning, and performance. Motivation, curiosity, interest, and application may be seen as emotional driving forces in the process of maturing. Flexibility in thinking is a necessary concomitant.

Rates of growth and levels of maturity are generally conceded to vary widely within a particular age or grade or class group. Within a group of children there are the less (or least) mature, those of (more or less) "average" maturity, and those who are more (or most) mature. A particular child within the group may be said to be more mature math-

101

ematically than he was formerly, less mature than he is in another aspect of mathematics, more mature than the other children in the group, less mature than he is likely to be next year, etc.

Maturation in terms of the entire mathematical growth period, from infancy through all the years of formal and informal learning, is of particular importance to those concerned with planning curriculum programs. These may be curriculum specialists, researchers, child development specialists, supervisors, administrators, and classroom teachers.

Levels of maturity within a class group are the teacher's particular concern. Teachers need to know: How many children and which children are mature enough to apply themselves to the tasks considered appropriate for the grade? What levels of maturity (mathematical and emotional) have been reached by various groups of children in the class? What teaching procedures and available materials of instruction are best suited to the children in the class? How can procedures and materials be adapted to meet the needs of children who are less mature and those who are more mature? What procedures for grouping children are most effective, that is, provide for maximum learning opportunities for all children in the class?

The concepts of readiness for learning mathematics have been extended considerably in recent years. It is known today that children develop mathematical concepts from their first year of life. Not only are children ready to learn mathematics when they enter school, but actually they have been learning a great deal of mathematics for years; and they have enjoyed such learning. The emphasis has shifted from "Are children ready?" to such questions as: How did children learn so much mathematics in their pre-school years, and so enjoyably? Why do some children appear to have learned relatively little mathematics? How can opportunities for experiential learning be provided in school? What is the role of classroom experiences in a sequential mathematics program? How can we provide for differences among children in need of experiential learning? What procedures will help children proceed, under classroom conditions, to develop from learning mathematics by referring to experiences to learning mathematics by referring to mathematical symbols only?

The concept of readiness is also extended to pertain to all school levels and to all learning tasks. The teacher conceives of the task of teaching as one of continuous evaluation as well as that of leading children to higher and higher levels of thinking and performance. Questions are asked to stimulate thinking. Children are given time to think out responses. The teacher listens carefully to determine whether responses are more or less mature for the particular task and group of children. Children are observed as they work independently —individually, in pairs, or in small groups. Pertinent questions or comments by the teacher stimulate more mature performance; levels of performance are observed and noted by the teacher.

Mathematical maturity is encouraged not by "giving" children concepts or by "motivating" children to learn. The development of concepts and motivation for learning *come from within the child*. But, a skillful and mature teacher can establish relationships with the child so that whatever learning potentialities he possesses will be realized to the fullest not only during school hours but during the many hours when he may not be consciously attending to mathematical situations at all. The influence of a teacher on the lives of children cannot be overestimated; children, their parents, and the teachers themselves know this or, at least, sense this.

PART I: READINESS AND MATHEMATICAL MATURITY

ARITHMETIC READINESS—WHAT IS IT? HOW IS IT ACHIEVED?

Ben A. Sueltz

What is involved in arithmetic that is functionally important? It involves such things as definitions, information, concepts, principles, relationships, computations, problems, understandings, and judgments. This is

[From "Arithmetic Readiness—What Is It? How Is it Achieved?" *New York State Education*, XXXVII (April, 1950), pp. 514-17. By permission of the author and *New York State Education*.]

much broader than the arithmetic too often found on typical tests and in books. Since the end product will deal with real things, it would seem only common sense that many of the learnings should also deal with real things. Certainly it is true that the individual responds in terms of his experience.

Let me prove this. When a small wire frame has been exhibited before groups of teachers they have identified it as a frame for a lamp shade, a waste basket, or some other familiar object within their experience. The frame actually is used commercially to hold the cork in a champagne bottle—but very few school teachers have experience with champagne bottles.

In the older pattern of teaching arithmetic, the pupil was not expected to think; he was furnished a ready-made answer and told never to forget it. But now, in the newer pattern, we want the pupil to be an active participant in learning. How can he find the answer to a problem in addition: Several ways: by counting, or by association with another known combination. Then it becomes his, the pupil's answer. Perhaps the most important feature of this newer pattern of learning is that it is a method that is transferable, for it can be used in many similar situations, and when fostered by an intelligent teacher it is constantly used.

What Is Arithmetic Readiness?

Readiness in arithmetic is the stage in a child's development when it is opportune for him to proceed into a new experience or phase of learning.

Readiness is really an integral part of modern education. It is not a thing apart. It involves physical, emotional, social, and mental development. Experience, broadly conceived, is an important factor in readiness for arithmetic. It is the job of the school to provide the stimulus in terms of experiences which will provide for each child the readiness he needs to proceed.

Readiness—Younger Children

First, let us consider readiness in young children. A four-year-old child said to her father, "Dad, two and three are five, aren't they?" The father a bit startled, said, "Yes. How do you know?" The child responded, "There were five, and when I took two away, there were three left."

Note that this discovery; it is thoughtful and meaningful; it is not mechanical. It employs a method that is useful in many similar situations, but note also, that it was done by separation and not by direct $2 + 3 = 5$. This child has readiness for simple addition and subtraction combinations.

But all children do not have this readiness. The school must assume the responsibility for developing readiness. Readiness is not automatic; it is the result of experience, of thinking, of growth. Consider the five-year-old who knew the answers to certain doubles combinations of addition. "Two and two are four." "Three and three are six; stick 'em up, I'm Tom Mix." She did not include "seven and seven," "nine and nine," and "eleven and eleven," but did say, "Twelve and twelve are twenty-four; shut your mouth and say no more." This child had learned by rote and enjoyed the sing-song of the sounds. But she had no knowledge that this was the language of addition. She was not educationally ready for what she was learning. It had no meaning or significance. Sometime later she did ask about the missing combinations. Note the element of curiosity. Curiosity is an element of readiness. But we cannot, nor should we, teach and learn things merely because we are curious about them, and especially is this true if we are committed to meaningful learning and hold the aim of functional competence.

What do these cases demonstrate? They demonstrate that initial arithmetic readiness is concerned with ideas, with speculation, with classifying, with seeking order and refinement and not with the skills of abstract addition and subtraction. As McConnell has stated in summary,

> The newer point of view emphasizes relatedness rather than itemization. It stresses generalization instead of extreme specificity. It conceives of learning as a meaningful, not a mechanical process. It considers understanding more important than mere repetition or drill. It looks upon learning as a developmental process, not one of fixation of stereotyped reactions. It encourages discovery and problem solving rather than rote learning and parrot-like repetition.

Yes, readiness for learning arithmetic must be a readiness for learning the kind of arithmetic we want. As illustrated, children often are ready for an arithmetic of ideas that grow out of their association with real things. This is different from their rote repetition of the sayings of adults and other children. Therefore, the way to achieve arithmetic readiness is to provide experience. Here are some examples of the things all schools should have and use for both readiness and learning.

Arithmetic	Materials
For counting and number sense	Pupils, sticks, blocks, papers, etc.
For size and shape	Balls, mats, brushes, pupils, etc.
For measure	Clocks, money, rulers, cans, weights, calendars, etc.
For number combinations	Sticks, number cards, blocks, etc.

Building Readiness

But the building of genuine readiness depends upon how the teacher uses these things. The presence of things alone is not enough. A kindergarten teacher told a pupil to get one large and two small rugs for the play house. She defeated real experience, speculation, and child growth by making the decision herself. Practically all pupils seem to possess a curiosity about arrangement, size, shape, and number. This curiosity is an initial stage of readiness. It is wisely fostered by providing things for pupils to handle and see and not just to talk about. Arithmetical ideas seem to be fostered in children's minds when a kinesthetic approach is included. The types of materials mentioned should be used by the pupils both visually and manually. The stage of writing numbers and of learning number combinations and recording them comes after meanings and significance have been developed. Professor Brueckner of the University of Minnesota has produced a test of arithmetic readiness for grades one and two. This is described in the *Journal of Educational Research* for March 1947.

Readiness for Arithmetic Computations

We have considered readiness as a stage or approach in learning when a child is prepared to proceed. Meaningful learning, seeing the sense in what is being learned, is a potent factor in readiness and learning. The old psychological doctrine of "felt need" is still important. The fact that normal children delight in learning, that they are curious, that they wish to explore ideas as well as things enters into readiness and learning. Let us look at arithmetic computations. Readiness for addition and subtraction may be achieved by illustration of the meaning of these processes: let the children select four blocks and four more blocks in two piles and then move them together into a pile of eight. Then record this as 4. It can

$$\frac{4}{8}$$

also be used to show $8 - 4 = 4$. The alert child senses that 8 is made up of 5 and 3, of 6 and 2, and of 7 and 1. This manual manipulation and visualization provides readiness for the written stage. The written stage of the one combination also provides a means of discovery for others.

Readiness for Written Arithmetic Problems

In problem solving, the role of experience is also important. The pupil who can picture a situation mentally has a good start on problem solving. Remember that we respond in terms of our experience. Experience with things and situations is needed as a readiness step for written problems. The girl in grade seven who seemed to have no mathematical sense about problems improved very rapidly when her mother began to send her to buy groceries and pay for them. Again, if experience is lacking in the homes of children, we in the school must provide it. That is the prime role of such activities as the post office and the grocery store in the elementary school. These will reveal the stage of development of the individual pupils.

Readiness in Measurement and Geometry

Psychological investigations have shown that young children are organizers and classifiers of things and ideas. They want to "pin things down." They are experimenters. It is enlightening to watch a young child experiment; for example, a five-year-old girl playing with colored tiles first sorted them by color, and that proved puzzling because there were different shapes of the same color. Then she sorted by shape (squares, triangles, and diamonds). She used these tiles to build mosaics and tried to fit two triangles into a space for a square and a square into a diamond space. She was developing ideas for size and shape. A six-year-old boy experimented similarly with balls and blocks but he introduced the additional concept of weight. With materials available and with just the slightest suggestion from another person, children can be real discoverers.

We are all familiar with children and their sense of comparison, particularly comparison of length or height. The school can build meaningfully not only ideas but also needed vocabulary of such concepts as smaller, taller, longer, more, etc. These are first steps leading to readiness for "How long?" "How much longer?"

What Is a Quart? The idea of quart is interesting. Most children have the language element and a partial understanding from having seen and heard of such things as quart of milk and quart of ice cream. Take your pupils of age six or seven and fill a quart milk bottle with water. Then pour the water into a larger pan and ask how much water is in the pan. With children who are a little older, take a quart of milk or water in a bottle and a quart of paint in a can. Let the children compare them and lift them. They look like different amounts, and certainly they have different weights, but each is a quart of liquid or the same amount. Again let us note that experience is a potent element in readiness and in learning.

Experience Develops Readiness

This experience develops readiness and understanding not only of such important measures as quart, foot, year, and pound but also establishes their use and significance in the world. Experience leads to readiness and readiness leads to further experience and learning. Because the experiences of children in their several homes are so varied, their readiness to proceed with arithmetic is also varied. Therefore the school must assume responsibility for providing experiences of readiness.

PART II: MOTIVATION AND MATHEMATICAL MATURITY

EMOTION AND THOUGHT

Robert B. Davis

If I may speak of the human mind, somewhat roughly, as a computing machine, then it is certainly a machine which is formidably intricate and incredibly delicate. Moreover, and this is the point which I wish to discuss, it is devastatingly subject to the influence of the emotions. The teacher who is trying to improve the problem-solving ability of a student is consequently involved in the manipulation of an awesome piece of machinery. The result of this manipulation may range all the way from permanent improvement to permanent damage. The matter is worth discussing largely because it lies within our ability to secure a maximum of improvement and a minimum of damage, provided we know how to go about it. But it is not always done the way one might expect. Goals like accuracy and precision must be approached with some caution; under certain circumstances they can become, surprisingly, not the desirable things we usually think them, but rather obstacles and sources of difficulty. This occurs chiefly when these goals are overstressed, or when they are used as the vehicle for expressing such emotions as resentment or hostility.

The Subtlety of Emotional Influences

Recently I was working to generalize a theorem I had just proved. I found myself not really trying. I was not really trying because I

[From "Emotion and Thought," *The Mathematics Teacher*, XLVIII (March, 1955), pp. 133-42. Reprinted by permission of the author and *The Mathematics Teacher*.]

suspected that no improvement was possible. Probably, also, I was not really trying because I wanted to be done with the matter, give the existing version to the typist, and get on with something else. Finding an improvement would force me to alter everything that had been written.

I did, finally, establish the extended version of the theorem. But this became possible only after I had settled three preliminary matters:

First, I had to recognize that I was *not* really trying.

Second, I had to make myself believe in the *possibility* of success.

Finally, I had to persuade myself that the improved version was worth striving for, that it really *was* something I *wanted*.

This influence of the emotions on one's rational thought processes—especially as it appears in students—is a central problem of good teaching. As a sheer guess, we might estimate that the teacher is well advised to devote one-tenth of his effort to the objective presentation of material (which should be an easy task for him, anyway, if he is well qualified), and to spend the remaining nine-tenths in establishing a suitable emotional background for the student's efforts. Obviously, not everyone would agree with this estimate, but I think there is much evidence to support it.

The teacher who is to be cognizant of emotional influences must possess, among other qualifications, these two: he must be able to perceive the student's needs, and he must be able to adjust his own behavior in response to these needs. In doing this, the teacher's chief obstacle is the large heritage of attitudes which are inappropriate to the situation. On the other hand, his chief asset is his understanding of his own mental processes and feelings and his knowledge of what works well in his own case.

The important influences in the teacher-student relation are very *small* things: an inflection in the voice at the end of a question, or perhaps even a glance, with no words spoken. We must be careful not to become so concerned with the gross, macroscopic phenomena that we overlook the nuances. Which teachers terrified us, when we ourselves were students? Did it depend upon what they actually said, or upon the *way* that they said it? Or even upon the way that they acted and looked, when they weren't speaking at all?

As a further example of the sort of thing we are dealing with, it is worth noticing how many different matters are involved in "wanting to learn": wanting to win the teacher's approval, wanting to avoid punishment, wanting to stand on one's own feet without the teacher's help, wanting to be able to defend one's own ideas against any criticisms of the teacher, wanting to develop self-confidence, wanting to contribute a new idea, and many other things. I might add: wanting to satisfy one's own sense of what is right. The diversity and depth of these phenomena are never exhausted, however long and carefully the teacher may observe the student's motives. He who is not alive to the subtleties of student desires and student motivation—indeed, he who is not thrilled and intrigued by them—has little likelihood of being a good teacher. But the phenomena are of the greatest subtlety, and many teachers find them easy to overlook. He who thinks of motivation as rooted in good grades and later earning power is a poor observer indeed.

Student Needs and Teacher Attitudes

Perhaps we should consider a few typical needs of students, and a few of the attitudes that frequently appear as obstacles to the teacher. This is no easy matter. It is this very subtlety of the phenomena which confounds us. The inter-relations between two people consist of a perfectly evident verbal part, and of a nonverbal part that is not at all evident. Unfortunately, the "invisible" nonverbal part is usually the more decisive. However much we dislike someone, it is not at all easy to say exactly *why* we dislike him. If we are strongly attracted to some other person, it is not to be explained, ordinarily, on the basis of something he has *said*, but rather because of something he has communicated without using the literal meaning of words.

Let us give an example. In the final scene of the recent movie version of Herman Wouk's *Caine Mutiny*, the captain and a young officer named Keith are standing on the bridge of a minesweeper, about to take her out to sea. Keith has been distinctly arrogant, and remarkably incompetent, in his past performances. As if this were not enough, he has made matters considerably worse by voicing a dislike for the captain, and by becoming involved in a mutiny. Keith, in short, is a problem. Now for the scene on the bridge: it is simple in the extreme. The captain looks at Keith. "Keith," he says, and pauses for a memorable piece of nonverbal communication, "take her out!"

By facial expressions, by tone of voice, by whatever other subtle mannerisms—as well as by the act itself of entrusting the ship's safety to Keith—the captain has said, in effect: "Go ahead. You will find yourself. If you try to take the ship out, nothing terrible will happen. I trust you; you can afford to trust yourself a bit."

Undoubtedly, any exceptional nervousness on the part of the captain would have been communicated to Keith and would surely have impaired his performance. Any insincerity, ambivalence, resentment, or similar feeling would also have been communicated. Each of us has everyday experiences which demonstrate how easy it is to "get rattled" —often in response to someone else's anxiety. The teacher's feelings are likewise transmitted to the student, and have the strongest influence on how well he likes a subject, how hard he works in it, the quality of the work, and his use of the subject in years to come. This last point alone would suffice to direct a great deal of attention to the communication of attitudes between teacher and student. After all, in later life, the student can go out of his way to make use of a certain subject, or he can go out of his way to avoid it; if he does use it, he can do so creatively, or he can do so in a thoroughly routine way. Much of this is determined by minute nuances experienced in the classroom.

In one of my own classes I recently had a student who presented a picture rather like Keith. I am sure this student disliked teachers. He had accumulated a long record of failures in mathematics. I believe he found the subject incomprehensible. His own ideas of what was important within a problem had, I suspect, never seemed to coincide with the ideas of his teachers. (Incidentally, I might add that the teacher who is not able to explain his ideas so that the student willingly accepts them, and understands them, but who is nonetheless prepared to insist upon these ideas, is one of the major sources of resentments and feelings of inadequacy among mathematics students.) He appeared to be left with the feeling that it was impossible ever to please the teacher, that mathematics was a magical subject where any reasonable decision would later turn out to be wrong, for some reason of the most unpredictable sort. It doubtless seemed to him to defy understanding. Mathematics looked to him like a combination of witchcraft and the capricious misuse of authority.

Toward the end of the term he began to work diligently, if somewhat uncomprehendingly. I take some credit for this spurt of activity. I imagine I had made him feel that success was a more *real* possibility than he had formerly thought it to be. On one occasion he volunteered to go to the board and solve a problem. This already indicated a great increase in his belief that "nothing terrible would happen." By this I refer especially to the nonverbal relations between him, the class, and me. The achievement which I claim for myself is that I had made him feel, after a term's contact, that my *attitude* toward him would continue to be friendly and encouraging, whatever came of his efforts at the blackboard. This, of course, was a nonverbal matter. It makes little difference what the teacher *says;* the crucial thing is his manner.

When this student went to the board, he was noticeably anxious. He worked most of a difficult problem with fair accuracy (getting almost the right answer), though he omitted some parentheses and made a few similar errors. When he had finished, I told him that I thought he had used a lot of good ideas (which was entirely the truth, and may consequently have sounded sincere). Then I asked him, without specification, if he had written exactly what he had intended in each of the lines of work. With no further comment from me, he turned and corrected most of his minor errors.

This is in many ways the crux of the matter. By building self-confidence, by pointing out the positive paths to achievement, by encouraging faith in the possibility of success, we do the optimal job of teaching. What we really have to do is to show each student that something he *wants* can be achieved *by his own efforts* in a certain direction. The use of negative inducements, threats, intimidation, or ridicule is a more dangerous and far less satisfactory approach. Veiled threats are no better. The trouble with inhibitions, as everyone today seems to know, is that they have an alarming tendency to spread. If we say "don't" to someone often enough, he soon becomes unable even to do those things which *are* permissible. (One encounters students of piano who have been told so frequently, and with such convincing feeling, not to make noise and disturb the rest of the family, that this has finally become a factor in their striking wrong notes during a performance. After all, music is a communication between performer and hearer, and if the hearer has habitually interpreted it as a hostile communication the player may gradually come to accept this evaluation, and to develop the guilt feelings which one would then expect.) In mathematics, I have seen students reject a simple and satisfactory solution to a problem, because they have acquired the feeling that things just are not that easy. Anything that nice must be immoral!

I can summarize the question of student needs by saying that the student does need someone to point out the paths to satisfaction; he does not need someone to stand by and threaten or intimidate. Every human being is trying, in a profound sense, to do his best. We can be most helpful by keeping open at least some paths to satisfaction, by showing that these paths are a real answer to his needs and desires, and by not confronting the student with desperate and unsolvable dilemmas.

Attitudes Which Are Obstacles

Many teachers overemphasize the demands of accuracy and precision. They can make a misplaced minus sign appear as the epitome of total failure. They can create a state of anxiety in the student, until he is unable to approach any problem in mathematics without a terrifying sensation of tottering insecurely at the brink of a bottomless pit of absolute incompetence (not to mention ridicule) into which he may at any instant be pushed by the fatal error of misplacing a decimal point. I do not mean to counsel indifference to the need of obtaining a correct answer. The point is that one is *more likely to get* the right answer when one is relaxed and self-confident than when one is anxious and insecure.

In the hope of making these ideas more concrete, I should like to refer to a recent article by Catherine Meehan.[1] This article gives something of a converse to the point of view which I am describing. Her point of view is that, by presenting mathematical techniques, the teacher influences the attitudes of the student. Our present interest is in the converse: the attitudes of the teacher are communicated in a subtle, nonverbal way to the student, and give rise to certain definite attitudes in the student which have a decisive influence on his problem-solving ability. I should like to join Miss Meehan in emphasizing that the flexibility or dogmatic rigidity of the graduate, his creative zeal or his apathy, his responsiveness to new ideas or his rejection of them, all date back in large part to his student days, to the subtle examples set by the attitudes of various teachers.

Miss Meehan writes:

> ... we meet local employers, day after day, who beg us to teach *attitudes,* good old-fashioned *attitudes.* If this could be done by means of another course, someone would have tried it before now. It used to be done in the regular classroom. It is still being done in mathematics classes led by alert, enthusiastic, well-prepared teachers. ...[2]

I hope that I may be forgiven my use of a couple of excerpts as a springboard to plunge into my own remarks. In regard to this first quotation we might emphasize these points.

1. Attitudes certainly are taught by countless *little* experiences, all day long, in class and out. This is the very aspect of education which we wish to emphasize. A teacher who counsels self-confidence in all of the big things, but who induces diffidence in all of the little things, will have a harmful effect in the long run. Perhaps, for example, he is inclined to interrupt impolitely at times when the student is talking, implying a real lack of respect for the student's presentation—perhaps also for the student.

2. The potentialities for inducing good attitudes or bad are tremendous. Many adults possess excellent thought processes which they owe,

---

[1] Catherine Meehan. "Mathematics and the Development of Good Citizens," *The Mathematics Teacher,* XLVII (April, 1954), 226-30.

[2] *Ibid.,* p. 226.

in part, to certain of their teachers. Alternatively, many adult cases of anti-intellectualism, lack of self-confidence, over-expression (or over-inhibition) of hostility, distaste for certain subjects, or failure to appreciate abstract thought can be traced back to teachers who have been instrumental in establishing such patterns. As an example, we might cite the case of the teacher who always insists upon being right, and who may thereby create in students a "what-does-it-get-you" attitude toward logic and rationality. Logic may appear as an inadequate defense against the capricious authority of the teacher. The good teacher always tries to make it clear whether he is stating his opinion, or is dealing with objective fact. As much as possible, he guarantees the student a secure refuge in logic. Contrariwise, I have heard poor teachers brush aside the student's logic even when it was largely correct. One might say: in a good school, a freshman with a rational line of reasoning will prevail over a dean who cannot thus support his conclusions. In a poor school, the dean is always right. What place has logic in such a school?

3. As we have mentioned earlier, it is not what you do, but the way that you do it. The attitudes of the teacher are decisive, for it is these which influence the attitudes of the student. The question is not, for example, whether the teacher *tries* to state the need for logic, but rather whether the teacher himself trusts his own logic, and genuinely believes in the student's ability to be logical. If the teacher is over-controlling, and interferes too much in the student's thought processes, the student has no opportunity to develop his own logical facility. That the over-controlling teacher makes speeches extolling logical thought means little if he continually interferes, as some teachers do, in all of the student's attempts to think for himself.

Permit me to interrupt myself. It occurs to me that I may not be understood, because the reader may be saying to himself: "But, after all, isn't the internal logic the important thing?" Yes, of course. That is to say, it is the important thing to the mathematical structure itself; it is the important thing once it is all set down on paper. But there is a stage, or even many stages, prior to that. One must select strategies, or lines of attack. One must recall this, and see the possibility of using that. In later life, one must choose between various problems, and decide which are feasible and which are not. If a line of attack is not leading to success, one must choose between abandoning it or persevering, and extreme error in this direction is not uncommon; often people have long continued attempts in a hopeless direction, or have left an approach just short of victory. One must decide when to resort to a search of the literature, and when to figure the matter out for oneself. Often there are many different *types* of solution, and one must decide which type to look for, as in choosing between finding a primitive function in integration, or resorting to numerical methods. For the student, who has not yet achieved such a high level of integration of his knowledge, there is often the choice of whether to use the method learned in trigonometry, and when to use the method learned in analytic geometry. One must sometimes decide either to try a certain change of variable, or else to reject it as unlikely. One can give literally millions of examples; indeed, one cannot solve even the simplest trigonometric identity without making many choices of this sort. I believe this is one of the functions of *inspiration* in teaching—to provide insight into how to make these decisions. This is done chiefly by the example of the teacher, and is one reason why I believe that it is virtually impossible to teach mathematics unless one is really extremely proficient in the subject. I know many teachers who are a few pages ahead of the students in the textbook, and who are known for the clarity of their lectures and are considered adequate teachers. I feel they are not. They are usually incapable of showing the student the important example of a man who knows how to make all of these choices, and without this, teaching is meaningless.

The reader may further ask: "Still, isn't student performance a question of aptitude or ability? If the student hasn't got what it takes, what is the teacher to do then?" Well, there is no doubt that there is such a thing as ability, or aptitude, or intelligence, just as there is such a thing as body weight. But just like body weight, this is relatively constant just so long as we do not make any intelligent effort to change it. The student's aptitude in a subject is the historical summation of his experiences relating to that subject. It is not even necessary to argue over the question of heredity. There is so much plasticity and potentiality for change in virtually every student that hereditary differences, even if they do exist, are not ordinarily the decisive factor. Heredity, or aptitude, or intelligence is usually neither more nor less than the excuse which the teacher offers when he has failed to understand the needs of a certain student or has been unable to meet these needs. Most "student" failures can be traced back to some adult, often a teacher though not always the current teacher. Sometimes one must look to the teacher of an earlier course who has left a residue of distaste, lack of self-confidence, indecision, and anxiety.

But after all, how can I say to the teacher: This is your job; look to it! Many good teachers have recognized this as their job, as far back as we know the history of teaching. To teach is to inspire. Many teachers (whom I unhesitatingly label inadequate) say: No, it is not my job. My job is to present material; if the student can get it, well and good. But if he fails, do not blame the failure on me.

And I would be the first to agree that it is not an individual matter. The cumulative effect of previous teachers may be more than one can counteract. It is precisely for this reason that the criteria of teaching are so complex. A teacher may say he has taught successfully this way for years; ah, but what sort of problem has he been leaving for the teachers who had to deal with these students in following years? Did he teach the students to think for themselves? Did he teach them to like the subject, and to want to work hard in it? Did he teach them to approach problems with self-confidence? Or perhaps just the opposite?

What of the person who, in later life, carefully avoids the use of mathematics as much as possible? Can we say that his mathematics teachers were successful, simply on the basis that he was once able to solve quadratic equations? The simplicities of examinations and grades are no substitute for the complex criteria of later life, and teachers, if not students, must be judged by these long-range criteria.

Suppose that we consider a second excerpt from Miss Meehan's article:

> I believe that we give our attention to developing the individual as a person who will be able to really *live*—happily, successfully, and peacefully in our democratic society—and who *will know* and will fight fiercely when his standards are imperiled. . . .
>
> What are *some* of these standards?
>
> *Accuracy*—By this standard we hope to develop attitudes of promptness, precision, honesty, etc.
>
> When Sammy, in the early grades, is given this problem, "There were five birds on a branch of a tree; two flew away; how many are still on the branch?" his answer must be "three" and only "three." "Two" is not acceptable on the theory that if there are three left there are certainly two! What kind of a city treasurer or a club treasurer or a banker would Sammy make if we took "two" for his answer? Equivocation is not honest and we just won't have it.[3]

One could discuss this excerpt at great length; let me settle for two remarks:

First, suppose that Sammy does in fact argue that there are two birds left. I think we would make a mistake if we brushed aside his logic here. We would run grave risk of forcing him to profess a belief in *our* logic, while he acquires more than a shade of doubt as to his own ability to look at the phenomena and follow out their intrinsic logic himself. Is he wrong in saying that there are two birds left? As a matter of fact, he evidently is not; he has seen a real truth concerning number which we should not brush aside. Perhaps he has been more astute and more profound than we have been. He has pointed up a weakness, not in his logic, but rather in our question. "Two birds are left" is a true statement! What

---

[3] *Ibid.*, pp. 226-227.

we are really asking for is the strongest statement of this kind that can be made, and "Three birds are left" is also a true statement, is stronger, and is in fact the strongest true statement, hence the answer. We would do Sammy an injustice—hardly the example which we mean to set—if we made him feel that our question was properly posed and his logic was fallacious. In truth, our question was vague, and he responded with a correct statement whose logical validity is unassailable. There *are* two birds left. That there are three implies *a fortiori* that there are two.

Sammy has looked at the situation clearly and realistically. Do we wish to brush this aside? Do we *want* him to take our word for it? If he does, he runs grave risks for the future. What criteria will be left him later on? Is he to try to remember what people have *told* him is true, or is he to try to figure it out for himself?

There is a digression here which I cannot resist. Miss Meehan argues that we want Sammy to be a good club treasurer. Well, if we are to take ultimate social values into account, as Miss Meehan essentially implies, is a numerical error in arithmetic so much worse than pathological gullibility, which we seem to instill in many a student today? Neither is desirable but in social terms, the mathematics teacher might well give a thought to the question of whether he is preparing his students to believe the worst lies of propagandists, because he has taught them to disbelieve the evidence of their own senses and their own logic, and to accept a logic which is foisted upon them from without.

But that is really irrelevant to my central theme. I claim that we must have a care lest Sammy soon find himself unable to do mathematics, irrespective of whether or not he becomes grist for the mills of the propagandist. There is no foundation for science other than logic mastered within one's own mind. There is no rote approach to science. There is no acceptance of external logic. The acceptance of external logic is itself illogical.

My second comment is this: "Promptness, precision, honesty, etc." are worthwhile virtues, but we must use the words with caution, lest we be utterly misunderstood. There is a kind of compulsive promptness which is virtually nothing more than a weapon with which some individuals belabor an easy-going world. Is our ideal the rigid individual who reproaches acquaintances when they are two minutes late for a luncheon engagement? Or the individual who demands absolute punctuality from his employees? I should say these are hardly the ideal; the ideal person is flexible, adaptable, easy to get along with, and reasonably forgiving and generous. Training in "promptness, precision, honesty, etc." is a strong medicine which we must take care not to administer in over-large doses. To do so is detrimental to the way the student relates to other people, is harmful to his own creative thought processes, and exerts a pernicious influence on the way he feels about himself.

I have mentioned various things which I feel the good teacher does or does not do. It is worth adding one more: I believe every really good teacher is frequently struck with a sense of awe at the consistent logic of nearly all of his students. (True, this may be most remarkably obscured by the fact that the student did not trouble himself to glance at pages nine and ten of the text, and so on.) Students, youngsters, even infants show an almost incredible natural gift for logic. I recently watched a nine-month-old baby trying to escape past a gate that had been put in place with him in mind. In back of him was an unfastened gate of identical construction, not needed at the moment. After unsuccessful efforts at moving the fastened gate, the baby returned to the unfastened gate, which he could move with ease. He repeatedly went from one gate to the other, clearly attempting to use the one as an example of how to solve the problem of the second. I am awe-struck by the extreme cleverness of such an approach.

Many remarks along the present lines could be appended to various other excerpts from "Mathematics and the Development of Good Citizens." I may as well confess that, taking that article as a whole, I feel a lack of sympathy with the tone of it all, though perhaps I misunderstand the true meaning. To arrive at a proper balance in educational matters requires constant discussion, a constant meeting of different minds. Teachers must be especially alert to recognize any harmful tendency in themselves toward being over-controlling or overly rigid. The teacher is so frequently right, and stands so unmistakably in a controlling position, that he must make great efforts to yield to the correct logic of students, and to permit them the generous amount of freedom which is necessary for learning. Students must be allowed to make mistakes, to try out their own ideas, to think for themselves. Good teaching cannot be built on the attitude that the students are stupid. In point of fact, the logic of students, as has been remarked above, is nearly always at least partly correct. The good teacher builds on the correct part, whereas the poor teacher attacks the weaker part. Hence the good teacher leads the student along the path to self-reliance and self-confidence, while the poor teacher induces feelings of inadequacy and distaste for the subject.

Unfortunately, a correct evaluation of oneself is extremely difficult. Many of the best teachers struggle prodigiously for self-improvement; many poor teachers, over-controlling and rigid, continue complacently in the same course year after year. It has been wisely said that one must distinguish twenty years of experience, which some teachers have, from one year of experience repeated twenty times, which other teachers have.

Few poor teachers show any real awareness of their inadequacy; rather, they have countless rationalizations to justify themselves.

Two Remarks

The reader who is familiar with certain sociological critiques of the culture of the United States (and perhaps especially of New England) may have recognized that many of my comments have been expressed in other language by saying that we have inherited a culture which, if it has a major defect, suffers chiefly from this: it *prevents* too many things, in the general sense. It is itself over-controlling, overly rigid. It seeks to mold youth too much, and to let it grow too little. Somehow this all adds up to an effect of stifling creative expression. Mathematics teaching might be said to tend to reflect this cultural characteristic. It would not be appropriate to consider the issue on broad sociological grounds in this article, and I do not mean to do so. Right within the needs of the creative teaching situation itself we can find ample motivation for encouraging individuality and *not* emphasizing routine acceptance of externally imposed logic.

It occurs to me that I have not used the word *rote* in this article—not yet, in any event. By *rote* teaching I mean the presentation of facts and techniques which are simply to be memorized by the student, with perhaps a certain amount of practice on some of the techniques. This, I claim, is not teaching at all. At least, it is not the teaching of mathematics. Mathematics is not a tool. It is a way of thinking which is creative, flexible, perceptive of reality, and based upon certain good judgment as to what may be eliminated, and what must be retained, in the process of abstraction. It recognizes objectives, and selects strategies. *None of this is taught by rote presentation.* That some teachers will tell me they can achieve high quiz grades by rote teaching is irrelevant. They have taught all of the inessentials, they have tested all of the inessentials, and they have found their students well versed in all of the inessentials. What has that to do with what I have to say?

Summary

But to return to my basic theme. Talk about teaching has a tendency to be unsatisfactorily vague, and I would wish to be as concrete and precise as the nonverbal nature of the subject will permit. My chief remark is that rational thought processes are under the influence of emotional factors. This is not a slight influence. On the contrary, emotional factors have a decisiveness which the teacher cannot afford to ignore. If one looks at a school, the over-all pattern of students doing well in courses they like, badly in courses they dislike, and so on, is the first thing that hits the eye. The cumulative effect of this sort of preference, over many years, gives rise to what we call aptitude for one subject, or lack of aptitude for another. (I do not, of course, mean to restrict attention to experiences within the classroom only, nor even to the experiences of school years alone. The bases of aptitudes, as the toy-makers have lost no time in pointing out, extend far back and into experiences of all sorts. The teacher is only one influence, but he is *one*.)

I wish the classroom experience were not so intangible. It is a most refractory matter for discussion. I should like to give an example of some instance where a teacher has, in a subtle and nonverbal way, exerted an influence toward creative thought in students, or, perhaps, an instance of the opposite sort of thing. As a matter of fact, fate has just handed me one example, and, inadequate as it is, let it do. I just interrupted this article to meet a class for the first session of the term. One problem was checking students' names against class cards. Now, the pronunciation of students' names is one of the less certain and predictable phenomena of the universe, and the teacher is not unlikely to be occasionally in error. Just how he handles this situation, the extent to which he encourages students to feel free and secure in correcting him—after all, here is one case where the student is the absolute authority—the way he responds when students do criticize him (and they may not do it gently) sets a good deal of the tone of the class, for that day at least. Or perhaps I should say, this is a very little thing. It is one case where the contest between power and truth is being fought, in the subtlest of ways. The basic principle of psychology, however, seems to be that everything is the outcome of the summation of all of these *little things*. They are small tokens, but they add up to a potent currency.

In case my meaning is not clear, I might add that the mature teacher, who wishes the student to learn to stand on his own feet, will show a generous ability to accept criticism, and will not respond by threatening the student in any way. Do we want the student to think for himself, or don't we? If he is right and we, the teacher, are wrong, we cannot ever be too ready to admit it. The more willingly we do it, the better.

What can be done in the classroom, to improve student performance, is in its way as definite and as important as any of the phenomena of science and art. Unfortunately, it is sadly neglected. I cannot say there is anything like the optimal amount of freedom, democracy, consistent objectivity, and inspiration in the average classroom. Too often one sees a teacher who insists upon being right, who is unreceptive to new ideas, who is unperceptive of the subtler needs of students, or who lacks the vital interest in his subject matter which is necessary if he is to inspire his students. The teacher is rarely able to evaluate himself accurately, especially in view of the nonverbal nature of the subject; though his words be generous and accepting, it matters not—the real question is whether or not his manner is threatening.

The constructive use of atmosphere to enhance problem-solving ability is strikingly akin to the psychoanalyst's use of "conversation" in treating neuroses. In either case, one is amazed at how much can be done, and by such subtle influences. It is to be regretted that the present-day acceptance of the psychiatrist's "conversational" methods as something definite and real (and even dramatic) does not extend more fully to include the similar techniques and problems of the teacher. One can hope for the day when a profound understanding of emotional dynamics will be recognized as an ordinary tool of the teacher's trade, virtually on the same level as the ability to speak his or her native tongue. The teacher *must* be alert to the needs and attitudes of the student, and must be able to modify these attitudes, or respond to these needs, wherever the occasion arises. If the teacher is less than this, he is nothing more than a textbook, and may strongly influence the student away from creativity and toward sterile routine.

PART III: INDIVIDUAL DIFFERENCES AND MATHEMATICAL MATURITY

DIFFERENTIATED INSTRUCTION IN ARITHMETIC: AN OVERVIEW AND A PROMISING TREND

J. Fred Weaver

"We hold these truths to be self-evident": that children differ; that they differ markedly in many ways and as a result of many causes; that no uniform instructional program, the same for all children, can provide learning experiences which are equally beneficial for each child; and that effective provision for individual differences is dependent in large measure upon appropriate differentiated instruction. These truths are as evident in the teaching and learning of arithmetic as they are in every other area of instruction.

[From "Differentiated Instruction in Arithmetic: An Overview and a Promising Trend," *Education*, LXXIV (January, 1954), pp. 300-5. Reprinted by permission of the author and *Education*.]

Arithmetic Abilities and Individual Differences

Effective differentiated instruction in arithmetic can be planned only in light of our knowledge of quantitative abilities and of individual differences in relation thereto. Among other things we know that:

1. Arithmetic competence is not a unitary thing, but a composite of several types of quantitative ability: e.g., computational ability, problem-solving ability, etc.

2. These abilities overlap to varying degrees, but most are sufficiently independent to warrant separate evaluation.

3. Children in a given class or grade show a wide range of ability in each phase of instruction. Furthermore, these variations generally increase from the lower to the upper elementary grades. For example: Based on results from the Stanford Achievement Test administered in a small school system, Brueckner and Grossnickle [1] have reported ranges of 4.8 years for children in Grade III in Arithmetic Reasoning and 3.2 in Arithmetic Computation. For children in Grade VI the reported ranges were 6.0 years in Arithmetic Reasoning and 6.1 years in Arithmetic Computation.

4. Children exhibit considerable variation in their profiles or patterns of ability in the various phases of arithmetic instruction.

5. The several quantitative abilities correlate differentially with general intelligence. Observed relationships between IQ and computational skill and between IQ and problem solving are too low to permit accurate prediction of success or failure in these quantitative abilities on the basis of IQ alone.

6. Reading comprehension bears little relationship to computational skill, but is more significantly related to problem-solving ability. However, improvement of general reading achievement-level is no guarantee that improvement in problem-solving will follow, although attention to certain specific reading skills related to the comprehension and interpretation of quantitative situations and data frequently proves beneficial.

Differences Between Extreme Deviates

Frequently studies of children who are extreme deviates give valuable data regarding the problem of individual differences and differentiated instruction.

In this present discussion it is possible only to emphasize the fact that characteristic differences between superior and retarded children are largely matters of *degree* rather than *kind*. Some of the most significant

---

[1] Leo J. Brueckner and Foster E. Grossnickle, *Making Arithmetic Meaningful* (New York: Holt, Rinehart & Winston, Inc., 1953), p. 82.

differences between these two groups of children are found in their rates of learning; in their ability to sense quantitative relationships, to form quantitative generalizations, and to reason abstractly; in their need for a rich background of concrete and manipulative experience; in their need for drill and practice; in their initiative, resourcefulness, and independence when meeting new or novel quantitative situations; in their ability to transfer quantitative learning; in their attention span; in their reaction to routine; and in their interests and attitudes, especially in relation to emotional adjustment and stability. Knowledge of differences such as these is most helpful in providing effective differentiated instruction in arithmetic.

Some Methods of Differentiating Instruction

Many plans for differentiating arithmetic instruction have been advocated and implemented, with varying degrees of success. Most commonly these programs seek to provide for adjustment in factors such as rate of learning, subject matter, instructional procedures and materials, etc. It will be advantageous to overview briefly a few of the frequently used techniques for differentiating instruction in arithmetic.

Plans Emphasizing Individual Rate of Progress. The Winnetka Plan undoubtedly is one of the best known instructional programs which permit each child to progress at his own rate. This emphasis upon individual rate of progress also is a feature of the plan for teaching arithmetic in the primary grades in Cleveland.[2] Numerous modifications of these and similar plans exist, of course.

Obviously, adjustment of rate of progress *alone* is not an adequate provision for individual differences in arithmetic. It is of little value to permit children to progress at their own rates through uniform experiences and assignments in a uniform way. Various other adjustments are equally necessary. Plans such as the Winnetka and Cleveland programs recognize this fact, of course, although they differ in those adjustments which are emphasized. To be most effective, any plan of individual instruction and rate of progress must be sensitive to all the many other instructional modifications and differentiations which are necessary.

"Ability" or "Homogeneous" Grouping. Frequently we have sought to provide for individual differences in arithmetic by some form of homogeneous grouping. Most commonly this grouping has been effected on the basis of IQ. When considering the effectiveness of such plans, we must not overlook several important facts.

---

[2] Herschel E. Grime, "Adapting the Curriculum in Primary Arithmetic to Abilities of Children," *Mathematics Teacher*, XLIII (October, 1950), 242-44.

Even within a "homogeneous" group there remains a marked degree of heterogeneity. Individual differences within each group have not been eliminated; at best they have only been reduced.

The mere formation of homogeneous groups is, in itself, no provision for individual differences. All too often all the various groups are handled in about the same way, which makes the very formation of such groups rather pointless. Homogeneous grouping will help provide for individual differences only to the extent that such grouping facilitates differentiated instruction.

IQ alone is a very inadequate basis for forming homogeneous groups. This is quite evident in light of the low relation cited previously between IQ and factors such as achievement in arithmetic computation and in problem solving. If "ability" grouping is to be used effectively, groups must be formed with IQ as only *one* of the determining factors—and not necessarily the most important one.

Differentiated subject-matter and instructional methods and materials. Some of our effective provisions for individual differences in arithmetic are to be found in variations in the depth and scope of subject-matter and in related instructional methods and materials. The study of any given arithmetic topic embraces understandings, skills, and applications. Each is fostered by appropriate, but different, kinds of learning experiences.

For most arithmetic topics, through differentiated instruction we can provide variations in the depth of understanding emphasized, in the complexity of skills to be mastered, and in the type of social application stressed. The slow learner will have experiences which lead to a less penetrating understanding of a topic, to the mastery of the simpler skills, and to an awareness of the more immediate social applications. He will rely more heavily on the use of concrete materials, and will have need for larger amounts of practice. He will profit from shorter units of work and from more specific assignments.

The superior child, on the other hand, will be challenged by experiences which develop a greater depth of understanding, a mastery of more complex skills, and an awareness of a wider variety of social applications. He will rely less heavily on the use of concrete materials, and will need smaller amounts of practice. He will profit from larger units of work and from broader assignments.

Anderson [3] has observed the differential value of two instructional meth-

[3] G. Lester Anderson, "Quantitative Thinking as Developed under Correctionist and Field Theories of Learning," *Learning Theory in School Situations,* University of Minnesota Studies in Education, No. 2. (Minneapolis: University of Minnesota Press, 1949), pp. 40-73.

ods or emphases for children of different ability-achievement patterns. He found that when the development of quantitative thinking is an instructional objective, drill procedures are more helpful than meaningful procedures for children of relatively low ability and high achievement, whereas just the opposite is true for children of relatively high ability and low achievement. Our remedial cases most frequently fall into the latter category.

Evaluation, Diagnosis, and Remedial Work

Any effective program of differentiated instruction in arithmetic must include provision for comprehensive evaluation, periodic diagnosis, and appropriate remedial work. These are not adjuncts to the instructional program; rather, they are some of its vital, integral parts.

We recognize clearly today that *all* phases of instruction—understandings, computations, applications, etc.—must be evaluated, and that pencil-and-paper tests alone are frequently quite inadequate as measuring instruments. Greater use of observational and interview-type procedures, as well as other appropriate techniques, is essential to comprehensive and effective evaluation.

Diagnosis is far more than a matter of showing the existence, if any, of quantitative trouble or difficulty. More importantly, it seeks to determine the specific place and nature of, and cause or reason for, an observed difficulty. In a sense diagnosis is a continuous process and has a place at all *stages* of instruction—from the development of readiness to the attainment of mastery. Diagnosis likewise is relevant to all *phases* of instruction—to the development of quantitative understandings, etc., as well as to the development of computational skills and problem-solving abilities. Although pencil-and-paper tests have a role to play as instruments of evaluation in relation to diagnosis, we have great need for techniques of an observational and interview-like nature. Especially do we need to be conscious of effective ways for studying a child's pattern of thinking in various quantitative situations.

Diagnosis is not an end in itself. Rather, it is a means to more effective differentiated instruction. Only when we have diagnosed the difficulties and determined the needs of children, quantitatively, can we provide the kind of instruction designed to remedy those difficulties and meet those needs. Except for extreme cases of disability which demand the aid of clinicians and special services, remedial teaching is basically *good* teaching, differentiated to meet specific instructional needs.

A Promising Trend

The most encouraging trend in improving the effectiveness of differentiated instruction in arithmetic is to be found in our increased attention to *levels of learning.* Smith [4] has given much attention to this concept in his recent discussion of individual differences in mathematics.

The same quantitative situation may be experienced by different children at different levels of representation, ranging from the concrete to the abstract. Different levels of quantitative thinking may be involved, and different levels of mastery may be achieved. Full recognition of these various levels of learning can lead to highly effective grouping and differentiated instruction. A specific illustration may clarify this idea.

Levels of Learning in Action

Let us assume that children are being introduced to the new topic of multiplying a fraction by a whole number, and that a simple socially significant situation has been presented at the outset of instruction: e.g., "There are 6 persons in Betty's family. If Betty's mother wants to serve each one with ½ a grapefruit at breakfast, how many grapefruit will she need?"

The teacher will do well to let the children in her class suggest and follow their own methods of attack upon this new situation. Some will resort to the manipulation of cut-out fractional parts. Others will draw a diagram. Still others will tackle the new situation at the abstract level of representation. Some will think basically in terms of the addition process (½ + ½ + ½ + ½ + ½ + ½), whereas others will think merely in terms of counting the halves. Still others may recognize the applicability of multiplication and express the problem as an example to be solved (6 × ½). Some children will think directly that 6 × ½ is 6 halves, or 3. Others may think in terms of ratios, recognizing that 2 persons could be served with one grapefruit, so 3 grapefruit would be needed to serve 6 persons. For some few children the teacher will need to suggest a method of attack *at an appropriate level of learning.*

The various attacks and thinking patterns should be discussed with the children in the class. A second or third problem can be presented in a similar manner. (One of the problems might involve a multiplication such as 4 × ⅔.) The teacher will observe that children begin to gravitate to

4 Rolland R. Smith, "Provisions for Individual Differences," *The Learning of Mathematics: Its Theory and Practice,* National Council of Teachers of Mathematics Twenty-first Yearbook (1953), 271-302.

one or another of the different levels of representation and thinking, and she will guide each child to the level of learning at which he appears to be most successful. Groups definitely are taking shape. The teacher now may group the children for further instruction on the basis of these levels of learning, or she may retain a "grouping effect" without actually dividing the class into distinct and identifiable separate groups. In either event, further instruction is differentiated in terms of each child's level of learning.

Of course, children do not remain statically at a given level. Many move to more mature levels as they are able, and sometimes encouraged, to do so. This is accomplished with ease, especially if a "grouping effect" has been utilized without the formation of separate and distinct groups. Even if the latter is the case, however, these groups are not static in structure but permit a child to move from one group to another as he is able to advance to a higher level of learning. This is possible because the basic difference between groups is not one of subject-matter so much as it is a difference in levels of learning in relation to much the same subject-matter.

"Mastery" in arithmetic is a relative rather than an absolute term. We rightfully may speak of levels of mastery in connection with levels of learning. One child may master the topic in question at the abstract level, whereas another child may be able to attain mastery but only at a lower level of representation and thinking. Each has mastered the topic at the level of learning at which he is capable. Thus, our attempts to differentiate instruction in terms of level of learning embrace a recognition of differentiation in terms of level of mastery.

A Final Word

This emphasis upon differentiated instruction in arithmetic through increased attention to levels of learning does not in any way exclude differentiations of the type overviewed earlier in this discussion. We cannot provide fully for individual differences in arithmetic in any *one* way, by any *one* method or technique. Many are necessary, and must be integrated wisely. Of the methods which have been discussed, however, differentiation in terms of levels of learning has been the most commonly neglected procedure, yet it is one which is extremely valuable and effective. In fact, it is a method of differentiation which, if overlooked, can only mean inadequate provision for individual differences in arithmetic. Our increased attention to this technique truly is a promising trend in our attempts to make more adequate provision for individual differences through more effective differentiated instruction.

TYPES OF CLASS ORGANIZATION FOR
MEETING INDIVIDUAL DIFFERENCES

Frances Flournoy and Henry J. Otto

If a school faculty is sincere in wishing to do the best it can in meeting individual differences in arithmetic, there should be some school-wide plans whereby a teacher may deviate from teaching a heterogeneous group of achievers by conventional "class as a whole" procedures by which all pupils are taught the same topics at the same time and all are expected to do the same amount of work and attain approximately equal proficiency. The discussion which ensues presents the pros and cons of six types of class organization designed to facilitate the task of meeting individual differences. Perhaps it would be well to recognize at the outset that no plan of organization will solve the problem per se; what the teacher does and how she does it still remains as the key to success in any plan of organization. One should also remember that class organization for meeting individual differences in arithmetic has many similarities to comparable plans for adapting instruction to differences in reading, science, spelling, social development, music, or art, *but there are also important differences.*[1] Content in arithmetic has an internal sequence that is more definite and exacting than is the content of any of the other fields. Most of the new steps in arithmetic require at least reasonable facility with background skills. In arithmetic readiness for a new topic or process has much more specific meaning than it does in art, handwriting, or reading. The order in which a child learns to sing three songs, or to spell *cat, rat,* and *hat,* or to form the letters *a, b,* and *c* probably makes little difference, but a child cannot do column addition until he knows the addition facts nor can he do long division involving two-place quotients until he knows the addition, subtraction, multiplication, and division facts, plus a variety of other skills.

A second difference between arithmetic and the other subjects lies in

[From *Meeting Individual Differences in Arithmetic,* Bureau of Laboratory Schools, Publication No. 11 (Austin, Texas: The University of Texas, 1959), pp. 12-19. Reprinted by permission of the authors and the Bureau of Laboratory Schools.]

---

[1] Mary Clare Petty, *Intraclass Groupings in the Elementary School* (Austin: University of Texas Press, 1953).

the availability of materials for meeting individual differences. We now have readers and social studies books written for use in the same grade but at different levels of reading difficulty. Basal texts in science, social studies, and reading can be supplemented readily with books from the school or public library which are easier or more difficult than the basal text or which are helpful in expanding content for the pupil who should go beyond that which is offered in the basal text. As yet we do not have arithmetic books for a given grade written at different levels of difficulty; nor do we have at hand diversified supplementary resources in the library; nor does the typical teacher have access to a reservoir of diversified practice materials or teaching aids. These and other differences between arithmetic and the other subjects should be kept in mind as one examines the six types of class organization discussed below.

1. Ability grouping is a plan whereby the children of a given grade are divided into two or more sections and placed in different classrooms on the basis of mental age and I.Q. The plan is feasible only in schools in which there are enough pupils in a given grade to form at least two sections so that those in the lower half in ability can be placed in one section while those in the upper half in ability are placed in the other section. Schools which follow this plan usually classify the pupils of a given grade into three sections so that each section contains one-third of the ability range. The plan has strong advocates as well as vociferous opponents. The opponents remind us of the parent relations, children's mental health, and social policy problems raised by its use. They also call our attention to the fact that few children present an even front in their achievement; a child may be a good reader but not so good in arithmetic or music. The advocates point out that if three ability groups are formed the achievement range in each will be about 20 per cent less than it would be if the same children were grouped heterogeneously. In other words, ability grouping into three groups reduces the task of meeting individual differences by 20 per cent. However, each teacher still has a fairly heterogeneous group as far as achievement in any one subject is concerned. Ability grouping per se cannot solve the problem of having to meet individual differences.

2. Completely individualized instruction is a plan whereby each pupil proceeds from one topic to another at his own rate. In a class of thirty pupils it is possible to have the different children working on thirty different assignments and at thirty different levels of achievement. The individual instruction plan was initiated by Frederic L. Burk in the training school of the San Francisco State Teachers College in 1913. Its use in public schools was begun as Winnetka, Illinois, in 1919 and in some of the Chicago schools a few years later. Since its use in Winnetka was widely

publicized the plan became known as "The Winnetka Plan." Actually it was used in whole or in part by several school systems in different parts of the country.

Theoretically the plan has many points in its favor. Its practical limitations have curtailed widespread usage. Its primary prerequisite consists of carefully prepared self-teaching materials so organized that each child can move forward with a minimum of teacher time and with maximum self-directed individualization to care for differential pupil needs in the developmental as well as the practice phases of each topic. The task of preparing, merchandising, purchasing, and managing such materials has not been solved to the satisfaction of many practical-minded school teachers and administrators. Another practical limitation is the diminishing level of pupil motivation when each child works entirely by himself. The motivation problem is particularly acute for slow learners or others who are encountering many difficulties. Completely individualized instruction makes little provision for the motivation that comes from being a member of a group engaged in the same task; class spirit tends to reach a point of no consequence. Research evidence is as yet too meager to tell us how much and in what directions individualized instruction affects motivation and ultimate achievement.

3. Some teachers use a combination of the whole class plan and the small achievement grouping plan which preserves the uniform forward movement of the class as a whole. All children in the class have each successive topic in the course of study introduced to them at the same time but intraclass groups are used to differentiate the methods, materials, and aspects of the topic which are presented. The following illustration from a fourth grade class exemplifies this plan.

Work with this class during the early weeks of the school year had enabled the teacher to become reasonably well-acquainted with each pupil and to determine that all members of the class had sufficient command of addition and subtraction of whole numbers so that all were ready to study the multiplication of whole numbers. Hence the latter topic was introduced to the class as a whole through a developmental approach involving a problem which could be solved easily by addition or multiplication. The teacher tried to make sure that every pupil understood the relationship between addition and multiplication and that all pupils comprehended the multiplication idea. Enough other problems, including some of greater difficulty, were used to develop these understandings and to bring into use those multiplication facts (such as the 2's, 3's, and 4's) introduced in grade three. Through these activities the children were introduced to the terms *multiply, multiplication, times, multiplier, multiplicand,* and *product.* Of course a few pupils already knew all these terms and their meaning. The 5's, 6's, and 7's were also introduced to the class as a whole.

As the preceding activities aimed at developing the concept and processes of multiplication were progressing, children were asked to achieve mastery of the multiplication facts involving 2's, 3's, 4's, 5's, 6's, and 7's as multiplicands and multipliers. An inventory test given at this stage in the teaching program revealed four pupils who needed much additional work with the multiplication facts involving 2's, 3's, and 4's. Time was provided at the beginning of each arithmetic period for these children to work in pairs with multiplication flash cards. The last part of the period was spent in performing computations using these facts and in doing simple reasoning problems. Concrete materials were used in proving the problem. Addition and drawings were also used as methods of proving. These children then went on to work on the 5's, 6's, and 7's as soon as they were able. Worksheets and other supplementary materials were needed for this group since they were working below grade level at the beginning of the study of this topic. Later in the year they were introduced to the 8's and 9's.

There were fifteen children in the class who had made average progress in the multiplication of whole numbers. They needed and were given more work for mastery on the 5's, 6's, and 7's, and with the help of the Multiplication-Division Facts Chart they were able to do examples with one-digit multipliers and two- or three-digit multiplicands with carrying while working for mastery on the 5's, 6's, and 7's. They were also able to do more difficult one-step reasoning problems. This group used the state-adopted text for the major part of its work. However, supplementary materials were used for practice and to provide enrichment activities. Soon after mastery of the 5's, 6's, and 7's, they were introduced to the 8's and 9's and studied for mastery. After giving this group further practice with all the multiplication facts in compound multiplication with a one-digit multiplier, the teacher introduced this group to multiplication with two-digit multipliers. They were also given much work in reasoning with two-step problems. Some enrichment activities were provided for this group. They learned to check their work by dividing the product by the multiplier and by casting out nines. They learned to use the "Scratch, Gelosia, and Lightning" methods of multiplication and to do number puzzle exercises. Some of them were urged to learn the multiplication facts through the 11's and 12's or even higher. Textbooks and supplementary materials on a higher level were required to meet the needs of this group.

The essential features of this plan are: (*a*) the topic was started with the whole class; (*b*) the whole class stayed with the topic until the whole class could undertake a new topic; (*c*) sub-groups were formed enroute as the need for them became evident; (*d*) the sub-groups were formed on the basis of achievement and instructional needs in a particular phase of arithmetic; (*e*) although not described in the narrative, membership in the sub-groups was kept fluid and several pupils shifted group membership before the topic was concluded; (*f*) all pupils were taught all the multiplication facts on a long range basis and all were taught to multiply two, three, and four place numbers by a one place multiplier and with carrying; (*g*) some pupils were introduced to several more complicated mathematical aspects of proficiency which every child was expected to reach before he was permitted to go on to a new topic; (*h*) expected level of understanding of mathematical terms and processes as well as computational proficiency were differentiated for groups and individuals; (*i*) the total time devoted to the study of arithmetic was approximately the same for all pupils except that teaching 8's and 9's to the below-average achievers was delayed; (*j*) method and materials were differentiated for individuals and groups; and (*k*) the enrichment activities pursued by some pupils were reported to the whole class so that each pupil obtained at least a glimpse beyond the immediate horizon at which he was working.

4. Teachers sometimes prefer to use a plan in which the class is divided into two achievement groups according to general arithmetic achievement on standardized tests. The two groups are about equal in size with one group consisting of pupils above-average to middle-average and the other middle-average to below-average in arithmetic achievement.

This plan preserves the uniform forward movement of the class as a whole. All children in the class are working on generally the same topic in arithmetic at the same time. The teacher alternates time spent directly with each group so that while the teacher works directly with one group, the other group works independently. In this plan of organization some teachers feel that time, practice exercises, and materials may be more satisfactorily varied to meet the needs of children in each group than in a whole class type of organization.

5. Another plan of intraclass grouping makes no effort to keep the entire class together as the successive topics are studied. At the beginning of the school year, and periodically thereafter, the teacher divides the class into two, three, or more sub-groups on the basis of general arithmetic achievement and instructional needs. Each sub-group starts with the topics and level of difficulty at which the group can experience reasonable success. Each group moves forward according to the logical sequence of arithmetic topics and at its own rate; the teacher divides her time per week as equitably as possible in working with each group. Actually the teacher must plan and provide for as many arithmetic programs as she has sub-groups in her class.

One teacher described her use of this plan in the following manner. In this fifth grade class the teacher discovered that she had six pupils who were retarded in general arithmetic achievement; 16 pupils had made normal progress and seemed ready for the new topics to be taught in the fifth grade; while nine pupils revealed advanced achievement and could probably push forward with sixth grade topics after making sure that they had good mastery of the topics usually treated in the fifth grade. The teacher therefore organized the class into three sub-groups and proceeded in planning the work for each group in accordance with its readiness and capacity to move forward.

The basal text, workbooks, and supplementary learning aids were essential materials of which differentiated use was basic to the success of the plan. The state-adopted basal text for the fifth grade was used as the general frame of reference and point of departure for work with each group. The sub-group of 16 pupils seemed ready to move forward with the review and new topics in the fifth grade basal text. In the early part of the year the low achievers used materials from fourth grade basal and supplementary texts but by mid-term this group had begun to work in the fifth grade text. The superior achievers' group started with the basal text and completed new topics in it before moving into topics usually reserved for the sixth grade.

Workbooks were used with all three groups, but each group had one or more different workbooks and each group used selected pages from its workbooks. The group representing retarded achievers used teacher-selected pages in two workbooks before the year ended; they started out with a fourth grade workbook and later began using the fifth grade workbook. If pupils cannot purchase two workbooks per year the plan can be modified so that this group does not use a workbook until it is ready to use the one for the fifth grade. The advanced group used sixth grade workbooks on sixth grade topics which members of this group pursued. In all three groups children were urged to use the workbooks as a reservoir for practice and as a device for checking their own proficiency and progress. All pupils capable of doing so were urged to check their own work individually or in small groups.

The teacher used visual aids along with the basal texts and workbooks. Some enrichment activities were provided for all pupils but most of the enrichment emphasis was placed with the rapid learners. Occasionally an all-class arithmetic activity was carried out to preserve some degree of class unity.

6. The sixth type of class organization described here consists of a class-as-a-whole procedure as the teacher and pupils move through the program during the school year, giving individual help as needed. This

plan assumes that all pupils are to be exposed to the basic list of topics taught in each grade and that the whole class moves forward as a group. There is usually no variation in time or content in the basic instructional plans. Individual children may devote extra time to the study of arithmetic through self-assigned or teacher-assigned tasks but the pacing of the instructional program is uniform for all. Uniform minimum attainments are expected but everyone knows that what children take away from such a program varies greatly among pupils. Efforts at meeting individual differences find expression through helping individual pupils as much as time will permit during the arithmetic period, extra assignments the teacher might direct toward certain pupils, and whatever enrichment activities the teacher might encourage rapid learners to pursue under their own steam. Actually this plan is little more than the conventional way in which most teachers have taught arithmetic in the past. Its major innovation is a more deliberate effort to provide for individual differences by putting forth special effort to give individual help to the slow learners and to effect some enrichment for rapid learners.

One teacher described the use of this plan as it was applied to the topic of *perimeters* in a sixth grade. With the use of the basal text the teacher introduced the idea of perimeter. Objects in the room were used to demonstrate perimeters. The main purpose in these initial stages was to impress the idea that the perimeter of a rectangle meant "the distance around" the rectangle. Using rulers, the children found the perimeters of their desk tops. At this point scale drawing was introduced as enrichment for the entire class. Each child made a scale drawing of his desk, indicating the perimeter. By this time many of the pupils were able to form a generalization or "rule" for finding the perimeter of a rectangle. Children helped each other and the teacher gave help where needed.

The next step consisted of working out problems of perimeter at the board, children being given problems commensurate with their ability. After considerable practice, a teacher-made test was given as an additional check to determine mastery of the procedure. Scale drawing was now continued. The teacher proposed, "Using a large sheet of paper, do a scale drawing of the room and the equipment within it. Arrange the furniture as you would like to have it and we will all select what we think is the best arrangement. From the best drawings chosen we will actually rearrange our room." A scale of 1 in. = 1 yd. was cooperatively decided on by the class. On a project of this type pupil performance will vary. The drawings can be as refined as individual skill can make them. All the drawings were shown to the class. The pupils selected what they thought were the five or six best arrangements and these were used in the manner originally planned.

PLANNING FOR EFFECTIVE TEACHING AND LEARNING IN ARITHMETIC

John R. Clark and Laura K. Eads

A teacher who tries to provide for the optimum learning of all of the children in her class soon finds that *the better she teaches*—that is, the more opportunities for growth her children have—*the greater will be the differences within her class group.* The rapid learner retains more, sees more relationships and sees them faster, more readily applies to new topics what he has already learned, wants to show and to tell what he has discovered, wants to be accepted in the class group. The slower learner wants to think (and can); he wants to understand (and can); he wants to move along with the class group (but cannot); but even more he wants to be considered acceptable by the teacher and by the other children in the class group. He tries to remember, and feels confused and unhappy when he cannot; he clutches at any cue or device that might make it appear that he is learning. The bright child hurries through an assignment; the slower child, too, tries to hurry and gets hopelessly lost.

Not only are there wide differences among the children in a class, but each child has his own pattern of growth. For any one child, growth does not proceed at an even tempo; at any one time a child will operate at a level that seems mature or immature for him. Moreover, learning and performance in different strands of mathematics also differ for individual children. A particular child, for example, may be among the less mature children in thinking about fractions but among the more able children when it comes to adding long columns of figures.

In this chapter we shall present some of the problems teachers face as they plan their arithmetic program, and some suggestions for meeting these problems to the end that elementary school children may grow in ability to think mathematically.

Readiness for Learning

If parents or teachers try to hurry a child's learning before he is ready or mature enough for it, his struggle with insurmountable tasks may im-

[From *Guiding Arithmetic Learning* (Yonkers-on-Hudson, N. Y.: World Book Company, 1954), pp. 242-51. Reprinted by permission of the authors and the World Book Company.]

pede or retard his learning later when he might otherwise be ready for the learning. For example, instead of learning to *think* mathematically, a child who has been pressed to do computation before he is ready to do so thoughtfully may continue throughout his life to make an effort to remember rules and formulas for solving mathematical problems. Moreover, a child's efforts to learn what he cannot yet learn properly may prevent his growing along lines for which he *is* ready. Thus a child's efforts to memorize and to write meaningless number facts may prevent his developing real number sense. Or struggles with rules for computing with fractions may interfere with his being able to use fractions when he should do so in life situations.

On the other hand, the more mature child needs guidance and encouragement when *he* is ready for more complex learning situations. He needs encouragement and opportunities to do thinking at his level of growth. Often this is possible within a topic other children are learning.

The concept of readiness applies to the learning of arithmetic in every grade in school. Here are some guideposts to help teachers decide whether children are ready to learn a particular arithmetic topic (multiplication by two-place numbers, for example):

1. Children are interested in and are able to use the topic in experiences they understand.

2. Children are interested in and are able to derive relationships involved in the topic.

3. Children are able to achieve ready success when they are given some mathematical help.

4. Children remember what they have been taught.

5. Children are interested in and are able to see in the world about them the mathematics they have learned.

6. Children are able to build on the mathematics they have learned with relatively little help.

Growth in Concepts a Continuous Process

The teacher faces another problem that makes it difficult for her to provide for effective learning of all of the children in her class. The traditional idea of grade placement—that is, the idea that certain topics are allocated to specific grades to be "covered" in these grades—places the emphasis in the teacher's mind on the topics she is to teach rather than on the learning that individual children or groups of children actually do. Some teachers and parents believe that certain topics taught in earlier grades should have been learned by the children in those earlier grades. They probably believe that the teaching and learning of mathematical concepts have fixed beginnings and fixed ends. They may think or say: "Have they *had* fractions?" "My children *know* long division." "I *taught* the smallest common denominator." "He *should* know that." "Where did he get *that* idea? I didn't teach him that." "You *knew* it yesterday." "What is the *fifth-grade work?*" "When can we *expect* these children to *know* their multiplication tables?" "John is a *remedial case;* he just cannot *learn* arithmetic."

If the development of concepts and generalizations is understood to be an on-going process, from the simpler to the more complex, it is apparent that it will take years for children to grow in the development of most mathematics topics after their introduction. Since children progress through mathematics sequences at different rates of speed, some ten-year-olds may still be dealing mathematically (and meaningfully) with the addition of two-place numbers; others in the class may be dealing mathematically (and meaningfully) with the addition of larger and more complex numbers, with multiplication as a short-cut process for addition, with division by two-place numbers, etc. Some sixth-grade children may be dealing mathematically (and meaningfully) with halves and fourths; others in the same class may be dealing with tenths and hundredths.

Thus the teaching of specific mathematical concepts is not concentrated in one lesson, one week, or one year, but is developed over a period of years. Beginning concepts of fractions and of adding may be developed in the first grade. There is a long way to go, however, from being able to cut an apple into halves, or being able to pour half a glass of water, to being able to deal meaningfully with the symbols for adding one third and three fourths.

Teaching Children in Groups

Because of the wide differences among the children in her class the teacher plans for group teaching. She knows that individual teaching of thirty or more children is impossible if children are to receive guidance in their growth in mathematical thinking and mathematical power. When she thinks she has placed her children in groups that she may call bright, average, and slow, she discovers that soon these children, too, differ markedly from each other—children grow at differing rates of speed, and individual children learn some topics in arithmetic more easily than they do others.

Guiding principles for group teaching. A few ideas about children the teacher might keep in mind as she thinks about teaching in groups follow:

1. *Children know quite well that they are being differentiated in some way when they are grouped for teaching.* Some children and some parents

react to this in more mature ways than do others, regardless of whether particular children are placed in the "highest," "middle," or "lowest" group.

2. *Children sometimes prefer groups, not necessarily for co-operative action but as a means of controlling others or as a means of winning social acceptance.* The beginnings of co-operative attitudes and behavior are developed in the elementary years.

Elementary school children grow toward co-operative effort by participating in small groups—at first not more than three or four children in each group, and gradually a few more. Many children need to spend some time in the same group day after day, in order to learn to understand others, to learn that others see things in different ways, to share willingly with others, to gain satisfaction because others gain satisfaction, to begin to think of others without expecting too much from them, to begin the long road toward becoming socially mature persons.

3. *Children's values reflect those of the adults about them and those of other children.* A teacher can do a great deal to guide children toward values that lead to a more mature growth by the way she *sees* children and by the way she thinks about what they need to learn in order to grow to maturity in a democratic society. If she believes that emotional and physical growth are as important as academic achievement, this belief will be reflected in the way she plans her program.

4. *Children feel secure or insecure in a classroom as they are accepted for what they are by adults at home and at school and by other children.* If certain children are commended and featured in any way and others are not, the others may feel rejected. Children generally learn better when they feel that they "belong."

5. *Every child can make a worthwhile contribution in a classroom.* The more opportunities there are for pupil participation in organizing and experiencing, the more opportunities there will be for pupils who find it difficult to learn the Three R's to make contributions that will *really* be valuable.

Class teaching as group teaching. Teaching children in groups does not necessarily mean that there are several separate groups of children in the classroom, all working independently and at different things. By teaching the entire class at one time, the teacher can often make a greater contribution as a *guide toward more mature thinking.* She *thinks about groups of children as she teaches the entire class,* and she makes plans for them to be thinking on different levels as she teaches the same topic to all of them. Some of the ways in which a teacher can teach the whole class the same topic and yet provide for group teaching follow:

1. The teacher discusses with the children the problems created by having one's thinking interrupted. She plans with them ways to avoid

interruptions such as raising hands or calling out while a child is "thinking out loud," even though he makes a mistake or hesitates. She is particularly alert early in the year to help the children listen to other children when they are expressing themselves. She does this so that she can listen herself and so that other children may think about and evaluate what has been said *after* a child who was given the opportunity to talk *has finished*.

2. The teacher listens carefully to children as they express their thinking, taking into consideration what their level of maturity may be. She encourages more thinking by asking children to say it in another way, or by asking them to tell a little more. She learns in this way what kind of thinking to expect from children at different levels of ability.

3. As she makes her plans for teaching a phase of a topic, the teacher includes in her teaching sequence for the topic many earlier steps. She calls on the less mature children for thinking about these early-level steps; this gives them an opportunity to learn *at their level* of achievement, and orients more mature children to the topic for the day. Gradually she proceeds with more advanced steps, calling on more mature children. She can challenge the thinking of the most mature children in her class by asking them to give other ways of finding solutions, to do as much computation as they can without using paper and pencil, to keep records too difficult for less mature children to keep.

4. The teacher plans to have different children deal with the topic of the day at various stages in concept development. The least mature children may perhaps re-enact an experience situation to help all children become oriented to the problem under consideration. More mature children may do the demonstrating with representative materials, some using simpler materials at their seats and others using more advanced materials. Still more mature children may be thinking orally or in writing without materials or with only occasional reference to them. The most mature children may be keeping mathematical records for the class.

5. The teacher appreciates that when she teaches a large group of children she is not teaching all of the children all of the time. Some of the children are not ready to learn all of the things being taught. Other children may seem to be learning but forget quickly. The teacher expects this. As a check, if she is not sure how much certain children are learning or remembering, she asks them to explain or show what a more mature child said or did. She makes a mental note of these children's needs as she checks. Some of them may find it difficult to pay attention to long explanations made by others. The teacher encourages them to listen by asking for explanations from time to time.

Some children find it difficult to pay attention when they are not talking. They may interrupt or call attention to themselves in various ways. When such children are directly in the teacher's view, she may be tempted to call on them while other children still need time to think. It is not necessarily the children who know the most arithmetic who want to do most of the talking. Such children make it difficult for others to think out or to explain problem situations.

Teaching small groups. Although the teacher may teach the class as a whole quite skillfully, there are times when she will find it necessary to plan to work with small groups as well. This may not be every day, but such teaching requires advance planning. Some reasons and procedures for teaching children in small groups follow:

1. One or two children may not be able to profit from class teaching. They may be very immature and/or emotionally disturbed. While the teacher teaches the other children, these children may be given the opportunity to work at the easel, to work with clay, or to engage in any other quiet, satisfying activity. Later that day the teacher may take a few minutes to give these children the attention they need and want, and plan some work with them. Other children who can profit by helping these children can do so under the teacher's guidance. It is generally unwise, however, to use children as helpers unless they themselves are learning.

2. Children who engage in experiences that take place outside the classroom may be assigned in pairs—one child more mature than the other. Each child may be given an assignment that he can accomplish: for example, the less mature child counts the money received and the more mature child computes totals and makes change. Since these children are getting data for use by the rest of the class, these data will need to be recorded in an efficient manner. The less mature child may ask for the information and data, and the more mature child may do the recording.

3. Children who engage in classroom experiences in groups may also have responsibilities in keeping with their abilities. Some children check, others recheck, others record, etc.

4. All children may work together in pairs to check each other as they work, as they manipulate materials, as they think out solutions, as they compute. These pairs may be matched so that both members of each pair are stimulated to do better thinking and more effective work. Such a procedure requires careful guidance by the teacher: pairs may need frequent changing, and assignments may need to be different for children of different levels of ability. It is sometimes advisable to have friends work together in pairs if they are reasonably well matched in ability.

5. When children are ready to develop mastery in number facts or skill in computation, they may be taught separately. Since drill procedures involve helping children see relationships, a teacher's guidance is required. Usually the drill period should not be long. The other children may work

at independent activities in their experiences or in other areas of the curriculum.

6. The teacher may plan to test a group of children. She may test the group orally (if the group is small) or have the children record answers on paper.

7. The teacher may give different assignments to different groups of children. Some may use experience materials or representative materials and record their discoveries. Others may write their solutions in a variety of ways. Others may devise problems based on their experiences in or out of the classroom. Others may make charts and records for later use by all of the children. The teacher may walk about the classroom asking questions, noting progress, and helping children as they work. She may have one or two pupil assistants helping her if these children, too, are learning as they give such assistance.

8. The teacher may teach children in two or three separate groups—for development in multiplication, for example. As she works with the groups, she may make a particular effort to have the children express their thinking orally or in written form at the blackboard. She notes which children need to be shifted to a different group, and changes the groups often.

9. Several of the least mature children may be ready for the development of a topic well understood by the other children. The teacher avoids thinking of these children in terms of remedial work. She realizes that they need earlier steps in arithmetic sequence because they may not heretofore have been ready for such steps. She knows that she must teach them what they are ready to learn. She is not doing remedial teaching; she is actually teaching these children.

Suggestions for teaching bright children. In many classes the children able to do the best thinking in arithmetic are the most neglected. Suggestions for encouraging bright children to learn and to think at levels commensurate with their potentialities follow:

1. Bright children should generally be commended only for responses that reflect superior thinking. They are asked from time to time to tell how they arrived at answers, and are expected to use more mature methods than other children.

2. When bright children are found to be using immature methods (such as counting by ones to find answers to addition or subtraction facts) they should be helped to learn more mature methods so that they can think on higher levels.

3. Bright children should be encouraged to get data for the rest of the class. They might make investigations in the neighborhood. They might refer to—sometimes even make—maps, charts, tables, diagrams, advertisements, financial reports, etc. They might report on the results of science

experiments, putting their data in writing so that the data may be used for computation by the other children. They might examine reference books or other materials for problem situations pertinent to the mathematics being emphasized. Such tasks can help bright children make judgments, do rapid mental computation, and develop skills (classifying, selecting, evaluating, etc.) that are of particular importance to them.

4. Bright children should be able to solve many problems without using paper and pencil. (They should first estimate the answers, however.) Occasionally they might also devise problems that could be used for solving by other children.

5. As the teacher presents a lesson, she might occasionally change the numbers being dealt with to much larger numbers for the bright children.

6. Bright children might be asked to help less mature children (but only if the bright ones profit from such a relationship). For example, bright children who still need some help in fixing multiplication facts might present facts for less mature children according to specific relationships, as 2 sevens, then 4 sevens; 3 sevens, then 6 sevens; 10 sevens, then 5 sevens; etc. As they organize such relationships, the bright children reinforce their knowledge of them.

BIBLIOGRAPHY

Adams, Olga. "Arithmetic Readiness in the Primary Grades," *Elementary School Journal,* XLVIII (October, 1947), 91-96.

Boyce, Loretta U. "Arithmetic for Kindergartners," *The Mathematics Teacher,* XLIV (November, 1951), 458-62.

Brown, Francis. "Arithmetic—Friend or Foe?" *The Arithmetic Teacher,* IV (February, 1957), 1-9.

Brownell, William A. "Arithmetic in Grades I and II," *A Critical Summary of New and Previously Reported Research,* Duke University Research Studies in Education, No. 6. Durham, N.C.: Duke University Press, 1941.

———. *The Development of Children's Number Ideas in the Primary Grades,* Supplementary Educational Monographs, No. 35 (August, 1928).

———. "Readiness and the Arithmetic Curriculum," *Elementary School Journal,* XXXVIII (January, 1938), 344-55.

———. "Teaching of Mathematics in Grades I through IV," *Review of Educational Research,* XV (October, 1945), 276-88.

———, and Doris V. Carper. *Learning the Multiplication Combinations,* Duke University Research Studies in Education, No. 7. Durham, N.C.: Duke University Press, 1943.

Brueckner, Leo J. "Deferred Arithmetic," *The Mathematics Teacher,* XXXI (October, 1938), 287-92.

———, and others. "Arithmetic," *Review of Educational Research,* VII (December, 1937), 453-63.

Buckingham, B. R. "When to Begin the Teaching of Arithmetic," *Childhood Education*, XI (May, 1935), 339-43.

———, and Josephine MacLatchy. "The Number Abilities of Children When They Enter Grade One," *Report of the Society's Committee on Arithmetic*, National Society for the Study of Education, Twenty-ninth Yearbook (1930). Chicago: University of Chicago Press, 473-524.

Burch, Robert L., and Harold E. Moser. "The Teaching of Mathematics in Grades I through VIII," *Review of Educational Research*, XXI (October, 1951), 290-304.

Burns, P. G. "Intense Review as a Procedure in Teaching Arithmetic," *Elementary School Journal*, LX (January, 1960), 205-11.

Carper, Doris V. "Seeing Numbers as Groups in Primary-Grade Arithmetic," *Elementary School Journal*, XLIII (November, 1942), 166-70.

Clark, Eileen. "Number Experiences of Three-Year-Olds," *Childhood Education*, XXVI (February, 1950), 247-50.

Clark, John R., and Laura K. Eads. *Guiding Arithmetic Learning*. Yonkers-on-Hudson: World Book Co., 1954.

Court, S. R. A. "Numbers, Time and Space in the First Five Years of the Child's Life," *Pedagogical Seminary*, XXVII (March, 1920), 71-89.

Davis, O. L., Jr., and Carolyn Crigler. "The Growth of Pre-School Children's Familiarity with Measurement," *The Arithmetic Teacher*, VI (October, 1959), 186-90.

Deans, Edwina. "The Contribution of Grouping to Number Development," *Childhood Education*, XVII (March, 1941), 307-10.

Dickey, J. W. "Readiness for Arithmetic," *Elementary School Journal*, XL (April, 1940), 592-98.

Douglass, Harl R. "The Development of Number Concept in Children of Pre-school and Kindergarten Ages," *Journal of Experimental Psychology*, VIII (December, 1925), 443-70.

Drummond, Margaret. *Five Years or Thereabouts*. London: Edward Arnold and Co., 1921, 119-135.

Durell, Thomas J. "Connecting Arithmetic with Children's Experiences," *Curriculum Letter No. 22*, Department of School Services and Publications. Middletown, Connecticut: Wesleyan University Press, 1956.

Eads, Laura K. "Teaching Mathematics in the Kindergarten. "Teaching Mathematics in Grade Four," *Grade Teacher*, LXXVI (October, 1958), 55, 134-35 (February, 1959), 22, 80, 82.

Flournoy, Frances. "Meeting Individual Differences in Arithmetic," *The Arithmetic Teacher*, VII (February, 1960), 80-86.

Gunderson, Agnes G. "Number Concepts Held by Seven-Year-Olds," *The Mathematics Teacher*, XXXIII (January, 1940), 18-24.

———. "Readiness for Number," *Instructor*, LV (February, 1946), 34.

———, and Ethel Gunderson. "What Numbers Mean to Young Children: Number Concepts Compared with a 1940 Study," *The Arithmetic Teacher*, VI (October, 1959), 180-85.

Harrison, M. Lucille. "Nature and Development of Concepts of Time Among Young Children," *Elementary School Journal*, XXXIV (March, 1934), 507-14.

Hollister, George E. and Agnes G. Gunderson. "Number Concepts of the Pre-School Child," *Teaching Arithmetic in Grades I and II*. Boston: D. C. Heath and Co., 1954, 51-58.

Hunter, Maude W. "Arithmetic for Beginners," *Instructor*, LIII (January, 1944), 14-15.

Junge, Charlotte. "The Arithmetic Curriculum—1954," *The Arithmetic Teacher* (April, 1954), 1-6.

Koenker, Robert H. "Arithmetic Readiness at the Kindergarten Level," *Journal of Educational Research*, XLII (November, 1948), 218-23.

————. "Arithmetic Readiness for the Primary Grades," *Arithmetic 1949*, Supplementary Educational Monographs, No. 70. Chicago: University of Chicago Press, 1949, 26-34.

MacLatchy, Josephine H. "Number Abilities of First-Grade Children," *Childhood Education*, XI (May, 1935), 344-47.

————. "The Pre-school Child's Familiarity with Measurement," *Education*, LXXI (April, 1951), 479-82.

————. "A Test of the Pre-school Child's Familiarity with Measurement," *Educational Research Bulletin*, XXIX (November, 1950), 207-8, 222-23.

Marks, John L., C. Richard Purdy, and Lucien B. Kinney. *Teaching Arithmetic for Understanding*. New York: McGraw-Hill Book Co., Inc., 1958.

Martin, William E. "Quantitative Expression in Young Children," *Genetic Psychology Monograph*, XLIV (November, 1951), 147-219.

McLaughlin, Katherine L. "Number Ability of Pre-school Children," *Childhood Education*, XI (May, 1935), 348-53.

McSwain, E. T., and Ralph J. Cooke. *Understanding and Teaching Arithmetic in the Elementary School*. New York: Henry Holt and Co., 1958.

Moser, Harold E. "Advancing Arithmetic Readiness Through Meaningful Number Experience," *Childhood Education*, XXIV (March, 1948), 322-26.

Mott, Sina M. "Number Concepts of Young Children," *The Mathematics Teacher*, XXXVIII (November, 1945), 291-301.

Mueller, F. J. "Building Algebra Readiness in Grades Seven and Eight," *The Arithmetic Teacher*, VI (November, 1959), 269-73.

New York City. *Mathematics: Grades 1-2*. Brooklyn, New York: Board of Education of the City of New York, 1955.

————. *Mathematics: Grades 3*. Brooklyn, New York: Board of Education of the City of New York, 1957.

New York State Department of Education. "Arithmetic Has Its Problems," *Letter to Supervisors*, Letter No. 8, 1948-49 Series. Albany, New York: The Department, April, 1949.

Piaget, Jean. *The Child's Conception of Number*. New York: Humanities Press, 1953.

Polkinghorne, Ada R. "Young Children and Fractions," *Childhood Education,* XI (May, 1935), 354-58.

Priore, Angela. "Achievement by Pupils Entering the First Grade," *The Arithmetic Teacher,* IV (March, 1957), 55-60.

Riess, Anita. "An Analysis of Children's Number Responses," *Harvard Educational Review,* XIII (March, 1943), 149-62.

——. *Number Readiness in Research: A Survey of the Literature.* Chicago: Scott, Foresman and Co., 1947.

Rosenquist, Lucy Lynde. *Young Children Learn to Use Arithmetic.* Boston: Ginn and Co., 1949.

Russell, Ned M. "Arithmetical Concepts of Children," *Journal of Educational Research,* XXIX (May, 1936), 647-63.

Springer, Doris. "Development in Young Children of an Understanding of Time and the Clock," *Journal of Genetic Psychology,* LXXX (1952), 83-96.

Stokes, C. Newton. *Teaching the Meanings of Arithmetic.* New York: Appleton-Century-Crofts, Inc., 1951.

Sueltz, Ben A. "Arithmetic Readiness and Curriculum Construction," *Mathematics Teacher,* XXX (October, 1937), 290-92.

——. "Arithmetic Readiness—What Is It? How Is It Achieved?" *New York State Education,* XXXVII (April, 1950), 514-17.

Thiele, C. L. *The Contribution of Generalization to the Learning of the Addition Facts,* Contributions to Education, No. 763. New York: Teachers College, Columbia University, 1938.

Woody, Clifford. "Arithmetic," *What Does Research Say?* Lansing, Michigan: State of Michigan, Bulletin No. 308, 1937, 56-58.

——. "The Arithmetical Backgrounds of Young Children," *Journal of Educational Research,* XXIV (October, 1931), 188-201.

——. "A General Educator Looks at Arithmetic Readiness," *The Mathematics Teacher,* XXX (November, 1937), 314-21.

V IDENTIFYING THE ROLE OF MATHEMATICS WITHIN THE TOTAL PROGRAM

W. Robert Houston, Principal, Midland, Texas

INTRODUCTION

BIBLIOGRAPHY

INTRODUCTION

Mathematics, as a basic area of study, is related to all subjects in the elementary school curriculum. This relationship may be examined in two ways: (1) the extent of relationship; and (2) the extent to which integration with other subjects should be basic to the teaching of mathematics.

A number of research studies have been conducted which investigated the amount of quantitative material found in

146

other school subjects.[1] General conclusions of these studies indicate that mathematical terms permeate all phases of the elementary school. Since the high relationship which exists between mathematics and other school subjects has been established, it is not considered a basic issue. However, the *extent* to which mathematics should be integrated with other school subjects continues to be one of the critical issues in educational planning. This aspect of the teaching of mathematics will, therefore, be the major concern of this chapter. At least three points of view are reflected in the literature:

1. Complete lack of integration of mathematics with other school subjects.

2. Total integration or fusion in the curriculum of the school.

3. A synthesizing viewpoint recognizing the need for two phases of a mathematics program: (*a*) a functional phase achieved through integration, and (*b*) a mathematical phase.

Lack of Integration

For many years educators failed to recognize a need for integration of mathematics with other subjects in the elementary school curriculum. Mathematics was considered a discipline, containing a body of knowledge that should be taught only as a separate subject. If integration was to take place at all, it was to be done by the individual after he had studied the various subjects separately.

Historically, this point of view represents the thinking of many educators prior to the 1930's. Up to that time, the idea of integrating mathematics with other areas of the curriculum was seldom considered.

Total Integration

During the thirties, a strong movement toward total integration of the curriculum swelled and burst forth. Many educators recommended the integration of all areas of the curriculum. This was to be accomplished through fusion of existing subject fields or through the organization of activity

---

[1] Bibliographical notations of many of these research studies are presented at the end of this chapter.

units around a central theme, not identified with specific subject areas. It was thought that students within a pattern of total integration would develop a better understanding of mathematical concepts and would be able to use them better in out-of-school activities.

Synthesized Concept

The third concept of integration attempts a synthesis of the first two approaches. It maintains that there are two phases to be considered in a mathematics program. The first recognizes the need for a functional phase which can best be accomplished through the integration of mathematics with other subjects in the curriculum; whereas the second is commonly referred to as the mathematics phase of instruction.

The society in which man lives is not compartmentalized into the categories of reading, writing, social studies, or arithmetic. In the school program, mathematical concepts can contribute to a better understanding of the other areas of the curriculum. Ernest Horn pointed out that as many as one out of every seven words in geography textbooks is a quantitative term.[2] Similar examples will be noted in other subjects of the school curriculum. The understanding of the meaning of such indefinite quantitative terms as "more" or "larger" or "greater than" as well as the understanding of their meaning in context is necessary for comprehension of the material. Each area of the curriculum thus provides an opportunity to use mathematical concepts.

The second phase of the synthesizing viewpoint recognizes the need for mathematics instruction as a separate subject in the curriculum of the elementary school. Mathematical concepts are best learned when taught in a systematic, meaningful manner. Integration, per se, does not provide the systematic approach that is required. In a well-organized instructional program, both phases should be dealt with in a balanced, well-integrated way, so that neither phase is neglected nor over-emphasized.

[2] Ernest Horn. "Arithmetic in the Elementary School Curriculum," *The Teaching of Arithmetic*, Fiftieth Yearbook of the National Society for the Study of Education (Chicago, Ill.: University of Chicago Press, 1951), Part II, 10.

Although many educators have recommended this synthesizing concept of a mathematics program, there has been relatively little research undertaken to determine its effectiveness. The nature and amount of mathematical terms found in the materials of other subject areas have been widely studied. However, research studies are needed to determine the relative effect that the understanding of these mathematical terms has upon achievement in the other subjects of the curriculum. Conversely, research is also needed to determine the probable or potential contributions of other school subjects to the development of mathematical concepts.

Organization of Remainder of Chapter

Part I of this chapter includes two articles which indicate the value of total integration of mathematics with other subject areas of the elementary school.

Part II includes two articles which point out the inherent weaknesses of the total integration approach to the teaching of mathematics.

Part III is composed of an article which supports the synthesized approach to the teaching of mathematics in the elementary school.

Additional sources reflecting each of the three points of view will be found in the bibliography at the end of the chapter. Also included in the bibliography are a number of research studies referring to the amount of quantitative material found in various subject areas of the elementary school curriculum. And finally, several references are listed which include illustrations of classroom practices which have been effective in integrating mathematics with the total school curriculum.

PART I: TOTAL INTEGRATION OF MATHEMATICS WITH OTHER SUBJECTS IN THE ELEMENTARY SCHOOL CURRICULUM

AN EXPERIMENTAL COMPARISON OF DRILL AND DIRECT EXPERIENCE IN ARITHMETIC LEARNING IN A FOURTH GRADE

Lowry W. Harding and Inez P. Bryant

During the early part of the present century the development of standardized tests focused attention upon the teaching and learning of specific items of knowledge and the mastery of discrete skills. In no subject was this trend stronger than in Arithmetic, where major emphasis could be placed so easily upon the computational skills. The effectiveness of the teaching-learning process was increasingly judged by the speed and accuracy of performing computational processes. As a result, drill became the almost universal mode of instruction.

Drill methods did not succeed in developing in pupils the ability to apply arithmetical skills to the solution of practical problems. In some cases drill appeared to be a handicap. As evidence accumulated that intelligent mathematical behavior was not learned through drill, many teachers began using experimental, liberalized procedures. This took various forms, such as delaying formal teaching of the subject, striving for more "exact" grade-placement in terms of Mental Age and other factors, or of developing "activity" programs.

The trend away from drill toward the teaching of arithmetic through functional activities gained much ground during the past decade. Many reports indicated that the functional approach was effective, although most of the reports were from the lower grades. It began to appear that the "arithmetic problem," the biggest obstacle to curricular reorganization and the bugbear of so many children and teachers, was being solved. With teachers having learned to use standardized tests as tools, rather than allowing them to direct the teaching process, and learning to teach func-

[From "An Experimental Comparison of Drill and Direct Experience in Arithmetic Learning in a Fourth Grade," *Journal of Educational Research*, XXXVII (January, 1944), pp. 321-37. Reprinted by permission of the authors and the *Journal of Educational Research*.]

tionally, it seemed that arithmetic might become interesting and teaching programs effective.

During the past few years this trend appears to be reversed. Opinions of individuals and reports from influential organizations indicate that functional programs of arithmetic teaching are being considered inadequate, especially for the intermediate and upper grades. These reports and the pressures of the present world situation are causing many teachers to abandon liberalized procedures. The thorough understanding and mastery of arithmetic assumes critical importance in view of the increasing need for technical services which require mathematical ability. Complaints to the effect that schools have failed in teaching the "Three R's" are heard with increasing frequency. The results of the Army tests and reports from personnel departments of industry concerning the results of their "fitness" tests are far from reassuring. Not understanding the techniques of a "functional" program or lacking faith in their effectiveness in its use, and realizing the importance of "results," teachers are rapidly reverting to the most formalized drill.

In view of the confusion and conflict in the thinking and practices of teachers of arithmetic, there is need for all available information concerning the effectiveness of various materials and procedures. The experiment reported in this article is pertinent because it was conducted in an intermediate grade of a public school in a large city system with no unusual material or equipment. It bears directly upon the larger problems of method and "results" or outcomes of instruction. It is hoped that readers will consider it "reportorial" rather than controversial, and make whatever practical uses of it as seem feasible.

The Problem

It is generally assumed that different instructional procedures result in different kinds of learning. That assumption gives rise to the many arguments concerning methodology. Questions concerning what instructional procedures are most effective in promoting understanding, developing computational skills, improving ability in problem-solving and in providing for individual differences have not been answered conclusively. It has been suggested that social problems furnish a vitalizing basis for teaching and that experience with problems may aid children in solving them, although both are frequently questioned. All these questions need further inquiry.

Many teachers agree that experience learning, through functional activities, offers unusual opportunity for practicing democratic relationships, developing "personality" and stimulating independent thinking. They are less certain that such procedures are practical in "traditional" schools, especially in the intermediate and upper grades, or that they yield results as satisfactory as more formal procedures in subject-matter achievement. Studies are needed which bear upon these points.

The problem of the study reported here was whether pupils taught through functional procedures would attain as high achievement on standardized measures of computation and reasoning as would pupils taught by formalized drill methods. There were several related problems which are stated below. Could concrete experiences involving mathematical procedures be introduced into one classroom of a public school without disturbing other teachers or disrupting the school program? Is a vitalized program possible within the limits of instructional materials regularly provided or obtainable without special expenditure by the teacher or school treasury? Is it possible to cover the material included in the Arithmetic Course of Study for one grade by means of concrete experiences and is such a method practical in terms of teacher time and energy expended? What are the comparative achievements, from the two methods of instruction, in social adjustment and emotional stability?

The experiment was conducted on the fourth grade level in a departmentalized school in a city system (population approx. 350,000) where classifying, marking and promoting are on the basis of subject-matter achievement. The pupils used as subjects were those regularly enrolled in the fourth grade of the school. They came from within the confines of the school district and represented a typical cross section of its constituency, a lower middle class group.

As the school system uses the semester plan, the study included two groups of "4A" pupils. It covered one semester's work with each group. The same teacher worked with both groups, thus avoiding questions concerning the relative efficiency of several individuals in terms of personality or teaching ability, although raising the questions of the teacher's personal preference of approach and relative skill in each. These questions may be answered by the school principal, the members of the teaching staff and the director of the experiment. In the judgment of these individuals the teacher's preferences were not evident in the proceedings used in either part of the experiment. Their opinion, based upon frequent observation, was that each of the two methods was used conscientiously and effectively. No difference in skill was observed, although any difference in teaching skill should have favored the drill method, due to longer experience with drill techniques.

By starting the experiment in the last semester (spring) of one school year and finishing it during the autumn (first semester) of the next school year, the intervening summer decreased the danger of a "halo" effect from the use of one method influencing the use of the other. As a further safeguard, the records kept on each group were stored, without being summarized, in a place inaccessible to the teacher or director. They were made available for study, summary and analysis only after the work of both groups was completed. Possible seasonal influence upon learning was recognized and taken into consideration in evaluating the results of the study.

Throughout the discussion following, the two groups will be designated as "experimental" and "control." The group with which personal experience projects were used to the exclusion of drill is termed the experimental group. The class which followed a textbook and had formal drill procedures of the usual type is designated as the control group.

Procedures with the Experimental Group

Because of limitations inherent in a departmentalized school situation—disintegration of total school experiences of pupils, lack of complete planning among the teachers, and difficulties in securing full use of building and equipment—the activities and projects used were those which could be carried out during the period when the teacher conducting the experiment was in the room with the pupils; that is, during the "Arithmetic" period. The problems for the experimental group were found in activities which were selected because of richness in mathematical possibilities, adaptability to the situation, simplicity of execution and appeal to the children. Every idea and activity used was decided by majority vote of the pupils, after discussion, investigation of materials, costs and probable results. The evaluation of these factors by the pupils often furnished experiences which were as educative as the actual project.

The pupils in the group sold candy to the other children in the school—after lunch, for they investigated and found that it was not well to eat candy before a meal. Some of the candy was purchased from a wholesaler and sold at retail, some bought from a retailer at reduced prices for quantity purchases, and some was made by the children after purchasing the necessary ingredients.

They weighed and measured themselves for the grade health chart; they kept a temperature chart and a weather chart for the classroom. They bought material—after much pricing and comparing of samples—and made curtains for the windows of their classroom, using the profits from the candy sales. The school having decided to have a kite-flying contest, the pupils of the experimental group constructed their own kites, as well as a few extra ones for sale. They conducted a paper sale, measured and diagrammed the room for a rearranged seating plan, sold and served lunch to the other children, and conducted a number of less ambitious activities involving use of arithmetic.

All of the activities were happenings of timely interest to the group. Being their own suggestions, decided upon after much discussion, they were performed wholeheartedly and enthusiastically. The experiences were rich in possibilities for developing quantitative thinking, for giving practice in computation, for developing habits of intelligent behavior in dealing with problems, and in opportunities for democratic living. Of course, the pupils made mistakes. But they did not make many, for they were intensely interested in the jobs they were doing. Seldom did a child make the same mistake twice, for the consequences of mistakes were made clear in concrete terms. Children checked and rechecked their work, frequently asking other children to go over it with them.

Perhaps no other activity offered as many possibilities as the lunch which the group prepared, sold and served to the other children in the school. It furnished practice in comparing price and quality of materials to determine what and where to buy; in estimating quantities to order; in figuring costs; in measuring quantities; in figuring proportional parts; in adjusting numbers of workers to amounts of work to be done in various jobs; in making out and checking bills; in collecting and counting money; in paying bills and figuring profits. Plans were made concerning the most practical and attractive menu to serve, the best way of preparing food and the most efficient division of labor; the best way of serving, the way to save most time in order to serve quickly and keep warm food warm and cold food cold, keeping in mind limitations of space and equipment. This enterprise, in which responsibility for real work was assumed by the group, collectively and as individuals, was a real adventure in social living, giving experience in planning, executing and evaluating.

Another typical example was the kite flying contest. This gave experience in buying string and paste, in measuring, and in cutting without waste. It also brought up such problems as wind resistance, the relationship of length of tail to size of kite and the weather, the problem of bowing a kite and techniques of flying. Since approximately two hundred children were to participate, rules for the conduct of the contest had to be developed, involving a wholesome exchange of ideas, opinions and experiences.

All activities, projects and problems carried on by this group were used for the "arithmetic" portion of the curriculum. They were solved by individuals, by small groups and sometimes by the class as a whole. When a new process was needed it was discussed, explained and demonstrated. A few sample applications were made and the work of the group proceeded. Not infrequently children developed understandings of new processes and operations in terms of their needs for using them, without outside help. Arithmetic textbooks were used occasionally, as references or for explanations of processes, but not for systematic teaching or practice. The teacher prepared a chart of the textbook assignments following the course of study and, as processes listed in it occurred in classwork, checked them. However, this was kept only as a private record and reference. It was not used to influence or direct the activities of the group.

Table 1 was prepared from that chart and shows the number of days on which various processes were used by individuals or groups in their work upon various enterprises. It should be remembered that the work with this group covered one semester, or ninety school days.

TABLE 1

FREQUENCY OF OCCURRENCE OF ARITHMETIC PROCESSES IN ACTIVITIES

	Adding	Subtracting	Multiplying	Dividing	Finding Averages	Measuring	Estimating	Counting Change	Fractional Parts	Reading Thermometer	Making Graphs
Candy Sale	76	76	44	32	5	11	16	70	15	0	0
Health Record ...	24	41	13	18	16	24	12	0	19	0	8
Keeping Attendance..........	77	23	34	27	14	0	13	0	11	0	12
Making Bookshelves........	12	12	9	10	7	12	12	0	8	0	0
Making Curtains..	12	12	12	9	4	11	7	5	7	0	0
Making Display Cases.........	11	11	11	8	3	10	9	3	7	0	3
Making Kites	5	10	10	7	5	17	13	6	11	0	0
Paper Sale	7	7	7	5	3	5	5	2	4	0	2
School Lunch	32	36	36	20	6	30	32	36	19	0	6
Scoring Games ...	61	24	16	27	17	0	11	0	13	0	14
Temperature Chart	11	32	9	14	8	9	26	0	0	62	17
Weather Chart ...	9	7	4	8	6	5	17	0	0	45	11
Other Activities...	33	51	18	18	9	62	49	17	53	0	18

Procedures with the Control Group

The control group followed the adopted text for the grade in its arithmetic. Page by page assignments were made. Addition, subtraction and multiplication were reviewed. Besides this review, the course of study assignment for the semester included the more difficult aspects of multiplication, the easier steps in division, drawing to scale, and introduction of ideas of parts of numbers.

The major portion of the work was division. The drill method was used in teaching this process. Work involving a review of the first three fundamental processes was given regularly throughout the semester by means of problems and mixed drills. All drill exercises were individualized rather than competitive, children being urged to improve their own records. The records of individual children were not compared with records made by others.

Daily assignments were made with seat work, checking of papers, making corrections and blackboard work. Explanations and demonstrations were usually made by means of blackboard and pointer. Every effort was made to exemplify the more efficient of "typical" procedures.

Findings and Comparisons

The results of the two methods of instruction were determined by comparisons of the growth of the two groups in computational ability, reasoning ability, social adjustment and emotional stability. Subject matter results were determined by comparing the gains made by the two groups on alternate forms of the Stanford Achievement Test. Relative progress of the groups in the other aspects of growth was determined by comparisons of anecdotal records kept for each group and by comparisons of full school records of each child, made before and after the experiment.

TABLE 2

INTELLIGENCE QUOTIENTS

I.Q.	Experimental Group	Control Group
111–115	0	1
106–110	3	2
101–105	1	6
96–100	5	2
91– 95	4	3
86– 90	5	6
81– 85	2	7
76– 80	5	2
71– 75	1	1
66– 70	3	0
61– 65	2	3
Total *	31	33
Range	50	55
Median	88	89
Mean	86.7	89.4
S. D.	± 12.95	± 12.85

* Three children in the experimental group and two in the control group transferred to another school before the end of the experiment. The records of these five children were omitted from all computations and comparisons. The totals shown in the above table represent those pupils in attendance throughout the study.

Comparisons of the achievement of the two groups can be made intelligently only in terms of some estimate of their ability and subject-matter understandings at the beginning of the study. Table 2 shows the range and distribution of intelligence quotients of the children in the two groups. The I. Q. ratings were secured on the Stanford-Binet Individual Intelligence Test, administered by the staff psychologist.

While the children composing the two groups were not selected, they were approximately equal in I. Q. ratings. The differences in range and distribution are minor so that, for all practical purposes, the two groups may be considered comparable.

The standing of the two groups in computation and reasoning, at the beginning of the experiment, is shown in Table 3. For easy comparison the scores have been reduced to grade levels and grouped.

TABLE 3

ACHIEVEMENT RATING BEFORE THE STUDY

Grade Level	Computation		Reasoning	
	Exp.	Control	Exp.	Control
5.0–5.4	0	1	1	2
4.5–4.9	3	3	8	7
4.0–4.4	12	11	7	11
3.5–3.9	9	6	7	2
3.0–3.4	7	12	8	10
2.5–2.9	0	0	0	1
Total	31	33	31	33
Range	2.0	2.5	2.5	3.0
Median	3.7	3.9	4.0	4.2
Mean	3.88	3.80	3.99	4.00
S. D.	±.47	±.56	±.61	±.67

Both groups were slightly below the fourth grade achievement standard of the test. Since they were leaving 4B and just entering 4A when subjected to the test, both groups were approximately one-half grade or five months below the test standard for that stage. The control group had a slightly wider range but not sufficient to make a serious difference in comparisons of achievement.

The standing of the two groups in computation and reasoning, at the end of the experiment, is shown in Table 4. As in Table 3, the data have been grouped in school grades by months or tenths of school years.

TABLE 4

ACHIEVEMENT RATING AT END OF EXPERIMENT

Grade Level	Computation		Reasoning	
	Exp.	Control	Exp.	Control
6.0–6.4	1	0	1	1
5.5–5.9	1	1	2	2
5.0–5.4	5	5	8	1
4.5–4.9	6	7	4	3
4.0–4.4	11	9	8	13
3.5–3.9	6	5	6	6
3.0–3.4	1	6	2	6
2.5–2.9	0	0	0	1
Total	31	33	31	33
Range	3.5	3.0	3.5	4.0
Median	4.38	4.31	4.47	4.14
Mean	4.54	4.35	4.62	4.21
S. D.	±.66	±.69	±.76	±.77

It is noticeable that the range of scores for both groups is greater than at the beginning of the experiment, indicating that the fourth grade work in arithmetic, more difficult than in previous grades, causes individual differences in ability and effort to become more evident. It is also evidence of provision for individual differences, since the pupils were not forced toward an average. It is evident, from the data of Table 4, that both groups were below test standards at the end of Grade 4A. However, their achievement is slightly better than the normal expectation for pupils with mean I. Q. ratings of 85–90.

The gain of the two groups in computation and reasoning, as evidenced by achievement test ratings, is shown in Table 5. The Range, Median, Mean and Standard Deviations are shown for each group. The reliability of the difference between the two means in Computation and in Reasoning is also reported, since the reliability of the difference in the achievement of the two groups is an important question in deciding the significance of the findings.

TABLE 5

COMPARATIVE GAIN IN COMPUTATION AND REASONING

Index	Computation			Reasoning		
	Exp.	Control	Diff.	Exp.	Control	Diff.
Total Gain (school yrs.)..	20.46	18.15	2.31	19.53	16.93	2.60
Range	1.70	1.40	.30	1.90	1.20	.70
Median (gain)	.7	.5	.20	.6	.2	.40
Mean (gain)	.72	.55	.17	.68	.26	.42
S. D.	±.40	±.34	$\left(\frac{\sigma}{D}\right).098$	±.46	±.23	$\left(\frac{\sigma}{D}\right).092$
σM.................	.072	.059		.083	.040	

From the above table it may be seen that the experimental group did slightly better than the control group in computation, making approximately two and one-half months greater gain. This is significant in view of the fact that they were not subjected to drill or "practice" procedures. There were more high scoring individuals in the control group, evidenced by the fact that their median was higher. The greater range of scores made by the experimental group is evidence that their achievement of computational skills was not as uniform as that of the control group. In reasoning the experimental group clearly surpassed the control group in their development, although again the range is much greater. This indicates greater flexibility of provision for individual differences in ability, the more able pupils of the experimental group making greater progress and the less able pupils making smaller gains than the corresponding pupils of the control group. This is what one might expect from the liberalized and regimented programs.

The standard deviations are rather high, as might be expected with small groups and wide ranges of scores. The difference in mean gain in computation may be interpreted as follows: The chances are approximately sixty-eight in a hundred that the obtained difference of .17 does not differ from the true difference by more than ±.093; the chances are ninety-nine in a hundred that the obtained difference of .17 does not differ from the true difference by more than ($\pm 3 \times .093$) ±.28. Then the true difference lies between −.11 and +.45 and, since the lower range is negative, the obtained difference is not statistically significant. However, as $D/\delta D$ (.17/.093) is 1.8 the chances are ninety-six in one hundred that the true difference is greater than zero, favoring the experimental group.

In Reasoning, the chances are approximately sixty-eight in a hundred that the obtained difference of .42 does not differ from the true difference by more than ±.092; the chances are ninety-nine in a hundred that the obtained difference of .42 does not differ from the true difference by more than ($\pm 3 \times .092$) $\pm.28$. Thus the true difference lies between .14 and .45 and, as the lower range is positive, the difference is statistically significant. The $D/\delta D$ (.42/.092) of 4.5 indicates that the chances are 99+ in 100 that the true difference is greater than zero, favoring the experimental group. This result gives practical certainty that the experimental group is superior to the control group in problem solving.

There were seventeen pupils in each group whose intelligence quotients exactly matched. The gains made by these individuals on before-and-after applications of the achievement test are shown in Table 6. The amount of gain is shown in tenths of school-grade achievement levels. That is, .8 represents a gain of eight tenths of a grade, according to the interpolation table of the test.

TABLE 6

GAINS IN COMPUTATION AND REASONING MADE BY PUPILS OF MATCHED
INTELLIGENCE QUOTIENTS

Pupils	I.Q.	Computation			Reasoning		
		Exp.	Control	Diff.	Exp.	Control	Diff.
A–A′	110	.5	.4		.8	.6	
B–B′	109	.3	.3		.5	.4	
C–C′	100	.7	.1		1.2	.3	
D–D′	98	.7	.4		.2	.3	
E–E′	95	.7	.3		.9	.4	
F–F′	88	.5	.3		.6	.3	
G–G′	88	.3	.4		.7	.4	
H–H′	87	.8	.7		.3	.0	
I–I′	86	.4	.2		.1	.4	
J–J′	84	.2	.8		.0	.2	
K–K′	82	.0	.4		1.7	.1	
L–L′	80	.2	.6		.6	.7	
M–M′	80	.3	.3		.6	.2	
N–N′	78	.3	.8		.5	.2	
O–O′	68	.1	.1		1.5	.0	
P–P′	67	.0	.3		.6	.4	
Q–Q′	64	.2	.0		.1	.1	
Total Gain	......	6.2	6.4	.2	10.9	5.0	5.9
Range	......	.9	.9	.0	1.8	.8	1.0
Median	......	.36	.39	.03	.55	.35	.2
Mean (gain)	......	.37	.38	.01	.63	.29	.34
S. D.	......	$\pm.24$	$\pm.23$		$\pm.43$	$\pm.19$	
σM	......	$\pm.058$	$\pm.056$	$\pm.08$	$\pm.104$	$\pm.046$	$\pm.11$

Table 6 shows that, for the pupils of equal intelligence test scores, those in the experimental group approximately equalled the growth of the control group in computational skill. They made a gain more than twice as great as the control group on the reasoning section of the achievement test. This would indicate that the learning of arithmetic through direct personal experiences may be as effective as formal drill in mastering the fundamentals and more effective in the development of ability to understand and solve problems. Comparisons of these matched pairs of pupils indicate that there may be little relationship between intelligence quotient, within the limits of the range of this group, and growth in computational skill or problem solving ability.

As in Table 5, the Standard Deviations are high, probably for the same reasons. In computation, the chances are ninety-nine in a hundred that the true difference lies between −.24 and +.25. This indicates that the mean difference of .01 is not statistically significant. In fact, the $D/\delta D$ (.01/.08) of .125 means that the chances are fifty-five in a hundred that the control group will score above the experimental group in computation.

In reasoning, the matched pupils show the same trend as the entire groups. That is, those pupils in the experimental group were clearly superior in their gains. The chances are sixty-eight in a hundred that the obtained difference of .34 does not differ from the true difference by more than ±.11. The chances are ninety-nine in a hundred that the obtained difference of .34 does not differ from the true difference by more than ($\pm3 \times .11$) ±.33. Thus, it is practically certain that the true difference lies within the limits of +.01 and +.67 and, since the lower range is positive, the obtained difference of .34 is significant. The $D/\delta D$ is 3+, indicating that the chances are 99.9 in 100 that the experimental group will consistently score above their matched opposites of the control group in reasoning.

Comparisons were made of the habits of study, school marks in arithmetic, and classroom behavior of the two groups for the semesters immediately preceding and following the experiment. That is, autumn and autumn for the group taught in the spring, spring and spring for the group taught in the autumn. Thus, the entire study covered four semesters or two school sessions. Table 7 shows these comparisons in terms of the number in each group making improvement, no improvement, or making poorer ratings during the semester following their participation in the experiment than they made during the semester preceding it.

It may be seen from the above table that the experimental group had a larger number of individuals making gains in all three items than did the control group. Also, fewer of them showed "no improvement." It is interesting to note that both groups had very nearly the same number making poorer grades after the experiment than during the semester preceding it and that the control group had more individuals showing deterioration in study habits and behavior. Although the differences are small, this may indicate that pupils experiencing a liberalized, functional program have less difficulty adjusting to a formalized program than has been assumed. Further study is needed on this point.

TABLE 7

STUDY HABITS, ARITHMETIC GRADES AND CLASSROOM BEHAVIOR COMPARISON OF GROUPS DURING PRECEDING AND FOLLOWING SEMESTERS

Aspects Rated	Study Habits				Arithmetic Grades				Behavior			
	Exp.		Control		Exp.		Control		Exp.		Control	
Classification	No.	%	No.	%	No.	%	No.	%	No.	%	No.	%
Improvement...	14	.45	7	.21	17	.55	11	.33	12	.39	8	.24
No Improvement	12	.39	16	.49	11	.36	18	.55	14	.45	20	.61
Deterioration ...	5	.16	10	.30	3	.09	4	.12	5	.16	5	.15
Total	31	1.00	33	1.00	31	1.00	33	1.00	31	1.00	33	1.00

The comparative ratings of the two groups in emotional stability, initiative and qualities of democratic living were determined by comparison of anecdotes which had been written by the teacher and by selected observers. They were validated by three judges who inspected them carefully, grouped them according to aspects of behavior treated, and rated them according to whether they showed evidence of that behavior being conspicuously present or absent. Approximately eight hundred anecdotes were written and used. Table 8 shows the comparisons of the groups on eight aspects of behavior. The ratings are given in percentages to make comparison clearer.

Table 8 offers evidence that the children in the experimental group showed desirable attitudes, social behavior, and evidences of emotional stability with more frequency than did the control group. It is significant that the control group was rated lowest in emotional stability (53 per cent) and in cooperation and habits of self evaluation (68 per cent), while the experimental group was rated highest in self evaluation (97 per cent), initiative (92 per cent) and in consideration for others (91 per cent). Emotional stability was rated lowest of the eight aspects of behavior for both groups (71 per cent and 53 per cent respectively) but the experimental group was considerably higher than the control.

The evidences from the judges' ratings of the anecdotal material indicate that the "activity-experience" program was more effective in developing desirable personality attributes than was the formalized program. However, one cannot extrapolate from the data on this aspect of the study with any considerable degree of certainty, as the total field of experiences contributes to personality development and, while the experiment dealt with arithmetic primarily, the pupils were subject to many other influences, both within and outside the school. On the other hand, the fact that the anecdotal material was collected during the arithmetic period exclusively does give some basis for conclusions drawn from the comparisons.

TABLE 8

COMPARATIVE RATINGS OF THE TWO GROUPS ON EIGHT ASPECTS OF BEHAVIOR

Aspects of Behavior Rated	Experimental Group		Control Group	
	Behavior Present	Behavior Absent	Behavior Present	Behavior Absent
Consideration for Others	.91	.09	.76	.24
Cooperation	.79	.21	.68	.32
Emotional Stability	.71	.29	.53	.47
Initiative........................	.92	.08	.81	.19
Intelligent Inquiry	.81	.19	.71	.29
Responsibility—Assumes	.89	.11	.87	.13
Self-direction	.88	.12	.86	.14
Self Evaluation	.97	.03	.68	.32

Conclusions

The authors of this report wish to emphasize the point that the experiment was quite limited, being restricted to one subject on one grade level in one school, to one teacher and two groups of pupils, and to one semester's work with each group. Within these limits all practical precautions were taken. However, in view of the limitations of the study, the data secured should be regarded as tentative in character and received openmindedly. The study indicates the importance of continued research upon similar educational problems.

The results of the experiment indicate that different instructional procedures do result in different kinds of learning. Direct, first-hand experiences with projects and enterprises in which children have a personal interest proved more effective than vicarious experiences and drill procedures in developing the ability to solve problems as this ability was measured by the "Arithmetic Reasoning" section of the achievement tests.

The functional use of arithmetic proved as effective as drill procedures in developing computational skill, as that is measured by the achievement tests. True or "functional" learning emphasizes discovery, thinking, and problem solving. Learning "facts" or "tool skills" as a prerequisite to their use in "thinking" apparently is not as effective as mastering the facts or tools through use in thinking upon problems of personal concern to the child.

The other members of the school staff expressed themselves as being undisturbed by the activities and procedures of the functional program. In fact, several stated that they used incidents from that program in their teaching by reference or as examples of topics under discussion. Thus it may be concluded that individual teachers may develop functional programs of instruction in their own classrooms without waiting for the entire school to be reorganized.

The experience from this study indicates that a vitalized instructional program is possible within the limits of the materials regularly provided or procurable without personal expenditure of money by the teacher. The necessary requirements seem to be initiative, originality and insight into the possibilities for learning which various activities may have. The teacher must do more planning. She must know the individual needs, interests and capabilities of pupils, but will spend less energy in review, re-teaching and general motivation for study.

The results of the standardized achievement tests indicate that it is possible to cover the material in a course of study for a fourth grade by means of concrete experiences. Also, that concrete materials and "alive" problems are more effective than abstract examples and "artificial" problems for learning.

From the information secured, the experience program appears more effective than the formal program in developing emotional stability, desirable social behavior and study habits in children.

A challenging item in the findings is the evidence that, within certain limits, methods and materials of instruction may be more important than I. Q. in the development of certain skills and abilities. Further research is especially needed on this problem.

Many individuals have emphasized the need and importance of a general spirit of inquiry throughout the school system with a continuous process of evaluating educational processes and products. It has also been stated that much of the needed research should be done by teachers since they are usually the first to feel the pressure of unsolved problems as well as the group to put into effect the solutions found. One of the major results of this study may be the evidence that, without unusual equipment or elaborate organization, individual teachers may conduct small experiments in trying out various methods of teaching and in attacking problems of which they have become aware.

THE LEARNING OF FUNDAMENTALS
IN AN ARITHMETIC ACTIVITY PROGRAM

Henry Harap and Charlotte E. Mapes

The writers set out to discover the extent to which the fundamentals are learned in an arithmetic activity program. In this particular study we were not experimenting with an integrated activity program. Such a procedure is more complex, involves more variables, and should logically come after some experience with a program of activities limited to one subject. In fact, the experiment reported in this article made several concessions to the conventional content and order of learning arithmetic.

The study was limited to the multiplication and the division of fractions and to denominate numbers which are commonly learned in the second term of Grade V. The activities were selected deliberately because they were rich in the applications of the fundamental processes in the multiplication and division of fractions and in denominate numbers. Nevertheless, the activities were genuinely real on the child's level of maturity. They were based on meaningful situations in the child's experience in school and out of school. The children participated in selecting and planning the units of work. The actual life-situations were, as far as possible, reproduced in the classroom. The materials utilized were those which occur in life. The activities included weighing and measuring materials, cooking meals, sewing garments, serving meals, purchasing goods, eating meals, reading recipes, entertaining children and adults, decorating classrooms, making baskets, assembling and arranging furniture and other equipment, cutting paper, consulting parents, obtaining estimates, comparing prices, organizing into committees, calculating costs, calculating quantities of materials, preparing food baskets, estimating the needs of families, handling foods, and so on. There was maximum participation on the part of the pupils. The pupils communicated and associated freely as the need arose. They had abundant opportunity to choose, to judge, and to evaluate. Every unit came to a logical and natural close.

The time devoted to arithmetic was the usual daily period lasting between fifty and sixty minutes. Much of the time ordinarily devoted to drill

[From "The Learning of Fundamentals in an Arithmetic Activity Program," *The Elementary School Journal*, XXXIV (March, 1934), pp. 515-25. Reprinted by permission of the authors and The University of Chicago Press.]

and problem-solving was devoted to construction, manipulation, and other activities. Actually, therefore, much less than the customary allotment of time was used in computations.

The Class and Its Resources

The experimental class was an ordinary class in a typical metropolitan school in Cleveland. It should, however, be pointed out that the school is designated as the arithmetic curriculum center, in which new units of work are developed for eventual distribution throughout the city or for inclusion in the next city-wide course of study. The teachers in the school are selected because of their special ability in teaching arithmetic. According to records of the general ability of the pupils based on the National Intelligence Tests, Scale A, Form 1, the intelligence quotient of the pupils ranged from 92 to 135, the average being 113. Unlike other experimental, laboratory, or private schools, the class was a typical crowded group of thirty-seven pupils. The classroom had practically no permanent learning equipment or supplies other than movable desks. The materials and equipment used in the several units were improvised and assembled when they became necessary, the resources of the school and the homes of the children and the neighborhood stores being drawn on.

The Functional Arithmetic Course

The units which comprised the course included the following: (1) a candy sale, (2) understanding the advantage of an inclined plane (clarifying the science of the grade), (3) a mothers' party, (4) baskets for two needy families, (5) preparing a luncheon for Grade I, (6) making a quilt for a children's hospital, and (7) serving a teachers' luncheon. Each of these units lasted from eight to twelve periods. With the exception of one, all the units involved some purchasing transactions by the pupils. All except two of the units involved the selection and the preparation of food. The quilt-making unit involved some designing and sewing. Four of the units involved selling transactions.

To illustrate, we give here a brief outline of the first unit, the candy sale. To raise funds for a mothers' party, the class decided to make and sell candy. The children estimated that they would need to earn five dollars. On the basis of a fifteen-cent profit on the pound, it would be necessary to make $33\frac{1}{3}$ pounds of candy. From a study of recipes five kinds of candies were selected. After testing the recipes to find out how much candy each would produce, the pupils determined how many times each recipe would have to be increased to yield $6\frac{1}{2}$ pounds of candy.

Before the materials could be purchased, the ingredients, which were given in cupfuls, teaspoonfuls, and tablespoonfuls, had to be converted into pounds and ounces. Prices were obtained from two stores, and the cost of materials was calculated. The actual making of the candy required several days. The cost a pound was determined and then the selling price. Most of the candy was sold by the half-pound. The estimated cost of materials was $4.43; the actual cost was $3.82 because of a decline in prices. The cost of a pound of candy was 12 cents; the selling price was 27 cents. The gross receipts amounted to $9.87. The profits from the sale amounted to $6.05.

New arithmetical steps did not occur in the order of progressive difficulty. In fact, the most difficult step in the multiplication of fractions came first, namely, the multiplication of a mixed number by a mixed number. The simplest step ($\frac{1}{2}$ of 4) was the twelfth in the actual order of occurrence. In five of the units the more difficult steps occurred before the simpler steps.

The pupils sensed a new step at once. Very often they were asked to suggest how to perform a new process. The pupils were never allowed to attack a new process incorrectly. Each new difficulty was taken up and explained in a few minutes. For example, in the luncheon unit in Grade I, when the children were deciding which would be the most economical loaf of bread to buy, a new step was met for the first time: dividing a number by a larger number. The five-cent loaf yielded 16 slices; the ten-cent loaf yielded 40 slices.

$$5 \div 16 = 5 \times \tfrac{1}{16} = \tfrac{5}{16} \ \cent$$
$$10 \div 40 = 10 \times \tfrac{1}{40} = 1 \times \tfrac{1}{4} = \tfrac{1}{4} \ \cent$$

The pupils' attention was drawn to the size of the divisor. It was shown that 5 could be divided by 16 but that the answer would be a fraction. In the same unit cookies were made. The recipe called for $2\frac{1}{2}$ dozen, but the class wanted to make 7 dozen. To determine how many times to increase the recipe, the pupils found it necessary to divide 7 by $2\frac{1}{2}$. This process was a new step: dividing an integer by a mixed number: $7 \div 2\frac{1}{2} = 7 \div \frac{5}{2} = 7 \times \frac{2}{5} = \frac{14}{5} = 2\frac{4}{5}$ times. The teacher called attention to the divisor and asked what must be done with such numbers before dividing. The mixed number was changed into an improper fraction, and the usual procedure in division of fractions was then applied.

Some new steps developed so naturally and imperceptibly that the pupils were barely aware of the newness or the difficulty of the process. Frequently a step belonging to an advanced grade was met. The step was explained briefly, and the pupils were told that they would meet it again later.

In this experiment we decided to dispense completely with any form of practice or drill sheets or any other supplementary exercises. We gave no diagnostic tests nor any other tests in order that the repetition of the processes might be limited exclusively to their natural occurrence in the units of work. There were, of course, many repetitions, but none of them was deliberate or extraneous. For example, when the party for mothers was being planned, it was necessary to increase the recipes of three kinds of cookies. Since each recipe required eight ingredients, there resulted twenty-four repetitions of the multiplication of fractions.

All the work of the pupil was kept in a notebook, which was frequently checked by the teacher. No child was permitted to leave an error uncorrected. The notebooks proved to be a valuable source of information, the pupils referring to their records frequently. No textbook or any other printed material was used in this experimental course.

The conditions under which the experimental course was conducted may be summarized as follows: (1) The units were based on socially real situations or activities. (2) The situations were selected because they were rich in the use of fractions. (3) No attention was given to the order of the occurrence of the steps in fractions. (4) No external practice or drill was introduced. (5) No more than the usual time allotted to arithmetic was devoted to computation. (6) The experimental class was an ordinary group of 37 children having an average intelligence quotient of 113 on the National Intelligence Tests, Scale A, Form 1. (7) The teacher was one of a group especially selected for this school because she excelled in the teaching of arithmetic.

Recording the Data

The fundamental steps. It will be recalled that the purpose of this experiment was to determine whether the arithmetical processes were learned. The fundamental arithmetical steps or processes have been isolated repeatedly. For our purpose we used the analysis made by the staff of our local curriculum center for arithmetic. The list of basic steps included eight steps in multiplication of fractions, six steps in the division of fractions, and twelve steps in denominate numbers.

The preliminary and the final tests. This list of fundamental steps formed the basis of the preliminary and the final tests containing seventeen items of three exercises each. The two forms actually used were those designed by the Milford School, the experimental center, to test the mastery of the processes for the grade. A step was considered mastered when the pupil worked correctly two of the three exercises involving that step. The results of these tests furnished our main conclusions. In addition to this test of mastery, the pupils were given a preliminary and a final test in practical problems involving the basic steps, as a further check on our experiment.

Sequence of steps and number of repetitions of steps. With the aid of a chart we kept a daily record of the order in which each step occurred. Thus, we knew the exact sequence in which the arithmetical steps occurred in each unit. We were interested to know whether the random sequence of steps had any effect on the children's mastery of the steps. Again, using a chart, we kept a daily record of the number of times each step was repeated. We therefore had an exact record of the amount of practice on each step as it was provided by our selected functional units of arithmetic. These data enabled us to determine whether there was any relation between the amount of practice and mastery.

The units themselves were recorded in detail, the actual development of the learning experiences and the arithmetical computations as they arose being shown. These records served not only as complete records of the experiment for us but also as records of learning experiences which other teachers may wish to try. The units,[1] the tests, and our detailed records are available to anyone at the cost of copying.

In summary, the following data were recorded: (1) the fundamental arithmetical steps, (2) a detailed account of the development of each unit, (3) the score of each pupil on the preliminary test of processes, (4) the score of each pupil on the final test, (5) the sequence of the processes in each unit of work, and (6) the number of times each process was repeated in each unit and in the whole term.

The Data

Were the fundamentals learned? It will be recalled that the primary purpose of the experiment was to discover whether denominate numbers and the fundamental processes in the multiplication and the division of fractions could be mastered in an arithmetic activity program based on situations in school and social life. With the exception of eleven pupils who had had some work in the multiplication of fractions, the preliminary test showed that the pupils possessed little ability to use the basic processes correctly. Table 1 gives data on the number of steps mastered, as measured by the final test. The final test showed that the average number

---

[1] The units have recently been made available in mimeographed form and may be secured from the senior author for fifteen cents a copy.

of steps learned by the class was 14.2 out of the 17 processes included in the tests. This showing is equivalent to a mastery of 84 per cent of the processes. Seven pupils mastered all the steps; eight pupils mastered sixteen steps; five pupils mastered fifteen steps. Seventy-three per cent of the pupils mastered at least 75 per cent of the steps included in the half-grade. Only one pupil mastered less than 50 per cent of all the steps. The group did especially well in denominate numbers, only one pupil failing to make a perfect score on this part of the test. This showing represents a mastery of 98 per cent for the whole class. The degree of the pupils' mastery of the processes in the division of fractions was greater than the degree of their mastery of the processes in the multiplication of fractions. In division of fractions they mastered 83 per cent of the processes, and in multiplication of fractions they mastered 79 per cent of the processes. The supplementary test of problems applying the processes confirmed the results of the basic test, the pupils making a composite score of 86 per cent of correct answers.

TABLE 1

Distribution of Pupils According to Number of Arithmetical Steps Mastered in Arithmetic Activity Class in Grade V A

Number of Steps Mastered	Percentage of Steps Mastered	Pupils Mastering Steps	
		Number	Per Cent
17 (all)	100	7	18.9
16	94	8	21.7
15	88	5	13.5
14	82	4	10.8
13	76	3	8.1
12	71	5	13.5
11	65	3	8.1
9	53	1	2.7
6	35	1	2.7
Total	84	37	100.0

Did the average intelligence of the group affect the results? It may be charged that the good showing of the experimental class resulted from the superiority of the group, the average intelligence quotient on the National Intelligence Tests being 113. To determine the accuracy of this charge, we divided the class into two halves. On the National Intelligence Tests the upper half had an average intelligence quotient of 121.4, and the lower half had an average intelligence quotient of 104.4. Table 2 shows that the upper half of the class mastered an average of 14.9 processes, or 87.6 per cent of the total. The lower half of the class mastered an average of 13.5

processes, or 79.4 per cent of the total. It is clear, therefore, that the average intelligence of the group was only a minor factor in accounting for the outcome of the experiment.

TABLE 2

DISTRIBUTION OF PUPILS IN UPPER HALF AND LOWER
HALF OF ARITHMETIC ACTIVITY CLASS ACCORDING TO
NUMBER OF ARITHMETICAL STEPS MASTERED *

NUMBER OF STEPS MASTERED	NUMBER OF PUPILS MASTERING STEPS	
	Upper Half	Lower Half
17 (all)	4	3
16	6	2
15	2	3
14	1	3
13	2	1
12	2	3
11	1	2
9	0	1
6	0	1
Average number of steps mastered	14.9	13.5

* On the National Intelligence Tests the average intelligence quotient of the upper half of the class was 121.4; that of the lower half, 104.4.

How much did the pupils add to their initial mastery? The conclusions thus far have been based entirely on the result of the final test because we were primarily interested in answering the question: Are the so-called "fundamentals" learned? This procedure is precisely the same as the procedure one would follow to determine the mastery of the basic arithmetic steps in the conventional class. However, we went one step farther in our inquiry and found the percentage of mastery of the steps which the class did not know at the beginning of the half-grade, as revealed by the preliminary test. In other words, we wished here to eliminate all steps which according to the preliminary test the pupils already knew. After the steps which the pupils already knew had been eliminated, the data showed that the experimental class learned 79.5 per cent of the basic steps in the half-grade.

Were the steps learned in sequence? It is obvious to anyone who has read thus far that the arithmetical steps were not learned in the order of progressive difficulty, as they are learned in the conventional arithmetic course. For years it has been taken for granted that most economical learning occurs when a system of habits is built up in carefully determined

TABLE 3

ORDER IN WHICH STEPS OCCURRED IN SEVEN ARITHMETIC ACTIVITY UNITS
IN A FIFTH-GRADE CLASS

STEPS INCLUDED	ORDER OF OCCURRENCE OF STEPS						
	Unit I	Unit II	Unit III	Unit IV	Unit V	Unit VI	Unit VII
1. Finding fractional part of an integer using unit fractions only; product an integer	12	....	13	....	3	....	4
2. Multiplying integer by a common fraction and vice versa. If cancellation possible, one term is common factor	5	2	9	1	1	3	5
3. Multiplying fraction by fraction. If cancellation possible, neither term is common factor	6	4	....	....	....	....	....
4. Multiplying mixed number by integer or common fraction	2	1	1	9	6	2	3
5. Multiplying mixed number by mixed number	1	3	4	8	....	7	7
6. Multiplying integer by mixed number using vertical form	10	....	6	....	....	....	6
7. Multiplying mixed number by integer using vertical form	9	....	8	....	....	....	.
8. Multiplying three common fractions or mixed numbers	....	....	....	....	....	....	....
9. Dividing an integer by a common fraction	....	....	....	....	....	....	....
10. Dividing a common fraction by a common fraction	....	....	....	....	....	....	....
11. Dividing a common fraction by an integer	....	....	....	....	....	....	....
12. Dividing a mixed number by an integer or a common fraction	8	....	3	2	....	4	....
13. Dividing an integer or a common fraction by mixed number	7	....	5	10	....	6	....
14. Dividing mixed number by mixed number	4	....	2	....	....	5	....
15. Changing ounces to pounds	3	....	11	....	....	....	....
16. Changing pounds to ounces	....	....	....	....	....	....	....
17. Adding ounces and pounds	....	....	....	....	....	....	....
18. Subtracting ounces and pounds	....	....	....	*	....	....	....
19. Changing inches to feet	....	....	12	....	....	1	....
20. Changing feet to inches	....	....	....	....	....	....	....
21. Changing yards to feet	....	....	....	....	....	....	....
22. Multiplying United States money	11	....	....	4	5	9	1
23. Adding United States money	....	....	7	7	4	10	2
24. Subtracting United States money	....	....	10	....	2	....	8
25. Dividing integer by larger integer	....	....	....	3	....	8	....
26. Changing pints to quarts	....	....	....	6	....	....	....

* In Unit IV Step 18 might have occurred nine times, but pupils preferred to change the ounces to a fractional part of a pound. Both methods were explained to the pupils.

sequence from the simple to the complex. Table 3 shows that in none of our units was there the slightest approximation to an orderly arrangement of arithmetical steps. For example, in the first unit, the candy sale, the order of appearance of the processes was 5, 4, 15, 14, 2, 3, 13, 12, 7, 6, 22, and 1.

TABLE 4

RELATION BETWEEN NUMBER OF REPETITIONS AND MASTERY OF STEPS

STEP NUMBER	REPETITIONS		MASTERY		DIFFERENCE IN RANK *
	Number of Repetitions	Rank of Step	Percentage of Mastery	Rank of Step	
4	112	1	87	8	7.0
2	50	2	94	5	3.0
5	31	3	71	13	10.0
12	24	4	84	9	5.0
13	14	5.5	76	10	4.5
15	14	5.5	60	15	9.5
25	11	7.5	94	5	2.5
1	11	7.5	97	1.5	6.0
14	10	9	73	11.5	2.5
6	9	11	55	16	5.0
7	9	11	68	14	3.0
18	9	11	94	5	6.0
3	8	13	94	5	8.0
8	0	15.5	42	17	1.5
9	0	15.5	97	1.5	14.0
10	0	15.5	94	5	10.5
11	0	15.5	73	11.5	4.0

* The average difference in rank is 6.0.

Was there any relation between the repetition of a step and the degree of mastery of the step? We were interested to find out whether the number of incidental repetitions of a process resulted in any learning advantage. We found that there was absolutely no relation between the number of repetitions of a step and the degree of mastery of the step. We arranged the steps (1) in the order of the number of repetitions and (2) in the order of degree of mastery, as is shown in Table 4. We found that there was an average difference of six places between the order on the basis of repetition of steps and the order on the basis of degree of mastery of steps. This difference does not, however, show the complete absence of connection between the two. To take a specific instance, Step 4, the multiplication of a mixed number by an integer or a common fraction, occurred 112 times in the course of the seven units and resulted in a degree of mastery of 87 per cent. On the other hand, Step 9, dividing an integer by a common fraction, did not occur at all, and yet it resulted in a degree of mastery of 97 per cent. It is most interesting to observe that the first three of the six steps in the division of fractions (Steps 9, 10, and 11) did not occur at all in the seven functional arithmetic units of work, yet the percentages of mastery of these three steps were 97, 94, and 73, respectively. This finding in itself is worth further study because it suggests, what others have pointed out, that learning depends on factors other than mere repetition. Furthermore, it throws doubt on the value of the meticulous attention given to the amount and the distribution of practice by many authors of textbooks in arithmetic.

Summary

1. In an arithmetic activity program based on real situations in school and social life, the pupils mastered 14.2 of the 17 fundamental processes included in the test on denominate numbers and on the multiplication and the division of fractions. This average is equivalent to a mastery of 84 per cent of the processes. If it is desired, the degree of mastery might be increased by the administration of two diagnostic tests at the middle and the end of the term followed by individual practice exercises.

2. The average intelligence quotient (113 on the National Intelligence Tests) for the experimental group was a very minor factor in accounting for the outcome of the experiment.

3. If what the pupils already knew at the beginning is eliminated, it is found that the pupils learned 79.5 per cent of the basic steps in the half-grade.

4. The fact that the arithmetical steps appeared in random order did not hinder the learning process.

5. The number of times which a step was repeated had nothing to do with the degree to which it was mastered.

6. Finally, at least under the condition of good teaching, an arithmetic activity program based on real situations in school and social life incorporating the basic arithmetical steps of a grade may be undertaken with considerable assurance that these steps will be mastered.

PART II: CRITICISMS OF THE TOTAL INTEGRATION APPROACH TO TEACHING MATHEMATICS

THESIS 5. WE MUST ABANDON THE IDEA THAT ARITHMETIC CAN BE TAUGHT INCIDENTALLY OR INFORMALLY

William David Reeve, Editor

It has been a popular notion in the last fifteen or twenty years that arithmetic can be satisfactorily taught in terms of pupils' "interests and needs" which result spontaneously from casual happenings or which are intentionally stimulated through planned units of work. The limitations of this instructional program have been pointed out many times.

1. It is unlikely that children left to themselves will have enough number experiences or an adequate variety of experiences to develop a feeling of need for any but the simplest of arithmetical ideas and skills (e.g., counting).

2. Few teachers are sufficiently sensitive to the quantitative aspects of events to recognize them and to call attention to their presence in ordinary situations or to arrange for their presence in activity units.

3. When an effort is made to infuse arithmetic into activity units, not all children profit equally. Usually the more capable children "run away" with the project, and the less capable gain little if anything.

4. Number ideas and skills are not *learned* as such when they occur only as parts of larger experiences. True, these larger experiences may arouse a feeling of need for a new idea or skill, and so motivate learning; true, also, they may provide excellent opportunities to apply ideas and skills that have been already acquired. But they cannot produce or guarantee the learning. One learns little about the chemical nature of sea water by being immersed in it, or about the mechanical principles of a machine by operating it.

5. Mathematics, including arithmetic, has an inherent organization. This organization must be respected in learning. Teaching, to be effective, must be orderly and systematic; hence, arithmetic cannot be taught informally and incidentally.

[From "The Second Report of the Commission on Post-War Plans," *The Mathematics Teacher,* XXXVIII (March, 1945), pp. 195-221. Reprinted by permission of the author and *The Mathematics Teacher.*]

SYSTEMATIC AND FUNCTIONAL
APPROACHES TO ARITHMETIC

Paul R. Hanna

The Important Rôle of Arithmetic

The Committee believes that some facility in arithmetic is indispensable to the life of any normal child. Each week brings scores of situations in which a child must make use of number to carry on his work and play: he must be able to count his marbles or the number of children invited to his party; to measure the ingredients for a batch of candy, or the length, width, and thickness of the board for a model ship; to handle money in his purchases at the store, or to add up the cost of his lunch or total the cost of an order for stamps; to divide equally, or otherwise, the contents of a bag of fruit among his friends, or apportion the cost of an entertainment among the members of the group; to keep the moving hands of the clock in mind in order to terminate the music practice or to know when it is time to hasten home to eat; to differentiate between more and less, larger and smaller, heavier and lighter; etc. For these and countless other everyday activities in school and out, children use number to solve their difficulties and promote their interests. Arithmetic is, as we have said, indispensable. There is no difference of opinion on this point between those who would have children learn through an activity program and those specialists who hold that arithmetic should be taught systematically through a separate subject approach. And because arithmetic does serve so important a rôle, all educators desire that the child acquire his use of number by the most efficient learning techniques and be able to use these acquisitions at later times to enrich his experiences of a quantitative and qualitative nature.

Purposes of This Paper

The purposes of this paper are to present:

1. A point of view held by a minority group in elementary school work concerning the learning of arithmetic.

[From "Opportunities for the Use of Arithmetic in an Activity Program," *The Teaching of Arithmetic*, National Council of Teachers of Mathematics, Tenth Yearbook (1935). Washington, D.C.: The Council, 85-120. Reprinted by permission of the author and the National Council of Teachers of Mathematics.]

2. A survey of opportunities for use of arithmetic in the "activities" curriculum.

3. Recommendations for the improvement of present practice.

There has been considerable innovation in curricular practice in elementary schools of America during the past decade. Innumerable public and private schools have attempted to break down the concept of formal education by bringing within the range of schooling the experiences and activities of normal child life. The typical child possesses a variety of interests and curiosities, a readiness which motivates him to participate actively in enterprises with almost tireless energy. Normal children find no particular "learning difficulty" in improving their roller-skating, or in mastering the rules and plays of a game of checkers, or in reading and following directions for assembling the parts of a model airplane. When the child has the purpose to achieve, those learnings which might otherwise involve difficult obstacles are with amazing agility mastered as necessary skills for achievement. And in those experiences where readiness attends the act, the learnings are freer to become a part of the next learning situation, to function when and where needed.

These curricular innovations and experimentations have led to many new departures in classroom practice. Education is now recognized as consisting of every activity in which children engage in and out of school. In many schools the daily program is not divided into separate periods for arithmetic, geography, spelling, composition, etc. In the classrooms of these schools education starts with an interest which absorbs the pupils and expands and deepens that interest into a series of related and worthwhile experiences. For example, a group of children may be enthusiastic about aviation. They may read some of the ancient stories and myths about flying—"Daedalus and Icarus," "The Magic Carpet," or "Pegasus." They may follow Commander Byrd to the South Pole and eagerly watch through newspaper and radio his airplane adventures into the unknown Antarctic. Undoubtedly, the group will write for aviation bulletins and seek information from various sources. Some of the group may plunge into the theory of air dynamics or experiment with the principles of the rocket plane. Thus the children develop joyfully a series of meaningful and related aviation experiences which will differentiate eventually into a great array of useful skills, facts, understandings, and attitudes. Yet, the children may not be aware at any time that they are really pursuing what is in the formal curriculum classified as "courses" in literature, geography, composition and spelling, science, arithmetic, etc.

It is obvious, however, that such a series of aviation experiences would demand arithmetic at many points. For example, Byrd's trip has to be financed; his cargo has weight and takes space, his ship is small, yet he must provide food, shelter, clothing, and equipment for a definite number of men and animals for an extended period of time. The determination of these supplies is largely arithmetical. Any study of air dynamics or rocket planes will necessitate computation of a high order. Determining lift per unit wing surface, horsepower of the engine, fuel capacity and consumption, pay load, cruising range and speed, and a multitude of other problems can be solved only by the use of number.

A First Viewpoint: Functional Experiences Adequate. In schools where such related experiences constitute the curriculum, there is a difference of opinion in regard to the teaching of arithmetic. At one extreme are the teachers who believe that arithmetic should be taught only as it is needed to carry out the children's purposes in any given situation. These teachers contend that any live, forward-moving activity offers ample opportunities for learning the meaning and use of arithmetic. They would not make use of formal textbooks nor would they set aside a period in the daily schedule for drill in arithmetic. Should a problem of average speed arise in an aviation activity, the teacher and children would compute the answer and pause long enough to grasp the meaning of the arithmetic process involved in the solution. They declare they would not detract from the larger outcomes in the experience, however, by constructing a number of hypothetical problems in average speed and then practice the process in order to fix the particular arithmetic learnings used in the solution. This practice, they hold, would interfere with the larger drive—the aviation interest. This group of educators leaves the mastery of any number skill or process mainly to the dynamic quality of functional situations and argues that if educational experiences are sufficiently rich and varied, those skills and processes that are truly important are mastered by the demands of constantly recurring life situations.

A Second Viewpoint: Systematic Arithmetic Mastery the Goal. A second point of view concerning arithmetic and the activity curriculum starts from a different set of assumptions. In many classrooms, a definite body of arithmetic knowledge and skills is selected in advance to be learned. The teacher then seeks to find or to stimulate the children's interests which will demand the arithmetic content which has been selected for the year and to develop these interests into activities largely for the purpose of giving meaning and readiness to the arithmetic lesson. In these classrooms, the pupils find the stage continually set to arouse their feeling of need for a particular arithmetic skill or process, then drill and exercise follow to fix permanently these learnings. This point of view holds certain selected arithmetic content to be so valuable socially that activities must be found or stimulated in order to motivate the work. The arithmetic content is the immediate end-point and the activity becomes the method of teaching it.

Formal systematic daily arithmetic which follows a course of study or textbook governs the selection and initiation of activities.

A Third Viewpoint: Recognizing Two Goals. There is still another—a third—point of view concerning this issue and the majority of the members of the committee responsible for this report subscribe to it. To some extent it is a synthesis of the two positions previously discussed. In the first place, in the classroom of those adhering to this third position, the aim is to develop in children those interests and urges which seem most worthwhile when all things are considered, i.e., no large activity is selected solely because it offers unusual opportunities for arithmetic. In the full development of most activities, as is illustrated in the case of the study of aviation, arithmetic will be necessary many times. Here arithmetic serves as a tool or as a means to the solution of the larger purpose, rather than as an end in itself. Arithmetic is a part of the process by which the child refines—resolves his problem. There is no forcing of artificial experiences in order to make opportunities for arithmetic, but whenever the situation functionally calls for arithmetic solution, it naturally comes into the activity. Furthermore, whenever the arithmetic process or skill is a new one to the children or has not been adequately fixed in their neural patterns, time is set aside in arithmetic periods for practicing these aspects of the subject. (The intelligent teacher, of course, passes over a process which she believes too difficult for the pupils to master or which is not apt to come up again until several grades later in the school career. She will need to check such judgments against standards held in her school system.) The skill or process is first called into meaning by the demands of the problem and then effort is devoted to the fixation of the process or skill through utilizing the best methods of learning known to the teachers.

This point of view further recognizes that there are undoubtedly certain aspects of arithmetic which can best be learned by a systematic practice when the learner has once grasped the meaning of a process. Also, many arithmetic manipulations depend upon a mastery of more elemental processes—multiplication can be done when one can add figures, etc. Much of the mathematics work in the high school is predicated on the mastery of certain skills in the lower grades. A mobile population adds to the desirability of some common consent among schools concerning the placement of the major learnings. All these considerations presume a need for some minimum understanding and facility of quantitative thinking and some minimum skill in fundamental processes.

This position differs from the first position presented in this paper in denying that functional experiences of childhood are alone adequate to develop arithmetic skill. On the other hand, this committee does not agree with the usual program of systematic mastery goal. The committee feels that their experience in teaching children has shown them that the traditional course of study is faulty in its selection of skills to be learned and in their grade placement. This committee holds that the teaching of arithmetic must take account of the following:

1. The demonstrated greater effectiveness of learning which results from the pursuit of a meaningful and purposeful activity.

2. The maturation of the insight and the interests of children at various ages.

3. The "logical" development of many aspects of arithmetic.

A Survey Undertaken

In order to find out more definitely whether the viewpoint held by the members of this minority group is sound, a survey was next undertaken in order to discover the extent to which opportunities for arithmetic in the activities program were possible. Six teachers of Grade 3 and six teachers of Grade 6 were invited to co-operate. These teachers were chosen from public and private schools in New York City, from suburban communities adjacent to New York City, and from rural communities of New Jersey. The necessity for group meetings to discuss survey techniques made it unwise to extend the survey widely throughout the Unitd States in this initial undertaking. The two levels, Grades 3 and 6, were selected in order to sample the elementary school. These schools for the most part teach some formal arithmetic, but on the whole these schools are organizing and integrating the children's experiences around worthwhile interests rather than following a strictly separate subject approach with a systematic course of study.

Each teacher was asked to record on prepared blanks every situation faced by individuals or by her entire class, in which there was a need for quantitative thinking and manipulation. These arithmetic situations were not to be those suggested by arithmetic courses of study, textbooks, or workbooks, but those problems which arose in the pursuit of some child-selected activity. An effort was made to explore the out-of-school arithmetic experiences whenever possible. For the most part, however, the recorded problems grew out of class activities rather than individual problems of a nonschool nature.

. . . .

Some General Comments

A few general comments seem to be in order at this point in the summary.

1. It was planned originally to check the findings of this survey with courses of study to discover inarticulations. However, the newer courses vary so greatly in the grade placement of number facts and processes that it seemed impractical to set up a standard against which to measure the findings of this survey. Consequently, each city or state may make its own comparison to see how well it squares with the findings of this study.

2. The present study is decidedly not a comprehensive survey. It takes into account only Grades 3 and 6. It does not run throughout the twelve months of the year. It lacks a record of many out-of-school number situations. It is not a fair geographic sampling of the pupils of the United States. For these and other reasons, this study should be considered only as a preliminary investigation.

3. The authors of this study feel that a national survey of situations in which children find a need for arithmetic is highly desirable. It is their belief that considerable inarticulation would be found between even the most modern arithmetic courses and the actual needs of pupils. Undoubtedly, there are many aspects of arithmetic now taught much too early—before the meaning and need have been experienced by the pupils. Also, many aspects considered essentially as parts of a carefully planned, sequential, and systematic program would be learned inductively, out of their logical order. Nevertheless they are learned and perhaps, in the long run, better learned as far as functioning when needed in subsequent behavior is concerned. A survey would focus attention on such inarticulations and unique learning characteristics of children. Such a study might contribute much to facilitate developing control over arithmetic facts and processes where meaning has been made clear through personal experience.

4. While the committee presenting this report believes the survey demonstrates a richness and vitality of arithmetic experiences in the activity program which may serve to give the pupils significant meaning and purpose, yet they point out again (see paragraphs under *A Third Viewpoint: Recognizing Two Goals*) that "functional experiences of childhood are alone not adequate to develop arithmetic skills." The teacher should recognize these meaningful arithmetic experiences as readings preceding the practice or drill necessary to fix the fact or process for the learner and the teacher must provide sufficient periods of practice to assure mastery.

5. Further, the authors recognize that the present activity program does not assure a comprehensive orientation in arithmetic.* It is evident

---

* EDITOR'S NOTE: The 234 third grade problems represented the total number of problems that arose in the six third grades during a period of four months. This is an average of about 60 problems per month for the entire six grades, or an average of 10 problems per room per month. These 234 problems included both computational

from the survey that each classroom found a very small number of experiences per week. In addition, there is a large element of chance operating in the selection of units of work in the present activity school. In the typical activity program, there is no check to assure that the total experiences of the six years of elementary school will introduce a child to most of the significant phases of comprehensive living in our contemporary world. If the activity program had in it some principle guaranteeing the development of a comprehensive understanding of most of the important social areas, then this committee would be willing to leave to the demands of such activities, the development of the necessary arithmetic fact and process, utilizing, of course, these meaningful situations as the occasions for drill sufficient to give the required degree of facility. They do not feel, however, that a survey of the opportunities found in the *present* activities program is a sufficient guide to the selection of arithmetic materials. Some guide or criterion in addition to opportunities-found-in-activities is essential, especially in an age where accurate quantitative thinking and computation is yearly becoming more basic to planning our collective enterprises. The most obvious source of this second criterion is the arithmetic needs of this collective society. When course-of-study makers can determine more clearly what constitutes full and comprehensive living in our society, then the teacher will have the important guide by which she may progressively select units of experience which will demand the quantitative thinking and skills commensurate with modern living. The school has an obligation to society to see that all citizens develop sufficient arithmetic competency to carry intelligently their mutual responsibilities. Only as the units of work or activities in which the children engage are selected in terms of a total social experience today is there any assurance that the school can meet its obligations to society and the individual. In other words, the authors of this report contend that units of experience should be as comprehensive and as all-inclusive of social problems as is possible. Then and only then will a survey of arithmetic opportunities in such units give the major cues to selection and organization of classroom materials.

6. Until such time as the activities program is fundamentally recon-

---

and noncomputational varieties. On page 101 it is stated that 56 per cent of these problems were computational, which means that, on the average, only 5 computational problems per room per month were encountered.

Similarly, the 205 sixth grade problems represented the total number that were found in all sixth grades in four months. This makes an average of 8½ problems per room per month, of which 72 per cent were computational and the rest noncomputational. This gives about 6 computational problems per month for each sixth grade room. It is this very small amount of number work encountered in each grade that leads the authors to the conclusion, stated above, that it is not possible to teach arithmetic solely through an activity program.

structed and a survey of these arithmetic opportunities made, a teacher will find it advantageous to approach the teaching of arithmetic through her own survey of the needs of her own pupils. If no opportunities are found for certain of the present courses-of-study requirements, she will probably do the best she can to build meaning before drill. But constantly, she will urge a revision of the curriculum in terms of a more socially comprehensive experience which will surely present the necessity to gain control over important arithmetic skills and processes.

PART III: THE CONCEPT OF THE INTEGRATION OF MATHEMATICS WITH OTHER SCHOOL SUBJECTS

ARITHMETIC IN THE TOTAL SCHOOL PROGRAM

James Curtin

Effective arithmetic instruction is not confined solely to arithmetic periods. The demands placed upon the arithmetical knowledge of the children are inherent in all subjects in the elementary school curriculum. In some areas of study these demands are enormous while in others they are less significant. However, if we can generalize at all, we can say that knowledge of arithmetic or a knowledge of quantity is necessary in every subject that is taught in the elementary school. Indeed, we might go further to say that the understandings derived from studying the sciences, social studies, even spelling, music and art are dependent in some measure upon the quantity involved.

Brownell cites three large areas that might comprise desirable arithmetic outcomes.[1] They are: (1) computational skill; (2) mathematical understanding; (3) sensitiveness to number in social situations and a habit of using number effectively in such situations. Should these outcomes be assiduously sought in arithmetic programs, it would be no exaggeration

[From "Arithmetic in the Total School Program," *The Arithmetic Teacher*, IV (December, 1957), pp. 235-39. Reprinted by permission of the author and *The Arithmetic Teacher*.]

―――――――――

[1] W. A. Brownell, "When Is Arithmetic Meaningful?" *Journal of Educational Research*, March, 1945, 481-98.

to state that arithmetic instruction would have come of age. A program characterized by such objectives would be a balanced one, and the balance would be struck by the application of arithmetic understandings in the other areas of the curriculum.

Curriculum workers commonly define the curriculum as those experiences offered under the supervision of the school. It would then be fair to assume that the arithmetic curriculum would be those quantitative or number situations that are encountered anywhere in the school day. Thus, there would be a time and a place for systematic teaching of arithmetic and the appropriate knowledge applied when demanded to further understanding in other curricular fields. Perhaps this observation might be in order . . .

> An arithmetic course which does not have as a very definite objective the development of ability to compute with accuracy and facility is wholly inadequate. However, the curriculum which tries to accomplish nothing but accuracy and facility in figuring is woefully one-sided. Moreover, a curriculum which sets out to do that and only that will not even serve its own purpose satisfactorily.[2]

The Place of Arithmetic in the Curriculum

The place of arithmetic in the curriculum is conditioned somewhat by the curriculum pattern in vogue in various school systems. If a school system is dedicated to an integrated program, the program in arithmetic instruction will differ from that of a school which is concerned with a more subject-centered curriculum. There is a good deal written about experience units, child centered curricula and so forth in the literature these days. However, in examining this literature it is a bit difficult to determine just what these terms mean and, consequently, it is a bit difficult to determine what the place of subjects in these kinds of curriculum might be. One of the complicating factors lies in the fact that many experience units are advertised as being integrated when, in fact, the arithmetic or any other subject in the curriculum is taught systematically and in an orderly fashion. In a subject centered curriculum we are less doubtful about the place of arithmetic in the curriculum for it has a special place and time is set aside for it. However, the point remains that the quality and kind of arithmetic instruction will be heavily conditioned by the particular type of curriculum organization in effect.

---

[2] Ernest Horn, "Arithmetic in the Elementary School Curriculum," *The Teaching of Arithmetic*, National Society for the Study of Education 50th Yearbook, Part II. (Chicago: University of Chicago Press, 1951).

No matter what kind of curriculum or organization is in vogue there are still some considerations that must be faced. For example as Horn points out, the kinds of arithmetic experiences that are to be offered in the content fields should be determined by the nature of learning undertaken in these fields. Units in science and in the social studies, if well taught, will not be able to avoid arithmetic concepts and abilities. This is true whether the curriculum is organized in terms of subjects or in terms of an integrated curriculum or experience units. It might be further pointed out that in these situations the arithmetical understandings are often crucial to the success of the learning in these fields. In dealing with this problem, Horn has suggested that such questions as these need to be raised:

1. What are the nature and amount of the demands which other areas make upon arithmetic?

2. How adequate are the pupils' abilities to meet these demands?

3. What are the probable or potential contributions of these areas to the development of arithmetical abilities?

4. Is there a need for specially planned instruction in arithmetic and, if so, what is the relation of that instruction to the arithmetical instruction incident to the attack on the mathematical aspects of other areas? [3]

Frequency of Arithmetical Terms in Texts and References in Other Fields in the Elementary School Curriculum

Practically all investigations concerned with this particular problem have indicated that the number of arithmetical terms in other elementary school subjects is quite extensive. However, this extensiveness is dependent somewhat upon how the arithmetic term is defined. If marginal terms such as *more* or *none* or *often* are included, then there are very many indeed. For example, one investigation which looked into geography books indicated that one out of every seven running words was concerned with some idea of quantity.[4] The most casual perusal of social studies materials will reveal the enormous number of quantitative statements that are encountered. The following is taken from a primary social studies text:

> Eight-year-old Sally sat in the doorway knitting. Knit, knit, knit! Was there ever an end to it?
>
> There were two brothers to knit stockings for. Sally's fingers were never still. She must work all summer to be ready for winter.
>
> In winter, feet were often cold and wet. There were no rubbers or overshoes in those days. There were no hard, dry sidewalks. In Jamestown there

---

[3] *Op. cit.*, page 12.
[4] *Ibid.*

were only dirt paths and they were often muddy. Warm knitted stockings
were a comfort to cold feet in wet shoes.

Knit, knit, knit! Sally's fingers flew.

'Sally!' called her mother. 'Watch the kettle that is hanging over the fire.
Don't let the dinner burn. And mind the baby. I'm taking the clothes to the
river to wash.'

In just this one item of reading there are eleven quantitative ideas,
most of them highly unspecific. This comprises approximately 8 per cent
of these running words, and it might be normally expected, as books get
a little more difficult in terms of readability, that this percentage would
increase. The following passage from an upper grade text will illustrate
this.

Not many years ago there were few symphony orchestras in the United
States. Today there are many, and quite a number of them may be heard
over the air in regular weekly programs. The radio has accustomed more
people than ever to the music of orchestras, and the United States has probably taken the first place as a nation of music lovers and music sponsors.
Music has come to be a part of American life, and a large part of our recreation and entertainment is connected with music.

The number of quantitative elements in this short selection is extremely
heavy. There are approximately eighty-eight words and sixteen of these
eighty-eight words, or 18 per cent, are quantitative in nature. Moreover,
this is complicated by the fact that these terms do not exist in isolation.
Notice the very first few words—"not many years ago"—a little further on
we come to—"quite a number." These are ideas that are not specific and
consequently difficult to appraise. It is, perhaps, unfortunate that many
textbooks deal with these unspecific terms rather than dealing in precise
statements of quantity. Then children could come to grips with them and
show either manipulatively or by our number system just what is meant
by statements such as these. There is evidence that indicates that children
have difficulty with this kind of quantitative statement. For example, some
years ago in a study conducted by Buswell and John [5] it was pointed out
that children's understanding of quantitative terms was weak. For example, the percentages of correct responses in grades four to six for the
following terms were these: Acre—38.9 per cent; area—28 per cent; average—43 per cent, difference—71 per cent; rectangle—33 per cent. More
pupils thought an acre to be larger than a square mile than believed it to

[5] G. T. Buswell and Lenore John. *The Vocabulary of Arithmetic,* Supplementary
Educational Monographs, No. 38 (Chicago: University of Chicago Press, 1931),
Chapters 3 and 4.

be smaller than a city block, and among the most flagrant misconceptions might be these: Acorns—an acre is acrons: 100,000 miles is an acre; acre is a man's name; houses—acres are houses, and one child, working on the principle of assonance, decided that an acre was to have a stomach ache. The terms tested in this particular study were taken from elementary school textbooks and, as a result of this study, the authors recommended that increased attention be given to the development of common arithmetical terms. Another study [6] (Horn's *Methods of Instruction in the Social Studies*) that looked into definite and indefinite terms came up with these examples: Ten square miles meant to the various pupils—about the size of Chicago; about the size of the state of Iowa; about the size of Washington Park; about as large as ten acres; about one lot; and one child said without any idea of square measure, "here to Key West in a straight line." Getting back to indefinite terms such as *a great deal; many; far; thick;* it might be shown that these are more difficult than are definite statements of quantity. A few years ago the writer became interested in this problem and devised a test for a group of sixth grade children of superior ability. These children had completed a social studies course on Canada and Latin America, and this short test attempted to measure their understandings of some of the indefinite terms that they had encountered. Quotes were taken from their textbooks and the children were asked to interpret them. The first item was this: " 'Many of the plants in Canada use hydro-electric power.' About how many does this mean to you?" The answers ranged from four to ten thousand. Another question was: " 'Large numbers of the people (of Quebec) are French-Canadians.' About how many do you think are French-Canadians?" The answers ranged from 180,000 to 7,000,000, despite the fact that these children had the understanding that there are about 14,000,000 people in Canada. Another question included: "Montreal is an old city founded long ago by the French." The children were directed somewhat in this question with the following multiple choices:

1. Montreal is about a hundred years old.
2. Montreal is about five hundred years old.
3. Montreal is about three hundred years old.
4. Montreal is about a thousand years old.

Each one of these choices was selected by some children. Four children indicated that Montreal was a thousand years old, which would have put its founding date at 954, somewhat antedating the discovery of America.

---

[6] Reported in Ernest Horn. *Methods of Instruction in the Social Studies* (New York: Chas. Scribner and Sons, 1937).

Perhaps these illustrations point up the fact that quantitative elements in other curricular areas in the elementary school, particularly the social studies, are extremely abundant. And we might further draw this generalization: that many of these concepts, particularly the indefinite ones, are not handled very efficiently by the children.

What Contribution Can Arithmetic Make to Understanding in the Content Areas?

First, it should be emphasized that effective instruction in arithmetic goes beyond the teaching of operations and vocabulary. Indeed, perhaps the thing that ought to be stressed is the ability to think quantitatively. One means of doing this is to establish with the children reference points which will enable them to deal with these ideas. For example, a large farm in Vermont is different from a large farm in Saskatchewan. In addition, a thick coat of ice in Greenland is different from a thick coat of ice in Illinois. In other respects, teachers might deal with something known to the children as being an acre. In fact, a good way of dealing with this, if your playground is large enough, is to have the children step off an acre. A child can be placed at each corner of the acre. All the children looking at this will undoubtedly get some idea of the size of an acre, and none of them could possibly conceive of an acre as being even remotely the size of the State of Iowa. It is particularly important that the unit to be used as a standard of reference be appropriate. As Spitzer [7] points out, it is of no use to the child to know the distance of one foot in determining the distance of a linear mile even though he may know that a mile contains 5,280 feet. Perhaps the most important thing that can be done in the content areas to deal with these terms is to make the children aware of them and hold them to the meaning that these quantitative ideas are intended to convey. A good deal of this work of sensitizing children to quantitative ideas can be done in the arithmetic time. This will then free the other curricular areas from the annoyances of interruptions, stopping instruction to point out ideas that can be better taught in the arithmetic period, and in general impeding the work in the content areas by dealing with them as such and by keying them in at the appropriate times. For example, something like this can be done:

> Boys and girls, yesterday when we were discussing the fact that Canada has a population of approximately 14,000,000 people, we had some difficulty in comparing this with something that was a little closer to us. Now, how

---

[7] Herbert F. Spitzer, *Teaching of Arithmetic* (Boston: Houghton-Mifflin Company, 1954).

many people live in the state of Minnesota? How many more people live in Canada than live in Minnesota?

In this fashion a comparison of the number of people can be made; and then to make this comparison more fruitful and to add some meaning to the social studies, it might be pointed out that the area of Canada is many times the area of Minnesota and yet, despite this immense space, there are relatively few people living there. In dealing with the density of population, this operation can be pointed out in arithmetic classes; it would serve as a good review for long division; it would help teach children this operation so that when they were confronted with these problems in the social studies, they could attack them with confidence and success. Thus, sound instruction in arithmetic, together with a knowledge of what is going on in the content fields, will combine to make more fruitful the teaching of arithmetic by means of supplying reasons for doing certain things in the arithmetic period and by giving children means of working out their problems in the content area. There should be no such thing as arithmetic versus the social studies or arithmetic versus science; the two are extremely complementary.

What Contributions Can the Content Fields Make to Arithmetic?

Perhaps the foregoing remarks have indicated that the content fields can make a contribution to arithmetic by the very nature of the fact that they have many quantitative elements. However, the method of dealing with these situations in the content areas will influence heavily the enhancement of arithmetic instruction in the general curriculum. Those people who favor incidental teaching have made many claims for this approach, many of which, unfortunately, are not documented. In many studies reporting the effect of incidental learning it was found that teachers did a considerable amount of systematic teaching of arithmetic which resembles very closely those practices which we call "the meaning approach." What this simply means is that without systematic attention to arithmetic, experience units alone cannot run the gamut of the developmental skills needed for arithmetic instruction. Some people have tried to assess the incidental learning of arithmetic by constructing special units. Some of these are loaded with mathematics. In the hands of a good teacher it would be expected that the children's arithmetic would be enhanced. Certainly, when units are highly motivated, are socially significant, and filled with arithmetic, arithmetic is bound to improve. This improvement will be enhanced even above this if there is sound arithmetic instruction going on in an arithmetic period. The point that ought to be raised at this time is simply this: Units in the social studies and units in science, indeed teaching in any other field, ought to be determined on the basis of what is to be learned from these fields. Thus, a social studies unit ought not to be chosen because of the contribution it can make to arithmetic. It should be chosen in terms of the contribution it can make to the social studies. The relationship with arithmetic need not be limited if the selection is made on this basis, for no matter what kinds of units are developed in the social studies and in science, the vast number of quantitative terms indicate that the arithmetic instruction will be hard put to keep abreast of the emerging arithmetic concepts in the content fields. There will be no slow down in arithmetic integration. The point is simply that teachers do not need to go out of their way to select units for their arithmetical value because all units, if properly taught, have this value.

BIBLIOGRAPHY

Amsden, Dorothy, and Edward Szado. "Fish and Arithmetic," *The Arithmetic Teacher,* V (April, 1958), 155.

Blouch, Adelaide. "The Contribution of Arithmetic to the Study of Geography," *School Science and Mathematics,* LII (December, 1952), 697-702.

Brown, Lawson J. "Arithmetic Comes to Life," *The National Elementary Principal,* XXXV (December, 1955), 36-37.

Brownell, William A. "Psychological Considerations in the Learning and Teaching of Arithmetic," *The Teaching of Arithmetic,* The National Council of Teachers of Mathematics, Tenth Yearbook (1935). Washington, D.C.: The Council, 1-31.

Brueckner, Leo J. "The Social Contributions of Arithmetic," *The National Elementary Principal,* XXX (October, 1950), 7-10.

Buswell, G. T., and Lenore John. *The Vocabulary of Arithmetic,* Supplementary Educational Monographs, No. 38. Chicago: University of Chicago Press, 1931.

Curtin, James. "Arithmetic in the Total School Program," *The Arithmetic Teacher,* IV (December, 1957), 235-39.

Dubins, M. Ira. "Integration of Arithmetic with Science Through the Study of Weather in the Elementary School," *School Science and Mathematics,* LVII (February, 1957), 121-30.

Flournoy, Frances. "Interpreting Definite Quantitative Statements Occurring in Reading Reference Materials," *The Elementary School Journal,* LVIII (January, 1958), 208-11.

———. "Relating Arithmetic to Everyday Life," *The National Elementary Principal,* XXXIX (October, 1959), 29-32.

Gabel, Otto J. "The Effect of Definite versus Indefinite Quantitative Terms upon the Comprehension and Retention of Social Studies Material," *Journal of Experimental Education,* IX (December, 1940), 177-86.

Glennon, Vincent J., *et al. Teaching Arithmetic in the Modern School.* Bureau of School Service, School of Education, Syracuse University, 1953.

Gunderson, Agnes G. "Nature and Amount of Arithmetic in Readers for Grades I and II," *Elementary School Journal,* XXXVI (March, 1936), 527-40.

Hanna, Paul R., *et al.* "Opportunities for the Use of Arithmetic in an Activity Program," *The Teaching of Arithmetic,* The National Council of Teachers of Mathematics, Tenth Yearbook (1935). Washington, D.C.: The Council, 85-120.

Harap, Henry, and Ursula Barrett. "Experimenting with Real Situations in Third Grade Arithmetic," *Educational Method,* XVI (January, 1937), 188-92.

———, and Charlotte E. Mapes. "The Learning of Fundamentals in an Arithmetic Activity Program," *The Elementary School Journal,* XXXIV (March, 1934), 515-25.

———, ———. "The Learning of Decimals in an Arithmetic Activity Program," *Journal of Educational Research,* XXIX (May, 1936), 686-93.

Harding, Lowry W., and Inez P. Bryant. "An Experimental Comparison of Drill and Direct Experience in Arithmetic Learning in a Fourth Grade," *Journal of Educational Research,* XXXVII (January, 1944), 321-37.

Hartung, Maurice L. "Mathematics in the Total School Program," *The Mathematics Teacher,* LI (May, 1958), 336-43.

Hizer, Irene S., and Henry Harap. "The Learning of Fundamentals in an Arithmetic Activity Course," *Educational Method,* XI (June, 1932), 536-39.

Hooper, Laura, and Barbara Stratton. "Developing Number Concepts with Young Children," *Educational Method,* XVI (January, 1937), 193-98.

Horn, Ernest. "Arithmetic in the Elementary School Curriculum," *The Teaching of Arithmetic,* National Society for the Study of Education, Fiftieth Yearbook (1951). Chicago: The University of Chicago Press, Part II, 6-21.

Jarolimek, John. "Teaching Quantitative Relationships in the Social Studies," *The Arithmetic Teacher,* IV (March, 1957), 70-74.

Keso, Edward E. "The Relationship of Mathematics and Geography," *School Science and Mathematics,* XLIV (October, 1944), 598-600.

Mariani, Richard. "Mathematics in a Living Laboratory," *Grade Teacher,* LXXVI (May, 1959), 94-95.

National Society for the Study of Education. *The Integration of Educational Experiences,* National Society for the Study of Education, Fifty-seventh Yearbook (1958). Chicago: The University of Chicago Press, Part III.

Payne, William H. "Integrated Learning as a Result of Exercises in Mathematics and Science," *School Science and Mathematics,* LVII (January, 1957), 37-40.

Ragland, Elizabeth. "Art and Arithmetic," *The Arithmetic Teacher,* VI (March, 1959), 112.

Rahn, F. W. "Learning Elementary Arithmetic by Means of the General Store," *Exceptional Child,* XXVI (March, 1960), 364-65.

Reeve, William David, ed. "The Second Report of the Commission on Post-War Plans," *The Mathematics Teacher,* XXXVIII (March, 1945), 195-221.

Reid, Florence E. "Incidental Number Situations in First Grade," *Journal of Educational Research*, XXX (September, 1936), 36-43.

Riedesel, Alan. "The Theme in Arithmetic," *The Arithmetic Teacher*, VI (April, 1959), 154-55.

Rosenquist, Lucy Lynde. "Learning through Experiences," *Young Children Learn to Use Arithmetic*. Boston: Ginn & Company, 1949, 42-62.

Seay, Maurice F., and Leonard E. Meece. *The Sloan Experiment in Kentucky*. Lexington: Bureau of School Service, XVI, Bulletin No. 4, 1944.

Sherer, Lorraine. "Some Implications from Research in Arithmetic," *Childhood Education*, XXIX (March, 1953), 320-24.

Spitzer, Herbert F. "Elementary School Projects Which Require the Use of Numbers," *The National Elementary Principal*, XXX (October, 1950), 20-23.

Stern, Catherine. *Children Discover Arithmetic*. New York: Harper & Brothers, 1949.

Thiele, C. L. "An Incidental or an Organized Program of Number Teaching?" *The Mathematics Teacher*, XXXI (February, 1938), 63-67.

Tompkins, Jean B., and C. Newton Stokes. "Eight-Year-Olds Use Arithmetic," *Childhood Education*, XVI (March, 1940), 319-21.

University of the State of New York. *Mathematics for Boys and Girls*. Bulletin, Bureau of Curriculum Development, Division of Elementary Education, 1950.

Van Engen, H. "Twentieth Century Mathematics for the Elementary School," *The Arithmetic Teacher*, VI (March, 1959), 71-76.

Whittenburg, Clarice. *Making Arithmetic Meaningful for the Young Child*. Laramie: Bureau of Educational Research and Service, College of Education, University of Wyoming, 1949.

Williams, Catharine M. "Arithmetic Learning in an Experience Curriculum," *Educational Research Bulletin*, XXVIII (September, 1949), 154-62.

Woody, Clifford. *Nature and Amount of Arithmetic in Types of Reading Material for the Elementary Schools*. Ann Arbor: Bureau of Educational Reference and Research, Bulletin No. 145, University of Michigan, 1932.

VI PRODUCTIVE APPROACHES TO PROBLEM SOLVING

Lowry W. Harding, Ohio State University

INTRODUCTION

BIBLIOGRAPHY

INTRODUCTION

Some agreement on the meaning and nature of *problems* seems necessary to any serious consideration of issues and procedures in teaching children to be problem solvers. The attempt to define *problems* presents a major difficulty, if it is assumed that such an idea can include all mathematical situations. Although on a much smaller scale, this difficulty is similar to that of formulating a definition of man. It may be more effective to construct specific definitions than a comprehensive one. This will be done by the reader, of course, in terms of his own background and circumstances.

As ideas with which to begin, three levels of consideration are here suggested: that problems may be one, unperformed tasks, two, challenges to one's adaptive powers, or three, motives of the thinker. A competent problem solver may be considered as one who performs assigned tasks, one who responds adequately to situations previously unencountered, or one who achieves his motives. A problem may be considered solved when the task assigner is satisfied with the performance of the task, when the individual is himself emotionally and intellectually satisfied with the results of his efforts to adjust, or when the thinker's motives have been carried out.

The essence of problem solving is search and discovery. And discovery is creative—it requires originality. Thus, the teacher faces both temptation and opportunity. If he succumbs to the temptation merely to drill his pupils on routine operations he deadens their interest, inhibits their creativity, and hinders their intellectual development. But, if he stimulates the interest of pupils by considering what are problems to them and challenges curiosity and effort by suggesting other questions appropriate to their ability and knowledge, he may give them a desire for, and some competence in, independent thinking.

Some insist that mathematics, especially the arithmetic branch, is only a tool for manipulating symbols representing quantities. Others insist that mathematics, including arithmetic, is a way of thinking about problems. Deploring emphasis on manipulation, they point out that even brilliant children can be taught to behave stupidly. Too many children tend to be conditioned with the idea that they can and should take memorized arithmetic rules directly to quantitative situations and expect a perfect correspondence.

Typical of the questions raised about the issue, "How can children's problem-solving abilities be developed?" are these:

1. What is a problem? What is problem solving in any situation? Can most problem solving be broken down into discrete steps? To what extent are these principles applicable to the solution of all problems?

2. Can immature minds grasp the nature of problem solving? If so, at what stages of development and at what levels of complexity?

3. How can one be sure the pupil has a problem to solve when teachers present him with problems or tasks? Must problems be centered in the life of the pupil to insure competence in problem solving methods?

4. Is problem solving a specific ability or a constellation of abilities and skills? Is such ability achieved at a specific

time or is it a culmination of knowledge gathering and skill development?

5. Should the general principles of problem solving be taught concurrently with the operational skills of mathematics?

6. Are the so-called special methods of problem solving, as formal analysis, dependencies, etc., really helpful? When pupils are trained to follow specific steps in attacking material classified by type, can such performance be called "problem solving"?

7. What are the relationships between problem solving and other mental and physical activities of the individual? Between problem solving in arithmetic and in other school subjects, such as geography, history, or science?

8. What are the levels of difficulty in various types of problems, in structure, vocabulary, objects, or materials involved, etc., or can such variations be ascertained with any certainty?

9. What are the particular emphases which are needed in the problem solving activities in arithmetic? How may these be arranged by teachers?

10. Is problem solving best taught as an application of mathematical principles already learned? As a new or different skill? Directly? Indirectly? Independently of other topics, or in association with other activities?

In studying the trends of professional thought on these and related questions during the past half-century, more than 400 references were perused by the editor. One hundred and two were chosen for inclusion in the bibliography. Specific content for this chapter was selected from the following authors for the reasons explained below:

1. Kenneth B. Henderson and Robert E. Pingry for identification of the shifting nature of problems and description of the major parts of the process of solving them.

2. George Polya for a definition of the responsibility of the teacher in the pupil's process of learning to think through to solutions.

3. Max Wertheimer for illustrating the steps in helping pupils develop insight.

4. Abraham Luchins for findings and conclusions from a significant study of the effects of routinized instruction or "mechanization" in problem solving.

5. Henry Van Engen for suggesting a way in which inter-pretations of the subject matter and of the learning process affect method.

6. Catharine Williams for a description of actual proce-dures in guiding pupils' problem-solving activities.

7. Herbert F. Spitzer and Frances Flournoy for analyti-cal comparisons of typical schoolroom interpretations of the teacher's role in problem solving.

8. Leo J. Brueckner and Guy L. Bond for identification of the major sources of difficulty in teaching problem-solving and ways to improve the program.

PROBLEM SOLVING IN MATHEMATICS

Kenneth B. Henderson and Robert E. Pingry

What may be a problem for one individual may not be a problem for another. A problem for a particular individual today may not be a prob-lem for him tomorrow.

How a person solves a problem. It has been mentioned that a necessary condition for a problem to exist *for a particular individual* is the existence of a question. To identify other necessary conditions, it is desirable to analyze the psychological process of problem-solving; that is, how a per-son goes about solving a problem.

The first identifiable part of the process of solving a problem is the on-going, sustaining activity of the individual. If we were to probe into the causes of this behavior, we would always find a more or less ration-alized goal or an unresolved psychosomatic tension present. It is this goal or tension that causes and directs the individual's behavior. A student, for example, decides to do his mathematics assignment. He finds a place to work, takes a sheet of paper, and begins to work the assigned exercises. This student has a goal in mind. He wants to complete his assigned work.

The behavior of an individual may also be caused by a less clearly de-fined goal. To use the student again as an example, he completes the assignment and has some time on his hands. He listens to the radio a while, finds he has read all his comic books, looks out of the window, calls

[From "Problem Solving in Mathematics," *The Learning of Mathematics,* National Council of Teachers of Mathematics, Twenty-first Yearbook (1953). Washington, D.C.: The Council, 229-31. Reprinted by permission of the authors and the National Council of Teachers of Mathematics.]

a friend on the telephone—all in an attempt to relieve his feelings of boredom. He is under the impact of a tension, but he has not clearly defined the goal which will resolve this tension.

It is the difference between the given situation and the desired situation (goal) that evokes, directs, and sustains the individual's behavior. Other factors being equal, the clearer the individual is about his goal, the stronger is his will-to-do or motivation. A vague feeling of uneasiness is not conducive to behavior which will remove this feeling. A consciously held and clearly defined goal, on the other hand, helps the individual select and organize behavior so that there is greater likelihood of the goals being reached. Attainment of the goal by the individual is satisfying. Tensions are released, the individual's ego is enhanced, and he feels better.

The second identifiable part of the process of problem solving consists of a blocking of the behavior normally employed by the individual in attaining his goal. The blocking has to be of such a nature that well-established habits cannot immediately go into action to circumvent or remove it. Suppose a girl is considering the problem, "A recipe for making four dozen cookies calls for 1 cup sugar, ½ cup sweet milk, ¼ teaspoon baking soda, and 2 cups flour. How much of each ingredient shall I use if I want to make two dozen cookies?" If she immediately takes one-half of each amount, there really has been no blocking. But suppose she does not know what one-half of one-half and one-half of one-fourth are. Blocking has now occurred, and she has become aware of a "problem" in the sense of a question to be answered.

The third step in problem solving is now ushered in. (This is assuming the student continues to act in terms of his original goal. Should he decide to abandon the assignment, then he has changed his goal. There is no blocking and hence no problem.) The student begins to think, and to figure out ways of removing the block and thereby to attain his goal.

This analysis of the process of problem-solving allows us to identify the necessary conditions for the existence of a problem-for-a-particular-individual:

1. The individual has a clearly defined goal of which he is consciously aware and whose attainment he desires.

2. Blocking of the path toward the goal occurs, and the individual's fixed patterns of behavior or habitual responses are not sufficient for removing the block.

3. Deliberation takes place. The individual becomes aware of the problem, defines it more or less clearly, identifies various possible hypotheses (solutions), and tests these for feasibility.

Implications for the meaning of a problem. The second concept of "problem" discussed here holds that when these three necessary conditions are met, a problem exists for the particular individual. It can be seen that this concept differs from the former one. Every question that is proposed for solution is not a problem.

. . . .

It is not a question of *which* concept is the correct one; i.e., problems existing independent of persons who might face them, or problems as only existing relative to the persons who face them. It is rather a question of which is more useful for a certain purpose. The second concept of a problem appears to be the more useful concept in most educational contexts.

HOW TO SOLVE IT

George Polya

Helping the Student

One of the most important tasks of the teacher is to help his students. This task is not quite easy; it demands time, practice, devotion, and sound principles.

The student should acquire as much experience of independent work as possible. But if he is left alone with his problem without any help or with insufficient help, he may make no progress at all. If the teacher helps too much, nothing is left to the student. The teacher should help, but not too much and not too little, so that the student shall have a *reasonable share of the work*.

If the student is not able to do much, the teacher should leave him at least some illusion of independent work. In order to do so, the teacher should help the student discreetly, *unobtrusively*.

The best is, however, to help the student naturally. The teacher should put himself in the student's place, he should see the student's case, he should try to understand what is going on in the student's mind, and ask a question or indicate a step that *could have occurred to the student himself*.

Questions, recommendations, mental operations. Trying to help the student effectively but unobtrusively and naturally, the teacher is led to ask the same questions and to indicate the same steps again and again. Thus,

[From *How to Solve It* (Princeton, N.J.: Princeton University Press, 1945), pp. 1-2, 3-4. Reprinted by permission of the author and the Princeton University Press.]

in countless problems, we have to ask the question: *What is the unknown?* We may vary the words, and ask the same thing in many different ways: What is required? What do you want to find? What are you supposed to seek? The aim of these questions is to focus the student's attention upon the unknown. Sometimes, we obtain the same effect more naturally with a suggestion: *Look at the unknown!* Question and suggestion aim at the same effect; they tend to provoke the same mental operation.

.   .   .   .

Teacher and student. Imitation and practice. There are two aims which the teacher may have in view when addressing to his students a question or a suggestion of the list: First, to help the student to solve the problem at hand. Second, to develop the student's ability so that he may solve future problems by himself.

Experience shows that the questions and suggestions of our list, appropriately used, very frequently help the student. They have two common characteristics, common sense and generality. As they proceed from plain common sense they very often come naturally; they could have occurred to the student himself. As they are general, they help unobtrusively; they just indicate a general direction and leave plenty for the student to do.

But the two aims we mentioned before are closely connected; if the student succeeds in solving the problem at hand, he adds a little to his ability to solve problems. Then, we should not forget that our questions are general, applicable in many cases. If the same question is repeatedly helpful, the student will scarcely fail to notice it and he will be induced to ask the question by himself in a similar situation. Asking the question repeatedly, he may succeed once in eliciting the right idea. By such a success, he discovers the right way of using the question, and then he has really assimilated it.

PRODUCTIVE THINKING

Max Wertheimer

Although there are good teachers, with a natural feeling for what genuine thinking means, the situation in schools is often not good. How teachers act, how a subject matter is taught, how textbooks are written, all this

[From *Productive Thinking* (New York: Harper & Brothers, 1945), pp. 2-3, 10-11, 89-91, 94-95. Reprinted by permission of the author and Harper & Brothers.]

is widely determined by two traditional views about the nature of thinking: the view of traditional logic and the view of association theory. These
two views have their merits. To a degree they seem adequate to certain
types of thought processes, to certain jobs in thinking; but it is at least
an open question whether the way in which they interpret thinking does
not cause serious hindrance, an actual impairment of genuine abilities.

This book has been written because the traditional views have ignored
important characteristics of thought processes, because in many other
books those views are taken for granted without real investigation, because in such books the discussion of thinking runs largely in mere gener-
alities, and because, for the most part, the gestalt view is only superficially
known. Much is at stake and it seems proper to bring these neglected
issues to the fore, to examine the traditional views, to discuss the crucial
problems in concrete instances of fine, productive thought, and in doing
so, to give the gestalt interpretation of thinking.

.   .   .   .

Training in traditional logic is not to be disparaged: it leads to stringency
and rigor in each step, it contributes to critical-mindedness; but it does
not, in itself, seem to give rise to productive thinking.[1] In short, there is
the danger of being empty and senseless, though exact; and there is always the difficulty with regard to real productiveness.

.   .   .   .

Similar difficulties arose in association theory: the fact that we have to
distinguish between sensible thought and senseless combinations, and the
difficulty in dealing with the *productive* side of thinking.

If a problem is solved by recall, by mechanical repetition of what has
been drilled, by sheer chance discovery in a succession of blind trials, one
would hesitate to call such a process sensible thinking; and it seems doubtful whether the piling up of such factors only, even in large numbers, can
lead to an adequate picture of sensible processes. In order to deal somehow with processes which reach new solutions, a number of auxiliary
hypotheses were proposed (for instance, Selz's constellation theory, or the
concept of the habit-family-hierarchy) which, by their very nature, do
not seem to give decisive help.

Now I shall tell the story of young Gauss, the famous mathematician.
It runs about as follows: he was a boy of six, attending grammar school

---

[1] The discussions of methodology in traditional logic, though meritorious in various
respects, do not give real help at this point. Cf. the heuristic ideas (or also, veritable
logical machines) of Buridanus, of Raimundus Lullus, of Jevons.

in a little town. The teacher gave a test in arithmetic and said to the class: "Which of you will be first to get the sum of $1 + 2 + 3 + 4 + 5 + 6 + 7 + 8 + 9 + 10$?" Very soon, while the others were still busy figuring, young Gauss raised his hand. "Ligget se," he said, which means "Here it is."

"How the devil did you get it so quickly?" exclaimed the surprised teacher. Young Gauss answered—of course we do not know exactly what he did answer, but on the basis of experience in experiments I think it may have been about like this: "Had I done it by adding 1 and 2, then 3 to the sum, then 4 to the new result, and so on, it would have taken very long; and, trying to do it quickly, I would very likely have made mistakes. But you see, 1 and 10 make eleven, 2 and 9 are again—must be— 11! And so on! There are 5 such pairs; 5 times 11 makes 55." The boy had discovered the gist of an important theorem.[2] In diagram:

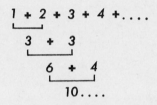

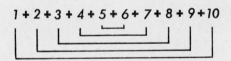

As the teacher had put the problem to the class, I put it to many subjects, including children of various ages, to see whether a good solution would be found, and what helps, what conditions, might bring it about. In order to study the steps and the features involved, I employed systematic variations some of which I shall describe later. Sometimes I gave very long series. I said directly: "Solve the problem without using the cumbersome additions," or I simply waited for reactions.

Here are the best types of genuine processes that I found.

At first no way was seen of dealing with the problem. Then: "If a sequence of numbers is to be added, it is certainly correct to add them as

---

[2] $S_n = (n+1)\dfrac{n}{2}$

they come—but tiresome." Suddenly: "This is not just any sequence; the numbers increase consistently, one by one—this fact may ... it must have something to do with the sum. But how the two hang together—the form of the sequence and its sum—what the inner relation is between them—is dark, unclear; I feel it somehow but I cannot clarify it."

After a while: "The series has direction in its increase. A sum has no direction. Now: the *increase* from left to right involves a corresponding *decrease* from right to left! This *has* to do with the sum. ————————→more and more;←————————less and less; in the same amount. If I go from left to right, from the first number to the second, there is an increase of one; if I go from right to left, from the last number at the right to the next preceding, there is a decrease of one. Hence the sum of the first and the last numbers must be the same as the sum of the next inner pair. And this must be true throughout!

"There remains only the question; how many pairs are there? Obviously the number of pairs is one-half of all the numbers; hence of the last number."

Essentially there is involved the regrouping, the reorganization of the series in the light of the problem. This is no blind regrouping; it comes about reasonably as the subject seeks to grasp the inner relation between the sum of the series and its structure. In the process the various items clearly gain a new meaning; they appear functionally determined in a new way. Nine is no longer viewed as 8 plus 1, it has become 10 minus 1, and so on.

. . . .

The teacher says, "To get the sum of such a series, write it out, then just write it below in the opposite order and add each vertical pair. They are equal."

$$1 + 2 + 3 + 4 \ldots\ldots\ldots + 58 + 59 + 60$$
$$60 + 59 + 58 + 57 \ldots\ldots\ldots + 3 + 2 + 1$$
$$\overline{61 + 61 + 61 + 61 \ldots\ldots\ldots + 61 + 61 + 61}$$

I found a number of persons who gave this procedure as the solution. They said they had learned it that way in school. Asked why they wrote the series twice, and in this inverted fashion, all were puzzled, did not know what to answer. When I insisted, "What I want is the sum of the series, why find twice the sum first?" for the most part I got the answer, "Well, it leads to the solution in the end." They were unable to say how the idea of doubling might have originated. I confess that I myself was for a long time at a loss to see how one could reasonably have come to the idea of doubling. It had looked to me like a trick, as it does to many, like a chance discovery.[3]

When I showed these results to a mathematician, he said, "Why do you bother about what you call 'functional differences,' 'differences in the meaning of terms'? What matters is the formula, which is identical in all cases."

This attitude is certainly justified if nothing matters but the correctness and validity of the final result. But the moment one tries to get at the psychological process in productive thinking, one *has* to investigate, to view the terms in their functional meanings. These bring about the solution in the sensible, productive processes; they constitute the basic difference between finding the formula in a sensible way and finding it by blind learning or by chance trial and error.

MECHANIZATION IN PROBLEM SOLVING: THE EFFECT OF EINSTELLUNG *

Abraham S. Luchins

Many of our subjects [in this research study] both in the college and in the elementary schools, because of their school training viewed arithmetic as composed of a heterogeneous manifold of definite facts and oper-

[From "Mechanization in Problem Solving: the Effect of Einstellung," *Psychological Monographs*, LIV (1942), No. 248, pp. 90-2. Reprinted by permission of the author and the American Psychological Association.]

---

[3] Cf. a similar procedure: getting the area of a triangle by doubling it into a parallelogram or, specifically, doubling a right triangle into a rectangle when the area is asked for.

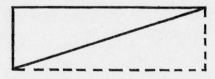

* *Einstellung* is "the set which immediately predisposes an organism to one type of motor or conscious act." H. C. Warren, *Dictionary of Psychology* (New York: Houghton Mifflin Co., 1934), p. 371. For the various meanings of "set" see James I. Gibson, "A Critical Review of The Concept of Set in Contemporary Experimental Psychology," *Psychological Bulletin*, XXXVIII (1941), No. 9.

ations, of fixed habits and skills; one must always try to remember the particular rule, formula, or method which works in any given type of arithmetical problem.

In some classes there was clearly an atmosphere of fear, tension, and tense competition. That such conditions may favor Einstellung responses has been noticed in the experiments.

. . . .

What could be done in school procedures if one wants to avoid "blinding" effects of Einstellung? We formulate some suggestions, the efficacy of which, of course, would have to be tested in actual teaching situations.

1. A change in the set of "assigned tasks": After illustrating a method the teacher would not present a series of problems all solvable by the same procedure; she would intersperse problems which are not solvable by the just before taught method, telling the pupils that the assigned tasks will not all be of the same type, but will sometimes have other methods of solution. In this way the child may be induced to examine the problem instead of merely repeating without looking at the problem's requirements.

2. Demands for *speedy instantaneous responses* may create conditions favorable to "blind" responses. It is certainly true that certain processes have to be reduced to quick, ready responses, but to focus all teaching on the production of such responses may mechanize the child. He may as a result of such teaching be able to give instantaneous responses in the drilled material, but not be able to solve new application tasks. In contrast, the child would in appropriate tasks be given time, would even be encouraged to think clearly himself, to weigh the problems before answering; and avoiding quick responses would rule out some of the competition.

3. On tests, not only the correctness or incorrectness of the final result but also the method of deriving the answer should be considered.

4. Not merely ability to reproduce what the teacher said or what the child read should be tested but interesting tests should be used in which some creative activity is demanded from the child, new situations in which the child cannot simply apply what he was taught but has to find ways himself.

5. In order to minimize the emotional and social conditions resulting from tests, the child should be made to realize that tests are not merely means of grading him but means of help—means to find out productively what further instruction or other assistance is required.

6. A "democratic" atmosphere would probably prevent the develop-

ment of the kind of teacher-pupil relationships and the social field conditions which we mentioned before.

. . . .

What the study has shown is that in mechanization there are certain dangers. When the individual does not adequately deal with problems but views them merely from the frame of reference of a habit; when he applies a certain habituated behavior to situations which have a better solution, or which, in fact, are not even solvable by the just working habit; when a habit ceases to be a tool discriminately applied but becomes a procrustean bed to which the situation must conform; when, in a word, instead of the individual mastering the habit, the habit masters the individual—then mechanization is indeed a dangerous thing.

We would consider our efforts well spent if this is realized; and if educators attempt to develop methods of teaching which possess the advantages of widely used methods but not their disadvantages. Methods are needed which will teach the child to stand on his own feet, to face the world freely and act through intelligent thinking rather than by blind force of habit.

TWENTIETH CENTURY MATHEMATICS FOR THE ELEMENTARY SCHOOL

Henry Van Engen

Problem Solving

The schools have not been successful in devising a sensible approach to problem solving. This audience is all too familiar with the various proposals for improving the problem-solving ability of the elementary school pupil. In spite of all the proposals and the research, it is probably not too far amiss to summarize the results of present-day research by the single statement: The best way to teach children how to solve problems is to give them lots of problems to solve. Certainly a fresh approach to problem solving is needed.

There is some reason to believe that the failure to achieve any degree

[From "Twentieth Century Mathematics for the Elementary School," *The Arithmetic Teacher,* VI (March, 1959), pp. 71-6. Reprinted by permission of the author and *The Arithmetic Teacher*.]

of success on the part of the various proposals for improving problem-solving ability is that the attention of the child is directed to the wrong element in the problem, namely, its answer. Now this may seem paradoxical, but it is put forth as a serious criticism of our efforts to teach children to solve problems. Arithmetic has been so "answer-minded" that teachers have forgotten that "first things must come first." This "answer-mindedness" is in keeping with the mistaken idea of what arithmetic is all about, namely, computation. Some twenty-five years ago, the idea was rather widely held that one should not attempt problem solving until all the basic facts had been memorized. After all, how could one solve a problem if he could not compute. While this attitude is not held today, we are still not far from it.

In our previous discussion, we have hinted at a more sensible and mathematically sound approach to problem solving. You will recall that we said that '3 + 2' and '2 + 3' were different names for the same number, but that these symbols have different senses. Let us follow this thought a little further.

Consider these two problems.

1. Mary has six apples. Her mother gave her five more apples. How many apples does Mary now have?
2. Mary has some apples. Her mother gave her five more apples. Mary now has 11 apples. How many apples did Mary have?

There can be no doubt that the symbol '6 + 5' is an appropriate symbol to transmit the sense of the situation in the first problem. But it is customary to change its name, and we indicate this by writing $6 + 5 = N$, where the N says to the child, "Find another name for $6 + 5$ and use it to replace N."

However, in the second case the situation is entirely different. A little thought will convince you that $11-5$ is not a good symbol for communicating the sense of this problem. The sense of this problem is not that of removing five apples. As we look at the two problems we begin to feel that whatever symbols are used for these problems they should possess some similarity, because the two problems are similarly structured as to physical events. After examining the problem, one feels that the symbol '$N + 5$' preserves the sense of the second problem and that this symbol must be another symbol for 11. So we write

$$N + 5 = 11$$

This approach teaches children to look for the sense of a problem and to select symbols which express this sense. In other words, we want the child to grasp the structure of the problem before he looks for the answer. The answer is obtained by finding the proper replacement for the placeholder symbol in the equation.

Certainly the basic differences between good problem-solvers and poor problem-solvers must reside in differences in ability to recognize the element which we have called *structure*. The good problem-solver knows "what's going on" in the problem even though he may not have been taught appropriate means for expressing this "going on." However, a knowledge of events leads the good problem-solver to the right answer. An "answer-minded" orientation in arithmetic has prevented us from giving the child a means for expressing these "goings-on" in problems and, consequently, the child has no systematic way to arrive at how to get the answer. Experience has shown that no reliance on words and cues will ever help the child to make these decisions.

The method of problem solving we have illustrated here is a mathematician's approach to problems in miniature. One first searches for the fundamental structure of a problem situation; then he finds the appropriate symbols to express this structure. Once the problem has been structured, a knowledge of previous problems and problem-solving techniques can be applied. Certainly, no "cue" method or mere admonitions to *think* hold the mathematical power that the search for the structure of the physical situation can command. The failure of the older methods over the past years should be reason enough to banish them from the classroom and search for methods with more mathematical power.

Arithmetic as Patterns vs. Drill

I have tried to convey to you that the study of mathematics is a constant search for patterns and that this search involves the ability to abstract and to generalize. This fact should cause all teachers to look carefully at their classroom activities. In fact, with the change in content of the curriculum there must come an entirely different concept of instruction. No drillmaster will ever be a mathematics teacher. Drill can do little more than teach children how to change the names of numbers. While this must be attained, it is not the end but only a means to an end. Once teachers sense this, there will be a profound improvement in both content and method of instruction.

TEACHING ARITHMETIC
IN THE ELEMENTARY SCHOOL

Catharine Williams

If teaching aims at critical thinking, it must treat problem solving in a different manner. Teachers must fully understand and consciously work to develop with children the concepts fundamental to problem solving.

Perhaps the following illustration will serve to show both the concepts fundamental to problem solving and how the problem-solving technique may be used to guide children to discover for themselves a process or a principle which is needed to carry forward some purposeful activity.

In a sixth grade classroom a boy whose hobby was astronomy appealed to his classmates for help. He wanted to find out how big around the planets are but the atlas gave only the diameters and he did not know how to proceed. Brief discussion enabled the members of the group to formulate their problem. At first no one had a plan for solution so the teacher suggested that if they worked in groups of two or three each and each group secured a round object, they might think out a plan. The clock, the barometer, a vase, a bracelet, a flower pot, a measuring cup, a mason jar were secured from the classroom; pans, petri dishes, tumblers, etc. from the science laboratory. When these articles were assembled, the teacher reminded the children of the problem. One boy suggested, "If we could measure across and around, we might find a way."

His peers accepted his hypothesis that this procedure might reveal a relationship; so plans were made to find all the diameters and circumferences and list this paired data for each object. Tape lines and pieces of twine and rulers which made crude tape lines were used as children set about collecting their data. They began to generalize when inspection revealed that constantly "the circumference is a little more than three times the diameter." However, they continued experimentation in order to further prove that the relationship was no accident. In order to find the more accurate relationship, children divided circumference by diameter and, because of inaccuracies with their crude instruments of measurement, got $3\frac{1}{4}$, $3\frac{1}{8}$, $3\frac{1}{7}$, etc. At this point they were given the scientists' $3\frac{1}{7}$. They formulated their own generalization: "If you have the diameter, you multiply by $3\frac{1}{7}$ to find the circumference."

[From *Teaching Arithmetic in the Elementary School* (Danville, Illinois: Interstate Printers and Publishers, 1946), pp. 22-25. Reprinted by permission of the author and the Interstate Printers and Publishers.]

They were helped to translate their thinking into "the short cut way to say the same thing," a formula, $D \times 3\frac{1}{7} = C$. They experimented further, constantly comparing their computations when using the formula with their actual measurements. When they finally referred to arithmetic texts, they were interested in the explanations which were given and their satisfaction with their achievement was expressed by one of the girls who exclaimed, "Why, we're almost as good discoverers as the scientists!" The more exact 3.1416 in place of $3\frac{1}{7}$ found in some texts brought about some further experimentation.

In this instance every one of the concepts fundamental to problem solving recognized by the Committee on the Function of Mathematics in General Education was essential. It was necessary to formulate the problem, to make plans for the solution, to gather data, to estimate results, to recognize functional relationships, to use operations for computation, and to work to establish proof of the validity of their solution.

Almost all of these concepts are essential to the solution of problems whether they are mathematical or not. Teachers have an obligation constantly to help children to refine these concepts as they mature.

Elementary school children should not be expected to develop the terminology nor be made unduly aware of these concepts. Rather through many experiences in solving problems which arise in the course of their work on purposeful activities these concepts should emerge as essential "things to do" in working out problems. It is quite enough if a child expresses himself as one child did following the situation just cited. He said, "Phil brought us a problem and we were stuck for a plan until Henry got an idea. We had to do lots of experimenting but we kept at it and proved that Henry's idea worked. It's neat the way it works for just every circle!" That this same problem-solving technique can be used to make even so advanced a topic as the diameter-circumference relationship meaningful to third grade children is shown in the following account written by the teacher.

A plan was finally evolved for making a wigwam which could be used for play in the woods. They experimented with paper patterns and the question came up as to how big a wigwam would have to be around the bottom in order to have it four feet in diameter. The teacher tried to help by drawing a circle on the board and marking the diameter. One of the boys looked at it and said, "It will have to be about three times as big around as it is across." The teacher marked it off into sections that appeared to be the length of the diameter and the other child said, "Yes, that is about right." The teacher helped them measure a piece of paper three times the length of the diameter. They held it in a circle, measured the diameter, and decided that the length around would have to be a little more than three times the length of the diameter. It is found that children can comprehend much of mathematics when they are given adequate experience background and permitted to reason out the proceedings, rather than to have formulas for operations presented without understanding the reason for such operations." [1]

Discovering a process or principle which enables children to carry forward their plans is a gratifying experience. Later when other instances arise which are a little different but to which the same principle can be applied, children often delightedly report that "It worked again, I thought it would." Generalizations take on more meaning with each extension of the experience.

DEVELOPING FACILITY IN SOLVING VERBAL PROBLEMS

Herbert F. Spitzer and Frances Flournoy

In view of the rather long time that instructors have been concerned with problem solving, it is very doubtful whether any one entirely new procedure of merit will turn up. Improvement will, then, most likely be the result of modification and refinement of plans now in use. This paper is concerned with steps which may lead to such refinements and modifications. Specifically, the paper will present a picture of some classroom and textbook practices illustrating the two broad types of problem-solving improvement procedures, followed by an analysis of the situations.

Examples of Classroom Procedures for Improving Problem Solving

Classroom 1. Miss R, the fifth grade teacher in this classroom, is putting into operation the "just solve problems" procedure for improving problem solving. She began by saying, "Open your books to page 124. Try to work the ten problems on that page. If you cannot work a problem or are not very sure of a solution, raise your hand and I'll try to help you." During

[From "Developing Facility in Solving Verbal Problems," *The Arithmetic Teacher,* III (November, 1956), pp. 177-80. Reprinted by permission of the authors and *The Arithmetic Teacher.*]

---

[1] Blanche Kent, from unpublished "Résumé of Activities for Third Week Ohio State University Summer Demonstration School," Ohio State University, Columbus, Ohio, 1933.

the ensuing work period Miss R gave assistance to various children. Her assistance consisted primarily of making suggestions, asking questions, and offering encouragement. She did not solve problems for the pupils.

When several pupils had finished the ten problems, Miss R said, "Let's stop our work for a few moments. All of you now have the answers for some problems and some have all. I'll read the answers. You check. When I get to the ones you haven't done, you may go back to work. For each incorrect answer try another solution for the problem."

After giving the answers, Miss R said, "If at any time you want to know an answer, you may look at the answer list. I'm leaving it here on my desk." She then again went about the room giving assistance to those who needed it.

Classroom 2. Miss D, the fifth grade teacher in this room, is also trying to improve pupil ability to solve verbal arithmetic problems. She began by saying, "Number downward on your paper from 1 through 6. As I read an arithmetic word problem aloud, try to solve it without using paper and pencil. Write only your answer by the number on your paper." She then read the following:

> For her birthday party, Jane bought 2 bags of candy with 20 pieces in each bag. She plans to serve each person 5 pieces of candy. How many persons can she serve?

After pausing for about 30 seconds to allow the children to think and record an answer, Miss D asked, "Who would like to tell how he thought in solving the problem and then give his answer to see if others agree with him? I will read the problem again."

Johnny explained, "I know that if there are two bags with 20 pieces in each bag, there would be 40 pieces altogether. A group of 5 pieces is to be served to each person, so I divided to find out how many groups of 5 could be made from 40 pieces. My answer is 8."

Sue explained, "I agree with the answer of 8, but I first divided to find out how many groups of 5 can be made from 20 pieces of candy. This is 4. I then multiplied 4 by 2 because there were 2 bags with 4 groups of 5 in each bag."

Miss D then said, "You worked in a different way but arrived at the same answer. I wonder if the other members of the class noted the reasons why you each began in a different way. What did Johnny want to know first that caused him to begin by multiplying 20 pieces by 2? What did Sue first want to know that caused her to begin by dividing 20 pieces by 5 pieces?" Miss D continued in a like manner with five other word problems to be solved without paper and pencil, each of which was followed by oral pupil presentation of various ways of thinking.

The use of oral or non-pencil-and-paper exercises is the problem-solving improvement suggestion illustrated in Miss D's room.

Classroom 3. The problem-solving improvement procedure which Miss L is using in this classroom emphasizes the use of drawings. She gave the following directions at the beginning of the class period.

"Use a simple drawing or picture to show how you are thinking as you solve each of the two problems I have written on the board." The problems were:

1. How much will Jane have to pay for 18 Christmas cards if they are being sold at 3 for 25¢?

2. Mrs. Green bought 4 yards of silk material. She plans to use 1¼ yards to make Ann a blouse and 2⅜ yards to make a blouse for herself. How much material will she have left from which to make a silk head scarf for Ann?

As the children worked on the assignment, Miss L went about the room giving assistance to those who needed it. As the work period progressed, she asked some pupils to place their drawing solutions on the chalkboard. The drawing solutions below are typical:

(1a)

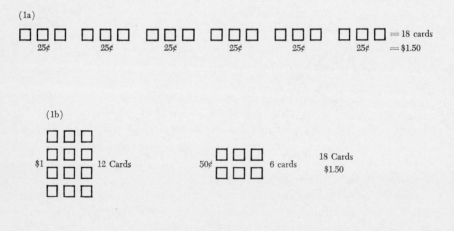

(1b)

(2)

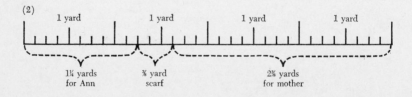

In the discussion period that followed, Miss D directed attention to these drawing solutions by such questions as "Can you tell how the person thought who put this solution on the board?"

Classroom 4. In School IV, Miss N and her fifth grade pupils used another procedure as they worked to improve in ability to solve word problems. Four word problems had been written on the chalkboard. Miss N began the class period by saying, "In problem number 1, there are really two questions to be answered, but only one is in written form. Can you find the unwritten question which is hidden from you? Let's do the first problem together. Read it silently."

> Ann divided 48 roses picked from her mother's rose garden into bouquets of 6 roses each. She sold each bouquet for 50¢. How much money did she receive altogether?

After a pause for reading and consideration, several suggestions were made. The class decided that the hidden question is, "How many bouquets did Ann make?" Miss N then wrote that question on the board and drew an arrow to the place in the original problem where the question might be inserted. She then said, "Try to state the unwritten or hidden number question in each of these other problems on the board and for the ones on page 116 of your book. Write your statement of the question." As the pupils worked, Miss N went about the room giving assistance where it was needed. At the close of the work period various suggested questions were compared.

Analysis of the Procedures

In the first classroom, with the emphasis on getting the correct answer, the pupil works primarily alone. All the pupil's time is given to work on his own solution with none or very little time spent in listening to questions, suggestions, and explanations of other pupils. Nor is any time spent in studying (observing) the solutions of others. Group spirit or group motivation, then, plays a minor role in this classroom.

In the second classroom emphasis is on the answer and also on various ways of solving problems, and since there is no writing of solutions, remembering the thinking done is at a premium. The consideration of the ways of thinking solutions, suggestions, and questions of others makes for class spirit and teamwork. The oral presentation of problems and solutions requires high order listening skills. This oral presentation also results in the pacing of work for all pupils and therefore does not permit fast workers to proceed at a rate that is up to their capacity.

In the third classroom the emphasis is on showing the thinking done in the problem solution, and the asking of pupils to figure out from a drawing how another person thought requires both clear drawing presentations and an understanding of the problem setting as well as its solution. While the assignment made required all pupils to use one type of solution (use of drawings), this type of non-standardized solution almost guarantees a variety of solutions and leaves pupils free to put into practice ingenuity and initiative. The consideration of various drawing solutions makes possible development of class spirit.

In the fourth classroom emphasis is on one specific aspect of problem solving, the formulation of the unstated question in two-step problems. To state this unwritten question calls for an understanding of the problem, and therefore the procedure actually gives more than experience with just a part of the problem-solving process. The specific nature of the assignment makes it easy for pupil and teacher to identify the learning task. The comparison of suggested questions in this procedure results in little disagreement except where errors are made. Therefore, the discussion period is primarily a checking period and does little for the development of class spirit.

In the opinion of the writers, the procedures used in Classroom 1 are definitely inferior to those used in the other classrooms. This conclusion is based on the belief that meeting with success or failure in the attempt to solve a problem contributes little to learning. The student who fails just tries again without benefit of suggestion, analysis from others, or knowledge of errors made. The pupil who succeeds goes no further. He doesn't explain his thinking and therefore his method is never analyzed or challenged.

Each of the procedures used in the other three classrooms calls for some analysis, and in Classrooms 2 and 3, for presentation of ways of solving, followed by an evaluation. Such analysis, presentation, and evaluation should make for learning for those who fail in the first attempts and should also enable those who succeed to acquire a more thorough grasp of the problems being considered.

Space does not permit further analysis and evaluation of the specific classroom procedures. The presentation, it is believed, has shown the value of looking critically at some specific problem-solving procedures.

THE DIAGNOSIS AND TREATMENT
OF LEARNING DIFFICULTIES

Leo J. Brueckner and Guy L. Bond

Improving Problem-Solving Ability

Changing Conceptions of Problem Solving. In recent years there has been a considerable shift from the concept of problem solving as the solution of traditional verbal problems formulated largely to illustrate the applications of number operations, but actually a form of "disguised drill" in arithmetic computations. Instead, it is recognized today that quantitative thinking in realistic social situations, in analyzing described situations, in discovering and using number relationships, and in using study skills in analyzing and interpreting graphs, tables, charts, diagrams, and the like, is a broad, even more valuable area of ability to develop. Consequently, modern courses of study and textbooks provide a wide variety of activities and interesting vital materials to give pupils experiences with arithmetic in all curriculum areas that will improve the ability to think quantitatively in the broad sense of the term *problem solving* described above.

.   .   .   .

Sources of Difficulty in Problem Solving. The deficiencies in problem solving fall into the following major categories:

1. Meaning of number operations and perception of relations among them.
2. Ability to compute with numbers.
3. Ability to sense quantitative relations involved in verbal problems.
4. Control of special types of reading skills required in problem solving.
5. Knowledge of vocabulary of a quantitative nature.
6. Knowledge of essential information, facts, rules, and formulas.
7. Breadth of knowledge about uses of arithmetic as applied in social situations.
8. Amount of practice in solving verbal problems.

These limitations arise from such causes as a low level of mental ca-

[From *The Diagnosis and Treatment of Learning Difficulties* (New York: Appleton-Century-Crofts, Inc., 1955), pp. 290-301. Reprinted by permission of the authors and Appleton-Century-Crofts, Inc.]

pacity of the pupil, a limited social and experiential background, inferior reading ability, and the limited scope and ineffectiveness of the instructional program and methods of teaching arithmetic.

General Program for Improving Problem Solving. Special exercises such as the following, adapted to the needs of the learner, should be used to remedy weaknesses revealed by diagnosis.

1. Discuss uses of number in social situations that arise, or in pictures and illustrations in textbooks to develop vocabulary and background experiences.

2. Give the pupil many opportunities to solve verbal problems that may arise in real social situations. Have pupil tell how he finds the answers and explain or give reasons for method of solution used.

3. Give the pupil abundant experience in reading and solving easy, meaningful verbal problems in textbooks and workbooks, beginning at or slightly below his level of development. Keep the numbers small at the start. Gradually increase the difficulty of the vocabulary, computations, and situations.

4. Be sure to help the learner to understand the meaning of each number process by manipulative experience and by exercises which embody the various types of situations or meanings each process implies. Textbooks often provide suitable exercises which visualize the meanings of the various processes. Have pupil give original problems.

5. Have pupils use manipulative materials to demonstrate and work out solutions of simple problems so as to help them to visualize the situations and the relations involved. Have them tell orally about the procedures they use.

6. Plan reading experiences which will develop the special reading skills in problem solving. . . .

7. Emphasize vocabulary development by suitable exercises similar to those used in reading.

8. Do special work on measures and their use in social situations. Help pupils to develop and then use tables of measure. Demonstrate or visualize the processes of conversion from "large to small" and "small to large," a basic element of difficulty in problem solving.

9. Develop basic rules, formulas, and procedures through real situations, involving manipulation of representative materials, drawings, visualization and thinking through the relations involved; for example, perimeter, area, costs, interest, percentage, etc.

10. Use problems without numbers to help the pupil learn to state in his own words how to find answers.

11. Emphasize the need of accuracy in all computations. Teach pupils to go over their work to check it.

12. Teach pupils above fifth grade procedures for approximating and estimating answers to see if their answers are sensible.

BIBLIOGRAPHY

Almy, Millie C. "Are They Too Young for Problem Solving?" *Progressive Education*, XXVII (March, 1950), 148-51.

Anderson, G. Lester. "Quantitative Thinking as Developed Under Connectionist and Field Theories of Learning," *Learning Theory in School Situations*, University of Minnesota Studies in Education, No. 2. Minneapolis: University of Minnesota Press, 1949, 40-73.

Banks, J. Houston. *Learning and Teaching Arithmetic*. Boston: Allyn and Bacon, Inc., 1959, 264-80.

Bathhurst, Effie G. *How Children Use Arithmetic*, U. S. Office of Education, Bulletin No. 7. Washington, D. C.: Government Printing Office, 1951. 6-9.

Beatley, Ralph. "Arithmetic for a Free Society," *Mathematics Teacher*, XL (October, 1947), 276-78.

Benezet, L. P. "Story of an Experiment," *National Education Association Journal*, XXIV (November, 1935), 241-44, 301-3; XXV (January, 1936), 7-8.

Berglund-Gray, Gunborg, and R. V. Young. "The Effect of Process Sequence on the Interpretation of Two-Step Problems in Arithmetic," *Journal of Educational Research*, XXXIV (September, 1940), 21-29.

Bingham, Alma. *Improving Children's Facility in Problem Solving*, Practical Suggestions for Teaching, No. 16. New York: Teachers College, Columbia University, 1958.

Blecha, Milo. "Helping Children Understand Verbal Problems," *Arithmetic Teacher*, VI (March, 1959), 106-7.

Bloom, Benjamin S., and Lois J. Broder. *Problem-Solving Processes of College Students*, Supplementary Educational Monographs, No. 73. Chicago: University of Chicago Press, 1950.

Bradford, E. J. G. "Suggestion, Reasoning, and Arithmetic," *Forum of Education*, III (February, 1925), 3-12.

Brownell, W. A. "Problem Solving," *The Psychology of Learning*, National Society for the Study of Education, Forty-first Yearbook (1942). Chicago: University of Chicago Press, Part II, 415-43.

——, and L. B. Stretch. *The Effect of Unfamiliar Settings on Problem-Solving*, Duke University Research Studies in Education, No. 1. Durham, N. Carolina: Duke University Press, 1931.

——, K. G. Kuehner, and W. C. Rein. *Learning as Reorganization: An Experimental Study in Third-Grade Arithmetic*, Duke University Research Studies in Education, No. 3. Durham, N. Carolina: Duke University Press, 1939.

Brueckner, Leo J. "The Social Phase of Arithmetic Instruction," *Arithmetic in General Education*, National Council of Teachers of Mathematics, Sixteenth Yearbook (1941). Washington, D. C.: The Council, 140-56.

———, and Foster E. Grossnickle, *Making Arithmetic Meaningful*. New York: Holt, Rinehart & Winston, Inc., 1953, 491-532.

———, and Guy L. Bond. *The Diagnosis and Treatment of Learning Difficulties*. New York: Appleton-Century-Crofts, 1955, 290-301.

Burack, Benjamin. "The Nature and Efficiency of Methods of Attack on Reasoning Problems," *Psychological Monographs*, No. 313, LXIV (1950), 1-26.

Burch, Robert L. *An Evaluation of Analytic Testing in Arithmetic Problem Solving*, Doctoral Dissertation. Durham, N. Carolina: Duke University, 1949.

Burt, Cyril L. "The Development of Reasoning in School Children," *Journal of Experimental Pedagogy*, V (1919-1920), 68-77, 121-27.

Burton, William H. "Problem-Solving Technique: Its Appearance in American Texts on General Method," *Educational Method*, XIV (January, February, March, 1935), 248-53, 338-42.

Buswell, G. T. "Relation of Social Arithmetic to Computational Arithmetic," *The Teaching of Arithmetic*, National Council of Teachers of Mathematics, Tenth Yearbook (1935). Washington, D. C.: The Council, 74-84.

——— (with the co-operation of B. Y. Kersh). *Patterns of Thinking in Solving Problems*, University of California Publications in Education, Vol. 12, No. 2. Berkeley: University of California Press, 1956, 63-148.

Chase, Clinton I., *The Relationship of Certain Skills and Intellectual Factors to Problem Solving in Arithmetic*, Doctoral Dissertation. Berkeley: University of California, 1958.

Clark, John R., and Laura K. Eads. *Guiding Arithmetic Learning*. Yonkers, N. Y.: World Book Co., 1954, 258-70.

Clendenon, E. "On Labeling Answers," *The Arithmetic Teacher*, VII (January, 1960), 37-38.

Connor, William L., and Gertrude C. Hawkins. "What Materials Are Most Useful to Children in Learning to Solve Problems?" *Educational Method*, XVI (October, 1936), 21-29.

Corle, Clyde G. "Thought Processes in Grade Six Problems," *Arithmetic Teacher*, V (October, 1958), 193-203.

Dewey, John. *How We Think*. Boston: D. C. Heath & Company, 1933, Chapter 6.

Dexter, C. E. "Analysis of Written Problems in a Recent Arithmetic Series," *Education*, LXV (April, 1945), 488-90.

Dickey, John W. "The Value of Estimating Answers to Arithmetic Problems and Examples," *Elementary School Journal*, XXXV (September, 1934), 24-31.

Doty, Roy A. *A Study of Children's Procedures in the Solution of Verbal Problems in Arithmetic*, Doctoral Dissertation. Durham, North Carolina: Duke University, 1941.

Douglas, Harl, and Herbert F. Spitzer. "The Importance of Teaching for Understanding," *The Measurement of Understanding*, National Society for the Study of Education, Forty-fifth Yearbook (1946). Chicago: University of Chicago Press, 7-25.

Duncker, Karl. "On Problem Solving," Translated by Lynne S. Lees. *Psychological Monographs*, No. 270, LVIII (1945).

Durkin, Helen E. "Trial and Error, Gradual Analysis, and Sudden Reorganization. An Experimental Study of Problem Solving," *Archives of Psychology*, No. 210, XXX (1937).

Glennon, Vincent J. *A Study of the Growth and Mastery of Certain Basic Mathematical Understandings on Seven Educational Levels*, Doctoral Dissertation. Cambridge, Massachusetts: Harvard University Graduate School of Education, 1948.

Goldstein, J. J., and others. "Thinking Can Be Learned," *Educational Leadership*, VI (January, 1949), 235-39.

Gunderson, Agnes G., "Problem Solving in the Primary Grades," *The Instructor*, LIV (October, 1945), 36-37.

Hall, Jack V. *Solving Arithmetic Problems Mentally*, Educational Service Publications No. 20. Cedar Falls: Iowa State Teachers College, 1954.

Hanna, Lavone A., Gladys L. Potter, and Neva Hagaman. *Unit Teaching in the Elementary School*. New York: Holt, Rinehart & Winston, Inc., 1955, 188-96.

Harding, Lowry W. *Arithmetoons; Arithmetoons #2; Arithmetoons #3*. Dubuque: Wm. C. Brown Co., 1956; 1957; 1958.

—— (with the assistance of Charlotte S. Huck and Martha Norman). *Arithmetic for Child Development*. Dubuque: Wm. C. Brown Co., 1959.

——, and Inez P. Bryant. "An Experimental Comparison of Drill and Direct Experience in Arithmetic Learning in a Fourth Grade," *Journal of Educational Research*, XXXVII (January, 1944), 321-37.

Hartmann, George W. "Insight vs. Trial and Error in the Solution of Problems," *American Journal of Psychology*, XLV (October, 1933), 663-77.

Haynes, Hubert C. *Relation of Teacher Intelligence, Teacher Experience, and Type of School to Types of Questions*, Doctoral Dissertation. Nashville: George Peabody College, 1935.

Heidbreder, Edna F. "Problem Solving in Children and Adults," *Journal of Genetic Psychology*, XXXV (1928), 522-45.

Henderson, Kenneth B., and Robert E. Pingry. "Problem-Solving in Mathematics," *The Learning of Mathematics*, National Council of Teachers of Mathematics, Twenty-first Yearbook (1953). Washington, D. C.: The Council, 228-70.

Herriott, Robert E. "An Aid in the Analysis of Verbal Problems," *Arithmetic Teacher*, V (April, 1958), 143-45.

Hilgard, E. R. *Theories of Learning*. New York: Appleton-Century-Crofts, 1948.

Hirsch, Martin. "Does Changing the Form of a Problem Affect Its Difficulty?" *High Points*, XXXIII (December, 1951), 19-25.

Husband, Richard W. "Cooperation versus Solitary Problem Solution," *Journal of Social Psychology*, XI (1940), 405-9.

Johnson, Harry C. "The Effect of Instruction in Mathematical Vocabulary upon Problem Solving in Arithmetic," *Journal of Educational Research*, XXXVIII (October, 1944), 97-110.

Katona, George. *Organizing and Memorizing.* New York: Columbia University Press, 1940.

Kingsley, H. L. *The Nature and Conditions of Learning.* Englewood Cliffs, N. J.: Prentice-Hall, Inc., 1946.

Koenker, Robert H. "Twenty Methods for Improving Problem Solving," *Arithmetic Teacher*, V (March, 1958), 74-78.

Kramer, Grace A. *The Effect of Certain Factors in the Verbal Arithmetic Problem upon Children's Success in the Solution,* Johns Hopkins University Studies in Education, No. 20. Baltimore, Md.: Johns Hopkins Press, 1933.

Leno, Richard S. *Children's Methods of Problem Solving in Arithmetic,* Doctoral Dissertation. Palo Alto, California: Stanford University, 1958.

Ligda, P. "The Systematic Solution of Arithmetic Problems," *School Science and Mathematics*, XXVIII (January, 1928), 24-33, XXVIII (February, 1928), 172-80.

Luchins, Abraham S. "Mechanization in Problem Solving: the Effect of Einstellung," *Psychological Monographs*, No. 248, LIV (1942).

———, and Edith H. Luchins. "New Experimental Attempts at Preventing Mechanization in Problem Solving," *Journal of General Psychology*, XLII (April, 1950), 279-97.

Lyda, W. J. "Direct Practical Experiences in Mathematics and Success in Solving Realistic Verbal Reasoning Problems in Arithmetic," *Mathematics Teacher*, XL (April, 1947), 166-67.

Maier, Norman R. F. "Reasoning in Humans. The Solution of a Problem and Its Appearance in Consciousness," *Journal of Comparative Psychology*, XII (August, 1931), 181-94.

———. "Reasoning in Children," *Journal of Comparative Psychology*, XXI (June, 1936), 357-66.

Marks, John L., C. Richard Purdy, and Lucien B. Kinney. *Teaching Arithmetic for Understanding.* New York: McGraw-Hill Book Co., Inc., 1958.

Mathematics in General Education, Report of the Committee on the Function of Mathematics in General Education for the Commission on the Secondary School Curriculum, P.E.A., Part II. New York: Appleton-Century-Crofts, 1940.

Matheson, Eunice. "A Study of Problem Solving Behavior in Pre-School Children," *Child Development*, II (1931), 242-62.

Miller, G. H. "How Effective Is the Meaning Method? A Report of the Los Angeles Study," *Arithmetic Teacher*, IV (March, 1957), 45-49.

Morton, Robert L. *Teaching Children Arithmetic.* Morristown, N. J.: Silver Burdett Company, 1953, 481-518.

McConnell, T. R. *Discovery vs. Authoritarian Identification in the Learning of Children,* University of Iowa Studies in Education, No. 5, IX, Iowa City: University of Iowa, 1934, 13-62.

McEwen, Noble R. *The Effect of Selected Cues in Children's Solutions of Verbal Problems in Arithmetic,* Doctoral Dissertation. Durham, N. Carolina: Duke University, 1941.

McLatchy, J. H. "Variety in Problem Solving," *Education,* LXI (April, 1941), 453-57.

McSwain, E. T., and Ralph J. Cooke. *Understanding and Teaching Arithmetic in the Elementary School.* New York: Holt, Rinehart & Winston, Inc., 1958.

Petty, Olan. "Non-Pencil-and-Paper Solution of Problems: An Experimental Study," *Arithmetic Teacher,* III (December, 1956), 229-35.

Piaget, Jean. *Judgment and Reasoning in the Child.* New York: Harcourt, Brace and Co., 1928.

———. *The Child's Conception of Number.* New York: The Humanities Press, 1952.

Poffenberger, Bonnie. "Thought You Might Like to Know," *Essays in Educology.* Dubuque: Wm. C. Brown Co., 184-85.

Polya, G. *How to Solve It: A New Aspect of Mathematical Method.* Princeton, N.J.: Princeton University Press, 1945.

Randolph, Adelaide. "Problem Making—A Creative Experience," *Childhood Education,* XIX (February, 1943), 271-74.

Reed, Calvin H. "Developing Creative Thinking in Arithmetic," *Arithmetic Teacher,* IV (February, 1957), 10-12.

Risden, Gladys. *How Big? How Many?* Boston: Christopher Publishing House, 1951.

Sauble, Irene. "Development of Ability to Estimate and to Compute Mentally," *Arithmetic Teacher,* II (April, 1955), 33-39.

Schaaf, William L. "A Realistic Approach to Problem-Solving in Arithmetic," *Elementary School Journal,* XLVI (May, 1946), 494-97.

Selberg, E. M., and J. D. Barnard. "Teaching Pupils the Method for Solving Problems," *Educational Method,* XVI (May, 1937), 413-16.

Spache, George. "A Test of Abilities in Arithmetic Reasoning," *Elementary School Journal,* XLVII (April, 1947), 442-45.

Spencer, Peter L., and Marguerite Brydegaard. *Building Mathematical Concepts in the Elementary School.* New York: Holt, Rinehart & Winston, Inc., 1952.

Spitzer, Herbert F. *The Teaching of Arithmetic* (2nd ed.). Boston: Houghton Mifflin Co., 1954.

Spitzer, H. F., and F. Flournoy. "Developing Facility in Solving Verbal Problems," *Arithmetic Teacher,* III (November, 1956), 177-82.

Stokes, C. N. *Teaching the Meanings of Arithmetic.* New York: Appleton-Century-Crofts, 1951, 187-220.

Swenson, Esther J. "Organization and Generalization as Factors in Learning, Transfer, and Retroactive Inhibition," *Learning Theory in School Situ-*

ations, University of Minnesota Studies in Education, No. 2. Minneapolis: University of Minnesota Press, 1949, 9-39.

Thelen, Herbert. "Social Environment and Problem-Solving," *Progressive Education,* XXVII (March, 1950), 152-55.

Thiele, C. L. "A Comparison of Three Instructional Methods in Problem Solving," *Research on the Foundations of American Education,* Official Report of the 1939 Meeting, American Educational Research Association, May, 1939, 11-15.

———. "Arithmetic in the Middle Grades," *The Teaching of Arithmetic,* National Society for the Study of Education, Fiftieth Yearbook (1951). Chicago: University of Chicago Press, Part II, 76-101.

Thorndike, Robert L. "How Children Learn the Principles and Techniques of Problem Solving," *Learning and Instruction,* National Society for the Study of Education, Forty-ninth Yearbook (1950). Chicago: University of Chicago Press, Part I, 192-215.

Treacy, J. P. "The Relationship of Reading Skills to the Ability to Solve Arithmetic Problems," *Journal of Educational Research,* XXXVIII (October, 1944), 86-96.

Ullrich, Anna. "Labeling Answers to Arithmetic Problems," *Arithmetic Teacher,* II (December, 1955), 148-53.

Van Engen, H. "Twentieth Century Mathematics for the Elementary School," *Arithmetic Teacher,* VI (March, 1959), 71-76.

Wertheimer, Max. *Productive Thinking.* New York: Harper & Brothers, 1945.

Wheat, H. G. *The Relative Merits of Conventional and Imaginative Types of Problems in Arithmetic,* Contributions to Education No. 359. New York: Teachers College, Columbia University, 1929.

White, Helen M. "Does Experience in the Situation Involved Affect the Solving of a Problem?" *Education,* LIV (April, 1934), 451-55.

Williams, Catharine. *Teaching Arithmetic in the Elementary School.* Danville, Ill.: Interstate Printers and Publishers, 1946.

———. "Portable Mathematical Laboratory for In-Service Teacher Education," *Educational Research Bulletin,* XXXIX (April, 1960), 85-91, 103.

Wilson, Guy M. "How Profitable Is the Usual Problem Work in Arithmetic?" *Arithmetic Teacher,* V (March, 1958), 94-96.

Woodworth, Robert S., and Saul B. Sells. "An Atmosphere Effect in Formal Syllogistic Reasoning," *Journal of Experimental Psychology,* XVIII (August, 1935), 451-60.

VII STRENGTHENING PRIMARY GRADE PROGRAMS

Agnes G. Gunderson, Formerly University of Wyoming

INTRODUCTION

BIBLIOGRAPHY

INTRODUCTION

An effective mathematics program for children in the primary grades makes use of many teaching methods, a variety of teaching materials, an understanding of child development, and above all a creative teacher. The mathematics program developed in the primary grades has distinctive characteristics when compared with mathematics programs for older pupils. Some of the issues growing from this distinctive character and the current thinking of educators are presented in this chapter. Readings have been divided into three areas:

1. Mathematical concepts of children
2. The mathematics program
3. The role of the teacher

Mathematical Concepts of Children

Pupils do not begin to develop "number sense" upon entering the first grade. Many number concepts have been developing for several years. An effective mathematics program in the primary grades takes into consideration this background of understanding. It considers the effects of intelligence as well as children's thought patterns in developing concepts. The understanding of the pupil, and his growth and development, then, is one of the cornerstones of an effective mathematics program.

The Mathematics Program

A second cornerstone is the development of a good mathematics program. An effective program for young children consists of not only workbooks, textbooks, film strips, and other commercially prepared materials but also various activities and experiences such as playing store with real or toy money, making number charts and scrapbooks, constructing a grocery store or postoffice, and measuring each other's heights and weights. Enrichment units such as the history of telling time or a unit on money are frequently used in primary grade classrooms. The making of original problems is also an important feature of an effective program. At first children solve problems orally, usually from their own buying or sharing experiences; later they can write and illustrate them.

Some words or terms which characterize a desirable program in mathematics for young children are: *discovery, meaning* or *understanding, manipulative materials* for all children, *number concepts* and *relationships, original problems*, and *fraction concepts*.

Discovery is an indispensable part of the good mathematics program in the primary grades. Through the use of manipulative materials the child discovers meanings and understandings of the various mathematical processes; he solves simple problems in addition and subtraction, in multiplication and division. Through the use of fractional parts or cut-outs, he also discovers fraction concepts and relationships.

The importance of "beginning mathematics" or "mathematics readiness" has only recently been recognized. As a result, greater emphasis is now being placed on these important features of a mathematics program. More and more, teachers are realizing that working with manipulative or semi-concrete materials is not merely preparation for later mathematics work. Discovering mathematical ideas or concepts through the use of these materials is mathematics. So-called readiness work usually consists of developing concepts, meanings, understandings, and relationships. The development of these aspects of mathematics is of great importance as they are the foundation of mathematical knowledge and understandings to be gained in later years.

The Role of the Teacher

The third cornerstone of an effective program concerns the identification of the role of the teacher. The skillful teacher questions more and tells less; she must listen while the child tells what he has discovered—perhaps the reverse of what she herself experienced in the primary grades when the teacher did the telling, demonstrating, and explaining, while the child watched and listened. Learning takes time; the child must not be hurried in his discoveries; he must be given time as well as opportunity to tell what he thinks and to explain how he figured it out. The teacher recognizes that there is more than one correct way of solving a problem; for example, a multiplication problem may be solved by addition, a division problem by subtraction. She frequently asks the class if they know a different way to work the problem. The effective teacher realizes that the development of thinking or reasoning skills involved in problem solving represents a major responsibility of the primary arithmetic teacher.

In selecting the readings which follow, the writer had in mind the graduate student, teacher, or supervisor working in the field of elementary school mathematics. It is assumed that the readers are familiar with basic texts in the methods of teaching arithmetic, so methods as such are not included. The aim was to select writings relative to present issues in the teaching of elementary school mathematics. These readings have been organized under three headings: mathematical concepts of children; the mathematics program; the role of the teacher.

PART I: MATHEMATICAL CONCEPTS OF CHILDREN

ACHIEVEMENT BY PUPILS ENTERING THE FIRST GRADE

Angela Priore

When asked "how many inches in a foot?" the five-year-old child, his first day in first grade, removed his shoe and counted his toes. The question again was repeated to him. Very arrogantly he eyed the interviewer and said, "Don't you know people have toes and not inches in their feet." Reluctantly the interviewer proceeded to ask the next logical question. "Johnny, how many feet are there in a yard?" To this question John hesitated for one moment. Then, appearing to be a little baffled, he could be heard in almost a whisper, speaking as if to himself, "Joey, Jimmy, Tommy, Peter—that makes four and me is five, five and five more is ten." "I know," he yelled, as pleased as punch. "There are ten feet in a yard." The interviewer gave quite a perplexed look, to which John grinned with all the satisfaction a five-year-old could possess, and said, "You didn't think I knew, did you?" When Johnny was asked how he arrived at this number he said, "Simple, all you got to do is add both feet of all the boys that play in your backyard."

Daily, children are confronted with arithmetical facts. How do they react to them? The child in the above interview was not familiar with the meanings of feet and yards, as we know them, but was able to compute five and five more. He remembered that children have two feet each, which was a factor in arriving at ten. Do we meet the needs of the individual children in our classrooms today? Do we attempt to discover how much understanding they have in arithmetic? Do we adjust our teaching to meet their needs, or do we adjust their needs to meet our teaching? These are typical questions which are asked constantly. The answers can only be arrived at after we conscientiously attempt to discover what

[From "Achievement by Pupils Entering the First Grade," *The Arithmetic Teacher*, IV (March, 1957), pp. 55-60. Reprinted by permission of the author and *The Arithmetic Teacher*.]

children know when they come to school, then adjust the curriculum to develop understandings from this point.

The problem is not only disturbing to the classroom teacher, but to parents, industrial leaders, college professors, etc. The cry has been that children are not gaining the understandings in arithmetic. Arithmetic is not being taught meaningfully.

In September, 1953, during the first two weeks of school, all the children entering the first grade for the first time in a school in upstate New York were tested by the same examiner in a room set up for the testing program.[1] The object of the test was to determine how much arithmetic boys and girls knew when they entered school. An assumption was made that the curriculum could be adjusted later to meet the needs of the children entering first grade.

In order to test all the various phases of arithmetic, it became necessary to make a test with 14 subheadings. The time for this would be approximately thirty minutes per pupil, with the test administered orally. The games were made varied and interesting to hold the interest of the child for such a long period of time. Many of the objects used in the test were blocks and pegs, which children had used in kindergarten. A number of these were placed in closed boxes to keep the children interested and not to sway their attention when working with one test.

A careful study had been made of all existing tests in this field on this level. An assimilation was made of all the types of items which are most helpful in a test of this nature. The test was then developed with the items placed according to their level of difficulty.

Test 1—Rote Counting

1. Counting by 1's
2. Counting by 10's
3. Counting by 5's

In the test of rote counting, the child was merely asked to count by 1's, as 1-2-3, by 10's, and by 5's. The results showed the average ability to count to 29.69 by 1's. This is a result that should be viewed carefully. A number of our workbooks for the first grade advocate spending weeks on counting from 1–10; however, a number of children can count beyond this their first few days in school. If this is true then some adjustment should be made immediately. Children were less able to count by 10's.

---

[1] This survey was made in a single school in a city of 100,000 population and involved 70 children. The clientele of the school is considered average.

Only 10 per cent could count to 100, while only 4 of the children tested could count to 100 by 5's. This is a revelation, since we do not attempt this until the later part of the first year or during the second grade. If children can count groups at the beginning of the year, maybe they are ready for instruction in group work.

Test 2—Rational Counting

1. Counting by 1's
   Scatter 100 discs on a table before the child.
2. Counting by 10's
   Place ten groups of tongue depressors, with ten in each group, in front of child. Take one bundle apart and show that it contains 10.
3. Counting by 5's
   Place 20 groups of colored pegs, with five in each group, in front of child. Take one bundle apart and show that it contains 5.

In the rational counting test a measure was being made of the child's ability to note the one-one correspondence of numbers with objects. In counting by 1's the children were able to count on the average to 29.77, which was slightly higher than the rote counting. Although the children were not familiar with counting by 5's and 10's, they seemed to be able to get the idea in rational counting and made some attempt at it.

Test 3—Reproducing

Ten colored blocks were placed on the table in front of the child. He was asked to give the examiner 5, 3, 6, 4, 7, 2, 8, 1, 9, and 10, of the blocks. The test showed that over 75 per cent of all the children tested could reproduce numbers to 10 by selecting the correct number of blocks when they enter first grade. Every child tested scored perfectly on the numbers 1, 2, and 3. An interesting observation made was that more children could reproduce 10 than 9. Perhaps they are more familiar with groups of 10.

Test 4—Identifying

This involves a more difficult task than reproducing. The child is shown a specific number of beads and asked to tell how many there are. The order in which they were asked was 5, 3, 6, 4, 7, 2, 8, 1, 9, 10. This, as had been expected, was more difficult. Fewer children were able to identify the correct numbers of beads. However, 59.9 per cent of the children could identify all the numbers up to 10. If over half the children can do this at the beginning of the grade, there appears a need for grouping in arithmetic.

Test 5—Combining with Objects

Small blocks were used for this test. The test was given in the following manner. The examiner would say, "If I give you 2 blocks (as this was said, 2 blocks were placed on the table, and covered with hand), and then I give you 2 more (cover these with hand), how many blocks would you have?" The following combinations were used.

5 and 1	6 and 2
2 and 4	4 and 1
9 and 1	1 and 2
2 and 3	3 and 2
3 and 7	

The most commonly known addition fact was 2 plus 2. Three-fourths of the children tested knew this combination. Closely following this was the combination 1 plus 2, which 74 per cent of the children were able to compute. It appears that in any combination when one was added to another number it was easy to get the answer. This probably implies that children understand the sequence relationship of numbers. They understand that any number following another number in counting, is one more than the number preceding it. The most difficult combination was 3 plus 7. However, in every other combination, over 34 per cent of the children could provide an answer. Some of these combinations are not taught until the second half of the first grade. Many schools will not teach any combination with answers more than ten in the first grade. Some adjustment will need to be made, if the truth is that children can combine to ten when they first enter first grade.

Test 6—Combining without Objects

No objects were used for this game. The directions given were to tell how many things Mother had brought us from the store. In investigating Mother's imaginary bag we found she brought many things which we already had at home. When these things were combined how much would we have all together? The combinations were the same as those used in Test 5. Some of the items which Mother brought were boats, balloons, oranges, bubble gum, crayons, cherries, peppermints, popsicles, airplanes, teddy bears. Items used were those which the author felt would appeal to boys and girls. We must keep in mind that the children had no objects to manipulate or visualize in this test. The child had the task of transposing the abstract number in his mind to something more concrete and then combine the two figures. The results of the test were close to those of Test 5. The test showed that 14.25 per cent of all the children tested could compute all the combinations. The most difficult combination also was 7 plus 3. Over 26 per cent or one-fourth of all the children could compute all the other combinations with 2 plus 6 being second in difficulty.

Test 7—Separating with Objects

Small beads were used for this test. The directions for this were "I will give you 2 beads (put 2 beads before the child) and when I take one back (remove 1 bead) how many beads do you have left?" The following combinations were used:

2–1	8–4
5–2	6–1
3–1	7–3
4–3	9–2
6–5	5–3

The hardest combination to subtract was 2 from 9, and the easiest was 1 from 3. Fifty per cent of the children were able to do most of the subtraction facts given. This may be due to a number of reasons. However, if they can do this much at the beginning, they may be ready for instruction in this phase of numbers.

Test 8—Separating without Objects

This test was given without any objects. It resembled Test 6 in scope. The children were told that they were to pretend that they were going to have a party. After giving some of the items away to the guests, how many would be left? The imaginary items used were pears, party hats, dolls, marbles, blocks, packages of gum, balls, books, drums, and kittens.

As you can recall, the test items (see Test 7) were listed in order of difficulty. This test was more difficult, although each combination received correct responses from some of the children. The most difficult was 2 from 9, which 14.3 per cent of the children knew. This test had the same type of difficulty as Test 6, which was to transpose the imaginary items to numbers in the head, and then obtain the correct response. The easiest combination was 1 from 2, which 91 per cent of the children were able to do. Although this test was rather difficult, the children seemed eager to continue and made attempts to discover the correct answers. No one was anxious to discontinue and everyone was interested in going on.

Test 9—Fractions

A felt board was used to test fractions. Three colored circles of the same size were divided into fourths, thirds, and halves respectively and placed on the felt board. The child was told to pretend that these circles represented pies. "If someone asked you (the child) for ½ a pie, which piece would you give him?" The same was done with ¼ and ⅓. The results of this test reveal that 50 per cent of the children knew ½, ¼ and ⅓. This concept of fractions is considered to be difficult and is not introduced into the grades for a while. However, if the children come to school with the ability to identify these fractions, they may be ready to learn a little more about fractions. The most difficult of the fractions was ¼ which 50 per cent were able to recognize. The next in difficulty was ⅓ which 51.4 per cent were able to recognize. The easiest was ½ and 77.5 per cent were able to recognize this. Children have many occasions to divide objects in half; half a candy bar, half an orange, and half a glass of water. They have recognized the connection between half and something divided into two parts. Perhaps they don't realize that half means two equal parts, at this point, but they connect half with two, which is a beginning understanding. The same is true of ¼ and ⅓.

Test 10—Facts

There are certain facts in arithmetic which children learn sometime. When are the children ready to learn these facts? Some of them have been included in this test. The fact that the largest percentage of children knew was the number of eggs in a dozen. The children who knew were asked how they knew the answer. A few of them responded that their mothers had egg containers. They said they had counted the number of spaces in it. Almost 10 per cent of the children knew the number of feet in a yard. The next fact according to correct responses was the number of days in a week. Closely connected with this and receiving almost the same amount of correct responses was the number of days a week you come to school. Following this was the number of inches in a foot. Only 4 per cent of all the children tested knew the number of hours in a day. It is interesting to note that more boys are cognizant of these number facts in arithmetic than girls are.

Test 11—Recognition of Symbols

We are under the assumption that children enter school unable to read and write. There are many exceptions to this rule, but it is an assumption which applies to the majority of situations. However, the next test was for the child to recognize the symbols that represent the numbers 1–10. These numbers were placed in random order on a 5 by 8 inch card. The children were asked to point to the number which represented 3–7–5–2–6–8–4–9–1–10. More children were able to recognize 3 than any other number. The number 7 was recognized by 60.15 per cent of the children. The same number of children who recognized the number 2 also knew the number 8. About 43 per cent of all the children recognized all the numbers through 10. The most difficult number to recognize was 6, which 43 per cent of the children knew. Next to this was 9, which 44 per cent knew. This combination is often difficult for children to recognize and some children continue in later months to write 6 when they mean 9 and vice versa.

Test 12—Judgments

Certain judgments are made daily by all of us. When do these have their beginnings? How do storekeepers estimate a pound of grapes before placing them on the scale? How can a dressmaker estimate 3 yards before measuring it? How can a baker estimate a quart of liquid? A few judgments were asked for. A quart of milk is a very familiar item in the home. Each child has been exposed to it by the time he enters school. However, when presented with it and asked to identify it, only 59.9 per cent of the children were able to do so. Practically the same number of children were familiar with half a pint which is not as frequently used as the quart. A little over 5 per cent of the children recognized a pint, which can be readily understood. The pint bottle is not often seen by children in their everyday experiences. In the questions concerning linear measure more children recognized the yard than the foot and inch. Forty-four per cent of the children could estimate which of four boxes contained a pound of candy. Twenty-nine per cent could recognize which of four lengths was an inch, while 21 per cent could recognize a foot. The results of this test may show that children have heard these terms and are familiar with them.

Test 13—Money

We realize that children have experiences with money long before they come to school. They are sent to grocery stores, are given allowances, have piggy banks, and other such means of handling money. Because of this a section on money was included. Over 75 per cent of the children tested knew which is more—3 pennies or a nickel. Next to this in order was, "Which is the same as a dime—6 pennies or 10 pennies?" which 71.3 per cent knew. Fifty-seven per cent knew, "Which is more—12 pennies or a dime?"; while 56 per cent knew, "which buys more, a nickel or a dime?" Fifty-three per cent knew, "Which is the same as a nickel—5 pennies or 8?" The next in order was the number of pennies in a nickel which 35.75 per cent knew and following this was the number of pennies in a dime which 25.5 per cent knew. The most difficult concept here was the number of dimes in a dollar. No girl was able to answer this and only 14 per cent of the boys knew the answer. Perhaps boys have more experience with more money earlier in life than girls do.

Test 14—Time

This test was sub-divided into two areas: identifying and reproducing. The results show that 41 per cent of the children could reproduce the number 2, and 35.5 per cent of them could reproduce the number 4. The number 12 was identified by 25.6 per cent of the children while 21.3 per cent could identify 9. The results show that children can reproduce time more easily than they can identify it. However, most people teach children how to identify first, which may be harder. The hour 9 was chosen because it is the time school begins and it was felt that children may have become familiar with it. In the same reasoning 12 was used because it is lunch time. Two and four were picked at random. However, more children were familiar with the two numbers which were picked at random.

Conclusions

From the results of this test some conclusions can be drawn. Children have many uses for arithmetic prior to entering school. This is evidenced by the amount of knowledge they possess when they enter school. They employ numbers in games, addresses, phone numbers, television, etc. Numbers are a part of their everyday experience. Consequently it is deemed advisable to begin the right kind of arithmetical instruction in the first grade.

The incidental approach to the teaching of arithmetic does not guarantee that the children will learn all the skills and concepts needed to better understand arithmetic. A systematic approach would provide for an orderly development of concepts. Since the development of skills takes time the teacher should provide varied experiences to direct children to discover higher and more mature procedures. The curriculum for teaching arithmetic in the primary grades should be based on the amount of arithmetic children know when they come to school.

The first question to consider is the ability of the children to learn arithmetic. We may assume that with proper instruction more arithmetic can be taught. It would be an insult to the intelligence of most of them to spend a number of weeks teaching what they already know.

Another question to be considered is the need of the first grade children to learn arithmetic. Since the children have "incidentally" gained so many skills before entering school, they must have had a need motivating them to learn. There are many "social" uses prevalent in young children's experiences for arithmetic. A number of games intended for five and six-year-olds demand some knowledge of arithmetic to be played successfully. The desire to use the telephone promotes the recognition of numbers in many cases. Judgment words, such as *pound, dozen, foot,* are used in store and play activities. According to these facts one may note that children do need arithmetic. If for no other reason, some may need it to be accepted by their peers.

It is not possible to outline a good program from the conclusions of this study alone. However, it may be seen that a revision in the present curriculum should be made to provide for a systematic program which is based on understandings and meanings. We owe this to the children who enter school with some background and a desire to learn.

WHAT NUMBERS MEAN TO YOUNG CHILDREN

Agnes G. Gunderson and Ethel Gunderson

Twenty years ago a study [1] was made at the University of Wyoming of number ideas or concepts held by a group of 17 pupils at the University Elementary School at the completion of the first half of the second grade.

[From "What Numbers Mean to Young Children," *The Arithmetic Teacher*, VI (October, 1959), pp. 180-85. Reprinted by permission of the authors and *The Arithmetic Teacher*.]

---

[1] Agnes G. Gunderson. "Number Concepts Held by Seven-Year-Olds," *The Mathematics Teacher*, XXXIII (January, 1940), 18-24.

This inventory or study showed that seven-year-olds have many contacts with the use and application of number in their daily work and play. It indicated that children learn many number concepts and associate various meanings and understandings with numbers 1–12.

The thought occurs: If a similar study were made now, 20 years later, how would the findings compare with those of the earlier study? This led to making such a study with a group of 26 seven-year-olds in Grade Two in the Willets Road School, East Williston, L. I., New York, at the beginning of the second semester of the school year 1958-59.

The same technique was used in this study as in the earlier one. The teacher asked the pupils to tell all they knew about the numbers 1–12. Questions such as: What does *five* mean? What is *five?* What does *five* make you think of? How can you show *five?* Do you know anything else about *five?* All work was oral, the teacher jotting down whatever responses the children made—most of these were in statement form.

Arithmetic work previous to the inventory had been with concrete and semi-concrete materials, using counters to show groupings and to solve problems. Learning and using measures: feet, yards, pints, quarts, dozen, hours, days, weeks, months, and years. Making a calendar for each month. Solving problems in addition and subtraction with sums and minuends to 10. Counting and writing numbers to 100, Roman numbers to XII. A chart with numbers to 100 used for meaning and sequence and referred to as our number system. Adding numbers to 10, such as 10 and 6, 10 and 3, Workbook for Grade Two. The number facts taught as related numbers.

$$
\begin{array}{cccc}
3 & 4 & 7 & 7 \\
+4 & +3 & -3 & -4 \\
\hline
7 & 7 & 4 & 3
\end{array}
$$

Fraction concepts of halves, fourths, sixths, thirds, and eighths. This content or subject matter is similar to that noted in the 1940 (Wyoming) study with this exception: in the earlier study pupils had had no work with fractions or fraction concepts. In the recent study the teacher had devoted one week, in early February, to the teaching of fraction concepts. A description of this work [2] is reported elsewhere. This work with fraction concepts preceded the taking of the inventory.

---

[2] Agnes G. Gunderson and Ethel Gunderson. "Fraction Concepts Held by Young Children," *The Arithmetic Teacher* (October, 1957), 168-73.

TABLE 1

Number Concepts

ONE

*One (word)
*1 (figure)
 1 is an odd number
*1 is the first number in the number system
*1 object (book, box, pencil, etc.)
 1 is my lucky number
 We have one universe
 We have one beautiful outdoor environment
 We have lived on only one planet
 We have one moon going around our planet
 You have one life; you should take care of it
 Do one thing at a time
 You are only allowed to have one wife at a time
 There is one Dr. Doolittle
 Pray to only one God
*One-year-old baby
*One month until my birthday
 One more year and we will be in Third Grade
*One more week we are moving to New York City
*Jack's baby brother is one month
*It is one minute after 2 o'clock now
*One o'clock in the morning I sleep
 George Washington was the first president
*January 1 is the first day of the year
*Last year I was in First Grade
 Here is one dollar

$$0 + 1 = 1 \qquad 2 - 1 = 1$$

TWO

*Two is the word for the number 2
 2 is an even number
*2 (figure)
*II (Roman number)
*2 objects
*2 arms, 2 legs, 2 feet, etc.
 Two is a homonym
 Channel 2 is a good channel
*Our easel has two sides on which we can paint
 We have two poles on the globe— South Pole and North Pole
 Two knobs on most doors
 You have two parents unless there is a divorce
*We have two days in our week-end
*My baby sister Amy is two years old
*We are in Grade Two
 Moses split the Red Sea in two parts
*I fell down twice on the ice
*It is 2 minutes after 9 o'clock A.M.
*Monday is the second day of the week
 November is second to the last month in the year
 B is the second letter in the alphabet
 2 tens make 20
*2 halves make a whole
*2 nickels make a dime
 2 pints make a quart
*2 counters measure 2 inches
 200 pennies make 2 dollars
 2 eighths make a fourth

$$1 + 1 = 2 \qquad 5 - 3 = 2 \qquad 4 - 2 = 2$$
$$100 - 98 = 2$$

THREE

*Three (word)
*3 (figure)
*III (Roman number)

---

* Similar comments were listed in the 1940 (Wyoming) study.

3 is an odd number
*3 objects
*My family has three children
*We had a three-layer cake
*Run has 3 letters
*Three Blind Mice
*I liked the story of The Three Bears
*At 3 o'clock we are home from school
X is the third letter from the last in the alphabet
C is the third letter in the alphabet
*Tuesday is the third day of the week
The middle finger is the third in line
March is the third month of the year
*3 feet make a yard
*3 counters measure 3 inches
3 sixths make a half
3 thirds of a pie make a whole pie
3 parts would be 1 third each
*Three 3's make 9

$$8 - 5 = 3 \quad 5 - 2 = 3 \quad 9 - 6 = 3$$
$$6 - 3 = 3 \quad 1 + 2 = 3 \quad 2 + 1 = 3$$

FOUR

*Four (word)
*4 (figure)
*IV (Roman number)
*4 objects
*Four is a homonym as four, for
*The number before 5 is 4
4 is an even number
*4 is the fourth number in our number system
On Saturday Channel 4 has basketball
4 is my lucky number
In the alphabet D is the fourth letter
A lucky clover has 4 leaves
*A square has 4 sides
*The word cent has 4 letters
*My dog has 4 legs
I have 4 dollars in my bank
A human being has 2 legs and 2 arms and that makes 4

When we buy butter there are 4 sticks in the pound
There are 4 second grades in our school
Without your thumb you have 4 fingers on a hand
*My sister is 4 years old
Every four years we elect a president
*Four o'clock is Junior Town on TV
My pencil is 4 inches
*It is 4 minutes to 9 now
The fourth finger is the one you wear a ring on
*Wednesday is the fourth day of the week
April is the fourth month of the year
*Two pairs of shoes are 4 shoes
*In fractions you need 4 fourths to make a whole
4 eighths make a half

$$7 - 3 = 4 \qquad 10 - 6 = 4$$
$$14 - 10 = 4 \qquad 1 + 1 + 1 + 1 = 4$$
$$2 + 2 = 4 \quad 3 + 1 = 4 \quad 5 - 1 = 4$$

FIVE

*Five (word)
*5 (figure)
5 is an odd number
*5 objects
*5 is the fifth number in the number system
*We count by 5's
5 is really 5 ones
*We usually have 5 schooldays a week
*5 pennies make a nickel which is 5 cents
We traveled in New England; we traveled in 5 states
*There are 5 fingers on one hand
If you cut a pie in 5 pieces that would be fifths
*At 5 o'clock I watch Abbott and Costello

*When you are 5 you are a pretty big boy

My hand is 5 inches long

Five years is kindergarten age

Five more minutes it will be 10 o'clock

Tom Thumb is a little above 5 inches

Michael is the fifth child from the lectern

*My birthday is January 5th

E is the fifth letter in the alphabet

*May is the fifth month in the year

If you are 15 and you take away 10 years you'd be 5 years old

*3 boys and 2 girls make 5 children

*1 girl and 2 boys and parents make 5 in a family

$$4 + 1 = 5 \qquad 7 - 2 = 5$$
$$2¢ + 3¢ = 5¢ \qquad 9 - 4 = 5$$

SIX

*Six (word)

*6 is a Hindu-Arabic number

*VI is a Roman number for 6

*6 objects

6 is an even number

*5 comes before 6

*7 comes after 6

Wonder has 6 letters

Channel 6 doesn't show a picture on our TV

Some insects have 6 legs

*After you are 6 you are a big boy

*Ellen is 6 years old

6 minutes before 12 noon

*3 feet is a yard so 6 feet are 2 yards

The average man is about 6 feet tall

*When you are 6 you are in first grade

*Our family eats dinner at 6

6 inches is half a foot

*F is the sixth letter of the alphabet

*Sixth Grade is the last grade in this school

Three pairs of mittens makes 6

Two 3's make 6

*3 dozen and 3 dozen is 6 dozen

If you cut a pie in sixths you have this

1 sixth of a pie is enough for me

$$9 - 3 = 6 \qquad 10 - 4 = 6 \qquad 8 - 2 = 6$$
$$7 - 1 = 6 \qquad 12 - 6 = 6 \qquad 3 + 3 = 6$$
$$2 + 2 + 2 = 6 \qquad 4 + 2 = 6$$
$$2 + 4 = 6 \qquad 1 + 5 = 6 \qquad 5 + 1 = 6$$

SEVEN

*Seven (word)

*7 (figure)

*7 objects

7 is an odd number

*6 comes before 7

7 ones make 7

On the back of Mickey Mantle's shirt is number 7

Good shows are on Channel 7

We cross the Seven Seas

Seven Voyages of Sinbad

Michael has 7 letters

*I am 7 years old

*Number 7 is the seventh number in the number system

*A week has 7 days

*Seven more years I will be as old as my brother

*We usually take 7 quarts of milk a day

*Seven minutes until 11 o'clock

From kindergarten it takes 7 years to get out of this school

700 pennies is 7 dollars

Some people have a shoe size 7
*July is the seventh month of the year
*Saturday is the seventh day of the week
1 nickel and 2 cents make 7 cents

$$6 + 1 = 7 \quad 5 + 2 = 7 \quad 4 + 3 = 7$$
$$3 + 4 = 7 \quad 3 + 2 + 2 = 7$$
$$8 - 1 = 7 \quad 14 - 7 = 7 \quad 9 - 2 = 7$$
$$10 - 3 = 7 \quad 11 - 4 = 7$$

EIGHT

*Eight (word)
*8 (figure)
*8 is the eighth number in our number system
*8 objects
An octopus has 8 legs
Charlotte (spider in book *Charlotte's Web*) has 8 legs
There are 8 planets besides the earth
We can't get a picture on Channel 8
*I am already 8 years old
When a Brownie is 8 years old she is happy
You have to be 8 to be a Cub Scout
*8 o'clock is bedtime
It takes a jet about 8 hours to go to France from here (Long Island)
If you went to the store and you wanted a half pound of something you could say, "Give me 8 ounces"
Each of my counters measures 1 inch so it takes 8 counters to make 8 inches
*The 8th of March is on a Sunday
Two pies cut in fourths make 8 pieces

If you cut a pie in eighths like this you have 8 pieces

$$5 + 3 = 8 \quad 4 + 4 = 8 \quad 16 - 8 = 8$$
$$2 \times 4 = 8 \quad 7 + 1 = 8$$

NINE

*Nine (word)
*9 is Hindu-Arabic
*IX is Roman number
*9 objects
*Counting by 3's
Counting 1, 3, 5, 7, 9
*9 is the ninth number in the number system
*8 comes before 9
9 boys on a baseball team
9 planets in the solar system
*My friend is 9 years old
9 feet is long
*Some people go to bed at 9 o'clock
9 inches
September, the ninth month
I is the ninth letter of the alphabet

$$3 + 3 + 3 = 9 \quad\quad 6 + 3 = 9$$
$$7 + 2 = 9 \quad\quad 2 + 7 = 9$$
$$4 + 5 = 9 \quad\quad 5 + 4 = 9$$
$$10 - 1 = 9 \quad\quad 18 - 9 = 9$$
$$11 - 2 = 9 \quad 100 - 91 = 9$$

TEN

*Ten (word)
*10 (figure)
*In Roman numbers 10 is X
*10 is the tenth number in the number system
10 is an even number
*10 comes after 9
Our whole number system is based on tens
*Counting by 2's to 10
*10 objects

*There are 10 fingers on two hands

There may be 10 planets but we are sure of 9

*I bought a microscope for 10 dollars

Once my father got something on Channel 10

Recreation has 10 letters in it

*We usually have recreation at 10 o'clock

There are 10 months in the school year

When you are 10 years old you are in Fifth Grade unless you skipped

This book measures 10 inches

The Long Island Railroad is usually 10 minutes late, my father said

*10 cents is a dime

When it is 10 degrees it is real cold

Sometimes in some parts of the world like Alaska it is 10 degrees below zero

It takes the bus about 10 minutes to come from my home to school

10 acres is a lot of land

Some trees are 10 feet tall

*May 10th is Shaarie's birthday

I weighed 6 pounds and 10 ounces when I was born

*2 nickels makes 10 cents

If you had 2 pies and you cut one in fourths and the other in sixths you would have 10 pieces of pie

$$5 + 5 = 10 \qquad 6 + 4 = 10$$
$$20 - 10 = 10$$

ELEVEN

*Eleven (word)

*11 (figure)

*XI is 11 in Roman numbers

Eleven rhymes with seven

*11 objects

11 is made up of 1 ten and 1 one

11 is an odd number

11 is my lucky number

*11 is 1 less than 1 dozen

Channel 11 has sports

Mickey Mantle hit 11 home runs

*My address is 11 Field Lane

11 inches is almost a foot

*At 11 o'clock A.M. we usually read

My brother gets out of kindergarten at 11 o'clock

Shock Theater is on at 11 o'clock

My baby brother is 11 months old

11 feet is the height of the classroom

11 hours is a long time, 11 minutes is not so long

*My brother is 11

*November is the eleventh month

*The eleventh grader is a junior in high school

$$5 + 6 = 11 \qquad 2 + 8 + 1 = 11$$
$$8 + 3 = 11 \qquad 3 + 8 = 11$$
$$6 + 5 = 11 \qquad 7 + 4 = 11$$
$$4 + 7 = 11$$

TWELVE

*Twelve (word)

*12 is Hindu-Arabic

*Roman number 12 is XII

*12 is the 12th number in the number system

*12 objects

"Time of Wonder," the name of our mural, is 12 letters

*A dozen things is 12

Most kids are in junior high school when they are 12

*12 years old

When a girl is 12 she usually gets a boy friend

*12 o'clock is our lunch time

*There are 12 hours from night until today

*Our poetry folder is 12 inches long

Lincoln's birthday comes the 12th day of February

L is the 12th letter of the alphabet

*12 is 10 and 2

I can buy 2 five-cent candy bars and 2 pieces of gum for 12 cents

One dime and 2 cents make 12 cents

I can buy 4 snack milks for 12 cents

I can buy 12 bubble gums for 12 cents

We have 6 windows in this room. Each window has 2 curtains. That makes 12

*Three 4's are 12

*Four 3's are 12

*6 and 6 are 12

TABLE 2

Fraction Concepts

ONE HALF

You could say the earth is divided in half by the equator; there is the north half and the south half

*Our library table is in two parts, each part is a half

Split a day in half and you have 12 hours

*From me down to Paul, the room is cut in half

*You have 10 counters; you divide them in half, you then have 5 counters

I can eat a half pound of meat

*Sometimes there is a half moon in the night sky

A half is to split something in two equal parts

*Two halves make a whole

Two half hours make a whole hour

*I can eat a half pie

2 fourths make a half

4 eighths make a half

3 sixths are a half pie

You can cut anything in half

If you cut a fourth in half you have 2 eighths

*A half quart of milk

Two sides to the world; one half is light, one half is dark

*A half dollar is 50 cents

A nickel is half of a dime

You can split a half dollar in half and you have 2 quarters

In some foreign money you have a half penny

By Wednesday noon half the week is gone

*We can buy a half pound of nuts

I weigh 65 and one half pounds

Monday divided in half: Mon-day

*If you have 4 pencils, half would be 2

$$10¢ - 5¢ = 5¢$$

ONE FOURTH

*If you had a pie cut in fourths you'd have 4 pieces

*A fourth is littler than a third

A fourth is bigger than a sixth

If I wanted 1 fourth of an English muffin, first I'd halve it in the center, then cut each piece in half

It takes 2 eighths to make a fourth

If you divide an hour in fourths you have 15 minutes or a fourth of an hour

*4 fourths make a whole

Three months is 1 fourth of a year

If I cut a pie in fourths and if I eat 1 piece I'd have 3 fourths of the pie left

In a fourth of an hour it will be 10 o'clock

Friends came over; we cut a pie in eighths. We ate 6 pieces; there were 2 eighths or 1 fourth of the pie left

One fourth of the moon is about like this (sketch)

I asked my sister for a fourth of the cake but she gave me 1 half of the fourth which is, as you know, an eighth

Put 8 children in a row

XX, XX, XX, XX

Ronnie and Richard make a fourth;
Amy and Debby make a fourth;
Penny and Shaarie make a fourth;
Ken and Gerri make a fourth

Put 4 children in a group

x

x   x

x

Each child would be a fourth: Paul, Ellen, Sally, Debby

A fourth of a banana isn't very much

ONE THIRD

One third piece of pie is big

*You have 3 pieces if you cut a pie in thirds

1 third is bigger than 1 fourth

2 sixths make a third

About 1 third of the planet is land; 2 thirds is water

*3 thirds make a whole

From January until April is 1 third of a year

20 minutes is 1 third of an hour

Sometimes we see just 1 third of the moon

On the hard-top where we play, it is 1 third of an acre

Conclusions

In comparing the responses given in this study with those of the study made 20 years ago, one notes many number concepts common to both studies. Each study reveals some ideas not shown in the other but the similarities are far greater than the differences. Both studies show that seven-year-olds understand the smaller numbers 1–12 rather well. They know: the word denoting the number, the Hindu-Arabic number, the Roman number, the number system, the cardinal and ordinal meanings of numbers. They are able to read the clock and the calendar; to compare numbers, e.g. 9 is more than 8. They know some of the easy addition and subtraction facts; they recognize numbers used as identification, such as "Channel 4" and "Fourth Street."

The pupils in the earlier study gave a larger number of addition and subtraction facts and a larger number of words denoting quantity, such as *double, couple, twins, duet,* but their comments did not reflect science learning nor much of social studies, whereas in the recent study a knowledge of science is revealed in comments about jets, planets, TV, etc. An awareness of social mores is seen in these comments: "You have two parents unless there is a divorce. When a girl is 12 she usually gets a boy friend."

It is interesting to note items 7–15 in Table 1. These comments show a more specific meaning attached to *one* than do the others. Do these seven-year-olds sense the "one and only one" meaning here, which adults often give to word *one* in similar comments?

This recent study shows changes in the school curriculum over the 20-year period, particularly the increasing attention given to the teaching of science—planets, television, jet planes, universe, were not mentioned in the 1940 study.

The responses given by children in this study reflect approved practices in the teaching of arithmetic which courses in teacher education, methods courses, professional magazines, modern textbooks and accompanying teachers' manuals are striving to promote. The key words of modern arithmetic teaching are *meaning* and *discovery*. The following comments indicate an understanding of the meaning of various measures:

11 hours is a long time; 11 minutes is not so long
11 feet is the height of the classroom
10 acres is a lot of land (this concept would vary with environment; it would be true for a child living in an urban area; to a child living on a large cattle ranch, for example, 10 acres would seem a small plot).
The hard-top where we play is 1 third of an acre
If you wanted half a pound of something, you could say, "Give me 8 ounces"
3 feet is a yard so 6 feet are 2 yards;
An average man is 6 feet tall (this from an adult's viewpoint would be an erroneous statement, but from a seven-year-old the statement is acceptable because 6 feet is more nearly the average man's height than is 5 feet.

That the number system can be meaningful to young children is seen in these comments:

4 is the fourth number in our number system
5 is really 5 ones
2 tens make 20
11 is made up of 1 ten and 1 one
Our whole number system is based on tens

In accord with modern theories of teaching arithmetic, fraction concepts are now taught a long time before children encounter the fraction symbol in their textbooks. Comparing the 1940 study (data taken in 1939) with this study (1959): the 1940 study lists very few comparisons of fractions or fraction equivalents; those are

2 halves in 1 whole
4 fourths in 1 whole
2 quarters is 1 half
1 fourth is less than 1 half
1 half of 1 half is 1 fourth

while the recent study lists these and many more. This greater knowledge of fractions shown in the recent study is, no doubt, a result of early teaching of fraction meanings or concepts wherein children through the use of fractional parts or cut-outs discover fraction concepts by superimposing one fractional part over another to see how they compare in size. Looking over the comments about fractions made by the pupils in this inventory one realizes this is time well spent. The comments show an understanding or insight into fractions far greater than that revealed by the pupils in the earlier study.

This inventory, like the 1940 study, is not exhaustive; the concepts listed are those which the child recalls. No doubt he would recognize many more than he is able to recall.

From the responses given above we see that seven-year-olds have a wide use for number; it is not relegated to the arithmetic class only; they use it in all their daily activities. As they are given further opportunities for discovering more and more meanings or concepts about number so will they become more efficient in their quantitative thinking.

FRACTION CONCEPTS HELD BY YOUNG CHILDREN

Agnes G. Gunderson and Ethel Gunderson

What can we do to help children gain a better understanding of what fractions are and what they mean? How can we give the child a longer acquaintance period with fractions before he is required to work with the written symbols?

In an attempt to find out what concepts and ideas young children have about fractions, a study was made with a group of children in Grade Two in the Willett's Road School, East Williston, Long Island, N. Y. Individual interviews were had with each of 22 children; two of the 24 children enrolled were absent that week. A separate room was available for the interviews which were held the first week in February, 1957. No attempt was made to get an exhaustive record of each child's knowledge of fractions. The interviews lasted only as long as the children talked spontaneously and easily; some of them kept talking and discovering all the while their

[From "Fraction Concepts Held by Young Children," *The Arithmetic Teacher*, IV (October, 1957), pp. 168-73. Reprinted by permission of the authors and *The Arithmetic Teacher*.]

replies were jotted down. Ten to fifteen minutes was the average length
of each interview.

Introductory Lesson

Because these children had had no work with fractions, the following
lesson was taught before beginning the interviews: Each child was given
four paper circles 5 inches in diameter. Then these directions were given:
Fold one of your circles in the middle. Open it. How many parts does it
show? Children answered, "2." What is each part called? "One half." How
many halves are there? "2." Take another circle and fold it the same way.
Fold it in the middle again. Open it. How many parts does it show? "4."
What is each part called? Here the children answered, "a quarter." The
term "quarter" is significant; it indicates that the children have had out-
of-school experience with fourths (the usual textbook terminology) but
in talking about these parts, they use the word "quarters." Through questions such as "How many parts does the circle show?" "What other word
could we use besides 'quarters' that would tell there are 4 parts in the
circle?" the word "fourths" was elicited. How many fourths does your
circle show? "4." What is each part called? "1 fourth." Color 1 fourth.
What part of your circle is colored? "1 quarter, 1 fourth." Color 1 more
fourth, one next to the one that is colored. What part of your circle is
colored now? Answers were, "2 quarters, 2 fourths, 1 half." Similar work
was done with another circle to get eighths. A set of flannel circles was
cut at the same time so as to have them for the flannel board. Another day
circles marked for thirds were given the children, and thirds and sixths
were taught in the same way.

All work was oral—not even the symbols $\frac{1}{2}$, $\frac{1}{4}$ were written on the
board.

Fractional parts of circles were used because it is easier for young children to recognize fractional parts of circular wholes than fractional parts
of other shapes. A square or rectangle such as a whole sheet of paper, for
instance, seems to become smaller wholes when cut in halves, thirds, or
fourths.

Interviews

The flannel board and circles (pies) cut in fractional parts were used
during the interviews.

In the interviews, not all children were asked the same questions. Some might be asked, "Which is larger, 1 *half* of a pie or 1 *fourth* of a pie?" others, "Which is more, 1 *third* of a pie or 1 *sixth* of a pie?" Always they were asked, "How do you know?" or "How can you be sure?" Besides defending their answers, the children were asked to think aloud as they worked and to tell other things they discovered about these parts. The word "fraction" was not used at all. The children had no difficulty in identifying fractions or fractional parts. When asked, "Give me 1 *third* of a pie; Point to 1 *fourth* of a pie; What is this piece called? Why is it called that?" they would respond, "This is 1 *third* because there are 3 of them; 1 *sixth* because the pie is cut in 6 pieces; 1 *eighth* because there are 8 parts." Only one child seemed a little uncertain but identified all parts correctly, talking as she did so: "I think this is 1 *fourth;* 1 *eighth?*, I might pick a small piece; 1 *third,* I think I'd pick a big piece; 1 *sixth?* I think I'd pick one of these (pointing to pie cut in sixths); 1 *half* (no hesitation), *that* is very big."

1. Asked "Which of these pies show half a pie?" Kathe said, "All these make half a pie" as she pointed to 4 of the *eighths,* 2 of the *fourths,* 3 of the *sixths,* 1 of the *halves.* Then pointing to the pie cut in *thirds,* she said, "I don't know how to get half of this pie." George, who was later asked the same question, said: "Two of these pieces (fourths) add up to one half; 3 *sixths* add up to one half. This ⊘ doesn't show 1 half (then folding 1 of the *thirds* double). Yes, if you cut 1 of these pieces (thirds) in half ⊕ it will show half a pie."

2. How does this pie ⊕ show half a pie? Steven: "2 *fourths* is half a pie; (then added) you need another 2 *fourths* to make a whole pie. 4 *eighths* is half a pie too."

3. How many *eighths* would I need to have half a pie? Janet replied, "4, because $4 + 4 = 8$. $8 - 4 = 4$; (then added) you would not need as many *sixths* for 1 half pie as *eighths* because *sixths* are bigger." To this same problem Barbara added, "3 *sixths* of a pie is 1 *half* pie."

Comparing Unit Fractions

While the question named the object as well as the parts, e.g. Which is bigger, 1 half of a pie or 1 third of a pie? the children did not always answer so fully, saying only "1 *half,* 1 *third,* 1 *sixth.*"

Questions dealing with unit fractions were given at the beginning of each interview as these seem simpler than other fractions. The responses indicate which fractions were being compared. Many responses were duplicated by several children; only different responses are given here.

Richard said, "1 *half* of a pie is bigger than 1 *third* of a pie." Another child placing 1 *fourth* over 1 *half*, said, "1 *half* is bigger than 1 *fourth*."

Stephen: "1 *fourth* is a bigger piece than 1 *sixth* because when you have more pieces they are smaller."

Cydney: "1 *third* of a pie is larger than 1 *fourth;* 1 *fourth* is a little smaller because there are more pieces."

Leslie: "1 *third* is more than 1 *sixth;* it is 1 *sixth* more."

Marian: "You need 2 *sixths* for 1 *third*."

4. Which is a bigger piece, 1 *third* of a pie or 1 *eighth* of a pie? Cydney: "One *third* is a bigger piece; (then superimposing) if you took 3 *eighths*, it would be about the same but 1 *eighth* is smaller."

5. Judy, you may take a piece of pie. (She chose 1 *half*). I'll take this piece (1 *fourth*). Which piece is bigger? Judy: "1 *half* is bigger because it takes 2 of the *fourths* to make 1 *half*."

6. Which is smaller, 1 *eighth* of a pie or 1 *third* of a pie? Susan: "1 *eighth* is a smaller piece than 1 *third* but the pie divided in *eighths* has more pieces."

7. Another kind of reasoning was revealed in Marian's answer to "Which is more pie, 1 *sixth* of a pie or 1 *fourth* of a pie?" "1 *sixth* is more 'cause 1 *sixth* is 6 (holding up 6 fingers); 1 *fourth* is 4 (holding up 4 fingers)." Talking on as she superimposed "I think it is more. No, 1 *fourth* is more." Such reasoning is frequently found among children who have difficulty with fractions.

Multiple Fractions

1. Which is more, 2 *halves* of a pie or 2 *thirds* of a pie? Laurence: "2 *halves* is more; 2 *halves* is a whole pie; 2 *thirds* is not a whole pie."

2. Which is less, 2 *eighths* of a pie or 2 *thirds* of a pie? Shep: "2 *eighths* is less. *Eighths* are the smallest pieces; *thirds* are next to the largest. 2 *eighths* are only 1 *fourth*, and 2 *thirds* are bigger than 1 *fourth*."

3. Stephen, you may have 7 *eighths* of a pie. I have 2 *thirds* of a pie. Who has more pie, you or I? Stephen: "3 of my *eighths* about cover 1 *third;* (talking as he superimposes) I'll see; that's the only way to find out. I have about 1 *eighth* more."

4. Which is more, 2 *thirds* of a pie or 2 *sixths* of a pie? Richard (superimposing): "2 *thirds* is more; 2 sixths cover only 1 *third*. If you had 2 *sixths* more they would cover. (Then added) You could make a whole pie with 1 *half*, 1 *third*, and 1 *sixth*."

5. Which is more, 6 *eighths* of a pie or 3 *fourths* of a pie? Stephen: "2 of these *eighths* make a *quarter;* (then as he covers each fourth with 2 *eighths*) they are the same."

6. In this problem an indirect solution was used: Which is more, 2 *fourths* of a pie or 2 *sixths* of a pie? Shep: "2 *fourths* is more; 1 *fourth* is

one-half of one half; put 2 *fourths* together, it is 1 *half*. 2 *sixths* is not 1 *half;* you need 1 *sixth* more."

7. Which is more, 1 *half* of a pie or 2 *sixths* of a pie? Robert: "2 *sixths* is more because more pieces; (then superimposing) No, 1 *half* is more."

Whole and Mixed Numbers

These children had no difficulty in carrying out directions such as: Give me 1 whole pie and half a pie; 1 whole pie and 1 third of a pie, and so on. For the whole pie they would select an uncut pie; for the fraction they would take a piece from the pie cut in the appropriate parts. One exception was Cydney who chose the pie cut in halves for the whole pie and 3 of the sixths for half a pie.

1. Give me 1 and 1 *half* pies. How many *half* pies can I have? Susan: "Cut this whole pie in *half* and you will have 3 *halves*. That is 1 *half* more than a whole pie."

2. Give me 1 whole pie and 1 *fourth* of a pie. If this pie were cut into *fourths,* how many *fourths* would I have in all? Marian: "1 whole pie is 4 *fourths,* add 1 *fourth,* that is 5 *fourths.*" Which is more, 5 *fourths* or 3 *fourths?* "3 *fourths* is only this (pointing to 3 of the *fourths*); 5 *fourths* is 1 more *fourth* than a whole pie. It is 2 *fourths* more or half a pie more than 3 *fourths.*"

3. Betty, you may have a whole pie. (She chose the one cut in eighths.) Will you give me 2 of those pieces? Now, how much pie do I have? Betty: "If you put them together, you'd have 1 *fourth,* but if you don't, it still would be 2 *eighths.* I have more than half a pie left. I have 6 pieces, 6 *eighths* of a pie; that is 2 eighths more than half a pie."

4. If you have 2 whole pies and give away 1 *fourth* of a pie, how much would you have left? Barbara took 2 pies (1 whole pie and the one cut in *fourths*). She then took away 1 of the *fourths* saying: "I would have 1 pie and 3 *fourths* left."

5. Another problem in subtraction: If you have 8 *eighths* of a pie and give me 3 *eighths,* how much pie will you have left? Mike: "5 *eighths,* that is 1 *eighth* more than *half* a pie."

6. Mary took 1 *sixth* of a pie, Jill took 1 *sixth,* and Linda 1 *sixth.* How much pie did all of them take? Janet: "3 *sixths.*" Barbara: "1 *sixth* and 1 *sixth* and 1 *sixth* are 3 *sixths.*" What part of the pie was left? "1 *half* of the pie was left."

Using Fractions

1. Which of these pies has the biggest pieces?
Jill: "The pie cut in *halves.*"

How many people could you serve with this pie?

Jill: "Two, you could serve 4 if you cut each piece (half) in *half*."

2. Which pie will serve the most people?

Shep: "The pie cut in *eighths* serves the most people, but the pie cut in *halves* has the largest pieces."

3. From which pie could you give 1 serving and have the most pie left?

Stephen: "The pie cut in *eighths* because that has 8 pieces. 8 *eighths* take away 1 *eighth* is 7 *eighths*."

4. Mrs. Gay wants to serve 5 people. Which pie should she take? Cydney: "She'd probably use this one ⊗ . She'd have 1 piece left over." Shep reasoned this way: "There is none cut in 5. She should get the one cut in *sixths*. She would have 1 left over. She could use this one ⊗ (*eighths*) but she'd have 3 pieces left over. It would be better to have only 1 left over."

5. If Mrs. Gay were serving 7 people, which pie should she take?

Richard: "She'd better take this one ⊗ (*eighths*). There will be 1 piece left over."

Billy: "She wants to serve 7, she must take the *eighths*. 1 *eighth* will be left."

Robert: "To serve 7 people, take the pie cut in *eighths;* she'll have 1 for herself. To serve 5 people, take the *sixths;* she'll have 1 for herself."

Marian: "To serve 7, choose this one ⊗ (*eighths*). The people who are served this pie get smaller pieces than those served from this pie ⊗ (*sixths*). When you cut more pieces, they are smaller."

6. Take 2 pies and 1 fourth of a pie. How many people can you serve with pieces of this size (¼)?

Janet, taking 2 whole pies and 1 fourth of a pie, said, "I can serve 4 from this pie and 4 from this pie. $4 + 4 = 8$ servings, and 1 more piece. I can serve 9 people."

The following comments reveal the generalizations reached: "If you want many pieces, cut them small. Big pieces make few pieces. The smaller you cut them, the more you get. When you cut many pieces, the pieces get smaller. If you cut pieces smaller you have more. Small pieces, many pieces."

Conclusions

This study indicates that the concept of fractions may well be introduced in Grade Two. These seven-year-olds showed an ability to grasp the meaning of fractions, some showing a deeper insight than others. It is significant, however, that all of them had gained (through their previous experience, including the introductory lesson) the ability to recognize fractional parts, to compare them, and to make the generalization that the more parts a thing is divided into, the smaller the parts become. But, note, the children were able to do this because they had these fractional parts before them—manipulative materials that they could see and superimpose —in other words, they told the answers as they discovered them by using these concrete representations of fractions. One would not say, nor should one expect, that they could have answered these questions without these objects, nor should one wish them to do so.

Note also that the problems were given orally. To hear some one *speak* of one half of a pie is far different and much more meaningful than merely to see the symbol ½.

The question may arise, "When second graders can do so well, why should fifth graders find fractions difficult?" To take a specific instance: much learning is needed to bridge the gap between discovering with manipulative materials how much is left of 1 whole pie after giving away 1 fourth of it, and working with numbers the example: $1 - \frac{1}{4} = ?$.

We are familiar with the three stages of learning number concepts: the concrete, the semi-concrete, and the abstract. Many courses of study plan as a year's work the meaning and use of numbers up to 6. Should we not give fraction concepts fully as much time as concepts of whole numbers? Yet when we compare the amount of time allowed for mastering the concepts of 1-place numbers with that of mastering concepts of simple fractions we can see that the child is rushed through the beginning work in fractions which develops the meaning and into the computation of fractions in their written form. Perhaps, he is given no more than a superficial introduction consisting of a lesson or two with concrete materials such as fractional cut-outs of paper, cloth, or wood. This introduction usually takes place a day or two before work with fractions as outlined in the textbook, which means that the pupils have only a few days' acquaintance with fractions before being asked to work such examples as these: $\frac{2}{6} + \frac{1}{6} = ?$ $\frac{3}{4} - \frac{1}{4} = ?$ True, children are older than they were when learning concepts of whole numbers, but maturity in dealing with arithmetic meanings does not come simply by getting two or three years older or through incidental out-of-school activities.

Even though the children interviewed in this study answered correctly almost every question asked, yet they are far from ready to do the computational work as presented in textbooks. A planned systematic program for developing the meaning of fractions is essential as readiness or preparation for working with fraction symbols.

What are the reasons for difficulties with fractions and what help can we give? Up to the time children encounter fractions in written form, they have dealt with whole numbers, each number retaining its intrinsic value; that is: 2 means 2 things; 3 means 1 more than 2; 4 means 1 more than 3 and so on. But in fractions such as $\frac{1}{2}$, $\frac{2}{3}$, etc. the numbers no longer retain their intrinsic value. Heretofore 2 has meant 2 things but in the fraction $\frac{1}{2}$, 2 means that something has been divided into 2 equal parts. Up to now when the child has seen the example: $1 + 2 = ?$ he has added 1 and 2. Likewise: $4 + 4$. Seeing these same numbers in this form: $\frac{1}{4} + \frac{2}{4} = ?$ is it strange that he gives the answer as $\frac{3}{8}$? He probably sees two examples in addition with one addition sign and one equal sign serving for both examples.

Then there are other things that may confuse or bewilder the child: the likeness in the sound of words, for instance, yet with such different meanings as seen in the following:

four	4	*fours*	$\begin{array}{r}4\\ \times 3\\ \hline\end{array}$
fourth	$\frac{1}{4}$	*fourths*	$\frac{3}{4}$
eight	8	*eighths*	$\begin{array}{r}8\\ \times 5\\ \hline\end{array}$
eighth	$\frac{1}{8}$	*eighths*	$\frac{5}{8}$

It is small wonder that the child becomes confused. Only through many meaningful experiences with each and all of these symbols and their number names can we expect children to become well acquainted with them and master fraction concepts.

It would seem that an interval of two years or more between a child's first introduction to fractions, as illustrated in these interviews, and the time he is expected to work such examples as: $\frac{4}{8} - \frac{2}{8} = ?$ and $\frac{1}{6} + \frac{3}{6} = ?$ is not too long.

This acquaintance period should provide for planned systematic work with manipulative and semi-concrete materials. Flannel boards and fractional cut-outs should be available for this work. Other shapes such as squares and rectangles as well as circles may be used. Children may play games with fractions, make up problems using them, and report any uses of fractions in out-of school activities. We should take advantage of every opportunity to teach fractions using apples, candy bars, cookies, birthday cakes and other school treats. Surely there is no better way to make fractions meaningful and delightful to children than to eat them.

In the beginning when writing or recording the work with fractions it is well to use the word rather than the symbol, i.e., writing "3 fourths" rather than $\frac{3}{4}$. Later the denominator as well as the numerator may be expressed in symbols. Fractional parts of a group may also be taught when children are ready, but this is more advanced work than fractional parts of a whole.

It may be wisdom to let the children set the learning pace. There is danger in hurrying. The teacher's task is to provide the materials and encourage children to make discoveries.

PART II: THE MATHEMATICS PROGRAM

ARITHMETIC IN THE PRIMARY GRADES

Edwina Deans

The time is ripe for a reconsideration of arithmetic in the primary grades. Concentrated study of the mathematics program in the junior and senior high schools is in progress. In addition to several foundation-sponsored projects, many school systems are taking a critical look at the elementary arithmetic program to re-examine goals, content, and method in relation to children's abilities and needs.

A many-pronged approach to the problem will be fruitful if the mathematicians who know arithmetic and the educators who know children and learning can work together effectively to achieve improvement. An open mind, free from preconceived set ideas, but with hypotheses to be tested, is an equally effective weapon to apply to the present curriculum and to new projects in the making.

The primary teacher has been a pioneer in knowledge of children, their growth, behavior, and learning. Yet, even at that level, in too many instances arithmetic has been taught mainly as application or as repetitive practice or drill. We need to take a long look at the missing elements as we recognize the value of application and repetition. One missing element is the large body of developmental learnings which help the child put meaning into arithmetic as a subject. Another missing element is the recognition that arithmetic embodies concepts, generalized ideas, and relationships, which, when carefully developed, help the child see the application to life situations and reduce the amount of repetition necessary for permanent learning.

[From "Arithmetic in the Primary Grades," *The National Elementary Principal*, XXXIX (October, 1959), pp. 22-8. Reprinted by permission of the author and *The National Elementary Principal*.]

Perhaps we can focus more clearly on these missing elements if we turn our attention to the purposes of the primary arithmetic program.

Purposes of Primary Arithmetic

The potential success of any program is affected by the purposes which have been established and accepted for it. The purposes of the primary arithmetic program may be summarized as follows.

1. To guide the child as he uses arithmetic to solve his day-by-day problems both in and out of school. Guidance by the teacher helps to insure meaning and application and provides a better understanding of the type of motivation that will enable the child to experience success with the arithmetic he needs and can use.

2. To help children learn that arithmetic is interesting and fascinating, that they can discover how it works, its systematic quality, its relationships, its laws, its possibilities. For example, $3 + 4$ gives the same answer as $4 + 3$; one added to any number gives one more; when zero is added to or subtracted from a number, the number does not change.

3. To help every child learn as much arithmetic as he is capable of learning at the time it can be learned most economically and efficiently.

The purposes of a program are partially met through the nature of the content, so our attention may now be turned to this important area.

Content of Primary Arithmetic

Manuals to the more recent arithmetic series outline the content which is generally presented in the primary grades. Differences in expectations by the end of grade three are slight, though there are variations in the amount of content to be covered in grades one and two. Until we have more evidence than is now available, school systems should probably continue to use text materials as a guide for the basic arithmetic program. Any adaptations that are made within a school system should be planned with county or city-wide approval so that gaps and repetitions in content will not occur.

With administrative approval, a school staff might well carry out action research in arithmetic to lend cumulative evidence on some of the questions on which there is still no uniform agreement.

1. Can the simple multiplication and division facts be discovered at the same time as addition and subtraction? As a child learns that $8 + 4$ are 12, can he also learn that 3 fours are 12? As he learns that $10 - 2 = 8$, $10 - 4 = 6$, $10 - 8 = 2$, $10 - 6 = 4$, can he also discover how many 2's

in 10 by finding that 2's may be arranged in single groups of 2 or in multiples of 2?

2. Can first- and second-graders gain a workable knowledge of the two subtraction ideas in problem solving known as the missing number and comparison? Can abstract understanding be expected or should the solution remain at the concrete level for most children?

Comparison: John has 5¢; Tom has 8¢. Who has more? How many more cents does Tom have? Is it not natural for a child to think of the comparison problem in terms of how many cents match and how many more there are? Both boys have 5¢; 8 is 3 more than 5 so Tom has 3 cents more. Is there a simple way for young children to record this thinking?

Missing Number: John has 7¢; he wants 15¢. How many more cents does he need? Some experimentation to find the simplest form for recording and solving problems of this type for young children would be helpful. Is it not natural for children to record the "how many more are needed" problem as missing number addition? E.g., $7 + ? = 15$.

3. To what extent can first- and second-graders gain a workable understanding of the number system as based on ten? Is teaching five as a subgroup of ten a useful learning for developing an understanding of ten as a base? For example, are number lines with the separation of the first five by color or spacing from six or seven useful for helping children see the subgroups which make up these numbers?

Providing for Differing Abilities

In addition to content, good arithmetic programs have certain characteristic features. The first of these is that *a good arithmetic program in the primary grades makes provision for the differences in abilities of children.* Some type of inventory testing at the beginning of the year is needed to ascertain where children are. Scores on the arithmetic section of the readiness test usually given to first-graders are helpful. At the second and third grade levels, group and individual informal inventories may be used.

One growing trend in administrative grouping places a teachable group of children with similar learning abilities and needs together as a subgroup within a class. This procedure enables the teacher to plan materials and activities which will better meet the needs of slow learners, very able children, children with a special interest in arithmetic, and those of just average ability.

To teach any primary class successfully the teacher must have a good understanding of the total arithmetic program for the elementary grades and specific knowledge of the methods and content for at least two grades below and two grades beyond the grade being taught.

According to most authorities on the teaching of arithmetic, the program for the more able children at the primary level should be enriched on a broad base rather than moving them into the work of the next grade level. Under ideal conditions, which would enable a subgroup of children to remain together over a period of years so that repetition could be avoided, both horizontal and vertical enrichment might well take place. At present, this seems a hazardous undertaking at the primary level because of turnover in staff and student population and the difficulty in maintaining a rapidly paced program throughout the child's school career. We might better lend our energies to discovering the possibilities for enrichment at each grade level, discover new and different applications of arithmetic, broaden the meaning for each process taught, and help children build appreciations for arithmetic.

Slower children need a wide variety of experience of every type, not just more drill as is commonly believed. It is indeed a challenge for the teacher to find a sufficient number and variety of experiences for effective initial presentation and for reteaching as necessary. It is sometimes difficult to realize that slow learners will be acquiring the same arithmetic abilities a year or more later than normal children and that this period of time must be profitably filled with meaningful arithmetic experiences.

While grouping children for arithmetic instruction within the classroom is not practiced as widely as in reading, it is essential for some activities. The occasions for grouping and the size of groups depend on the activity and the materials being used. If children are working with concrete materials, for example, the teacher may find it extremely difficult to foster a give and take of oral responses which reflect ways of thinking if the group exceeds ten or fifteen children.

As children approach the oral drill stage in learning, even smaller groups of two, three, or four children may be necessary in order to provide the opportunity for them to respond many times to the drill material.

Some teachers prefer to maintain ability groups for the developmental aspect of the arithmetic program. Others seem to achieve good results from introducing and demonstrating new arithmetic work to the whole class. Then flexible subgroups are selected on the basis of different group needs.

Often when a more advanced aspect of a process is to be introduced, there is need for reteaching the lead-up skills for the new learning. This necessitates setting up a subgroup of children who are weak in the specific lead-up skills involved. The subgroup works prior to or parallel with the new learning and stays together until their goal is accomplished. The teacher's purpose is to select the types of flexible grouping which permit discovery, emphasis on ways of thinking, and reasonable management. Each teacher must decide the types of grouping or combinations thereof which are consistent with his purposes and with which he is most successful.

Levels of Maturity in Learning

A good arithmetic program recognizes levels of maturity in learning. How many ways can a child find the answer to the abstract number fact $4 + 5 = 9$? Beginning with the lowest and progressing to higher levels, the steps might be somewhat as follows:

1. *Guessing:* Guesses wildly, indicating no idea of sizes of groups involved.
2. *Counting:* Counts by ones inaccurately, or counts by ones correctly
3. *Partial Counting:* Counts one group only:

$$4 - 5, 6, 7, 8, 9, \text{ or } 5 - 6, 7, 8, 9.$$

4. *Grouping:* Visualizes grouping patterns:

$$00 \quad 00 \qquad 0\ 0 \quad 0\ 0$$
$$00 + 00 + 0 \ ; \ 000 + 000 \text{ less } 1.$$

5. *Relationships:* Senses abstract relationship to a known fact:

$$4 + 4 \text{ are } 8 \text{ so } 4 + 5 = 9,$$
$$\text{or } 5 + 5 \text{ are } 10, 4 + 5 \text{ is } 1 \text{ less, so it's } 9.$$

6. *Knowing:* Knows fact immediately with understanding as evidenced by child's ability to prove his answer.

Other methods used by children are counting by multiples, a combination of counting and grouping, and relating to another process such as subtraction fact from an addition fact and division fact from a multiplication fact. The teacher needs to know this progression of steps in thinking so that children may be guided from the lower ones which show lack of understanding, are inaccurate, slow, and cumbersome, to those which show good understanding, are accurate, quick, and efficient.

It is difficult for the teacher to be sure of the levels of thinking children are using in written arithmetic work, though some children oblige by making marks or dots on their papers or by counting their fingers. The teacher's chief avenues for diagnosis are through the oral arithmetic periods and observation of the child's reactions to concrete materials. Group interaction is an excellent way of helping children progress to more mature ways of thinking. As a child listens to others describe their modes of thought, he may indicate his own readiness for a higher level by his apparent grasp of the idea and his willingness to experiment with it himself.

Experimenting by Children

A good arithmetic program makes it possible for children to experiment and to discover much of the arithmetic they will learn in the elementary grades. It is true that there are a few arithmetical learnings which must be learned by rote—for example, the number names and symbols. Fortunately, few learnings are purely of this nature. The basic understandings in the processes and in the application of processes to problem solving may be facilitated through experimentation. This indicates that teaching is far more than telling. It must provide the means for finding out. Children who experiment and find out for themselves tend to be more interested and to retain longer than those who parrot answers they have been told.

Discovery can take place on several levels. At one early stage in their development, children may discover facts in any of the processes by manipulating concrete objects. As they manipulate seven objects, for example, they discover that seven can be separated into two groups; that it makes no difference which of the two groups is read first (4 and 3 or 3 and 4; 5 and 2 or 2 and 5); the answer is still seven. As they work, they arrive at a fundamental law of addition and multiplication, the Commutative Law, which says that the answer is the same regardless of the order of the numbers.

Discoveries may also take place with pictured groups on a semi-concrete level. For example, geometric patterned arrangement of a number may be presented for children to discover all the various ways of making two groups:

0 | 00	000	00 | 0 |	0 | 00
0 | 00	000	00 0	0 | 00
0 00	000	00 0	00 | 0
2 and 7	3 and 6	1 and 8	4 and 5
7 and 2	6 and 3	8 and 1	5 and 4

Discovery may also take place by thinking through relationships on an abstract level: 8 and 9 as one more than 8 and 8; 8 fours as twice 4 fours; sixes in 42 as the number of sixes in 30 plus the number of sixes in 12.

Understanding the Number System

A good program in arithmetic helps children to develop understanding of the number system. They soon learn that:

1. Each of the numbers from one through nine and zero has a definite meaning in terms of quantity.

2. This quantity meaning gives each its place in ordered sequence.

3. Each has a name by which it is known.

4. Each is an abstract idea which can be represented with things, with pictures, with groups, or with line arrangements.

5. These numbers help to answer questions about how many and which one.

6. These numbers can be combined or separated, giving us many ways of referring to the same quantity. For example, 6 may be separated into 2 and 4, 1 and 5, 2 and 2 and 2, 4 and 1 and 1, 3 twos, 2 threes; it is what is left when we take 2 from 8; and it describes how much larger 8 is than 2.

As the number sequence is extended from ten through 99, children learn that:

1. Each number now has two meanings—a quantity meaning and meaning in terms of the place in which we put it. For example, 50 means 5 tens and 0 ones. Because two places are needed to express tens, the zero must be used. It must be used also to indicate that there are no ones.

2. Each number between 10 and 20 is made up of ten and a number quantity with which children are already familiar: 16 is 10 + 6; 16 is also 10 + (2 + 4) or 10 + (1 + 5).

3. For two-place numbers the number at the left describes the groups of ten; the number at the right describes the group of ones.

4. What we know about combining and separating numbers one through nine and zero also applies to combining and separating numbers above ten.

$$\begin{array}{r} 13 \\ + 2 \\ \hline \end{array}$$ 3 and 2 are 5; 13 is 10 and 3; so 13 and 2 is the same as 10 and 5 are 15.

$$\begin{array}{r} 38 \\ - 6 \\ \hline \end{array}$$ 6 from 8 is 2; 38 is 30 and 8; 6 from 38 is 30 and 2 or 32.

$$\begin{array}{r} 65 \\ - 8 \\ \hline \end{array}$$ 65 is six tens and 5 ones; we think of 65 as 5 tens and 15 ones; 8 from 15 is 7; so 8 from 65 is 57 because 8 from 15 is 7 and the tens number is decreased by one ten.

5. We use two places to record numbers between 10 and 99. We need another place to record numbers between 99 and 999. One-hundred-two may be thought of as:

H	T		
1	0	0	One group of a hundred, no tens, and a group of
		2	two ones; or
	10	2	ten groups of ten and two ones;
		102	one-hundred-two ones.

6. What we need or want to do with numbers helps us decide how we think about them. If we wish to take 48 from 64:

T	O
5	14
4	8
1	6

We know that 64 is 60 and 4; now it will help us to think of 64 as 50 and 14. The amount we have is the same in either case. We have changed the way we describe it because the new way makes it easier for us to subtract 48.

7. We need to change numbers or think about them in other ways when we combine certain groups.

T	O
3	5
+4	9
7	14
or 8	4

5 ones and 9 ones are 14 ones; 14 ones may be thought of as 1 ten and 4 ones; this ten may be combined with 3 tens and 4 tens to make 7 tens.

Children may be guided to discover when *numbers must be changed to make adding and subtracting easier. They can discover that:*

1. Whenever the combined number in one's place exceeds nine, they can think the groups of ten with other tens they have. They can extend this thinking to apply to tens and hundreds places.

2. When the number of ones to be taken away is more than they have in one's place, they must rethink the amount they have, changing one of the tens to ten ones and combining them with the ones they already have in one's place.

Providing for Sequential Development

A good program in arithmetic provides for sequential development. Sequence and order are inherent in the number system itself. A concept of any number is based on an understanding of the meanings involved because of the place the number holds and an understanding of the quantities expressed by the numbers. One place numbers aid in the understanding of two place numbers and two place numbers serve to make three place numbers more meaningful.

The sequence for teaching processes is largely a matter of judgment. Certain sequences are fairly obvious; others are less clear. There is some evidence that the pattern of difficulty of the addition and subtraction facts relates closely to the size of the numbers involved. While this is probably accurate in a general sense, it may not hold entirely for children who have been guided to build and apply generalizations with regard to the effect of zero on any number, what happens to any number when one is added or subtracted, or how number facts are related to their opposites, to doubles and near doubles, and to tens and near tens. For these children, the most difficult addition and subtraction facts are those for which they can find the least help in the generalizations they are able to apply at the time.

As a guide line, it is undoubtedly wise to proceed from the simple to the complex. It is not always easy, however, to decide what is simple and what is complex for children in terms of their readiness, their background, and their ability to profit from classroom experience. The experience of many classroom teachers tends to indicate that some of the simple multiplication and division facts may be learned successfully by children along with the addition and subtraction facts. To illustrate, children explore groups at the left looking across the rows and down the rows to discover:

0000	four twos and two fours;
0000	
0000	three fours and four threes;
0000	six twos and two sixes;
0000	there are twice as many twos as fours.

Thus the relationship between 8 as $2 + 2 + 2 + 2$, as 2 and 6, as 4 and 4, becomes apparent to the child. In this way, multiplication facts help to reinforce addition facts. The same relationships may be discovered with regard to subtraction and division.

Certainly, children can solve simple problems involving fractions long before they know all of the facts in the four fundamental processes. Ask a second grader how many halves his mother gets from two grapefruit or from three apples. He will know and can draw a picture to prove his answer.

One important guide line in a consideration of sequence is that "seeing, doing, talking, and thinking" arithmetic can come much earlier than recorded arithmetic. Written arithmetic makes sense to the child only when it stands for the "seeing, doing, talking, and thinking" which he has already experienced many times.

Some learnings such as problem solving and number language accompany all process learning. We do not teach problem solving after facts are learned, but at every stage along the way, because a child can solve problems on any level. By placing the learning in a familiar situation, it becomes more real for him, helps him to see its value, and often creates a need and desire for more learning.

Learning to Solve Problems Mentally

A good program in arithmetic helps children learn to solve problems mentally. The greater part of the arithmetic we use in our daily life requires an ability to approximate, rather than find exact answers. Often the approximation is sufficient. When an exact answer is needed, the approximation helps to judge the correctness of the answer and to prevent gross errors in calculation.

Successful approximation presupposes a good understanding of the number system. The following example, adding 38 and 46, illustrates some of the ways children approximate answers:

Approximation: 38 is nearer 40 than 30; 40 and 40 are 80. The answer is more than 80 but less than 90; it's around 85.

Mental Solution: Progressing one step beyond the approximation to an exact answer, the child may think: "38 and 40 are 78 and 6 are 84," or "30 and 40 are 70 and 8 are 78 and 6 are 84." While he has been led in pencil and paper arithmetic to start with ones and proceed to tens, in mental arithmetic the more efficient way is to deal first with tens and then with ones.

Children profit from opportunities to try out different mental solutions, to analyze them, and to evaluate their effectiveness. Through this process they gradually arrive at efficient methods of mental solution. Many teachers make good use of odd moments to practice mental arithmetic skills.

Sufficient Practice and Drill

A good program in arithmetic provides for sufficient practice and drill to make arithmetic learnings permanent and readily available when they are needed. There has been some disagreement as to whether practice and drill are the same or different phenomena. A useful distinction for the teacher is to consider practice as varied and drill as repetitive. Practice implies that the teacher is using a variety of procedures for teaching a given learning and that these procedures are accompanied by demonstrations with materials, use of materials by children, and oral discussion of the whys and wherefores of the procedures. Furthermore, it implies that the teacher is inviting questions on the part of children and is following them up with further explanation and is urging children to prove correctness of answers.

Drill, on the other hand, implies that the exploratory, discovery, and discussion stages are past and all that remains to perfect the learning is repetition of the same thing in the same way. Drill, therefore, may occur with any procedure or with any activity to the point that it is thoroughly understood and well learned. The way a child responds to drill may indicate a need for more practice. In other words, to be effective drill must be applied only when a high level of thinking has been reached; otherwise, the child repeats and perfects his immature ways of arriving at answers.

It must be remembered that repetition alone will not help a child move from an immature level, such as counting by ones, to a higher level, such as seeing relationships or actually knowing the facts. Levels of thinking are raised not by repetition, but by opportunities to react, to question, to experiment, to explore, to discover, to prove. Children can be helped to analyze their own thought processes, to recognize when they have control of an area of arithmetic and are ready for drill work. Viewed in this light, speed is seen as a by-product of improved thinking processes, to be achieved by the elimination of ineffective ways of thinking rather than by taking timed tests. Excessive drill will not compensate for a meager program devoid of a variety of practice activities. In fact, the opposite is more likely: a variety of well-planned, teacher-directed and guided activities will reduce the amount of drill necessary to fix learning.

Supplemental Materials

A good arithmetic program provides some basic materials in addition to textbooks and manuals for teachers and children. Some of the recent research on materials tends to indicate that a few materials, carefully chosen and explored thoroughly from the standpoint of learning possibilities for children, are as satisfactory as a wide variety of materials. This finding may serve as consolation for school systems with limited monies for materials.

Lists of commercial materials may be found in the yearbooks of the National Council of Teachers of Mathematics, in issues of *The Arithmetic Teacher*, or obtained from the American Association for the Advancement of Science. In recent years, publishers of arithmetic textbooks have also made available some of the materials they recommend. Good commercial materials have instructions or booklets to assist the teacher in their use.

Almost any of the purposes served by commercial materials may be accomplished by teachers and children working together to collect and organize materials. For example, each child may collect his own set of sticks and bundle some of them into sets of ten, and use them to explore the possibilities for changing numbers. The same idea may be taught using strips of one-inch cross section manila paper for tens and separate one-inch squares for ones.

A hundred chart cut from cross section paper has infinite possibilities for exploring the number system. Marking in quarters helps children to group by fives and to avoid excessive counting. Children can learn to find any number on the chart without the aid of symbols. They find numbers by thinking of the tens and ones contained in them. Fifty-six means 5 tens and 6 more so it may be represented by 5 rows and 6 on the next row. Higher decade addition and subtraction are easily shown on the hundred chart.

56	Find 56 and move over 3 squares.
+3	Read the answer. (59)

67	Find 67 (6 rows and 7 more).
−4	Move back 4. Read the answer (63).

Children can also discover that:

1. To add ten to any number they find the number and move to the same position in the next row below; to add 24 they move two rows below and over four squares.

2. To subtract ten from any number they find the number and move up to the same position in the row above; to subtract 20, they move up two rows, to subtract 24, move up two rows and back 4 squares.

A ten-strip and a twenty-strip (strips of 10 and 20 squares) may provide a number line for discovering addition and subtraction facts. Children may draw balls in the center of each square, coloring the first five one color, and the next five another color, or in the case of the twenty line they may make alternate fives of different colors.

5	Find 5; move over 3. Read the answer.
+3	

9	Find 9; move back 4. Read the answer.
−4	

Use the two number lines together to illustrate a companion problem such as: "How much more is 16 than 7?" Place the 20 number line directly under the 10 number line with left hand squares matching. Find 7 in the 10 number line; find 16 on the 20 number line; read the number of squares between 7 and 16 on the 20 number line to find the answer.

These illustrations provide only a few of the many possibilities of a relatively inexpensive and extremely useful material.

In Summary

A good primary grade arithmetic program fosters the natural curiosity which children have with regard to numbers, and helps them build more appreciation for arithmetic as they learn its uses and possibilities.

The teacher who provides a good arithmetic program knows arithmetic, knows children and how they learn, and knows how to provide the arithmetic experiences which will result in rich living today and will serve as a foundation for future success in mathematics.

PART III: THE ROLE OF THE TEACHER

TEACHING MATHEMATICS IN THE KINDERGARTEN

Laura K. Eads

Teach them *more* and teach them *sooner*. This is an all too simple solution to our present-day need for better mathematicians, for more mathematicians, and for higher-level mathematical competence on the part of all consumers of mathematics (which includes us all). Let us agree that we should teach children more mathematics and that we should teach them sooner. Let us agree, moreover, that kindergarten is not too soon. But *what* mathematics we teach kindergarten children, *how* we teach it, and *when* we teach certain children—these considerations determine what they will really learn, not only in the kindergarten, but in all of the years of school to come.

Let us consider first whether children are *ready* to learn mathematics at kindergarten age. They *are* ready. A four- or five-year-old child has actually been learning mathematics for some time. When very young a child learns that he needs one shoe for one foot and another shoe for the other foot. Later he discovers that he needs two blocks or sticks of the same length, that Jerry has more candy than he has, that he can build the house higher than Mary can, that one more plate and knife and fork are needed when Aunt Susie comes to dinner, that he has only a half glass of lemonade.

[From "Teaching Mathematics in the Kindergarten," *Grade Teacher*, LXXVI (October, 1958), No. 55, pp. 134-35. Reprinted by permission of the author and *Grade Teacher*.]

Not all children are immediately ready to learn mathematics *in school* —where there are new adults, where many other children are competing for attention from these adults, where surroundings are strange, where there is a new set of rules for behavior, where communicating with anyone at all requires special effort. The kindergarten teacher knows that most of the children cannot *tell* her whether or not they are comfortable in school, or ready to learn mathematics in school. She knows that she must look for signs in her children's actions, in what they do or do not do—that this is their way of "telling" her how they feel.

Individuals All

The kindergarten teacher observes that some children move from one thing to another; they can't seem to concentrate on any one thing. One or two of these children may even be disrupting. She watches to see what the actions of these children might "tell" her. Are they avoiding children— all children, some children? Which? How do they get what they want? What happens then? Do any of them seem to need her close by? How do they show this? She sees also that there are some children who just sit, waiting to be told what to do next. These "tell" her they are very troubled, that they are much too afraid even to move about, much less to "take hold" of mathematical ideas. She notices that there are some who are so "different" in speech, in behavior, in appearance that other children avoid them. This "tells" her that these children need to feel accepted without any reservation before they can meet school expectancies successfully. A kindergarten teacher who is gifted with sensitivity to children's real needs, who can accept children for their differences and their individualities, is far along the road to helping her children develop an awareness of their intellectual capabilities and potentialities.

Planning Mathematical Experiences

Before they come to school, young children *experience* mathematical situations. In school, they need many more such experiences. At home, however, children's experiences are more or less unique; in school, children necessarily have experiences *in common*.

The kindergarten teacher makes plans so that all children can build a large reservoir of experiences. Later, they draw on these to talk about, to reflect upon, to integrate into meaningful mathematical patterns. Kindergarten children are collecting appropriate experiences as they play house, play going to market, build with blocks, model with clay, paint with water or watercolors, string beads, play with puzzles, play the cymbals and drums, play games, go on trips, eat and drink at lunch or parties, hop and skip and dance, feed the fish, water the plants, get the things they need, put things back where they belong. Experiences such as these take into consideration the fact that kindergarten children are still essentially physically oriented, and that they need opportunities to explore, to observe, to look into things, before they will be ready to adjust to what we mean when we say "learning the three R's."

The kindergarten teacher looks for the proper time to focus attention on mathematical aspects of experiences—with one child, with a group of children, with all children. She may start with Johnny, who is building a tall tower: Why did you use these blocks here? How many floors high is your tower? How did you build this bridge over the second floor? How high do you think you can build the tower? She may go to the group chatting freely in the houseplay area as "Mother" is preparing "dinner" for their "family": How many are there in the "family"? What dishes will you use for the table? How many of each? She may ask two or three children to help her place the library books on the bookcase shelf: What shall we do with the tallest books? How many books do we still need to fill the shelf? She may help a group of girls keep score. She may encourage Tommy to talk about the colored cubes he is putting together. She may help Stella select chairs to place at the table. She may ask Teresa how she knows the number of containers of milk to take for her group.

Developing Mathematical Concepts

In the kindergarten all children should have opportunities to grow in developing concepts—geometric concepts, measurement concepts, quantitative concepts, and concepts of fractional parts. The kindergarten teacher differentiates among levels of concept development; that is, she knows when a lower-level or higher-level development is being manifested. She knows whether particular children are developing mathematical concepts while they are participating in experiences. She anticipates next steps for a particular group of children and guides them toward these.

The teacher listens to children to find out what erroneous concepts they may be developing, what concept level they may have reached, or what concept level they are now ready to develop. She encourages children to talk by asking such questions as: How did you do it? Can you tell me about it? Such questions reveal more than: *What* did you paint? *What* is its name? Is it bigger? Would you like to _____?

The teacher herself uses only language that is correct mathematically. She uses the word *circle* when she refers to an appropriate curved line (not to a surface, or disc, or sphere, or ellipse). She uses the term *rectangular* (not "long square"). She makes sure that when she says *three*, the children know that 3 things are referred to (not as in counting 1-2-3, saying *three* but referring to *one*). She makes clear what is being compared when she uses a measurement term: *taller* than Mary (not "Jane is *big*"); *warmer* than yesterday (not "*warm* today"); *heavier* than this box (not "*heavy* box"). She indicates that Sarah's entire length is 46 inches (not only the top of her head). She uses the term *one-half* when she means 1 of the 2 equal parts (not for *any* part of a container of water or milk).

In the kindergarten, as in all of the succeeding grades, concept development is interpreted as growth in perception, thinking and judging. Children proceed from mere name-calling, to matching, to comparing, to meaningful counting as follows:

1. Children learn the names of things through association in experiences; for example, they learn number names ("three" for a group of 3 things), names of coins, measurement terms, geometric shapes, and terms for fractional parts.

2. Children match related things in experiences: coat with hook, cup with saucer, one child with one container of milk.

3. Children match patterns as they string beads, arrange blocks: 2 red, 3 green; 2 red, 3 green.

4. Children compare two quantities: more blocks (cubes) in this pile, more candy in this basket.

5. Children compare two measurements (non-numerical): lengths of blocks, positions of puzzle pieces, weights of boxes.

6. Children create patterns: arrange blocks from longest to shortest, string beads by fives.

7. Children compare fractional parts as they share with another child: halves of an apple or sandwich, half of the clay for you.

8. Children count things if the number cannot be perceived at once: plates in a stack, stairs as they are climbed, beads on a string.

Levels of Counting

Young children are able to perceive the number in a small group *without counting*. They may need only to learn the number name. *Emphasis on rote counting to 10 (or more), and counting small groups by ones seems actually to interfere with group perception.* Early emphasis on counting by ones also interferes later with the learning of number facts, since children then persist in counting by ones (using fingers, toes and so on).

Children grow in *number sense* as they have mathematical experiences with groups of things. They pattern a particular group and then rearrange this group in various ways. They compare groups of different sizes. They count, beginning not with one, but with the number in a known group. They count by groups both forward and backward.

Through counting experiences, kindergarten children are developing beginning concepts of addition, subtraction, multiplication and division.

INTRODUCING OUR NUMBERING SYSTEM IN THE PRIMARY GRADES

William H. Hausdoerffer

There are many objectives for the teaching of arithmetic in the primary grades. One of the most basic of these objectives is that of helping children to understand the place value principle of our number system. It is in the early grades that foundations of understanding are developed, but it should be pointed out that not until the student has studied exponents in high school is it possible for him to consummate these understandings in the richest possible way. It is the purpose of this article to discuss some of the fundamental approaches that can be used successfully in the primary grades.

Pre-Number System Learnings

One of the first things the teacher should make sure of is that the pupil has a good understanding of numbers from one to ten. This should include such abilities as being able to count to ten with understanding, being able to read and write numbers from one to ten, being able to make comparisons involving these numbers, and being able to analyze numbers from one to ten so that eight, for example, may be thought of as being composed of a group of six and a group of two, or a group of five and a group of three, etc. This last point involves the important concept of grouping which should be introduced by experiences surrounding such questions as which group is larger? Which group is smaller? How much bigger is this group than that group?

As in all good teaching, especially at the elementary level, the general pattern should proceed from the concrete stage to the abstract stage as gradually as is feasible. Usually the teacher should attempt to include two intermediate steps in the form of pictures and semi-abstract representations such as dots, crosses, circles, etc.

[From "Introducing Our Numbering System in the Primary Grades," *The Arithmetic Teacher,* V (March, 1957), pp. 61-3. Reprinted by permission of the author and *The Arithmetic Teacher.*]

The group concept which was mentioned previously is an extremely important prerequisite concept to understanding our number system. As indicated, the concept should be developed through experiencing activities calling for the analysis of a number such as six. For example, a group of six children may be composed of the subgroups of two girls and four boys, or of five girls and one boy. Children should be encouraged to look for the various subgrouping possibilities. As an aid in developing the concrete and semi-concrete aspects of grouping, the teacher should have available, collections of various toys, erasers, pencils, books, bottle caps, clothes pins, jacks, checkers, etc.

There are also available many simple visual aids which will facilitate the work of the teacher in developing group concepts. Some of the more useful of these are the bead frame, the abacus, the flannel board, the magnetic board, a coat hanger from which one may suspend varying numbers of clothes pins, and a number fence.[1] (See Diagram 1.)

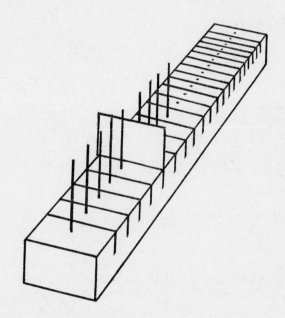

Diagram 1. (Number fence). Showing that a group of
nine is composed of a group of five and a group of four.

---

[1] A number fence can be constructed very easily from a piece of wood about two feet long, one or two inches thick and about two to four inches wide. Twenty evenly spaced holes should be drilled and then a saw cut about a half inch deep should be made between each of the holes across the width of the board.

Beginning the Place-Value Idea

To develop the number concepts from eleven to twenty it is merely necessary to extend the idea of grouping so that one of the subgroups will be ten and the other subgroup will be whatever is necessary to yield the number under consideration. For example, eleven should be emphasized as a group of ten and one more. At this point 11 should be written on the board and it should be emphasized that the digit "1" on the left indicates one group of ten, and the digit "1" on the right indicates one object more. The next step should be to demonstrate the meaning of twelve with an emphasis on the idea that twelve is composed of one group of ten and one group of two, rather than stressing the notion that twelve is one more than eleven. To help achieve this emphasis, it would be advisable first to remove the single object that was used to picture eleven as a group of ten and one more, and replace the single object with a group of two, rather than merely adding one to the existing eleven. Likewise, after writing 12 on the board and showing its connection to the subgroups it would be helpful to remove the two units before introducing 13. Thus 13 can be readily introduced as consisting of a group of ten and a group of three. A similar procedure should be followed with the other numbers from 14 to 20, with perhaps a little special emphasis on the 20 as containing 2 groups of ten and nothing more.

It is assumed, of course, that each of the preceding numbers will be developed in accordance with the pattern of going from the concrete to the abstract. Thus, the teacher will first deal with such concrete objects as books, children, blocks, tongue depressors, and beads. Then she can demonstrate the same number concept using pictures in books or cut-outs on the flannel board, and then before using the abstract symbols themselves, she can work with dots, squares, circles, or some other semi-abstract representations.

An analysis of our decimal money system helps to bridge the gap from the concrete to the abstract. For example, 13 cents should be thought of as one group of ten cents and one group of three cents, but it should also be thought of as one coin which stands for ten cents (the dime) and a group of three cents. The student's understanding, though, is not complete until he sees the connection between this last analysis and the technique used in our place value system of having the "1" in 13 stand for one ten just as the dime represents one group of ten.

By the time the pupil has had these experiences with numbers from 11 to 20, he should have a clear picture that the "1" in the left place indicates one ten and that the digit in the right place indicates how many ones are to be combined with the group of ten. This idea is extended and enriched through a similar study of the numbers from 21 to 99 and eventually beyond.

Here again there are many visual aids which can be utilized to sharpen and to test understandings. The conventional abacus, the open-end abacus (Diagram 2), and the loop abacus (Diagram 3) are among the most helpful devices.

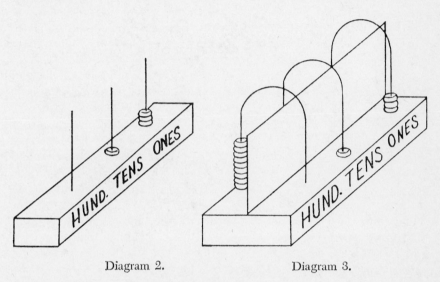

Diagram 2.   Diagram 3.

Place value cans, which are merely cans bearing one of the following labels: "Ones," "Tens," "Hundreds" are also very useful. Thirteen, for example, would be portrayed by placing one stick in the can marked "Tens" and three sticks in the can marked "Ones." Another useful device is the place pocket chart which is used in a similar manner and which is prepared in just a few minutes by pasting or stapling patch pockets on heavy cardboard. The pockets are then used just as the cans are. If the place pocket chart is made with three rows of pockets, it can be used very conveniently to demonstrate processes in addition and subtraction.

Some other useful devices include a string of 100 spools, a counting board (a board with three or four grooves cut into it in which the groove at the right stands for "ones," the second groove represents "tens," the third "hundreds," etc. It is used like an abacus. Pebbles, beads, or marbles may be used as the counters), a 100's chart, or a flannel board or magnetic board used to analyze groups or used somewhat as a place pocket chart with columns headed "Ones," "Tens," and "Hundreds."

It should be kept in mind at all times that numbers take on meaning for children slowly and that only after many varied experiences is it clearly understood that our number system is a place value system in which the idea of grouping by tens plays a basic role. The varied experiences should include concrete, semi-concrete, and abstract experiences enriched by a sufficient number of teaching devices to accommodate the varying needs and abilities of the pupils.

BIBLIOGRAPHY

Adams, Olga. "Arithmetic Readiness in the Primary Grades," *Arithmetic 1947.* Chicago: University of Chicago Press, 1947, 10-16.

Association for Supervision and Curriculum Development Committee. *The Three R's in the Elementary School.* Washington, D. C.: The Association, 1952, 99-152.

Bathurst, Effie G. *How Children Use Arithmetic,* United States Office of Education Bulletin, No. 7, *The Place of Subjects Series,* 1951.

Blom, E. C. "Developing Understanding Through Counting," *The Arithmetic Teacher,* II (October, 1955), 83-85.

Brownell, William A. *Arithmetic in Grades I and II.* Durham, N. C.: Duke University Press, 1941.

———. "Arithmetic in 1970," *The National Elementary Principal,* XXXIX (October, 1959), 42-45.

———, et al. *Arithmetic in Grades I and II: A Critical Summary of New and Previously Reported Research,* Duke University Research Studies in Education, No. 6. Durham, N. C.: Duke University Press, 1941.

———, and Harold E. Moser. *Meaningful vs. Mechanical Learning: A Study of Grade III Subtraction,* Duke University Research Studies in Education, No. 8. Durham, N. C.: Duke University Press, 1949.

Buswell, Guy T. "Deferred Arithmetic," *Mathematics Teacher,* XXXI (May, 1938), 195-200.

———. "Content and Organization of Arithmetic," *The Arithmetic Teacher,* VI (March, 1959), 77-83.

———, and M. L. Hartung. *Arithmetic 1949,* Supplementary Educational Monographs, No. 70. Chicago: University of Chicago Press, 1949.

Campbell, Dorothy. "Kindergartners Learn Arithmetic," *The Arithmetic Teacher,* V (April, 1958), 137-39.

Clark, Caroline Hatton. "To Tell, or Not to Tell," *The Arithmetic Teacher,* V (March, 1958), 65-68.

Clark, John R. "Issues in Teaching Arithmetic," *Teachers College Record,* LII (January, 1951), 205-12.

———, and Laura K. Eads. *Guiding Arithmetic Learning.* Yonkers-on-Hudson, N. Y.: World Book Company, 1954.

Dawson, Dan T. "Number Grouping as a Function of Complexity," *The Elementary School Journal,* LIV (September, 1953), 35-42.

Deans, Edwina. "Arithmetic in the Primary Grades," *The National Elementary Principal*, XXXIX (October, 1959), 22-28.

DeMay, Amy J. "Arithmetic Meanings," *Childhood Education*, XI (June, 1935), 408-12.

Drasin, Lillian Packer. "The Forgotten Level: Semi-concrete Materials, a Valuable Bridge," *The Arithmetic Teacher*, IV (November, 1957), 211-13.

Drew, Nellie L. "Creating Competition in Arithmetic," *American Childhood*, XXXIX (November, 1953), 10, 64.

Eads, Laura K. "Teaching Mathematics in the Kindergarten," *Grade Teacher*, LXXVI (October, 1958), 55, 134-35.

———. "Teaching Mathematics in Grade One," *Grade Teacher*, LXXVI (November, 1958), 52, 108, 110, 112.

———. "Teaching Mathematics in Grade Two," *Grade Teacher*, LXXVI (December, 1958), 56, 68-69.

———. "Teaching Mathematics in Grade Three," *Grade Teacher*, LXXVI (January, 1959), 52, 88-89.

Edwards, Phyllis O. "Guiding Primary Children's Arithmetic Growth," *American Childhood*, XL (October, 1954), 13-15.

Fehr, Howard F. "A Philosophy of Arithmetic Instruction," *The Arithmetic Teacher*, II (April, 1955), 27-32.

Fouch, Robert S., and Eugene D. Nichols. "Language and Symbolism in Mathematics," *The Growth of Mathematical Ideas, Grades K-12*, National Council of Teachers of Mathematics, Twenty-fourth Yearbook (1959). Washington, D. C.: The Council, 327-69.

Gibb, E. Glenadine, Philip S. Jones, and Charlotte W. Junge. "Number and Operation," *The Growth of Mathematical Ideas, Grades K-12*, National Council of Teachers of Mathematics, Twenty-fourth Yearbook (1959). Washington, D. C.: The Council, 7-64.

Grant, Albert. "Analysis of the Number Knowledge of First Grade Pupils According to Levels of Intelligence," *Journal of Experimental Education*, VII (September, 1938), 63-66.

Grossnickle, Foster E. "Discovering the Multiplication Facts," *The Arithmetic Teacher*, VI (October, 1959), 195-98.

———, and Leo J. Brueckner. *Discovering Meanings in Arithmetic*. New York: Holt, Rinehart & Winston, Inc., 1959.

Gunderson, Agnes G. "Arithmetic for Today's Six- and Seven-Year-Olds," *The Arithmetic Teacher*, II (November, 1955), 95-101.

———. "Thought-Patterns of Young Children in Learning Multiplication and Division," *Elementary School Journal*, LV (April, 1955), 453-61.

———, and Ethel Gunderson. "Fraction Concepts Held by Young Children," *The Arithmetic Teacher*, IV (October, 1957), 168-73.

———, ———. "What Numbers Mean to Young Children, Number Concepts Compared with a 1940 Study," *The Arithmetic Teacher*, VI (October, 1959), 180-85.

Gunderson, Mrs. Ethel. "Fractions—Seven-Year-Olds Use Them," *The Arithmetic Teacher*, V (November, 1958), 233-38.

Harap, Henry. "Experimenting with Real Situations in Third Grade Arithmetic," *Educational Method*, XVI (January, 1937), 188-92.

Hausdoerffer, W. H. "Introducing Our Numbering System in the Primary Grades," *The Arithmetic Teacher*, IV (March, 1957), 61-63.

Heard, Ida Mae. "Handmade Materials for Teaching Arithmetic—Materials for Kindergarten through Grade III," *Emerging Practices in Mathematics Education*, National Council of Teachers of Mathematics, Twenty-second Yearbook (1954). Washington, D. C.: The Council, 126-31.

Hickerson, J. Allen. *Guiding Children's Arithmetic Experiences*. Englewood Cliffs, N. J.: Prentice-Hall, Inc., 1952.

Hollister, George E., and Agnes G. Gunderson. *Teaching Arithmetic in Grades I and II*. Boston: D. C. Heath and Company, 1954.

Johnson, Lois V., and Avis S. Whipple. "Arithmetic and 'Block Work' in Primary Grades," *The Arithmetic Teacher*, VI (December, 1959), 306-9.

Junge, Charlotte. "The Arithmetic Curriculum 1954," *The Arithmetic Teacher*, I (April, 1954), 1-6.

Leodas, Costa J. "First Number Concepts: Cornerstones of Mathematics," *The Journal of Educational Sociology*, XXX (April, 1957), 343-45.

Love, Rose L. "Number Readiness in Grade One," *The Instructor*, LXIV (September, 1954), 82.

MacLatchy, Josephine H. "A Child's Thinking as a Source of Error," *Educational Research Bulletin*, XXVII (May, 1948), 113-20.

Maloney, John P. "Arithmetic at the Primary Level," *The Arithmetic Teacher*, IV (April, 1957), 112-18.

Martin, William E. "Quantitative Experiences in Young Children," *Genetic Psychology Monographs*, XLIV (November, 1951), 147-219.

Oesterle, Robert A. "What About Those Zero Facts?" *The Arithmetic Teacher*, VI (March, 1959), 109-11.

Olander, Herbert T., M. J. Van Wagenen, and H. M. Bishop. "Predicting Arithmetic Achievement," *Journal of Educational Research*, XLIII (September, 1949), 66-73.

Panek, Alice. "Providing for the Gifted Child," *The Arithmetic Teacher*, VI (November, 1959), 246-50.

Parker, Beatrice F. "Primary Arithmetic," *Grade Teacher*, LXXII (January, 1955), 16, 66, 74.

Plank, Emma N. "Observations on Attitudes of Young Children Toward Mathematics," *Mathematics Teacher*, XLIII (October, 1950), 252-63.

Polkinghorne, Ada R. "Young Children and Fractions," *Childhood Education*, XI (May, 1935), 354-58.

Priore, Angela. "Achievement by Pupils Entering the First Grade," *The Arithmetic Teacher*, IV (March, 1957), 55-60.

Reid, Florence E. "Incidental Number Situations in First Grade," *Journal of Educational Research*, XXX (September, 1936), 36-43.

Rezsek, A. N., and R. B. Norris. "Enrichment in Arithmetic in the Primary Grades," *Grade Teacher* LXXIII (October, 1955), 39, 116-17.

Riess, Anita P. "Pre-first Grade Arithmetic," *The Arithmetic Teacher,* IV (March, 1957), 50-54.

Rosenquist, Lucy L. *Young Children Learn to Use Arithmetic.* Boston: Ginn & Company, 1949.

Russell, Ned M. "Arithmetic Concepts of Children," *Journal of Educational Research,* XXIX (May, 1936), 647-63.

Sherer, Lorraine. "Some Implications from Research in Arithmetic," *Childhood Education,* XXIX (March, 1953), 320-24.

Shuster, Carl N. "Teaching the Digit Zero," *The Arithmetic Teacher,* IV (February, 1957), 13-14.

Spencer, Peter L., and Marguerite Brydegaard. *Building Mathematical Concepts in the Elementary School.* New York: Holt, Rinehart & Winston, Inc., 1952.

Spitzer, Herbert F. *The Teaching of Arithmetic* (2nd ed.). Boston: Houghton Mifflin Company, 1954.

Stains, Katherine G. "Number in the Everyday Living of Young Children," *American Childhood,* XXXVI (November, 1950), 22-25.

Stern, Catherine. *Children Discover Arithmetic.* New York: Harper & Brothers, 1949.

Swenson, Esther J. "Arithmetic for Preschool and Primary-Grade Children," *The Teaching of Arithmetic,* National Society for the Study of Education, Fiftieth Yearbook. Chicago: University of Chicago Press, 1951, Part II, 53-75.

Thiele, C. L. "Fostering Discovery with Children," *The Arithmetic Teacher,* I (February, 1954), 6-11.

Thomson, Alice P. "Evaluation by Observation—Grade 3," *The Arithmetic Teacher,* III (April, 1956), 104-8.

Tompkins, Jean B., and C. Newton Stokes. "Eight-Year-Olds Use Arithmetic," *Childhood Education,* XVI (March, 1940), 319-21.

Tuttle, Ruth H. "Counters? Yes, But . . . ," *The Arithmetic Teacher,* V (February, 1958), 25-28.

Weaver, J. Fred, and Cleo F. Brawley. "Enriching the Elementary School Mathematics Program for More Capable Children," *Journal of Education,* CXLII (October, 1959), 1-40.

VIII DEVELOPING EFFECTIVE EVALUATION PROCEDURES

Vincent J. Glennon, John W. Wilson, Syracuse University

INTRODUCTION

BIBLIOGRAPHY

INTRODUCTION

Evaluation is as essential to the effective guidance of the teaching-learning process as buying is to the selling process; in each case the former is the necessary complement of the latter. In the long history of systematic instruction in the American elementary school, the evaluation process and its specific techniques has been largely viewed in the narrow sense of testing. The testing programs of the seventeenth century Dame School, the eighteenth century Colonial Common School, and the nineteenth century Grammar School

276

were largely confined to oral testing of subject matter learnings.

The invention and widespread use in the nineteenth century of the steel pen (to replace the goose quill) and the individual slate and slate-pencil followed by an increasing availability of inexpensive writing paper—all served to provide an educational environment that allowed the written test to develop to the point of almost completely replacing the oral test as the sole evaluation technique.

The first half of the twentieth century witnessed a rapid flowering of the evaluation program. Several factors rendered this possible. Foremost among these was the popularization of a philosophy of education broadened to include the development of the whole child. It then followed logically that if the school was to be concerned with teaching the whole child it must also be concerned with evaluating the whole child. At the same time, the application of the method of intelligence, the scientific method, to the problem of improving the educational program of the elementary school brought with it an apparent need for more complete and more dependable ways to measure growth of the whole child. Measuring growth in the subject matter learnings was necessary but not sufficient.

The demand grew for improved ways to measure growth in the cognitive (subject matter) domain, and for new ways to measure growth in the affective (emotions, feelings, attitudes) domain. Then, too, there was some need for new and improved measures of growth in the psychomotor (motor-skills) domain, but this domain is of lesser importance in arithmetic learning than the other two domains.

Evidence of the fact that immediate and substantial efforts were made over the years to fulfill the demands of the elementary program generally and of arithmetic specifically is the listing of hundreds of testing instruments found in the first edition of Buros' *Mental Measurements Yearbook* and of several times that number in the most recent edition.

Within the purview of the paragraphs above, it is the purpose of this chapter to bring to the student selected readings and a bibliography of readings that will provide a starting place for becoming acquainted with the problem of evaluation in arithmetic. The reader should also refer to the chapters on evaluation that appear in most of the professional textbooks on the teaching of arithmetic. Also, the Twenty-sixth Yearbook of the National Council of Teachers of Mathematics is entirely devoted to the evaluation of achievement in mathematics.

PART I: AN OVERALL VIEW OF THE EVALUATION PROGRAM IN ARITHMETIC

THE EVALUATION OF LEARNING IN ARITHMETIC

William A. Brownell

For the best interests of both, we have sometimes been told, instruction and measurement must be kept apart. Considerations involving measurement are held to impede the solution of problems of measurement; and, conversely, the task of measurement is thought to require time and energy which teachers might more properly give to instruction. Some test technicians have not felt particularly handicapped by their ignorance of the purposes of arithmetic instruction. On the other hand, teachers, who supposedly know the nature and purposes of their subject matter, are regarded as unable to evaluate the learning they have directed.

This separation between measurement and instruction presents a curious anomaly. It exists only in theory; it cannot actually be maintained in practice; hence it is wholly artificial. Nevertheless, the attempt to establish the separation has been made, and the effects upon classroom evaluation and teaching alike have been most unfortunate. Let us start with these unfortunate effects, reserving for a moment consideration of the artificiality of the separation.

Effects of attempted separation of measurement and teaching. One effect of the attempted separation has been to remove measurement further and further from the immediate learning situation. Tests to be used for diagnosis and the evaluation of achievement have been standardized, and in the process of standardization have lost touch with the features peculiar to the local classroom. Indeed, it is the very essence of stand-

[From "The Evaluation of Learning in Arithmetic," National Council of Teachers of Mathematics, Sixteenth Yearbook (1941), pp. 225-49. Reprinted by permission of the author and the National Council of Teachers of Mathematics.]

ardization as a process to disregard local variations and to strive for a "national average" of subject content and teaching practice. For certain purposes, such as are comprehended in the survey function of measurement, for example, this averaging and this disregard for local conditions are precisely what is needed. For other purposes, however, especially for those purposes which relate most closely to the organization and direction of learning, it is the local conditions, lost in standardization, which are most crucial.

A second effect of trying to keep measurement and teaching apart has been to limit measurement to outcomes that can be most readily assessed. In arithmetic this has meant concern almost exclusively with "facts," with computational skills, and with "problem solving" of the traditional sort. The necessity for developing proficiency in these areas is obvious. Furthermore, measurement of these outcomes (or at least partial measurement) can be managed by objective techniques. As a result, many experts in test construction have confined themselves for the most part to these outcomes, as have also teachers who have followed their lead. But, as will be made clear below, there are other arithmetic outcomes, fully as important if not so obvious as those commonly attended to, and these outcomes under present practice are neglected.

A third ill effect of the effort to separate measurement from teaching has been to limit unduly the techniques which are serviceable for evaluation. It is not far from the truth to say that evaluation in the broad sense has been narrowed to measurement in the narrow sense, that such measurement has been made virtually equivalent to testing, and that testing has become the administration of paper-and-pencil tests, usually of an objective character. Valuable as are such objective tests, whether commercial or local products, they cannot readily carry the full burden of evaluation. There are other procedures which are now ignored. These other procedures to be described below, are easily managed by teachers and, what is more important, they uncover kinds of learning processes and products which at present elude paper-and-pencil tests.

The fourth harmful effect of the desire to separate measurement and teaching, and the last one here to be considered, has been to create confusion with respect to the purposes of evaluation. Learning may be evaluated for a number of reasons. One may be the diagnosis of failure; another, the measurement of progress over short units or sections of content; yet another, the pre-testing of abilities before starting a new topic, as a means of "establishing a base line" or determining a common ground for instruction in a given grade. Tests, commercial or otherwise, which are suited to one purpose are not thereby suited equally well to other purposes. Indeed, it might even be argued that the better a test serves one function, the less well it can serve others. For illustration, the better a test "surveys" (e.g., permits comparisons of a school system with other school systems or with national norms) the less effectively it "diagnoses." Yet, several survey tests in arithmetic incorrectly bear the label "achievement test" and are improperly used for the latter purpose, as well as for other purposes even more remote from the function for which they were devised.

The four consequences of the attempt to divorce measurement from instruction which have been mentioned reveal the essential artificiality and impracticability of the attempted separation. The fact of the matter is that, despite the effort to do so, measurement and teaching have not been kept apart. Classroom instruction has emphasized the outcomes and only the outcomes with which measurement technicians and some measurement theorists have worked, and it has used the evaluation procedures and only the evaluation procedures favored by them.[1] The poverty of the results of arithmetic teaching under this scheme of things has been all too well exposed. It has been exposed in the fact that children are not able to use the arithmetic they are taught in dealing with the simple personal quantitative problems of the adult world into which they are presently to enter; indeed they are not even sensitive to the quantitative aspects of their own daily lives. The poverty of our teaching has been exposed, too, in the arithmetical deficiencies of adults who have been subjected to eight or more years of school arithmetic. Witness the typical adult's efforts to evade the quantitative demands of his life and his embarrassment and uncertainty when there is no escape from them.

To some readers the foregoing discussion may appear to be somewhat academic and unreal. Among these readers will be the many excellent teachers who never have thought of separating measurement from teaching but have steadfastly evaluated learning in order to improve the effectiveness of their teaching. Admittedly, the past few pages have not been written for such persons. Instead, they have been intended for persons who have not yet accepted the full import of modern conceptions of education according to which children and the problems relating to their learning are the central consideration in the classroom.

The purposes of this chapter. The purposes of this chapter are two in number, the first of which has been already foreshadowed in the criticisms

---

[1] There are of course occasions when measurement and instruction must be separated. This is true when tests are correctly used in some kinds of research and for survey purposes. It is true at times when pupils are to be classified for certain reasons, as, for example, in making up sections in a cosmopolitan junior high school which draws from many lower schools. But this chapter deals with the evaluation *of learning;* in other words, with evaluation as it relates to the improvement of teaching. On this account the consequences of separating measurement from instruction, helpful in noninstructional situations, are here viewed as harmful.

offered in the paragraphs above. The purposes are: (1) to outline a point of view with respect to evaluation (*a*) which relates evaluation to teaching, and (*b*) which makes evaluation comprehensive enough to include all objectives or aims of arithmetic instruction; and (2) to illustrate as far as possible concrete procedures for evaluating outcomes now too often overlooked. In order to save space for the second and more obviously practical purpose, the statements to be made with regard to the first purpose must be held to what is essentially an outline.

A Point of View with Respect to Evaluation

As has already been suggested, the thesis of this chapter is that instruction and the evaluation of learning cannot be kept apart in theory and should not be kept apart in practice. Instruction and evaluation go hand in hand. As teachers develop new insights into learning—its difficulties, its stages or phases of development, the basic understandings required for each advance step in learning—as teachers acquire these insights, they will employ them in improved evaluation. And as they correct or modify their evaluations and devise procedures which are more comprehensive and more penetrating, they should come upon new data of great significance for the better guidance of learning. Viewed thus, instruction and evaluation are inseparable and mutually interdependent.

If the recommendations to be made in this chapter were accepted and practiced, certain values would accrue. In the first place, evaluation (the broader term will henceforth be used in place of measurement) and teaching would both start with arithmetic outcomes—with *all* the arithmetic outcomes which are deemed worthy of attainment.[2] Evidences would then

---

[2] It is no longer possible to assume that a test of computational or problem-solving ability measures all arithmetical outcomes—if indeed this assumption ever was tenable on logical grounds. Brueckner, using Vocabulary and Quantitative Relationships sections of the Unit Scales of Attainment with 453 children in grades four A to five B, obtained coefficients of correlation of .361 between "vocabulary" and "computation," and of .522 between the former and "problem solving." Scores on the Quantitative Relationships test correlated .576 and .661 with "computation" and "problem solving," respectively. (See Leo J. Brueckner, "Intercorrelations of Arithmetical Abilities," *Journal of Experimental Education*, III (September, 1934), 42-44. Since that date, Spainhour's investigation has confirmed these results. Spainhour devised special tests of "mathematical understanding" (reliability coefficients of .901 for grade four and of .933 for grade six), and administered them along with the New Stanford Reasoning Arithmetic Test and the New Stanford Computation Arithmetic Test to 143 children in grade four and 136 in grade six. In grade four the "understanding" test scores correlated .665 and .751 with "problem solving" and "computation," respectively. In grade six the corresponding *r*'s were .751 and .756. Richard E. Spainhour, "The Relationship Between Arithmetical Understanding and Ability in Problem Solving and Computation." Unpublished Master's thesis in education, Duke University, 1936.

be obtained, so far as can reasonably be done, on all types of growth and at all stages in this growth. In the second place, any procedure whatsoever which might shed light on learning would be accepted and utilized. Wider recognition would be given to observation, to the interview and conference, and to other techniques which can yield information on the progress of learning. In the third place, the various purposes for which evaluation is undertaken would be recognized in the kinds of procedures which would be used. In other words, evaluation procedures would be adapted to the ends for which they are best fitted. In the fourth place, evaluation would be continuous with teaching and learning. Evidence on learning would be collected daily (occasionally by tests, more often by informal procedures), instead of irregularly and spasmodically. In the fifth place, evaluations would be immediate and intimate; they would reflect the unique conditions, emphases, and factors affecting learning in particular classrooms. And for this reason they would provide teachers with the kinds of information which they most need in order to direct learning.

These gains are not to be won by wishful thinking. Admittedly, they represent an ideal state of affairs which now can be no more than approximated. But even so, the approximation in itself will mean important progress away from present practice in evaluating outcomes.

Comprehensive and functional evaluation in arithmetic is dependent upon the effective relating of a number of factors. We need, first of all, an adequate statement of arithmetic outcomes. Second, we need to recognize the peculiar demands of different purposes in evaluating learning as these demands affect evaluation procedures and instruments. And, third, we need to have a practicable program for evaluation. This third requirement involves (*a*) knowledge of effective procedures and their limitations, (*b*) a realistic understanding of what can and cannot be done by the classroom teacher, and (*c*) the actual planning and designing of evaluation procedures. This last named item (*c*) is reserved to the last part of this chapter. The other items listed above will now be considered in order.

Acceptable Outcomes. There are dangers in setting arithmetic outcomes. In the first place, there is the danger that the mere listing of outcomes separately may for some carry the implication that these outcomes are isolated from each other and are to be achieved independently of each other, one at a time. But outcomes are not thus distinct; rather they overlap in meaning, and they are probably best achieved when they are achieved more or less together in their functional relationships. In the second place, there is the danger that outcomes may be regarded as ends to be attained once and for all, the quicker the better. But outcomes are not so to be conceived; they really stand for directions of growth. In the third place, there is the danger that from a list of outcomes questionable teaching practices and forms of curriculum organization may be inferred. Not always should particular outcomes be at the immediate forefront of thinking when learning activities are being considered. After all, as we have been told almost too often, we teach "the whole child." Outcomes function best in teaching when they constitute the *background* of thinking, against which may be projected possible teaching plans. When, however, evaluation rather than teaching is the major concern, outcomes as such become more immediately important. In the fourth place, there is the danger of a suggestion of finality in any formal statement of outcomes. These outcomes work their way into educational thought; they come to be accepted as definitive, and they are modified only with great effort.

In full awareness of these dangers a list of arithmetic outcomes is given below. This list is not the result of Committee action; it does not bear the label of the Committee's authority. Instead, it is offered purely as the writer's own formulation. After all, if evaluation must start with outcomes, we must know what the desired outcomes are, and the list below seems to the writer to be adequate at present as a working basis.

1. Computational skill
   Facility and accuracy in operations with whole numbers, common fractions, decimals, and per cents. (This group of outcomes is here separated from the second and third groups which follow because it *can* be isolated for measurement. In this separation much is lost, for computation without understanding *when* as well as *how* to compute is a rather empty skill. Actually, computation is important only as it contributes to social ends.)
2. Mathematical understandings
   a) Meaningful conceptions of quantity, of the number system, of whole numbers, of common fractions, of decimals, of per cents, of measures, etc.
   b) A meaningful vocabulary of the useful technical terms of arithmetic which designate quantitative ideas and the relationships between them.
   c) Grasp of important arithmetical generalizations.
   d) Understanding of the meanings and mathematical functions of the fundamental operations.
   e) Understanding of the meanings of measures and of measurement as a process.
   f) Understanding of important arithmetical relationships, such as those which function in reasonably sound estimations and approximations, in accurate checking, and in ingenious and resourceful solutions.

    g) Some understanding of the rational principles which govern number relations and computational procedures.

3. Sensitiveness to number in social situations and the habit of using number effectively in such situations

    a) Vocabulary of selected quantitative terms of common usage (such as kilowatt hour, miles per hour, decrease and increase, and terms important in insurance, investments, business practices, etc.).

    b) Knowledge of selected business practices and other economic applications of number.

    c) Ability to use and interpret graphs, simple statistics, and tabular presentations of quantitative data (as in study in school and in practical activities outside of school).

    d) Awareness of the usefulness of quantity and number in dealing with many aspects of life. Here belongs some understanding of social institutions in which the quantitative aspect is prominent, as well as some understanding of the important contribution of number in their evolution.

    e) Tendency to sense the quantitative as part of normal experience, including vicarious experience, as in reading, in observation, and in projected activity and imaginative thinking.

    f) Ability to make (and the habit of making) sound judgments with respect to practical quantitative problems.

    g) Disposition to extend one's sensitiveness to the quantitative as this occurs socially and to improve and extend one's ability to deal effectively with the quantitative when so encountered or discovered.

Purposes of evaluation. Evaluations of learning are undertaken, or should be undertaken, for several different reasons. These differing purposes introduce variations into the procedures and instruments to be used. For example, as the learning area which is sampled is extended, the thoroughness of the sampling diminishes. What seem to the writer to be the five chief purposes of evaluation are listed below.[3] In each instance both the meaning of the purpose and the significance of that purpose for the kind of evaluation procedure to be used are illustrated in terms of paper-and-pencil tests. Tests are employed in this connection because teachers are more familiar with them than with some of the other procedures. Illustrations of other evaluation procedures will be given later with greater emphasis.

---

[3] Evaluation is also used to motivate learning, and this purpose of evaluation might have been included as the sixth discussed. This purpose was, however, omitted, first, because motivation is a general effect of evaluation regardless of the particular purpose for which it is used, and second, because abuses easily arise from this use of evaluation. For instance, when tests are used for this purpose, the motivation is likely to be extrinsic and harmful to sound learning, rather than intrinsic and beneficial.

The chief purposes of evaluation are:

1. *To Diagnose Class and Individual Difficulty.* Effectiveness of diagnosis is dependent upon the intensity or depth of evaluation. That is to say, diagnostic data increase in value as they pass from a mere locating of the places of difficulty to an analysis of the causes of difficulty. On this account, special care must be exercised not only to include (*a*) all critical steps, processes, uses, opportunities, and so on, and (*b*) enough samples of each to yield reliable measures, but also (*c*) to discover insofar as is possible the thought processes which children employ in dealing therewith. Diagnostic tests must usually be restricted in their range of coverage in order to insure such depth and intensity.

2. *To Inventory Knowledge and Abilities.* Inventories are made, for example, to determine "readiness" for a new topic or for the start of instruction in a grade. The usefulness of this kind of evaluation has been made steadily more apparent as we have sought better to adapt the pace of instruction to level of pupil ability. The inventory test resembles the diagnostic test in that it includes samples of all levels of thinking which are achieved in the critical aspects, or skills, etc. Its range, obviously, varies with the area under examination from a relatively few constituent abilities, thought processes, and evidences of social awareness with respect to basic skills and concepts (when "readiness" for a new topic is under consideration) to the many such aspects of skills and concepts of a whole year's work (when, for example, the "base line" for class instruction in grade four is being established). Usually the depth of evaluation is much less in an inventory test than in a diagnostic test, or it may justifiably be made less.

3. *To Determine the Extent of Learning over a Limited Period.* An example is the measurement of learning over a month's unit of work. When tests are used for this purpose, they may be called "instructional" or "progress" tests. They are commonly short enough to be given in one class period or less, and their content is restricted to what has been but recently taught. In this respect they tend to differ from inventory tests. They differ from diagnostic tests in that usually but comparatively little effort is expended to get at the source of difficulty. But, as is also true in the case of the first two purposes, this third purpose of evaluation does not necessarily require a test at all. Indeed, in the case of some kinds of learning other procedures are much more suitable.

4. *To Measure Learning over a Relatively Long Period.* One use of evaluation for this purpose is to secure a basis for pupil classification; another, to get a general view of achievement for a semester or year to be used in making up the term "mark." Usually paper-and-pencil tests are

employed exclusively for this purpose. Such tests are certainly valuable, but evaluation should not be limited to them since probably not all outcomes will be represented in them. Here, that is for evaluating learning over fairly long periods of time, the extent of the area is relatively much larger than in "progress" tests, and thoroughness of sampling must be sacrificed to some degree. As in the case of progress tests (Purpose 3) test content should be restricted to what has been taught in the period covered, except of course as skills, concepts, etc., taught earlier are indirectly involved. The purpose of "achievement" testing almost necessarily precludes diagnosis, save in the shallowest sense of finding places of difficulty, and by the same token it cannot, unless the test is unusually comprehensive, well serve the purpose of inventorying.

5. *To Obtain Rough Measures for Comparative Purposes.* Reference here is to the survey function of evaluation, as this is illustrated in comparisons between schools within a system or between school systems. Because of the purpose for which the measures are to be used, these measures must almost necessarily be obtained from paper-and-pencil tests. Objectivity in scoring and the reliability of measures are especially important. Unless comparisons are to be made grade for grade and on the subject matter of those grades, a single test for all grades is commonly used. This means that the learning area is very extensive, and that the sampling is correspondingly very crude. To use a test designed for the survey function for the purpose of achievement testing (Purpose 4), or for progress testing (Purpose 3), or for inventorying (Purpose 2), or for diagnosing (Purpose 1) is almost certain to introduce errors and to lead to misinterpretation of test results. Yet, precisely this practice frequently obtains in testing programs.

These five purposes of evaluation have been discussed in terms of tests and apparently in terms only of computational skills. But actually the points made apply equally well to other evaluation procedures and to all outcomes. The nature of other evaluation procedures is treated in the next section. Emphasis needs now to be given to the fact that in evaluating growth or learning toward all objectives, and not merely toward computational proficiency, one must keep in mind the purposes for which evaluation is undertaken. Thus, one needs to diagnose, to inventory, to note progress, etc., in the case of mathematical understandings and of sensitiveness to the quantitative in life, just as fully as in the case of computational skills. Growth takes place in understandings and in quantitative sensitiveness as truly as in computation, and just as truly learning in these areas needs to be assessed for difficulties, for status, for progress, etc.

Evaluation procedures. Four general classes of evaluation techniques will be briefly considered, namely, (1) paper-and-pencil tests (or simply tests), (2) teacher observation, (3) individual interviews and conferences with pupils, and (4) pupil reports, projects, and the like.

1. *Tests.* Though much of the preceding section has been devoted to the use of tests in evaluation, actually far more space than this whole chapter affords could be taken for this purpose. Of all the possible evaluation procedures no other has received the research and theoretical attention given to tests. With the limited space here available, only a few suggestions can be offered.

Valuable as tests are, they are subject to certain limitations: (*a*) Tests are essentially artificial: they are convenient substitutes for the ultimately valid trial by functional use. This is but another way of saying that the true measure of learning is the ability to use what has been learned in practical life situations. (*b*) Tests yield scores which are susceptible to errors of interpretation. We may infer, for example, that the score is a measure of the total ability tested, whereas it is but a description of a particular performance in a particular situation. Obviously, the more comprehensive our testing and the nearer our testing situation approximates functional use, the fewer will be the errors of interpretation. (*c*) Tests may be used too exclusively. We may rely on tests to furnish indirectly evidence of growth in areas to which tests are not very sensitive. It is exceedingly difficult to prepare tests (other than essay tests) to measure certain arithmetic outcomes. If tests alone are used, these other outcomes will almost certainly be excluded from evaluation. (*d*) In the attempt to secure reliable measures from tests, we may pay too high a price for objectivity in scoring. Consideration of such a factor as correct principle, or evident understanding, introduces variation in judgment and so makes for unreliable measures. If we hold to the superior value of reliable measures, we may lose much that we need in order to understand children's work habits and thought processes. If we hold to the superior value of these evidences of learning we tend to lose objectivity and reliability.

Another series of cautions relates to standard tests and the use of norms for such tests. It cannot be assumed that mere standardization of a test makes it a good test, even for the purpose for which it is designed: (*a*) The content may be quite different from what has been locally taught [4] and the norms may therefore be useless in the local situation (except for the purposes of the survey). (*b*) It has been shown that the arithmetical content of such tests varies considerably.[5] (*c*) It is not unlikely that many, or most, standard tests measure effects of arithmetical learning different

---

[4] Guy M. Wilson. "Choosing and Using Standardized Tests in Arithmetic," *Education*, XL (November, 1939), 177-79.

[5] Louise Beattie. "Standardized Tests in Arithmetic," *Educational Method*, XVI (January, 1937), 175-76.

from the achievement and abilities with which teachers are primarily concerned. (*d*) Moreover, norms on supposedly comparable tests have been found not to be equivalent.[6] (*e*) Still again, nation-wide norms are apt to be misleading. Thus, nation-wide norms are worse than useless in diagnostic tests. They are of little or no service in inventory tests, except possibly to ascertain "readiness" for some topic. Certainly when we seek to determine where to start instruction in a grade, what we need to know is not how our pupils compare with other pupils but precisely what they can do about the items of skill, knowledge, and understanding which are regarded as prerequisites. And last of all, norms are of little value in progress or achievement tests unless we follow slavishly the instructional organization in terms of which the test has been standardized. Norms come into their largest and most legitimate field of usefulness in connection with the survey function of testing.

What has been said about tests is deliberately negative. These negative comments imply no doubt of the values of tests for evaluating learning. The shortcomings and limitations of tests have not been stressed in any attempt to get rid of them. We should be in a sad state indeed if tests, local, commercial, or both, were abolished. To say that tests will not do the whole job of evaluation and to say that tests need to be constructed and test scores interpreted with reasonable caution is far from saying that tests should be abandoned. Rather, they should be retained and improved, and they should be supplemented by other evaluation procedures. The import of this whole section may be summarized in the statement that tests usually indicate the outward, objective, quantitative results of learning, not the inward, subjective, qualitative results; yet these latter both transcend and include the former.

2. *Teacher Observation.* The type of evaluation meant here is the type which the intelligent and alert teacher uses daily in analyzing and assessing the written and oral work of his arithmetic pupils. The observation

---

6 Stokes and Finch in 1932 reported a difference amounting to .77 grade between the medians of 65 pupils in grades seven to nine on the New Stanford Computation Arithmetic Test and the Van Wagenen Revision of the Woody Arithmetic Scales of Fundamental Operations in Arithmetic, and a difference of .74 grade in class medians on the New Stanford Reasoning Arithmetic Test and the Buckingham Scale for Problems in Arithmetic. C. N. Stokes and F. H. Finch, "A Comparison of Norms on Certain Standardized Tests in Arithmetic," *Elementary School Journal,* XXXII (June, 1932), 785-87.

The results of this study have since been confirmed by Foran and Loyes (Thomas G. Foran and Sister Mary Edmund Loyes, "Relative Difficulty of Three Achievement Examinations," *Journal of Educational Psychology,* XXVI (March, 1935), 218-22) and by Pullias (Earl V. Pullias, *Variability in Results from New-Type Achievement Tests,* Duke University Research Studies in Education, No. 2 (Durham, N. C.: Duke University Press, 1937), see especially Chapters 7 and 8).

referred to may be informal, as just described, or it may be more closely controlled, as when special settings are arranged in order to note children's behavior with respect to the quantitative aspects of their experience.

The possibilities of evaluating through observation are well-nigh limitless. That these possibilities have not been realized is explicable on two grounds. In the first place, teachers have had their confidence in their own judgment undermined by certain research which purportedly has demonstrated its unreliability. The implications of this research are that teachers' estimates and opinions are of doubtful worth and that they must give way to more trustworthy (that is, more objective and reliable) evaluation techniques. Some of the dangers inherent in this view have been pointed out,[7] and eventually the artificiality of the techniques in this research will be disclosed. In the meanwhile evidence is accumulating that teachers' judgments (in the form of scores on essay tests, of marks, and the like) need not be as unreliable as had been supposed.[8] But the reaction against the extreme position of the objectivists has not yet affected teachers to any large extent. Under the influence of the objectivists teachers tend to doubt the validity and reliability of their own observations and to minimize the usefulness of observational data for the purposes of evaluation. Nevertheless, it is probable that 90 per cent of teachers' (*good* teachers) activities in teaching and evaluating are still subjective and must remain so. If this be true, the wise course would seem to be to help teachers to get the most from their observations, rather than to continue to discourage their use.

A second obstacle to confident use of observation is of a different character. To observe accurately one must know what to look for. Teachers who regard arithmetic purely as a skill subject are hardly equipped to make useful observations of growth in arithmetical insight and quantitative sensitiveness. On the other hand, teachers who are committed to a more modern conception of arithmetic are handicapped by our general ignorance concerning learning. We do not yet know with certainty all that we need to know about growth toward the non-computational aims of arithmetic. As new information of this kind is acquired, and as teachers regain confidence in the value of observational procedures and in their

---

[7] W. A. Brownell. "The Use of Objective Measures in Evaluating Instruction," *Educational Method*, XIII (May, 1934), 401-8.

[8] The following studies are illustrative:

Howard Easley, "On the Limits of Predicting Scholastic Success," *Journal of Experimental Education*, I (November, 1933), 272-76.

James B. Shouse, "College Grades Mean Something," *Journal of Educational Psychology*, XXX (October, 1939), 510-18.

Ralph R. Wolf, Jr., *Differential Forecasts of Achievement and Their Use in Counseling*, Psychological Monograph, No. 227 (Columbus: American Psychological Association, Inc., 1939).

ability to use this method, evaluation by observation will become more precise and more comprehensive.

The advantages of evaluation by observation (only skillful observation, of course) are several in number: (*a*) Observation has few of the limitations of testing as to time and place. Informal observation requires no special planning and no special arrangements: one can seize each instance of significant behavior as it occurs. (*b*) Observation "catches" behavior in all its functional relationships. One sees not only the error, for example, but also the prior and the accompanying behavior which may account for the error. (*c*) Evidence for evaluation is obtained when it can be used. This is particularly true in the case of diagnosis. (*d*) Observation imposes no unusual restrictions and exposes children to no unnatural tensions. (*e*) Evaluation by observation enables teachers to secure evidence with respect to many arithmetic outcomes to which testing is ill adapted. Reference here is to the outcomes listed especially under mathematical understandings and quantitative sensitiveness on pages 283-284.

3. *Individual Interviews and Conference.*[9] As its name implies, this evaluation procedure, unlike observation, is limited to contacts with individual children. The teacher not only observes what the child does, but has him "talk out loud" as he works and questions him whenever the oral report is interrupted, is incomplete, or is ambiguous. The purpose is primarily to get at the way in which the child thinks about the given quantitative situation, be it a computation, a verbal problem, the use of technical terms, the interpretation of the number relations, etc. The usefulness of the conference for probing undesirable attitudes (indifference or open dislike) toward arithmetic, for finding out how extensively a child really uses arithmetic, and the like, should be apparent.

Readers of research are already familiar with the use of the interview for discovering children's work habits in dealing with number combinations and computation.[10] Good teachers have always employed the interview and conference to some extent, chiefly for purposes of diagnosis. No other procedure equals the interview in disclosing the nature of disability and thus in providing data for remedial instruction. If this procedure were

---

[9] Observation and the interview are not of course as unrelated as may be suggested from the separate treatment accorded them here. As a matter of fact, the interview multiplies opportunities for observation and makes these observations more intimate and penetrating.

[10] For example: Guy T. Buswell and Lenore John, *Diagnostic Studies in Arithmetic*, Supplementary Educational Monograph, No. 30, Department of Education (Chicago: University of Chicago, 1926); Lofton V. Burge, "Types of Errors and Questionable Habits of Work in Multiplication," *Elementary School Journal*, XXXIII (November, 1932), 185-94; Lenore John, "Difficulties in Solving Problems in Arithmetic," *Elementary School Journal*, XXX (May, 1930), 675-92.

used more commonly in connection with initial instruction, later diagnosis and remediation would be greatly reduced in amount.

Perhaps the chief reason why the interview is not more generally used
is the fact that it is time-consuming. To take a fourth grade child through
the whole addition section of the Buswell-John Diagnostic Test requires
between twenty-five and forty-five minutes. It is only rarely, however, that
such extensive interviewing is necessary. Five or ten minutes can hardly
be spent more profitably than in interviewing a child who is having trouble
at some point.

The interview and conference should be kept flexible. Questions cannot
be standardized, but must be worded and reworded until the child knows
precisely what is required of him. At the same time the interviewer must
avoid giving cues and must not ask leading questions. The child who is
in difficulty gropes for reasons and explanations and is especially likely to
seize upon any suggestion from the interviewer which may even temporarily rescue him from his predicament.

4. *Pupil Reports, Projects, and the Like.* Under this heading belong a
large variety of pupil activities which are useful for teaching, but equally
useful for evaluation. Individual children or groups of children can prepare reports on such topics as: How Number Is Used in the ... Bank,
How We Got Our Figure 7, Lucky Numbers, The Arithmetic I Use on
My Paper Route, Where Our Measures Came From, How Much Our
Automobile Costs Us a Month, Shortcuts in Addition, The Budget for Our
Camp Last Summer, and Number Tricks. Such reports are teaching devices, to be sure, but they also reveal unmistakably how sensitive children
have become to the mathematics of number and to the quantitative
aspects of life about them.

Trips and excursions to various points of interest offer other occasions
for detecting awareness of the quantitative. Children who during the trip
note and afterward can describe many uses of arithmetic are clearly more
advanced in their appreciation of the social significance of number than
are others who are less successful. Events in the history of number (e.g.,
the derivation of a standard unit for "foot") can be dramatized in such a
way as to permit evaluation of the level of quantitative thinking which
has been attained. In the primary grades the ability to act out or to picture the events in verbal problems reveals understanding of process meanings. The preparation of scrapbooks, models, posters, and special exhibits,
all of them involving number and quantity, may be used as much to reveal
the level which children have achieved in knowledge, understanding, and
quantitative sensitiveness as to teach them new concepts, new skills, etc.

It is precisely the meanings, understandings, and appreciations of
arithmetic that are the most difficult to evaluate objectively, reliably,

and validly by means of tests. However, these outcomes become more susceptible to evaluation, evaluation that is none too objective and none too reliable, it is true, but nevertheless valid—when evaluation escapes the limits of testing and takes the form of one or another of the procedures described above. The peculiar advantage of special reports, dramatization, picturization, and so on is that they instigate behavior in which these outcomes appear in natural relations and functional reality. The loss in objectivity need not be serious. In the first place, it is better to have some evaluation, even if somewhat unreliable, than to have none at all. In the second place, the reliability of the final evaluation by these subjective procedures increases materially and attains a respectable figure if enough observations are made.[11]

One last word should be said about the opportunities for evaluation afforded by activity units and pupil projects in which number and quantity are involved. Too often the arithmetical aspects of these units are overlooked both by teachers and by pupils. The alert teacher, however, can detect these arithmetical aspects of units and projects, can direct the pupils' attention to them, and eventually can lead pupils to discover them for themselves. When this has been done, many occasions will arise when children will be able to use number in units and projects. Whether they do so or not, the *chance* for evaluation in either case is present and should be fully utilized. That this chance is not generally so utilized is regrettable, for units and projects afford splendid opportunities to observe children thinking mathematically when the stage has not been deliberately set, as it is in the arithmetic period.

Evaluation and the classroom teacher. The program of evaluation outlined in this chapter is obviously impracticable if it is inferred that every classroom teacher must find or devise and use procedures for all the purposes of evaluation and for evaluating growth toward all outcomes. Under this assumption the teacher would be so busy evaluating that he could never get around to teaching. It follows that judgment must be exercised in deciding the extent to which evaluation is to be undertaken and the manner in which it is to be carried out. In this connection the following steps may be suggestive.

1. The first step toward effective evaluation is to know and understand the outcomes set for instruction. In a given situation these outcomes may

---

[11] This last fact is not sufficiently recognized. Assume that the reliability coefficient of a single observation is only .40. If the same kind of observation of the same performance and yielding the same result is made ten times, the reliability coefficient (Spearman-Brown formula) becomes .83. Fourteen observations would yield a reliability coefficient of .90. The writer recognizes at least some of the dangers in this statistical approach, but believes that the argument is nevertheless essentially sound.

or may not be those listed previously on pages 283-284, but whatever they are, teachers, supervisors, and principals should know what the outcomes mean.

2. The second step for the classroom teacher is to know the various kinds of behavior which evidence growth toward these objectives and to train himself to detect this evidence. Reference here is primarily to kinds of growth which cannot be evaluated by means of tests (chiefly the outcomes listed under mathematical understandings and sensitiveness to the quantitative. Admittedly, research has not yet identified all the significant evidences of growth which are needed for ideal evaluation, but this lack of research data should not greatly impede the teacher who understands what he is to teach in arithmetic and how his pupils learn.

3. Perhaps the third step is for the teacher to re-establish confidence in his ability to assess growth toward the more "intangible" outcomes. The values of observational procedures in the hands of the intelligent teacher have not been fully realized.

4. Closely related to the third step is the fourth: to take advantage of the close relation between teaching and evaluation and to seize every opportunity offered by everyday instruction to secure evidence of growth.

5. The fifth step, or another step, is to realize that evaluation for certain purposes (especially for purposes of measuring long-time achievement and of survey comparisons) is required rather seldom and then may be managed by others than the individual teacher. This means that the teacher can concentrate on diagnosis, inventorying, and measures of short-time learning—on evaluation for those purposes, in other words, which bear most directly upon the major concerns of his pupils.

The values of observational procedures are emphasized in this chapter. To some, large use of these procedures may seem to put excessive demands on the limited time teachers have. Such is not the case; observational procedures are actually time-savers. A few moments devoted to careful observation at the critical time are worth more than an hour of less intimate diagnosis at a later date. The more observational procedures are used, the less is the need for more time-consuming procedures (interviews, tests, and the like). As has been stated before, observation "catches" the behavior which is significant for directing learning at the crucial instant, and so can obviate or at least greatly lessen the necessity for more elaborate evaluation procedures later on.

Practical Suggestions for Evaluation

The plan of treatment in this section is to consider the possible means of evaluation for each group of outcomes in the order in which they are listed earlier in this chapter, and then to supply samples of procedures in the case of less easily measured outcomes.

Computational proficiency. Insofar as computation is interpreted to mean the mechanical manipulation of numbers in solving abstract examples and verbal problems of the traditional kind, the outcomes in this area are probably the most amenable to evaluation. For this reason, and also because both testing instruments and critical discussions [12] are generally available, the problems of evaluation in this area are passed over briefly, and no sample procedures are given.

The fact that most computational outcomes seemingly can be evaluated so readily by means of tests has given rise to certain unwise practices. Perhaps chief among these is that of using local uniform supervisory tests and commercial standard tests to coach children. It is not unusual for teachers and administrative officers to purchase all forms of a given standard test (or for teachers to maintain a library of all supervisory examinations over a period of years) to train children systematically on the content and skills involved in taking these tests.[13] It should be obvious that under such conditions the test scores later obtained are practically useless for purposes of evaluation. Other evil consequences of this practice should be equally apparent.

1. *Diagnosis.* For the purposes of group diagnosis on particular arithmetic skills (*a*) some standard tests are useful. Here may be mentioned the Brueckner Diagnostic Tests (Whole Numbers, Fractions, Decimals) and the Compass Diagnostic Tests (twenty forms). These tests show the places of difficulty, but not the reason for difficulty or even at times the specific nature of difficulties. The same tests may be used with the same limitations for individual diagnosis. Similar statements may be made (*b*) about the group diagnostic tests sometimes provided in textbooks and manuals by textbook authors and (*c*) about group diagnostic tests con-

---

[12] In the writer's opinion the best reference relating directly to arithmetic is the chapter by Greene and Buswell in the *Twenty-ninth Yearbook of the National Society for the Study of Education.* These authors employ a terminology somewhat different from that in this chapter, but the reader should encounter no difficulty in translating the one vocabulary into the other. See Charles E. Greene and Guy T. Buswell, "Testing, Diagnosis, and Remedial Work in Arithmetic," *Report of the Committee on Arithmetic, Twenty-ninth Yearbook of the National Society for the Study of Education, Part I,* Chapter V. Public School Publishing Co., Bloomington, Ill., 1930.

[13] A letter from the publisher of many educational tests, who must remain anonymous, states: "I could give you the names of several school systems in which cumulative files are kept of all forms of our tests. We have standing orders from these systems to supply them with each new form as it appears. Our agents tell us that in these systems the tests are available to all teachers who, if not encouraged to do so, are certainly not prevented from duplicating these tests and drilling their pupils in taking them. Then some form or other of these tests is used at the end of the year to measure achievement and to make comparisons between classes within the same system!"

structed by the teacher or the supervisor. (In this connection attention is directed to the earlier discussion, page 287, of diagnostic tests.) Diagnosis is better, the closer it comes to the immediate learning situation. On this account more crucial data than those obtainable from group tests are to be secured (*d*) from observation and, in the case of individual children, (*e*) from personal interviews. The Brueckner Diagnostic Tests, mentioned above as useful for group diagnosis, may also be used for interviewing individual children, and the Buswell-John Diagnostic Tests for Fundamental Processes in Arithmetic has been especially devised for interviewing in connection with the addition, subtraction, multiplication, and division of whole numbers only. In the latter, the test for each operation requires an average of more than a half-hour per child. Since the content in each case includes the whole range of skills taught, the first and easiest items may safely be omitted in the higher grades, and the later and harder items, in the lower grades. Or, following the model set by the Brueckner and the Buswell-John tests, the teacher can prepare his own test for interviewing. But tests as such are not indispensable to diagnosis. On the contrary, from watching his pupils day-by-day as they are busy with their arithmetic work the teacher may gain his most valuable insights. The daily lesson provides the ideal time and place both for diagnosis and for remedial teaching. As has been repeatedly emphasized, the practice of careful and continuous observation makes not only for help at the critical time, but also for economy of effort.

2. *Inventorying.* To determine "readiness" for the work of a grade or for some particular arithmetic topic, class evaluation is most practicably undertaken (*a*) through the testing programs provided in certain textbooks and teachers' manuals, (*b*) through specially prepared tests constructed according to the local course of study, and (*c*) through observation, particularly if cumulative records are kept. The last named, (*c*), does not, however, give an adequately general picture of the situation to aid in determining what should be done for the class as a whole. To the degree that instruction is individualized, however, evaluation should include observation (*c*) as well as (*d*) interviews whenever possible.*

3. *Short-Time Achievement.* For measuring attainment over a limited period of time or a single unit of work (*a*) textbook or manual tests, insofar as they fit the immediate situation, and (*b*) specially constructed local tests are to be preferred. The latter need to be carefully prepared; otherwise, important steps may be omitted. (*c*) Observation and (*d*) in-

---

* Since this chapter was written, Professor Brueckner has announced the publication of standard readiness tests for all processes with whole numbers, fractions, decimals, and percentage.

terviews serve supplementary purposes, which is to say that they are useful chiefly for evaluating outcomes which are important in the unit as a whole but are essentially non-computational. (*e*) Standard tests are of slight value, since rarely does their content agree with the local course of study.

4. *Long-Time Achievement.* For semester or yearly measures, the suggestions made with respect to short-time measures hold with equal force. The content of tests is chosen, of course, from a wider range than in the case of "progress" tests, since the learnings are wider in scope. Mistakes of interpretation are frequently made by obtaining measures of long-time achievement ("long-time" in the sense here used) from commercial standard tests which cover the arithmetic content of a series of grades.

5. *Surveys.* For comparisons between schools within the same system local instruments which are uniform in content may be used. These instruments, when intended for grade-by-grade comparisons, should probably contain only the content (skills, facts, etc.) taught in the given grade and in grades below that point. In this case as many separate tests may be needed as there are grades tested. Standard survey instruments are useful, particularly when the standings of school systems are to be compared with one another. In such cases the test contains a rough sampling of all skills, facts, etc., taught through grade three, grade six, grade eight, or some such point. Among the better known tests of this last kind are: Analytical Scales of Attainment in Arithmetic (grades three and four, five and six, seven and eight), Compass Survey Test (elementary and advanced), Metropolitan Achievement Test (primary, intermediate, and advanced forms), New Stanford Achievement Test (primary and advanced forms), Progressive Arithmetic Tests (primary, elementary, and intermediate forms), Public School Achievement Tests (Computation and Reasoning), and Unit Scales of Attainment in Arithmetic. For critical comments on these and other standard tests, the reader is advised to consult the various annual volumes under the general title *The Mental Measurements Yearbook,* edited by Professor Oscar K. Buros of Rutgers University. The non-equivalence of norms on survey tests, mentioned above as invalidating comparison of scores for individual pupils, does not seriously affect the comparisons of large numbers of children or of schools as wholes. Nevertheless, the interpretation of test results should always include appropriate recognition of the implications of differences in aims and objectives among the schools concerned.

Mathematical understanding. This section presents illustrations of evaluation devices useful in connection with the less commonly assessed outcomes of arithmetic.

1. *Purposes of Evaluation.* So far as evaluation for differing purposes is concerned, outcomes which can be classified under the term "mathemati-

cal understanding" can be discussed together, since the problems relating to evaluation procedures are much alike for all of them. Exceedingly little has been done either informally or systematically to find practicable and valid procedures for evaluating the outcomes under the heading above. There are, for example, no standard tests available, except (*a*) two sections of the Analytical Scales of Attainment, one devoted to forty items testing "Quantitative Relationships," and the other to forty items testing "Arithmetic Vocabulary" (these sections being available in the tests for grades three and four, five and six, and seven and eight), and (*b*) a shorter section in the Iowa Every Pupil Test. But these sections do not evaluate learning with respect to all the outcomes listed here under *Mathematical understanding;* they do not evaluate fully or for all different purposes with respect to any one outcome listed; nor do high scores on these tests guarantee that the knowledge revealed will actually function to affect conduct. They are, however, to be recommended to anyone interested in objective means of evaluating in this area.

For diagnosis, the best procedures in the order of their present practicability are: (*a*) observation (both of oral and of written work), of which samples are given below, (*b*) the interview and conference, also illustrated below, and (*c*) specially constructed tests. The last-named are hardly practicable for the average teacher, for the preparation of such tests is as yet highly technical. Few ventures would, however, pay larger returns on effort than the co-operative work of a group of teachers in attempting to devise testing instruments. For their benefit what seem to be promising devices are illustrated below. Procedures (*a*) and (*b*) are entirely practicable for the teacher who knows what to look for. The present methods of preparing arithmetic teachers, however, hardly equip teachers with this kind of knowledge.

Inventorying to determine "readiness" is likewise handicapped at present because of inadequate knowledge of the stages of development which characterize growth toward the various objectives. All understandings are matters of experience, but the essential experiences cannot all be had at once. Rather, learning activities must be arranged so as to encourage growth from stage to stage, or from level of meaning to level of meaning. In time, tests should be available to identify these stages of development. In the meantime, the situation is not hopeless. Teachers (*a*) by observations and (*b*) by interviews can determine whether pupils have attained requisite degrees of understanding, and have or have not carried a given generalization far enough to warrant either its use in a new context or its extension through new activities. It is not impossible that (*c*) tests can be worked out experimentally and improved with trial. In this case, the sample items below can be adapted to the special purpose of inventorying.

Evaluation of learning over short periods of time is subject to the same limitations as have been mentioned for the other two purposes of evaluation which have been discussed—restricted knowledge and lack of procedures which are certainly reliable and valid. Reliance for the time must be placed upon subjective judgment, that is, on (*a*) observation and (*b*) interviews, chiefly the former. Eventually (*c*) tests may be available, and groups of teachers may want to try their hand in this direction.

What has just been said applies also to evaluation of learning over longer periods of time.

For survey purposes, survey tests are required. The only ones to be had have been mentioned in the first paragraph above under *Purposes of Evaluation.*

2. *Samples of Evaluation Procedures.*[14] Below are given samples of procedures (test items, observation, interview) which can be used for evaluating growth in mathematical understanding. Space limitations forbid more than a few samples in each case. The same limitations make it necessary to present each item as briefly as possible, without indication of its grade level and frequently without its being cast into proper form for testing.

PART II: THE COGNITIVE DOMAIN

METHODS OF STUDYING PUPILS' THINKING

Guy T. Buswell

Some marked gains in our understanding of how pupils learn arithmetic have been made by purely objective studies of their behavior and of the results of their work. Analyses of the written work of pupils have revealed

[From "Methods of Studying Pupils' Thinking in Arithmetic," *Arithmetic 1949*, Supplementary Educational Monographs, No. 70 (November, 1949), pp. 55-63. Reprinted by permission of the author and the University of Chicago Press.]

---

[14] The writer is grateful to the following persons, in addition to those mentioned in the text, for assistance in suggesting sample items: Mr. Lester Anderson, of the University of Minnesota, Dr. Arthur S. Otis, and Professor Leo J. Brueckner, Professor Ben A. Sueltz, and Professor Harry G. Wheat, the last three being members of this Committee.

some of the troublesome operations in computation. Time and error studies have yielded useful information regarding the relative difficulty of number combinations. Objective investigations of methods of teaching have shown unmistakable differences in the results of different ways of teaching.

Objective methods of research need no defense, and I shall be among the first to acknowledge indebtedness to them. In fact, my personal inclinations have led me to follow the rigid techniques of laboratory research largely because of the high degree of objectivity that they afford. However, there may be many roads to the goal of truth, and the highway of objective methods, while hard and straight, need not blind one to other roads which may provide other views of the truth we seek.

In the present paper the truth we are seeking is an understanding of how pupils think when working with numbers. As a supplement to some of the very productive objective studies of this question, I am proposing that more attention be given to descriptive studies of how pupils think, even though the necessary methods for conducting such studies leave something to be desired in the way of quantitative evidence. They may provide leads which will later be followed by more objective methods. For example, pupils' descriptions of their own mental operations in computation or problem solving are subjective and may not always accord with the actual mental processes that occur. Yet they frequently supply insights into the pupils' difficulties which may escape the attention of the strictly objective studies of behavior. The pupils' statements may not be taken as valid truth, but they often supply hypotheses of value, which can in turn be studied by more refined techniques.

In my opinion, research in arithmetic is suffering from a lack of insights, which may be supplied only by exhibiting more daring and assuming more risks of failure in our methods of study. Research in arithmetic is in danger of becoming stereotyped and sterile. And this statement is in no sense to be interpreted as a disparagement of research already done. Rather it is a plea that the kind of ingenuity which initiated some of the research already proved significant be applied to new problems and the devising of new techniques.

One of the conspicuous gains of the last fifteen years has been the rather general acceptance of the idea that arithmetic must be taught meaningfully. We are no longer complacent about computational skill accomplished by routine practice without an understanding of the operations that are used. It was fairly simple to study and to control the frequency of number combinations in drill exercises. It is much more difficult to discover how pupils think when the outcome is understanding rather than confusion. Yet, if we mean what we say about "meaningful arithmetic," we must discover what these "meanings" are, not only to the teacher, but also to the pupils.

We are yet somewhat in the dark as to just what mathematical meanings are important to be learned in arithmetic, and we do not know with any certainty at what grade levels these various meanings should be taught. But even more serious is the fact that we do not know what meaning consists of to the pupil as contrasted with what meaning is to the teacher. We think we know that meanings for the teacher possess characteristics of logic and coherence, but what we do not know is the nature of the meaningful experiences which make up the thinking of pupils through the various levels of learning until full maturity of understanding is reached. And the main concern of the school is this process of learning by which pupils pass from the confusions of immaturity to the clarity of mature understanding. How can we ever understand this until we get more knowledge of the way in which pupils think at various stages of the process? More important still, how can we discover what goes on in the thoughts of the pupil as he tries to learn the arithmetic that we try to teach?

Methods of Studying Pupils' Thinking

The main purpose of this paper is to suggest some methods of studying pupils' thinking. I have no doubt that some of my readers may think of even more fertile ways of accomplishing this than the half-dozen ways that I shall propose as worth trying. All these ways employ simple techniques and no elaborate apparatus. They are adaptable to classroom situations and may be used by any teacher.

1. As a first proposal I would suggest that teachers study the development of meanings from year to year as pupils progress through the grades. This can be done by keeping a systematic record of pupils' responses to a common group of exercises or questions. Study of such records will indicate the nature of the pupils' understandings from grade to grade and will throw light on the problems of learning at various levels of maturity. My first use of this method was in studying the vocabulary of arithmetic, but it was not until later that I sensed its possibilities for studying the levels of pupils' thinking.

A concrete illustration from the vocabulary study [1] will indicate the

---

[1] G. T. Buswell and Lenore John. *The Vocabulary of Arithmetic*, Supplementary Educational Monographs, No. 38 (Chicago: University of Chicago Press, 1931), Chapter 4.

possibilities of the method. In that study forty pupils from each of the school Grades I-VI were asked to give the meanings of a list of twenty-five arithmetical terms. The words were typed on cards, and the teacher pronounced the words as they were shown to the pupil. A verbatim record was then kept of each pupil's response to the question, "Can you tell me what this word means in arithmetic?" The significance of the method becomes clear from a comparative study of the data from grade to grade.

For example, responses to the term *fraction* showed that no pupil in the first or the second grade had a correct concept of the term. In the third grade, three pupils gave a correct response, and in Grades IV, V, and VI, the number of correct responses were, respectively, 20, 29, and 34. However, the most significant aspect of the study does not lie in the statistical tabulations, enlightening as they are. The nature of the pupils' thinking is revealed better by the interesting views of what pupils are thinking. For example, no pupil in Grade I gave a correct meaning for the word *fraction*. Two of the forty gave wrong responses. One of the two said, "It's some kind of work—we do it in Brazil," while the other said, "I don't know, but I've heard my sister use it."

In Grade II no pupil had a correct understanding of *fraction*, but three of them said, "It is a number"; one said, "It is something in arithmetic," and one said, "It means you take numbers and add numbers." Vague as the latter responses were, they were at least placing the word in the area where it belongs.

Thoughtful analysis of such statements by pupils will throw much light on the character of their thinking. For purposes of teaching, it is more important to understand the devious ways through which a correct meaning is finally reached than to know how the meaning is finally stated.

A careful analysis of the pupils' responses in this investigation revealed a number of facts about how pupils think. It was clear that the meanings of words for pupils grew out of their experiences rather than out of definitions from textbooks or dictionaries. The meanings emerged gradually and were at first limited to concrete situations, with a gradual formulation of generalization and abstraction. When the meanings developed from the pupils' experiences, they remained as permanent attainments, but, if they were taught as technical textbook definitions, the meanings were soon forgotten. For example, for the word *quotient*, which was taught by definition, there were fewer sixth-grade pupils who knew it than there were in the fifth grade where the word was first taught. The essence of this method is that the pupils' own responses furnish the data and that a systematic record of responses to the same term or situation be made with enough pupils to show common tendencies and individual differences. A systematic analysis of pupil responses is very different from listening to them casually from time to time.

2. A second method of studying pupils' thinking also involves keeping verbatim records of their responses but goes farther than simply recording definitions of words. In this case it is based on "thinking aloud" while the pupil carries on arithmetical operations. The first requirement is that the teacher establish good rapport with the pupil so that he will express his thoughts fully and freely as he does his computations or his verbal problems. The teacher will also need some practice in rapid recording of what the pupil says. However, the method pays rich dividends in insight into pupil difficulties in thinking.

A concrete illustration of the use of this method may be taken from a study carried on in the Laboratory School of the University of Chicago. It revealed a type of difficulty which never would have been discovered by studying the pupils' written answers. As an illustration of this method I shall quote from a published study in which a systematic individual analysis was made of the methods of thinking of more than four hundred pupils. The following case [2] is an interesting example.

> Kurt was a bright boy in the third grade who had received his previous instruction at home and who entered school for the first time in this grade. He experienced many difficulties with both addition and subtraction. Some of his difficulties were of a peculiar type, especially those relating to his reading of numbers. In the example, 58 minus 4, he read the 58 as 85, then counted back to 81, and wrote the answer 18. He was frequently confused by 6's and 9's, not being sure which was 6 and which was 9. In the example, 79 minus 3, he said "67," both inverting and reversing numbers. He counted back "67, 57, 47," stopped, and wrote the answer 74. In the next example, 98 minus 5, he read the 98 as 86 and then began to count back as follows: "86, 76, 66." When he reached 66, he said, "Oh, no," and counted as follows: "86, 85, 84, 83, 82." He reversed the 82 and wrote his answer as 28. In the case of the example, 89 plus 7, he said, "89, 99, 100, 102, 103, 104, 105" and wrote 105 as the answer. In adding 53 and 8, he said "53 and 8 is 43, no, 53, 63, 73, 83, 93. Well, I don't know which number this is [pointing back to the 53]. Is it 50 or 30? He then counted, "54, 55, 56, 57, 58, 59, 60." In writing the final answer, he reversed the digits and wrote 06. The methods and processes which Kurt used were rich in variety. His work showed an interesting mixture of erratic procedure and erroneous logic. Nothing but a detailed analysis of his mental processes could indicate to a teacher the kind of help that he needed.

---

[2] G. T. Buswell, with the co-operation of Lenore John. *Diagnostic Studies in Arithmetic*, Supplementary Educational Monographs, No. 30 (Chicago: University of Chicago Press, 1926), 2-3.

A record of pupils' thinking when urged to think aloud is revealing at any time. However, there are now available in the published literature of arithmetic rather elaborate classifications of pupils' habits of work derived from this method of study, which enable a teacher to identify quickly the common types of difficulties that pupils experience. These catalogues of habits of work, with their accompanying concrete illustrations, furnish a useful tool for the teacher who wishes to enrich his understanding of how pupils think. These published studies of pupils' thinking cover the four fundamental operations with whole numbers, decimals, and fractions, and there are also some examples of the same technique applied to problem-solving. Some of our most useful techniques of diagnosis are derived from these studies of pupils' thinking.

3. A third method for studying how pupils think is to provide them with an ample supply of manipulative aids and then ask them to illustrate concretely some of the algorisms that they express abstractly in numbers. For example, pupils in the primary grades are expected to learn the decimal nature of our number system so that they can express numbers and simple combinations in terms of tens. If a child is given an abacus or bundles of sticks tied into tens and is asked to show how the number 365 is made up, his demonstration will very quickly show whether or not he senses that 365 is made up of 36 tens and 5 ones. At a later stage, his demonstration of borrowing or carrying by the use of various manipulative aids will again show whether he knows $34 - 18 = 16$ as an abstract verbal statement or as a meaningful relationship that he can demonstrate concretely.

We are only beginning to realize the important place that manipulative aids of various types can play in learning. We have usually thought of them as devices to help pupils get their answers. Much more important is their use as devices to show the thinking which lies back of the answers that pupils get. Of course, manipulative aids may be used both without contributing to pupils' thinking and without revealing how they think. But when used with intelligence and insight, they may contribute much to superior teaching.

4. A fourth method of studying pupils' thinking consists of making a diagram of the various possible procedures in solving a problem or verbal exercise and then, with this diagram as a diagnostic tool, tracing the steps of an individual pupil's thinking. This method makes possible an objective plotting of both the false and the true moves of a pupil. When applied to a number of pupils, the plotting supplies valuable insights into the variety of their thinking processes.

For example, a textbook exercise read as follows: "Mary has 15 hens which lay an average of 5 eggs each per week. If eggs sell for 50¢ per

dozen, how much should Mary get for her eggs in 4 weeks?" Pupil A
worked the exercise as follows:

1. $5 \times 15 = 75$ (5 eggs, 15 hens, 75 eggs per week)
2. $4 \times 75 = 300$ (4 weeks, 75 eggs per week, 300 eggs)
3. $300 \div 12 = 25$ (300 eggs, divide by 12 = 25 dozen)
4. $25 \times \$.50 = \$12.50$ (25 dozen, 50¢ per dozen, total $12.50)

Pupil B followed a different mode of thinking but got the same answer.
Her procedure was as follows:

5. $5 \times 4 = 20$ (5 eggs per week, 4 weeks, 1 hen lays 20 eggs)
6. $20 \div 12 = 1\frac{2}{3}$ (20 eggs, divide by 12, 1⅔ doz.)
7. $1\frac{2}{3} \times \$.50 = \$.83\frac{1}{3}$ (1⅔ dozen, 50¢ per dozen, $.83⅓ per hen in 4
   weeks)
8. $15 \times \$.83\frac{1}{3} = \$12.50$ (15 hens, $.83⅓ each, $12.50 total)

There are, obviously, other procedures which will also bring the correct
answer, and these in turn may be listed with appropriate serial index numbers. Furthermore, there will also be numerous incorrect procedures that
should also be listed, as, for example, the failure to reduce the 300 eggs to
number of dozen before multiplying by the price per dozen.

If a teacher has before him a page on which are listed all the various
possible steps or procedures for a given exercise, it is then a simple matter
to record by index number the thinking procedures of an individual pupil.
If this were done for a sample group of problems, a diagnosis of a pupil's
thinking could be expressed objectively and the pupil could be shown just
where his errors occurred. In the upper grades pupils could learn to diagnose their own difficulties and could compare procedures with those of
other pupils. The main point about this method is that it makes possible
an objective listing or plotting of the procedures in subjective thinking. It
is a method which deserves much wider use than it has so far received.

5. As a fifth method for studying how pupils think, I would suggest the
use of unusual procedures in computation and even the use of number
systems with a base other than 10 and with non-numerical symbols. One
becomes more aware of the thinking procedures involved in novel situations than in those which have become conventional, as for example, our
usual method of multiplying by beginning with the right-hand number.
However, one may begin with the left-hand number if he wishes, and to
do so occasionally is a good exercise in straight thinking.

Writing the full product of each partial multiplication, rather than carrying as we usually do, is an interesting variant which makes pupils more
conscious of the decimal nature of the number system and the advantages
and economies of learning to carry. Pupils in the upper grades can learn

to use a modified number system, based on 3 or 7 or any number other than the usual 10. In doing so, they will reveal many of the thinking difficulties in dealing with our usual decimal system. Letters of the alphabet may be substituted for digits. For example, a can represent zero, b stand for unity, and c and d be the following digits in a system based on 4 rather than 10. Counting would then proceed as follows: $a, b, c, d, ba, bb, bc, bd, ca, cb$, and so on. Computation would be carried on as usual, only with a base of 4 (in this case ba) rather than 10, and the usual number combinations could be learned, as $b + b = c; c + c = ba; d + d = bc$; etc.

Occasional exercises with variants from usual procedures produce wholesome thinking situations and give opportunities to observe how pupils think which do not occur in habitual, conventional procedures. Obviously, the teacher should master thoroughly the new procedures before using them with a class.

6. As a sixth method for studying pupils' thinking, I would suggest that, while much can be learned from pupil's subjective statements about their own thinking, there is always an advantage in getting objective evidence when possible. The methods of the laboratory are not feasible in a classroom, at least when elaborate apparatus is involved. But to the extent that they are possible, they are valuable adjuncts to less exact modes of study. For example, the first precise data on the irregular procedures that pupils follow in column addition were furnished by photographic records of the eye-movements of children while adding, and the subsequent explanations of these irregularities were enlightening and useful to teachers. There are, however, many possibilities of objectifying pupils' thinking through the use of relatively simple devices that can be used in a classroom. A simple string pendulum or metronome will make possible a time analysis of a pupil's operations in arithmetic, which in turn may be used to probe into the thinking done on operations requiring inordinate amounts of time. The objective time analysis identifies the trouble spots, which can then be studied in detail. As a principle, objective evidence is always preferable when it is possible to get it.

Levels of Thinking

The six methods of studying pupils' thinking that have been suggested all have a single purpose, namely, to understand better how pupils arrive at their answers in computation and how they solve arithmetical problems. We want their work to be meaningful to them, not a formal process of drilling on operations which they do not understand. If we help them, we must see their difficulties from their own point of view—we must understand what meanings are to children, not just to teachers.

If we are able to make a sufficiently clear analysis of the pupils' mental operations from grade to grade through the elementary school, we shall become aware that there are progressive levels of meanings as arithmetic is learned. The same operation will have different meanings to the child as his understanding of number processes develops. We need to give more study to these levels of meanings which characterize the child's work. A meaning which is entirely satisfactory at the third-grade level may be unacceptable at the fifth-grade level. These meaning levels change from the particularized, concrete expressions of the beginning period to the generalized, abstract relations of the later stages of arithmetic. Each level of meaning is equally appropriate in its place.

Difficulties arise when beginning levels persist into later grades. Adding by counting is one of the ways by which young children verify their sums. If the child does not know an addition combination and if there is no one present to ask what the sum is, the surest thing to do is to count to arrive at the answer. The meaning of so doing is clear to the child, and he has confidence in the result. Counting is a valid experience at the beginners' level. But when counting persists into the middle and the upper grades, it is entirely unacceptable as a mode of adding. At the upper-grade level, adding should become a process of dealing with abstract number symbols without counting and even without concern for the concretes for which the numbers stand. It is wrong to begin addition by asking first- and second-graders to master the abstract addition facts by rote, and it is equally wrong to complete the learning of addition in later grades by allowing pupils to count or to use concrete aids in carrying on what should have become an abstract operation.

In our concern for meaningful arithmetic we need to know both the array of mathematical meanings which make up the subject of arithmetic and the levels at which these various meanings can appropriately be learned. In doing the latter, the main consideration is not the logical sequence in which these meanings may be arranged but rather the sequence in terms of pupils' meanings and understandings. We are blocked, at present, in doing this by the inadequate research findings that would show us the nature of meanings from the child's rather than the teacher's point of view. It is difficult to construct an adequate course of study in arithmetic without such knowledge. And this kind of knowledge can be obtained only by studying pupils' methods of thinking.

Meanings for pupils are what *they* think, not necessarily what *teachers* think. The learning process is a developing process, advancing from level to level. Teachers need to understand the levels of thinking at which pupils operate. Answers to arithmetical exercises are less important to teachers than is knowledge of the mental processes by which pupils obtain the answers.

The "meaning theory" has produced marked changes in the teaching of arithmetic in the past two decades. It has been interpreted in various ways, sometimes emphasizing social meanings and sometimes mathematical meanings. At heart there is no dichotomy between social and mathematical meanings. Arithmetic deals with a number *system* and a set of processes and operations coherent and consistent within themselves. It is a closed system, not modified by pupils' wishes or interests. Pupils do not decide by democratic vote what will be the sum of 4 and 5 or whether the value of a fraction is unchanged when both numerator and denominator are multiplied by the same number. Within the frame of reference of our mathematical system these things are true because they are demanded by the consistency of the system. The number system is mature, logical. But children are neither mature nor very logical. The problem of the teacher is so to understand the successive levels of pupils' thinking that he can help the children develop clear meanings at every stage of the learning process. These meanings exist in the pupils' thinking. Arithmetic teachers must learn to understand how pupils think.

TESTING MEANINGS IN ARITHMETIC

Vincent J. Glennon

The application of the method of intelligence to the solution of problems in the area of education and its ancillary disciplines, the social sciences of psychology, sociology, and cultural anthropology, has been the most significant development in education in the past half-century. The scientific method, as it is commonly called, applied to educational problems has done much to supplant groundless opinions with established principles and facts. We shall never again find ourselves in that stage of development in which we advocate, as was done in an arithmetic course of study written in 1914, that "nothing but drill day after day, week after week, and month after month, will fix these memory facts."

The theory of education and of the learning process in particular that supported such a statement, although still widely prevalent in practice, is

[From "Testing Meaning in Arithmetic," *Arithmetic 1949*, Supplementary Educational Monographs, No. 70 (November, 1949), pp. 64-74. Reprinted by permission of the author and the University of Chicago Press.]

being undermined by the findings of competent research students. It is rapidly becoming an educational curiosity, and in its stead we have the theory of generalization. The group which accepts the generalization theory is small in number but large in influence. That group is the group of frontier researchers. It will be some time before practice catches up with present-day theory.

Causes of Lag

The lag in the development of adequate methods and devices for measuring growth in understandings and meanings in arithmetic has certain causes that are related to the lag in other aspects of the arithmetic teaching-learning situation. Let us consider a few of these causes.

The first cause is a direct outgrowth of the changing role of arithmetic in the curriculum of the schools during the many phases of the evolving culture. The role of arithmetic has shifted from that of a science of numbers, *numerorum scientia*,[1] in the Greek and Roman cultures to that of a so-called "tool" subject in our present culture; from that of a discipline with inherent relationships to that of a discipline with little or no inherent relationships; from that of a discipline which was studied as an end in itself to that of a discipline which was studied so that it might be used to achieve some other end; and from that of a discipline based upon a broad interpretation of the practical to that of a discipline based upon a narrow interpretation (or misinterpretation) of the practical. (The word *misinterpretation* is used advisedly, since our present interpretation of "practical arithmetic" does not at all agree with the ideas developed by John Dewey and McLellan.)[2] This change in the role of arithmetic has brought with it a change in the aims and objectives in the teaching and learning of arithmetic, and that change has in turn brought with it a changed emphasis in the methods of measuring the outcomes of learning in arithmetic. The aims and objectives have stressed speed and accuracy in selected and restricted segments of the total field, and the methods of measuring these outcomes have been limited to tests of speed and accuracy in computational and verbal problem situations.

The second cause of the lag in the development of adequate methods and devices for measuring growth in understandings and meanings in arithmetic lies in the great impact of physiological psychology on methods of teaching. A narrow interpretation of practical education or of the

---

[1] The Greeks and Romans used the word *arithmetic* to refer to the science of numbers (*numerorum scientia*) and used the word *logistic* to refer to the more humble type of learning involved in manipulating numbers or computing.

[2] James A. McLellan and John Dewey. *The Psychology of Number* (New York: D. Appleton & Co., 1895).

philosophy of pragmatism was well supported by the psychology of the teaching-learning situation. The usual or common interpretation emphasized atomization of the facts and processes of arithmetic, the selection of bonds to be formed, and habit formation or the strengthening of bonds through drill. This usual or common interpretation tends to eliminate reference to the necessity for learning the general principles and understandings inherent in the number system. This is not strictly as the writings were meant to be interpreted. In his *Psychology of Arithmetic* Thorndike gave a position of importance to the development of principles and generalization, as is indicated in the following quotation:

> The older pedagogy of arithmetic stated a general law or truth or principle, ordered the pupil to learn it, and gave him tasks to do which he could not do profitably unless he understood the principle. It left him to build up himself the particular habits needed to give him understanding and mastery of the principle. The newer pedagogy is careful to help him build up these connections or bonds ahead of and along with the general truth or principle, so that he can understand it better.[3]

The common misinterpretation of "bond" psychology was accepted readily and on a wide scale by teachers for two reasons: (1) the ease with which the teacher was able to understand it and tell others about it and (2) the ease with which the teacher was able to apply it through the drill lesson.

A third cause of the lag in the development of adequate methods and devices for measuring growth in understandings and meanings in arithmetic is the mental security which teachers and supervisors find in the present practices of telling, drilling, and testing. The thought of providing a learning situation in which the learner is given the freedom in which to discover number relationships and in which the learning is measured by more than pencil-and-paper tests, is a thought that is sufficiently threatening to the teacher to cause him to retreat to the security found in present classroom practices and procedures. The teacher will only move along in the acceptance and development of new ideas and methods of guiding growth and of measuring growth in arithmetic when he can find the same or greater security in the new than he finds in the present ideas and methods. This presents a herculean job for those persons responsible for the in-service and pre-service development of teachers.

A fourth cause for the lag in the development of adequate methods and devices for measuring growth in understandings and meanings in arithmetic lies in thinking of arithmetic as a series of arbitrary associations,

---

[3] Edward L. Thorndike. *The Psychology of Arithmetic* (New York: Macmillan Co., 1922), p. 74.

each association being an entity in itself and having no relation to other associations. This places the learning of arithmetic in the same category as the truly arbitrary associational learnings, such as word recognition in reading and the order of letters in the correct spelling of a word. Arithmetic is no more a series of arbitrary associations than an automobile is a series of arbitrary parts and systems. Arithmetic is as much a series of related understandings and meanings as an automobile is a series of related parts and systems.

To illustrate the folly of our present methods of teaching arithmetic as a series of arbitrary associations, we can elaborate this analogy. Assume that you are with a person who has never seen, heard of, or read about, an automobile. He is completely naïve about the meaning of *automobile*. You are to teach him the meaning of *automobile*, proceeding on the learning theory that an automobile is a series of unrelated parts, a series of arbitrary associations. You might begin by showing the learner one of the parts; let us say a fender. You tell the person that this is a fender; you ask him to repeat the name after you; you spell it for him and ask him to repeat the spelling until he knows it. You do not go out of your way to show the relation of this part of the automobile to any other part. After the learner has mastered *fender*, you put it aside and take up another part; let us say a lamp. Following the "correct" teaching procedure, you show him the part, pronounce the name of it, ask him to repeat the name, you spell it for him and ask him to spell it for you, and so the learner "masters" another part of the automobile. You proceed in like manner to teach the person all the several thousand parts of the automobile, "reviewing" whenever necessary the previous learning and testing occasionally the person's ability to associate the correct name with a given part. Having finished the course, you then tell the person that he now knows what an automobile is!

Does he know what an automobile is? No! He knows only that an automobile is a series of parts and that he was able to identify enough of the parts to please the teacher. He sees few relationships between the parts and the system; he does not see the automobile as a whole; and he does not know the uses of the automobile.

Arithmetic is a series of related meanings, principles, and generalizations. And to the degree that we approach the teaching and testing of arithmetic with that point of view, to that same degree we raise the subject from the level of a series of arbitrary associations to the level of the higher mental processes.

A fifth cause for the lag in the development of adequate methods and devices for measuring growth in understandings and meanings in arithmetic is the degree to which the presently available tests impinge upon and striate the aims and objectives of learning in arithmetic. Teachers tend to teach for the learnings that they know are included in standardized tests. When those tests include only learnings of limited scope, the teaching also includes learning experiences of limited scope. The tests presently available measure, with the exception of a few items in a few tests, ability to compute and ability to solve verbal problems. Therefore, teachers tend to teach for proficiency in these two abilities.

Although tests presently available have serious limitations, we cannot say that they are bad tests. No object is good or bad in itself. The goodness or badness of an object lies in the use to which it is put rather than in any inherent qualities of the object. The presently available tests are worth while if it is kept in mind that they measure only a small area of the total field of arithmetic.

At the present time little attention is given by the teacher and the supervisor to the need for measuring the degree to which the learner is growing in those outcomes which are the controls of behavior in number situations —outcomes such as the understandings and meanings that are inherent in the number system, the attitude toward number situations as they appear in life and in school, and appreciation of the uses of arithmetic. The teacher and the supervisor will seek out and use more adequate methods and devices for measuring the broader outcomes of instruction in arithmetic only after they have accepted these broader outcomes, these controls of behavior, as worth-while aims in arithmetic. Bringing about this acceptance on the part of the teacher is an important in-service and pre-service problem in teacher education.

A sixth cause for the lag in the development of adequate methods and devices for measuring growth in understandings and meanings in arithmetic is the lack of a definitive list of the understandings and meanings. In numerous sources in the literature we can find brief lists or single illustrations of the understandings. Quite often these brief lists tend to be poorly worded and ambiguous. By way of illustration, it is not sufficient to state as one of the understandings: *understanding higher-decade addition.* We must be much more specific than that. Understanding *what* about higher-decade addition? Higher-decade addition is a complex of several related but simpler understandings. We must know what these related but simpler understandings are.

We ought to have some insight into the relative order of difficulty of these understandings. We ought to have some insight into the mental age at which the understandings can be acquired. Only when we have this type of information shall we be able to tackle intelligently the problem of grade placement of topics. Only when we have this type of information will the teacher be able to guide the learner in experiences that include both social understandings and mathematical understandings that are meaningful. And only when we have this type of information shall we be able to develop adequate methods and devices for measuring growth in understandings or meanings.

The foregoing statements have treated briefly six causes for the lag in the development of adequate methods and devices for measuring understandings or meanings in arithmetic. The brevity of the treatment does not negate the importance of the causes, nor does it imply that the causes are easily overcome. We have come a long way in the development of a few aspects of a total evaluation program in arithmetic, but there is still much to be done.

A Frontier Research Study

The paucity of research studies in the area of testing for meanings justifies the conclusion that this is one of the most neglected educational problems of the day. The lack of research is a direct result of the general lag in the development of adequate methods and devices for measuring understandings and meanings, which in turn is a direct result of the six conditions listed previously.

The study to be reported here [4] is a frontier research study designed to make a small inroad into this problem. Like all frontier research, it has limitations. The major problem of the study is of more concern to the small professional research groups than it is to the classroom teacher. Subsequent research studies will refine the method, corroborate the findings, and determine their implications for classroom practice.

Purpose of the Study. The general purpose of the study is to determine the extent of growth and mastery of certain basic mathematical understandings possessed by representative groups on seven educational levels. It is an attempt to obtain evidence of the degree to which persons above the level of Grade VI have possession of understandings basic to the several computational processes commonly taught in Grades I through VI.

Method of the Study. The general type of investigative method used in the study is the normative method; that is, a method through the use of which we obtain an index of prevailing conditions within the group or groups of persons being studied. The first problem to be considered in the development of the study was a method for gathering the data. Two alternatives presented themselves. First, the researcher could use the method of the individual interview, or, second, he could use the method of mass

---

[4] Vincent J. Glennon. "A Study of the Growth and Mastery of Certain Basic Mathematical Understandings on Seven Educational Levels," Unpublished Doctor's dissertation. Cambridge, Massachusetts: Graduate School of Education, Harvard University, 1948.

administration of a pencil-and-paper test. The second alternative was selected because it would permit the researcher to study a larger and more representative group of persons in the same amount of time.

Selection of the second alternative brought with it the very immediate problem of choosing the pencil-and-paper test that would measure understandings and meanings. An analysis was made of all arithmetic tests published since 1915. Each of the tests was carefully examined for the purpose of determining the number of items that were designed to measure understandings or meanings. The examination revealed no single test that would meet the needs of the study. It also revealed that no test commonly used at the present time contains more than a few items designed to measure understandings.

It was necessary, therefore, to construct a new instrument for measuring basic mathematical understandings. The items included in the test had to be of such a kind that they eliminated entirely, or at least minimized, the effect of rote computational facility as a determiner of success on the test items. An example in multiplication would not be a valid item, since it would not discriminate between the student who performed on a rote level and the student who performed on a rational or understanding level. Since any test item that involved computation would not be a valid item, the general validity of the test would be raised to the degree that the items did not require computation.

To obtain objectivity, the items were built in the form of multiple-choice items. This type of item was chosen on the basis of such statements as that of Hawkes, Lindquist, and Mann: "The multiple-choice type is perhaps the most valuable and the most generally applicable of all types of test exercises." [5]

Among the five choices in each test item there were included, wherever possible, one or more choices that were typical pupil responses. These typical responses were secured by the preparation and administration of a completion test to several classes of seventh- and eighth-grade pupils. The answers which occurred most frequently were then built into the multiple-choice items. The original test contained 136 items covering seven areas of meanings and understandings basic to the computational processes, commonly taught in Grades I through VI.

The determination of the validity of the test was a big problem. Several commonly used validation procedures were considered in terms of their applicability for determining the validity of this particular instrument. Lack of a criterion test made it impossible to compare scores on the new

---

[5] Herbert E. Hawkes, E. F. Lindquist, and C. R. Mann. *The Construction and Use of Achievement Examinations* (Boston: Houghton Mifflin Co., 1936), p. 138.

test with scores on the criterion test to obtain the degree of statistical validity. The curricular or analytical validity was determined by making use of the combined judgments of sixteen well-informed experts in the subject matter covered by the test.

In the last analysis the best method for determining the validity of any test is an observation of behavior, keeping in mind the question: Does the test distinguish between the person who understands (or has a given ability, or has a given skill, etc.) and the person who does not understand? Keeping in mind this question, I worked with many groups of children, two children to a group, on the seventh-grade level over a period of two months. After selecting the choice which he believed to be the correct answer to a given question, the student was asked to tell why he thought that choice was correct. He was asked to explain his choice, to prove by an explanation or drawing that his choice was correct.

"Loaded" questions were discovered by the student's ability to select the correct answer without being able to describe or illustrate the understanding involved. Such questions were either revised or eliminated. The interview technique was continued until no new loaded questions were uncovered. During the interviews I noted evidences of reading difficulties stemming from the wording of the items. Whenever the item seemed to cause such difficulty, the students were asked to tell what they thought the item meant and were asked to state the question in their own words. This wording was noted, and the items were changed to conform with the wording that was the most meaningful to the students. Difficulties with sentence structure, vocabulary, and ambiguities were noted and the items modified or eliminated.

Through this procedure the original test of 136 items was reduced to 90 items. However, a test of 90 items of this kind is somewhat too long for use in a single classroom sitting, so the number of items was reduced to 80. The items covered five areas of basic mathematical meanings: (1) the decimal system of notation, (2) basic understandings of integers and processes, (3) basic understandings of fractions and processes, (4) basic understandings of decimals and processes, and (5) basic understandings of the rationale of computation. A preliminary tryout run on the seventh-grade level led to an arrangement of the items in an approximate order of difficulty within each of the five areas. Since the test was of a diagnostic rather than a power variety, a time limit was not used.

Let us look briefly at a few of the test items.

I.   Which statement best tells why we move the second partial product one place to the left when we multiply by the 6?
     A. Because the answer has to be larger than 729.   729
     B. Because the 6 means 6 tens.   ×68

C. Because 6 is the second figure in 68.

D. Because we learned to multiply that way.

E. Because the 6 represents a greater value than the 8 represents.

II. When you multiply by the 4 in 48 you will get a number that is how large compared with the final answer?

A. One-twelfth as large.

B. One-tenth as large.

C. One-half as large.

D. Five-sixths as large.

E. Two times as large.

$$485$$
$$\times 48$$

III. Which statement best tells why it is necessary to "borrow" in this example?

A. Because the top number is smaller than the bottom number.

B. You cannot subtract 92 from 67.

C. You cannot subtract 9 tens from 6 tens.

D. You cannot subtract 39 tens from 56 tens.

E. You cannot subtract 9 from 6.

$$567$$
$$-392$$

IV. Which statement best tells why we carry 2 from the second column?

A. The sum of the second column is 23, which has two figures in it. We have room for the 3 only, so we put the 2 in the next column.

$$251$$
$$161$$
$$252$$
$$271$$

B. The sum of the second column is more than 20, so we put the 2 in the next column.

C. Because we learned to add that way.

D. The value represented by the figures in the second column is more than 9 tens, so we put the hundreds in the next column.

E. If we do not carry the 2, the answer will be 20 less than the correct answer.

V. In this example you multiply by the 6, then by the 3. How do the two results (partial products) compare?

A. The second represents a number one-half as large as the first.

B. The second represents a number twice as large as the first.

C. The second represents a number five times as large as the first.

D. The second represents a number ten times as large as the first.

E. The second represents a number twenty times as large as the first.

$$749$$
$$\times 36$$

Administering the Test. The test was administered to a total of 1,139 subjects on seven educational levels as follows: Grade VII, 168; Grade VIII, 157; Grade IX, 163; Grade XII, 175; teachers' college Freshmen, 144; teachers' college Seniors, 172; and teachers in service, 160. Testing was begun on the seventh-grade level rather than a lower level bcause the seventh is the lowest grade at which we can be certain all the fundamental processes have been taught. The analysis of the data collected will give us some insight into the degree to which the students have acquired the meanings and understandings that are basic to the computational skills.

Some of the Findings. Let us look first at some of the broad findings in Grades VII-XII and then at some of the more specific findings. Several hypotheses were tested.

Hypothesis I.—There is no significant difference in achievement of basic mathematical understandings between a seventh-grade pupil and an eighth-grade pupil.

Findings I.—The findings show a significance ratio of 1.210, representing a significance level of 23 per cent. This evidence supports the hypothesis that there is no significant difference in basic mathematical understandings between a seventh-grade pupil and an eighth-grade pupil in the population sampled.

Conclusion I.—From the findings above we may infer that instruction in arithmetic on the seventh-grade level does not contribute sufficiently to the pupil's understanding of arithmetic to be able to say that a pupil at the beginning of Grade VIII is significantly better than a pupil at the beginning of Grade VII.

Hypothesis II.—There is no significant difference in achievement of basic mathematical understandings between an eighth-grade pupil and a ninth-grade pupil.

Findings II.—The significance ratio between eighth-graders and ninth-graders in the population sampled is 3.060. This indicates significance beyond the 1 per cent level. The evidence does not support the hypothesis.

Conclusion II.—In the population sampled, ninth-graders are significantly superior to eighth-graders in understandings basic to arithmetic. This growth may be due to the teaching that took place during Grade VIII. However, it may also be due in part to the fact that entering Grade IX is a more selective process than entering Grade VIII.

It will be recalled that the type of instrument used in gathering the data consisted of multiple-choice items. Multiple-choice items are aided-recall items and consequently are easier to answer correctly than unaided-recall or completion-type items would be. Since the students in Grade IX are, on the average, one year advanced in mental ability, and since entering the first year of high school is a selective process, these two factors would imply greater reasoning ability or ability to select the correct choice and hence better scores.

Hypothesis III.—There is no significant difference in achievement of basic mathematical understandings between a ninth-grade pupil and a twelfth-grade pupil.

Findings III.—Collation of data on the two groups produces a significance ratio of 10.685. This represents a confidence level at infinity.

Conclusion III.—The ninth-grade pupils were tested at the beginning of Grade IX; the twelfth-grade students were tested at the end of Grade XII. The growth represented is essentially that which took place during the four years of high school. We may say that the twelfth-graders represent a population that is significantly superior to ninth-graders in their achievement of basic mathematical understandings.

One might ask a question concerning the degree of relationship that exists among the orders of difficulty. Do the understandings which are difficult for one grade level tend to be difficult for another grade level? The rank-order correlations (rho) between the difficulty of basic mathematical understandings at the various grade levels were: between Grades VII and VIII, .898; between Grades VIII and IX, .885; between Grades IX and XII, .871. Within the scope of the study there is a strong tendency for the understandings that are difficult on one grade level to be difficult on other grade levels.

Now let us look at the data which will tell us how well the average student did on the test of understandings. These data are shown in Table 1.

TABLE 1

AVERAGE PER CENT OF ACHIEVEMENT OF BASIC
MATHEMATICAL UNDERSTANDINGS FOR
EACH GRADE LEVEL

Grade	Average Raw Score	Per Cent of Total (80 Items)
VII	10.00	12.50
VIII	11.21	14.01
IX	14.42	18.02
XII	29.60	37.00

The average seventh-grade pupil tested had acquired 12.5 per cent, or one-eighth, of the understandings basic to the computational processes taught in Grades I through VI. The scores increase with grade level, and by Grade XII the average student tested had acquired 37 per cent of the understandings basic to the computational processes taught in Grades I through VI. However, the data presented in Table 1 do not offer a favorable picture of our present practices in teaching meanings and understandings in arithmetic.

The responses of pupils in Grade VII on the five sample items previously presented are given in Table 2. Again, the picture is not bright. Apparently, the seventh-grade pupils were doing little more than guessing to arrive at the correct answers. They evidently had little background in meanings and understandings to help them select the correct choices on the five items.

TABLE 2

RESPONSES MADE BY SEVENTH-GRADE PUPILS TO FIVE TEST ITEMS

	Item I	Item II	Item III	Item IV	Item V
Number of subjects	168	168	168	168	168
Number of responses	96	104	116	111	88
Number of correct responses	12	6	7	16	7
Score *	−9	−19	−20	−8	−13
Frequency of Response A	19	24	25	43	34
Frequency of Response B	**12**	13	37	15	22
Frequency of Response C	18	25	**7**	13	**7**
Frequency of Response D	22	**6**	8	**16**	14
Frequency of Response E	25	36	39	24	11

* Corrected for guessing by formula: $S = r - w/4$, computed from number of responses. Correct responses are shown in bold-face type.

Summary

Despite the several factors which have militated against the advancement of a total program of evaluation in the field of arithmetic, and despite the difficulties involved in the construction of instruments and in the collecting and collating of data, some progress is being made throughout the country. The program of evaluation of growth in arithmetic is broadening at a fair pace. Teachers are beginning to respond to the present trends in the field. Influenced by in-service courses and local curriculum-development work, teachers are beginning to ask for materials and for help in broadening the program of evaluation, particularly with respect to the measurement of growth in meanings and understandings. This increased interest should encourage the leaders in the field to tackle with added vigor the many problems in the construction of valid devices and methods for testing meanings.

The data presented in Tables 1 and 2 are limited evidence of the meager degree with which teachers are succeeding at bringing about growth in meanings and understandings. The evidence does not lend much support to the argument often heard that "we are already teaching meanings." However, the data collected in this study are not enough to serve as a basis for broad generalizations. The same type of study should be amplified many times. Data should be collected at all grade levels and by a variety of techniques. Then, armed with sufficient data and knowledge, the teacher can begin to tackle intelligently and effectively the problem of teaching and testing for meanings in arithmetic.

BIG DIVIDENDS FROM LITTLE INTERVIEWS

J. Fred Weaver

There is no "get-rich-quick" scheme for improving the effectiveness of arithmetic instruction, nor will there ever be such a scheme. There are available, however, sound low-cost investments which often yield substantial dividends at high rates of compound interest. These every teacher can afford, regardless of present salary status!

A Promising Investment

One of the most promising of these investments is an outgrowth of a marked change that has been occurring in arithmetic instruction during the past two decades: namely, our increased concern for the *process* of learning as contrasted with the *product* of learning. We have come to a fuller realization of the fact that *how* children learn is as important, and at times more important than *what* they learn. We have come to attach as much, and often more attention to the way in which children think as we do to the observable result of that thinking.

We know that all children do not think uniformly, in the same way, when dealing with a given quantitative situation. We recognize that important differences exist in the *levels* of thinking which children employ. Their thinking patterns range from those which are almost pathetically immature on the part of some, to those which are rather startlingly mature on the part of others; from those which are stereotyped and inflexible to those which are insightful and ingenious.

We know, furthermore, that a given child does not tackle all quantitative problem-situations at the same level of thinking. There are differences for each child, just as there are differences among children, in the thinking patterns actually used.

Instruction in arithmetic cannot be most effective unless the teacher first is aware of the levels of thinking employed by the children in her class when dealing with various quantitative situations, and then differentiates her instruction appropriately in light of this knowledge. The teacher who seeks to become cognizant of these existing levels and who

[From "Big Dividends from Little Interviews," *The Arithmetic Teacher,* II (April, 1955), pp. 40-47. Reprinted by permission of the author and *The Arithmetic Teacher.*]

seeks to guide learning experiences accordingly, that teacher is the one who is making a promising investment—an investment that can and does yield substantial dividends, both present and future.

An Investment Technique

Various methods have been suggested and used to study children's thinking patterns in arithmetic. Buswell [1] discussed six of these in a significant article a few years ago. In the present paper the writer wishes to re-emphasize the importance of one of the techniques as a fruitful instructional procedure to be used by any classroom teacher. This is a form of *interview* in which children individually "think out loud" as they respond to specific quantitative situations, and related questions, which have been designed carefully for a specific purpose. The time spent in "interviewing" various pupils, and all children in a class upon occasion, will be well invested in terms of the dividends to be derived—the dividends of increased instructional effectiveness.

Planning the Investment

Probably a specific illustration of the technique in actual operation may be advantageous. In this particular instance the classroom teacher, Miss Watkins, was anxious to become aware of the thinking patterns used by the pupils in her fourth-grade class as they responded to a group of multiplication combinations. She was ready to begin systematic instruction in multiplication and wanted to be guided to some extent by the children's existing skills and understandings relative to the basic facts of this process. She knew that during the previous year the pupils had worked with the facts involving 2, 3, and 4 as both multiplier and multiplicand. However, from past experience she also knew that there would be differences among the children in their level of mastery of these previously "taught" facts and in their level of understanding of multiplication as a mathematical process. Furthermore, she also knew that the same child would not necessarily respond to all combinations in the same way or at the same level.

Miss Watkins decided to use six representative multiplication combinations as the basis for her study of pupils' thinking patterns. Four of the six would involve supposedly "known" facts; i.e., facts that had been a part of the previous year's program of systematic instruction. Two of these four combinations would be presented in horizontal form and two in vertical

---

[1] G. T. Buswell. "Methods of Studying Pupils' Thinking in Arithmetic," *Arithmetic 1949*. Supplementary Educational Monographs No. 70 (Chicago: University of Chicago Press, 1949), 55-63.

form. Finally, Miss Watkins planned to include two "untaught" facts in the form of combinations having both multiplier and multiplicand greater than 4. These would not have been the object of specific teaching and practice in last year's systematic instructional program. One of the two "untaught" combinations would be presented in horizontal form and the other in vertical form. (The reason for including two facts of this nature, if not obvious to the reader, will be clarified shortly.)

Although Miss Watkins did not plan to measure understanding of the multiplication process directly, she felt that she could get some evidence of this important aspect of learning in either or both of two indirect ways. On the one hand, children who were unable to respond more or less "automatically" to one or more of the four "previously taught" combinations often would give an indication of their level of understanding by the method used to find the product. On the other hand, virtually no pupils would be likely to respond "automatically" to either of the two "untaught" combinations. Each of these would have to be "solved" in some way. Thus the method of attack and solution used by any child, in transferring his existing knowledge of the multiplication process and facts to these two new situations, generally would give some valid indication of his level of understanding of the process in question.

Implementing the Plan

Each of the representative combinations was placed on a separate 3″ × 5″ card as shown below.

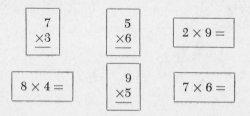

Miss Watkins presented these six cards, one at a time in the above order, to each of the children in her class. Whenever a pupil was unable to respond "automatically" to any combination, he "thought out loud" as he attempted to find the product. In these instances Miss Watkins would interject pertinent questions, etc., if she felt them to be necessary or helpful at any time. A class record sheet was employed to indicate the product given for each combination by every child and his method of response. When not "automatic," the thinking pattern used by the pupil was recorded as nearly verbatim as possible.

These "interviews" were not a new experience for the children. Consequently, Miss Watkins had no difficulty in establishing desirable rapport. The pupils knew what they were to do and responded freely and fully. They took the "interviews" seriously, and at the same time truly enjoyed them.

Such was not always the case, however. When Miss Watkins first tried the technique with these children in another type of situation, things did not run as smoothly! More time was needed, especially with some pupils, to establish rapport; to have them understand what they were to do; and to get them to respond naturally, freely, and fully. Nevertheless, with proper guidance and some degree of patience, it was not long before all children "caught on" and began to enjoy this type of experience thoroughly. Furthermore, Miss Watkins developed some short cuts and a scheme of coding which made the recording of responses much simpler and less time consuming for her.[2]

Studying the Investment Record

The pupils' responses and thought patterns were recorded in the form of a class chart to facilitate study of the data secured. An abbreviated illustration of Miss Watkins' completed chart is reproduced below. This shows the responses of five children to three of the combinations—two of the "previously taught" group and one of the "untaught" group. Undoubtedly the reader will want to look over the chart at this point, and also will have occasion to refer to it from time to time during the discussion which follows.

An Overview

Even a cursory glance at the illustrative chart brings to light a distinct advantage of the interview technique. Miss Watkins more simply could have had each child copy the combinations on a sheet of paper and then write the products. Had she done this, the *observable result* likely would have been the same for Sally, David, Linda, and Carole: all four would have written the correct product for each combination. Miss Watkins easily might have drawn the erroneous conclusion that these four pupils had comparable mastery of the facts and understanding of the fundamental nature of the multiplication process, and that the next learning experiences could be virtually the same for each of the four children.

---

[2] Some teachers have found the use of a tape recorder to be distinctly advantageous, in that it frees them from having to make rather complete written records during the course of each "interview."

TABLE 1

ILLUSTRATIVE SUMMARY OF THOUGHT PATTERNS

Pupil	Previously "Taught" Facts		"Untaught" Fact
	$\begin{array}{r} 7 \\ \times 3 \end{array}$	$8 \times 4 =$	$\begin{array}{r} 9 \\ \times 5 \end{array}$
Sally	Automatic Response Correct Product	Hesitated, then recited full "table": $1 \times 4 = 4,$ $2 \times 4 = 8,$ $3 \times 4 = 12,$ etc. to $8 \times 4 = 32.$	Hesitated, saying "I don't know that." Then put down 5 rows of 9 dots and counted by ones to reach 45.
David	Automatic Response Correct Product	Said, "Let's see: 6 fours are 24, 7 fours are 28, 8 fours are 32. That's it."	Looked up a bit, then said, "Now I know how to work that one! 5 tens are 50, so take away 5 and that's 45."
Linda	Hesitated, then said: "7 and 7 are 14–15, 16–17, 18 –19, 20–21."	Hesitated, then said: "Oh, I know! It's the same as 4 eights, and I remember that's 32."	Hesitated, saying "We never had that one before." Began to add 9 and 9; then suddenly she stopped and counted by fives to 45.
Carole	Automatic Response Correct Product	With seemingly no hesitation, said: "4 fours are 16; and 10, that's 26; and 6 more—30, 32."	Very little hesitation, then said: "Well, 4 nines are 36; and 10, that's 46; so take away 1, that's 45."
Jerry	Automatic Response Correct Product	Automatic response, but incorrect product of 36. When asked to "prove" it, looked puzzled and said, "I can't, but I'm sure that's what it is— 36."	Looked very confused, saying: "I don't remember *that* one. Did we have it before?" Was unable to attack it sensibly, asking: "Is it near 14?"

Such would have been far from the truth, however; Sally, David, Linda, and Carole actually differed significantly in various ways from the standpoint of the thinking patterns behind their ultimate overt responses. They differed in their level of mastery of the facts, in their level of understanding of the multiplication process, and in their level of ability to use other mathematical concepts and relationships. The same subsequent learning experiences would not be equally appropriate and effective for each of the four pupils. These facts were brought to light clearly through the interview technique but would have been obscured had Miss Watkins used a simpler alternative such as the one mentioned above.

Let us now look briefly at the record for each child listed on the illustrative class chart and direct attention to observations which deserve special comment.

Sally

Notice first that Sally used a common procedure in attacking the second fact when unable to respond automatically. She started at the beginning of the "four's table" and repeated the sequence of facts in order until she arrived at $8 \times 4 = 32$. Next observe that although Sally tackled the "untaught" combination at a relatively low level, she understood the meaning of the combination and proceeded accordingly. It is important to note that Miss Watkins could make no inference concerning Sally's understanding, however, from her response to either the first or second combination. The former response was automatic, and the latter might have come only from rote memory.

David

First observe that although David, like Sally, used the "four's table" to arrive at the second product, he did so in a more mature way. Rather than start at the beginning of the "four's table," David started with a "remembered" fact well along in the table ($6 \times 4 = 24$) and repeated the facts in sequential order from that point until he reached $8 \times 4 = 32$. Next notice the insightful method used by David to find the product for the "untaught" combination. Here is evidence not only of an understanding of the meaning of the combination, but also of a relatively mature attack based upon this understanding in relation to the distributive principle.[3]

Linda

This child had not reached the level of automatic response for either of the two "previously taught" facts. Each of these, as well as the "untaught" fact, had to be solved—but at different levels of thinking. All methods of attack, however, gave evidence of understanding of one kind or another. Linda's approach to the first combination was at a relatively low, but not

---

[3] This all-important principle is a *functional* one for many children even though they may not be able to express it concisely in the form of a verbal statement or mathematical equality: $a(b \pm c) = ab \pm ac$. In this specific instance, $5 \times 9 = 5 (10 - 1) = 5 \times 10 - 5 \times 1 = 50 - 5 = 45$.

uncommon level. She used a "known" addition fact at the outset $(7 + 7 = 14)$ and then resorted to partial counting. It is interesting to observe the rhythm employed in this latter connection.

Linda used the commutative principle [4] when dealing with both the second and third combinations, but at different levels. In the former instance she found the product for 8×4 by responding automatically to the "reverse" combination, 4×8. In the latter instance we see an interesting insightful procedure in which Linda applied this commutative principle in a way that enabled her to find the product much more easily than if she had continued to add nines as she started to do. It is significant to note that her attack upon the "untaught" combination was, in a sense, more mature (or at a higher level) than was her attack upon the first "previously taught" combinations.

Carole

The approaches used by Carole to the second and third combinations show effective use of the base of our number system (10) and its multiples (20, 30, 40, etc.), as well as functional application of other important mathematical relationships and understandings. In effect she recognized that 8×4 would be twice as much as 4×4, which she knew to be 16. Her method of doubling the 16 was far from stereotyped! In responding to the "untaught" combination, Carole worked from a related "known" combination (4×9) and then added 9 to the product by first adding 10 and then subtracting 1. In one way or another this child used more automatic responses to "known" facts than any of the other pupils did.

Jerry

This youngster's responses present an overall picture that is much different from any of the four which have been discussed previously. Nevertheless, the picture is far from unique or atypical—unfortunately! Multiplication as a mathematical process has very little meaning for Jerry, if any. He could respond automatically to "previously taught" combinations —sometimes correctly, sometimes incorrectly—but always mechanically to a meaningless stimulus. When questioned by Miss Watkins and asked to "prove" one of his products, he was unable to do so. He did sense that a "new" combination was involved at one point, but he had no way of cop-

---

[4] This useful principle asserts that if $a + b = c$, then $b \times a = c$. Although the interchange of factors does not affect the size of the product, it *does* alter the meaning of the situation. For example, 8×4 has the same product as 4×8, but the expression "8 fours" does not mean the same thing as the expression "4 eights."

ing with the situation. His ultimate response showed that he thought maybe he should add the 9 and the 5. Definitely, Jerry was in a class by himself when compared with the other four children.

Other Pupils

Obviously, the examples cited in the illustrative class record and just discussed do not embrace all of the thinking patterns, etc., revealed to Miss Watkins through her interviews. At times she needed to inject more questions of her own than she did in the illustrative instances. She found some difficulties, too, which were not in evidence for these five children. She observed that a few pupils were somewhat confused by the horizontal algorism and seemed uncertain about responding to combinations in this form. For one or two children just the opposite was true. Furthermore, she noticed that some pupils read the vertical algorisms downward rather than upward (e.g., "7 times 3" instead of "3 times 7"). Many of the patterns of thinking, etc., were similar to those observed by Brownell and Carper [5] when interviewing children in connection with their excellent research study, *Learning the Multiplication Combinations*. Of course, some different patterns were observed as well.

All in all, Miss Watkins gained invaluable information about the strengths and weaknesses of her fourth-grade children in relation to basic facts and understandings of multiplication at the outset of her proposed program of systematic instruction in this phase of arithmetic content. Miss Watkins had made her investment, but where are her dividends?

Earning the Dividends

Miss Watkins, and all teachers, must beware. Highest dividends from interview-investments do *not come automatically*. They must be *earned—* earned by putting the investment to use. Only in that way can the attractive dividends of increased instructional effectiveness be realized most fully.

Put the investment to use? In what way? By planning and implementing differentiated instruction based upon information brought to light through a study of the investment record. As is true of so many things, often this may be "easier said than done." To indicate in detail how Miss Watkins used the data she gathered through the interviews—that would be another paper in itself. However, we must look briefly to one of the possibilities,

---

[5] William A. Brownell and Doris V. Carper. *Learning the Multiplication Combinations.* Duke University Research Studies in Education, No. 7 (Durham, N. C.: Duke University Press, 1943).

to one of the things that might be done. We must catch a glimpse of one way in which the dividends could be earned.

A Promising Plan

Miss Watkins did *not* have her class organized formally in groups for arithmetic instruction in the same way that many teachers do. That is, she had not set up several groups (three, let us say) at the outset of the year's work and then provided mostly separate and independent instruction for each of the groups, permitting them to progress at their own rates —with all children in the class working together on common projects, etc., only rather infrequently.[6]

Although Miss Watkins did not organize her class formally in two or more groups and follow the instructional scheme just characterized, she did use groups many times in her teaching—but in a significantly different way. She employed a much more flexible plan of grouping—one that developed as the need arose, following her frequent exploratory work with the class as a whole in which a "grouping effect" generally prevailed. Miss Watkins had attempted to translate into action a promising plan advocated and illustrated by various persons,[7] including the present writer,[8] which places major emphasis upon differentiation in terms of *level* or *depth* of learning rather than rate of progress as we often conceive it in the frequent grouping procedure.

A Glimpse of the Plan in Action

When Miss Watkins began her reteaching of the understandings and skills of multiplication involving the basic facts with 2, 3, and 4 as multiplicand and multiplier,[9] her initial approach was through work with the

---

[6] For a recent exposition of this point of view, see Charles E. Johnson. "Grouping Children for Arithmetic Instruction," *The Arithmetic Teacher,* I (February, 1954), 16-20.

[7] See, for example:

John R. Clark. "A Promising Approach to Provision for Individual Differences in Arithmetic," *Journal of Education,* CXXXVI (December, 1953), 94-96.

John R. Clark and Laura K. Eads. "Teaching Children in Groups," *Guiding Arithmetic Learning* (Yonkers-on-Hudson, N. Y.: World Book Co., 1954), 245-252.

Rolland R. Smith. "Provisions for Individual Differences," *The Learning of Mathematics, Its Theory and Practice,* National Council of Teachers of Mathematics Twenty-first Yearbook (1953), (Washington, D. C.: The Council), 271-302.

[8] J. Fred Weaver. "Differentiated Instruction in Arithmetic: An Overview and a Promising Trend," *Education,* LXXIV (January, 1954), 300-5.

[9] It is to be understood that the basic facts involving 1 and 0 were included. Products for such facts were considered in relation to the broad generalizations governing the use of these numbers as factors.

class as a whole. The interview data were used to good advantage in this connection, giving her some idea of the strengths and weaknesses of each pupil and an indication of the level at which he might participate most successfully in the instructional activities.

Jerry and a few other youngsters definitely needed help in gaining an understanding of the nature of multiplication as a mathematical process. She knew that Sally and a number of other children would be able to interpret this meaning for Jerry and those like him at the concrete or semi-concrete levels. Still other pupils would be able to extend the interpretation to the more abstract levels, symbolically relating multiplication to addition, etc.

Thus, each child was enabled to contribute and profit at his own level of learning, and the interview data gave Miss Watkins a most helpful indication of the level at which she should encourage each pupil to work at this point of her reteaching. Actually, a "grouping effect" was in operation even though the children worked together as an entire class.

Frequently, however, situations arose which made it desirable for Miss Watkins actually to separate the class into several groups and work with each somewhat independently for a while. Often these groups would deal with the same broad aspect of multiplication, but at different levels.

For example, at one point in her reteaching Miss Watkins injected the idea of organizing related facts into a "table" for further study of relationships, etc. She had the entire class consider a situation such as the following:

> Some boys in the school shop were making 4-wheeled toy wagons for Christmas presents to be sent to children's hospitals.
> How many wheels would they need for 1 wagon?
> How many wheels would they need for 6 wagons?
> How many wheels would they need for 3 wagons?
> How many wheels for 8 wagons?
> How many wheels for 5 wagons?
> How many wheels for 2 wagons?
> For 9 wagons?
> For 4 wagons?
> For 7 wagons?

As the products were found and verified at different levels, they were recorded as follows:

$$
\begin{array}{ccccccccc}
4 & 4 & 4 & 4 & 4 & 4 & 4 & 4 & 4 \\
\times 1 & \times 6 & \times 3 & \times 8 & \times 5 & \times 2 & \times 9 & \times 4 & \times 7 \\
\hline
4 & 24 & 12 & 32 & 20 & 8 & 36 & 16 & 28
\end{array}
$$

Discussion of these recorded facts led pupils to rearrange or reorganize them in the manner indicated below:

$$
\begin{array}{ccccccccc}
4 & 4 & 4 & 4 & 4 & 4 & 4 & 4 & 4 \\
\times 1 & \times 2 & \times 3 & \times 4 & \times 5 & \times 6 & \times 7 & \times 8 & \times 9 \\
\hline
4 & 8 & 12 & 16 & 20 & 24 & 28 & 32 & 36
\end{array}
$$

Miss Watkins knew from her interview data, and from the work she had just done, that the children differed materially in the level at which they could deal with this type of situation and the depth to which they were able to perceive relationships among the facts.

Consequently Miss Watkins divided her class into separate groups—three, in this instance—characterized somewhat as follows:

Group 1. Those who still needed to use representative materials frequently and who showed very limited perception of relationships among the facts of a table.

Group 2. Those who generally could work at an abstract level and who had a somewhat better grasp of relationships among tabled facts.

Group 3. Those who showed definite ability to deal with higher-level relationships in abstract form.

The first group reorganized sets of facts into systematic tables and dealt mainly with an understanding of the presence of the constant factor in a table and its relation to the increasing products. Representative materials were used frequently as needed.

The second group worked with this idea as well, but more quickly and without the use of concrete or semi-concrete materials. Furthermore, they used their increased understandings to determine the next fact in a table following one given in isolation, and also used many "known" facts in this way to find the product for "unknown" combinations.

The third group dealt with the previous ideas only briefly, since these children already were rather secure and proficient in work of this nature. Most of their instruction centered around a deeper understanding of relationships inherent in the table of facts: recognizing that 6 *fours* would be twice as much as 3 *fours*, that 4 *fours* would be half as much as 8 *fours*, that 7 *fours* would be as much as 5 *fours*, and 2 *fours*, or as much as 4 *fours* and 3 *fours*, etc.

Later, Miss Watkins again was working with the class as a whole. Still later, she was dealing with separate groups once more. In any event, levels of learning were constantly in her thinking as she planned and implemented her instructional program. Children were encouraged to work at the highest level of which they were capable and to move to higher levels as quickly as feasible. Consequently, a given child was not always placed in the same group when Miss Watkins felt the need to form such;

nor was it impossible for a child to move from one group to another at virtually any time he showed evidence of working better at another level.

As her program of arithmetic instruction progressed throughout the year, Miss Watkins continued to use the interview procedure. At times she would study the thought patterns of only some of the children; at other times, of the entire class. In any event, she used the interview to gain helpful and truly *necessary* information—information that influenced her instruction greatly but which would have been obscured frequently without use of the technique.

Concluding Statement

Children's thinking patterns in arithmetic are highly important. Every teacher can make a sound investment by interviewing children in her class periodically to determine and study their levels of thinking when dealing with various quantitative situations. By then using the knowledge gained from such interviews to assist her in providing a helpfully differentiated program of teaching and learning experiences, every teacher can reap big dividends in the form of increased instructional effectiveness.

EVALUATION IN ARITHMETIC AND TALENTED STUDENTS

Vincent J. Glennon

This title implies that the first three difficult educational problems associated with talented students—the identification of, the objectives for, and the teaching of—have been solved, leaving for this article a brief discussion of the fourth problem—the evaluation of growth along the lines of the previously agreed upon objectives. These previously agreed upon objectives, whether for the talented, the average, or the slow, fall into three categories or domains that have been identified as the cognitive domain, the affective domain, and the psychomotor domain.[1]

[From "Evaluation in Arithmetic and Talented Students," *The Bulletin of the National Association of Secondary School Principals*, XLVII (May, 1957), pp. 134-36. Reprinted by permission of the author and the National Association of Secondary School Principals.]

[1] Benjamin S. Bloom, ed., *Taxonomy of Educational Objectives—Handbook I: Cognitive Domain* (New York: Longmans, Green and Co., 1956).

The cognitive domain is the subject matter domain and includes the three kinds of verbal learnings—understandings, concepts, and arbitrary associations (facts). The affective domain is the domain of emotional learnings and includes attitudes, appreciations, and feelings. And the psychomotor domain, the mind-body domain, includes mental skills, motor skills, and habits.

In the brief space allowed to this article I will limit this discussion of the evaluation of the learning of talented students to the cognitive domain; that is, to the learnings that take place *in* arithmetic. We recognize, of course, that the learnings that take place *through* arithmetic instruction, the so-called intangibles, are also important to teach for and to evaluate for.

We can save an extended discussion here by saying immediately that the standardized test is useful to some extent in the evaluation of growth by talented students in computational skill and verbal problem-solving ability. It is of little usefulness in the evaluation of growth in such important areas as insight into number relationships, basic mathematical meanings, knowledge and rationale of the symbolic representation used for number systems with bases other than ten, maturity of thought processes, and depth of understanding—to mention just a few.

Assuming for the moment then that the teacher is already making prudent use of presently available tests of computational skills and verbal problem-solving ability, the remainder of this article will be devoted to a discussion of a more penetrating approach to the gathering of pupil responses upon which to make up evaluative judgment of the arithmetic ability of the talented student.[2] It need hardly be said that the broader approach to evaluation techniques being used today, including such as the anecdotal record, sociodrama, play therapy, the observation and interview, and others, is as useful with the average and the slow as with the talented.

The most penetrating evaluation technique available to the teacher is the observation-interview. It is generally agreed that this is the only technique that enables the teacher to get at the thought processes being used by the learner. Its use assumes that the teacher is attempting to provide for depth, maturity, or quality of learning. So let us look at two learning situations to see how the observation-interview technique might be used by the teacher.

Assume that a fourth-grade group of pupils is concerned with the prob-

---

[2] For a more detailed discussion of the characteristics of children who are highly talented in arithmetic, the reader may wish to consult the *second edition* of *What Does Research Say About Arithmetic?* published by the Association for Supervision and Curriculum Development, 1201 Sixteenth St., N.W., Washington 6, D. C. (late 1958).

lem of sharing equally 154 marbles among 7 boys. Also assume they have no previously learned mature solution to the problem. During the learning process, the teacher is observing and asking questions to gather evidence of maturity of the learning. He might witness such as these:

A pupil of average mental ability begins by counting out 154 tongue-depressers. Then taking a group of 7, he places one in each of seven boxes —each box standing for a boy. Then he counts away another 7 which he also shares equally among the 7 boxes. He continues this until there are either zero tongue-depressers left or not enough to share equally among the 7 boxes. His answer is the number of tongue-depressers (marbles) in any one box.

Observing this performance the teacher would conclude that the pupil worked slowly and accurately, but on an immature level. This is not the performance of a talented pupil.

An above average pupil might also use the counting method, but show 154 as 15 bundles with 10 in each bundle and 4 singles. He would count away 7 tens, placing 1 ten in each of the 7 boxes. Then he would count away 7 more tens, leaving 1 ten and 4 ones. Showing the 1 ten and 4 ones, he would distribute them equally. Obviously this is a much more mature level of behavior than that of the pupil described above.

Now observing and interviewing the talented pupil, the teacher might see him demonstrate a high level of insight. He might go immediately to the level of symbolic representation of numbers, thinking and writing "Each boy will get $\frac{1}{7}$ of the 154 marbles. So, $\frac{1}{7}$ of 14 tens is 2 tens, or 20. $\frac{1}{7}$ of 14 ones is 2 ones. Each boy will get 22 marbles." Such a performance, when there has been no previously learned solution, should be evidence to the teacher that this is the thinking of a talented student.

Now let us look briefly at the maturity or depth of performance level of the talented student on the seventh- or eighth-grade level. While the average student is continuing in his attempt to master the decimal system and its applications to business practices as found in a typical arithmetic textbook, the talented student should be taking many side-trips for the purpose of both extending previous learnings and enriching his background with wholly new learnings. Evidence of the degree to which he is achieving these two objectives will be gathered by the teacher through observation and interview.

Having taught, let us say, the use of the two symbols 0 and 1 to represent numbers from 1 to 16 (1 to 10,000) the teacher could evaluate the depth of learning of the student by asking him to extend his learning to the writing of the numbers to 32 or to 64.

On a still higher level the teacher could gather evidence of the student's power by asking such questions as:

How many digits will be needed to represent the decimal number 83 in the binary system?

What decimal number has the value of the binary number 1,011,010?

Change to binary numerals and add: 43 + 76 + 29 = ?

Using binary numerals, find the product of 18 × 61.

Change to binary numerals and add: ½ + ⅔ = ?

Show as decimals in the binary system and add: 3.25 + 4.5 = ?

In summary, this brief article has attempted to show that the evaluation in arithmetic of the work of talented students makes use of the same tests, the same techniques, and the same procedures that are used with average students. The difference resides not in *how* we evaluate the talented student but *what* we evaluate for; namely, increasingly more difficult mathematical ideas.

PART III: THE AFFECTIVE DOMAIN

MEASURING ATTITUDES TOWARD ARITHMETIC

Wilbur H. Dutton

The significance of attitudes to teaching and learning has been consistently mentioned in recent educational literature.[1] However, the objective measurement of attitudes toward elementary-school subjects has been noticeably lacking.[2] The purpose of this article is to report attitudes of prospective teachers toward arithmetic as determined by an objective evaluation instrument.

Construction of Arithmetic Attitude Scale

Gathering and Selecting of Statements. Prospective teachers enrolled in education classes at the University of California were asked to write out

[From "Measuring Attitudes Toward Arithmetic," *Elementary School Journal*, No. 55 (September, 1954), pp. 24-31. Reprinted by permission of the author and the University of Chicago Press.]

---

[1] See J. Murray Lee and Dorris May Lee. *The Child and His Curriculum* (New York: Appleton-Century-Crofts, 1950).

[2] "The Educational Program," *Review of Educational Research*, XXIII (April, 1953), 111-90.

their feelings toward arithmetic. Two categories were used—favorable and unfavorable attitudes. Statements were collected over a five-year period from slightly more than six hundred students. Eighty-three statements were selected from these responses. These statements were carefully edited and subject to the following criteria:

1. The statements should be brief.
2. The statements should be primarily concerned with feelings toward arithmetic.
3. They should be easily indorsed or rejected by the reader.
4. The statements should not be ambiguous.
5. There should be adequate coverage of all attitude areas to be measured.

Forty-five statements were retained for use in the sorting procedures which were used in the further selection of desirable statements.

Sorting Procedures. One hundred and twenty students, representing all classifications enrolled in the University, were selected to sort the forty-five statements which had been mimeographed on slips of paper. The slips were numbered so that identification would be possible for tabulation, and only one statement was placed on each slip. Small groups of students, usually eight or ten, were seated at tables and given specific directions for sorting the slips into piles numbered from 1 (extreme dislike) to 11 (extreme liking). Since these students represented random samplings from larger classes, the number of students seemed to be adequate for the sorting process. The slips sorted by twenty students were eliminated because of faulty sorting procedures, such as placing eight or ten slips in one pile.

Scale Value and Q Value. The techniques developed by Thurstone and Chave were used to determine the scale value for each statement.[3] In these techniques a graph is plotted from the accumulative proportions into which the statements were sorted. For example, when the curve in the graphs crosses the 50 per cent level at the (interpolated) scale value of 7.0, this is the assigned scale value for the statement. This occurs when 50 per cent of the sorters classify this statement as more favorable than the position 7.0, and the remaining 50 per cent place the statement as less favorable than this position in the eleven piles.

The spread between the upper and the lower quartile is a measure of the ambiguity of the statement and is called the Q value. Ambiguous statements will be sorted into a wide range of piles on the scale, and the Q value will be high. Concise statements which convey nearly the same mean-

---

[3] L. L. Thurstone and E. J. Chave. *The Measurement of Attitude* (Chicago: University of Chicago Press, 1948).

ing to the readers will be placed in about the same position on the scale, and the Q value will then be small.

Preparing an Experimental Scale. Twenty-two statements of feelings toward arithmetic were selected from the forty-five statements used in the sorting process. The selection was made on the following bases:

1. Items with low Q value were selected.

2. Statements were chosen to give an adequate distribution of scale values for the scale.

3. About an equal number of statements were selected to represent favorable and unfavorable feelings.

4. Two statements were selected because they were very close to the neutral position—one was an experimental item beamed at the importance of arithmetic as a subject.

The statements were shuffled and then selected at random for placement on the first page of the scale. A second page was added to the scale to secure permanent data about those individuals taking the test, to obtain a self-rating of the student's general attitude toward arithmetic, and to provide data for studying the development of specific attitudes toward arithmetic. These data are summarized in a later section of this report.

Methods of Scoring the Scale. The purpose of this scale is to describe attitudes toward arithmetic more objectively. No attempt has been made to give a total score or an average score for the scale. The general pattern of responses may thus be studied for an individual or for a class. In many instances students will have both favorable and unfavorable feelings toward arithmetic. The scale value will be helpful in determining the intensity of feeling on any one statement.

The second part of the scale provides the opportunity for students to estimate their total general attitude toward arithmetic, since this section yields information pertaining to the causes for specific attitudes and to the particular phases of arithmetic that students like or dislike. The total scale is intended to be diagnostic in nature.

Reliability of the Scale. The reliability of the experimental scale was measured by the test-and-retest procedure. The correlation between the two sets of scores, taking an average scale value for the total test for each student, was 0.94. While there were enough statements for constructing a second scale and correlating the two scales, the writer chose to use the one form and to develop another comparable scale at a later date.

Application of Experimental Scale to Prospective Teachers

The experimental scale was administered to 289 students, 28 men and 261 women. This number was composed of 61 students enrolled in a methods course for kindergarten-primary teachers, 76 students enrolled in a methods class for the teaching of arithmetic, and 152 students taking a general course dealing with the teaching of elementary-school skill subjects. The classification of students is shown in Table 1.

TABLE 1

CLASSIFICATION OF 289 UNIVERSITY OF CALIFORNIA STUDENTS TAKING
THE ARITHMETIC ATTITUDE SCALE

Classification	Number of Students
Graduate	23
Senior	115
Sophomore	30
Junior	118
Nonclassified	3
Total	289

Responses on Attitude Statements. The record of responses for 289 students taking the attitude scale is shown in Table 2. These data are significant for numerous reasons. The total over-all feeling of the group tested is favorable toward arithmetic. This might indicate considerable advancement in the education of the young men and women who are favorably inclined toward arithmetic. Since the group is composed of prospective teachers, we should also be concerned with the students who express unfriendly feelings toward a subject that they must teach when they receive full-time employment in our nation's schools.

The most pronounced unfavorable feelings are expressed by Statement 2, "I don't feel sure of myself in arithmetic," chosen by 39 per cent of the students responding; Statement 18, "I am afraid of doing word problems," chosen by 29 per cent; and Statements 11 and 15, in which students express fear of, or a desire to avoid, arithmetic, each chosen by 16 per cent of the students.

Three statements, located near the center of the scale in value, indicate a profound respect for the subject, real enjoyment when problems can be worked with understanding, and pleasure in the challenge presented by an arithmetic problem. These statements (Nos. 14, 10, and 8) were indorsed by 70, 72, and 83 per cent of the students, respectively.

Other interesting interpretations could be made of these data, depending upon the particular purposes of the reader. For example, the writer found that 30 per cent of his summer-session class, dealing with the teaching of arithmetic and other elementary-school subjects, did not feel sure

TABLE 2

RESPONSES OF 289 UNIVERSITY OF CALIFORNIA STUDENTS ON ARITHMETIC
ATTITUDE SCALE SHOWING PER CENT OF INDORSEMENT AND
SCALE VALUES FOR EACH STATEMENT

Scale Value	State-ment No.	Attitude Statement	Frequency of Response Number	Per Cent
1.0	13	I detest arithmetic and avoid using it at all times	9	3
1.5	20	I have never liked arithmetic..................	27	9
2.0	18	I am afraid of doing word problems...........	85	29
2.5	11	I have always been afraid of arithmetic.........	45	16
3.0	22	I can't see much value in arithmetic	1	0.3
3.2	15	I avoid arithmetic because I am not very good with figures.............................	45	16
3.3	9	Arithmetic is something you have to do even though it is not enjoyable..................	78	27
3.7	2	I don't feel sure of myself in arithmetic.........	113	39
4.6	6	I don't think arithmetic is fun but I always want to do well in it.............................	97	34
5.3	7	I am not enthusiastic about arithmetic but I have no real dislike for it either..................	111	38
5.6	4	I like arithmetic but I like other subjects just as well	156	54
5.9	8	Arithmetic is as important as any other subject..	241	83
6.7	14	I enjoy doing problems when I know how to work them well..............................	201	70
7.0	10	Sometimes I enjoy the challenge presented by an arithmetic problem........................	207	72
7.7	5	I like arithmetic because it is practical.........	109	38
8.1	19	Arithmetic is very interesting..................	127	44
8.6	3	I enjoy seeing how rapidly and accurately I can work arithmetic problems..................	150	52
9.0	12	I would like to spend more time in school working arithmetic	46	16
9.5	1	I think about arithmetic problems outside of school and like to work them out	66	23
9.8	17	I never get tired of working with numbers......	55	19
10.4	21	I think arithmetic is the most enjoyable subject I have taken..............................	12	4
10.5	16	Arithmetic thrills me, and I like it better than any other subject.............................	9	3

of themselves in arithmetic (Statement 2). This finding has influenced his
teaching methods considerably and will prompt careful follow-up of these
students when they begin their student teaching.

Another significant factor, which is not apparent in Table 2, is the number of persons who may have mixed feelings toward arithmetic and who
need considerable guidance before they complete their student-teaching

assignments. This problem and the one mentioned previously are revealed
when the individual scales for each student are available.

Student Self-Rating of Their Attitudes Toward Arithmetic. Students
were asked to indicate their general feeling toward arithmetic by placing
a check on a number in an eleven-point scale ranging from 1 (strongly
against) to 11 (strongly in favor). The neutral position on the scale was
6. The results are shown in Table 3. Slightly over 32 per cent felt that they
were neutral or opposed to arithmetic. Eleven students were strongly opposed to arithmetic, 23 were opposed, and 59 were neutral or slightly
below neutral.

TABLE 3

SELF-RATING OF 289 UNIVERSITY OF CALIFORNIA STUDENTS ON
GENERAL FEELINGS TOWARD ARITHMETIC

Scale Value	Number of Students Checking	Scale Value	Number of Students Checking
1 (Strongly against) ..	..	7	37
2	4	8	57
3	7	9	47
4	23	10	33
5	25	11 (Strongly favor)	22
6 (Neutral)	34	Total	289

There were 196 students favoring arithmetic, or 67.8 per cent of the
entire group. Of this number 37 were slightly in favor, 57 were favorable,
and 102 were more strongly in favor of arithmetic.

Reasons Given for Liking or Disliking Arithmetic. Space was provided
for students to write their reasons for liking or disliking arithmetic. Their
statements are summarized in Table 4. The main reasons for liking the
subject were: arithmetic is practical; it provides a challenge; student
achieved success in the subject; arithmetic is definite and logical; and student finds satisfaction in working problems. Usually two reasons for liking
the subject were given. The total number of responses was 406 for the
196 students who liked the subject.

Lack of understanding, poor marks, difficulty in working problems, poor
teachers who punished students or used inadequate methods, and insecurity were the main factors causing dislike for arithmetic. Other causes
are shown in Table 5.

Of the 289 students who were sampled in this study, 93 declared themselves opposed to, or neutral toward, arithmetic. The total number of
responses was not large, but the factors were rather definite so that one
main cause seemed sufficient for many students. Students were not asked

TABLE 4

REASONS FOR LIKING ARITHMETIC GIVEN BY 196 STUDENTS
OF THE UNIVERSITY OF CALIFORNIA

Reason	Number of Responses	Reason	Number of Responses
Arithmetic is practical—everyday applications	100	Arithmetic is interesting	11
Arithmetic provides a challenge	67	Working problems was like playing a game—short cuts	8
Grades were good—easy to succeed	55	Encouragement from parents influenced attitudes	6
Arithmetic is logical, definite, exact answers	46	Enjoyed working with figures	5
Gain much satisfaction in working problems	42	Can do it mechanically without too much thinking	3
Arithmetic is fun, enjoy it	23	Had incentives such as competition	2
Good teachers influenced favorable attitudes	21	Total	406
Makes one think—helps one express self	17		

to list a specific number of causes for disliking arithmetic, just the main factors. Among the many interesting and revealing statements made by students, the writer found one especially descriptive: "Mother drilled and drilled me on arithmetic each morning while she combed my hair before going to school. I always went to school dreading arithmetic and any more mental punishment."

TABLE 5

REASONS FOR DISLIKING ARITHMETIC GIVEN BY 93 STUDENTS
OF THE UNIVERSITY OF CALIFORNIA

Reason	Number of Responses	Reason	Number of Responses
Lack of understanding—confused by thought-problems without practical applications	43	Not sure of self—insecure—mental blocks—fear of failure	21
Arithmetic was hard—made poor grades—irregular attendance	35	Time factors—not enough time—takes too long—pressure	16
		Arithmetic was boring, stale—slow learning, behind	9
Poor teachers—punishment—frightening experiences	25	Too much drill—memorization	8
		Total	157

Students' Estimation of When They Developed Their Feelings (Good or Bad) Toward Arithmetic. Student responses indicated that Grades III through VI were the main years when feelings were developed. Table 6

TABLE 6

ESTIMATION OF 289 UNIVERSITY OF CALIFORNIA STUDENTS ON
WHEN THEIR ATTITUDES TOWARD ARITHMETIC DEVELOPED

Grade	Number of Students	Grade	Number of Students
I	8	IX	17
II	16	X	10
III	52	XI	7
IV	38	XII	1
V	30	All grades	18
VI	24	College	6
VII	17	No response	27
VIII	18	Total	289

shows that 50 per cent of the responses named these grades. There were
52 students who stated that their feelings were developed in junior high
school grades.[4]

TABLE 7

ASPECTS OF ARITHMETIC LIKED BY 289 UNIVERSITY
OF CALIFORNIA STUDENTS

Aspect	Number of Students Indicating Liking	Aspect	Number of Students Indicating Liking
Fractions	71	Subtraction	27
All processes—everything	69	Percentage	16
Reasoning and thought-problems	69	Measurement	9
		Games, speed tests, drills	8
Addition	42	Work with equations	7
Multiplication	37	Mechanical aspects	3
Division	31	Square root	2
Practical applications—meaningful use, business	29	Graphs, charts, diagrams	2
		Total	422

Aspects of Arithmetic Liked and Disliked. Analysis of previous studies
of students' feelings toward arithmetic showed that students could like
some parts of arithmetic and could dislike other parts.[5] Provision was made
in this study for students to indicate their likes and dislikes for particular
aspects of the subject.

---

[4] The writer has recently taken a sampling of five hundred junior high school students. More data will be available based upon student responses while they are in school.

[5] Wilbur H. Dutton. "Attitudes of Prospective Teachers toward Arithmetic," *Elementary School Journal,* LII (October, 1951), 84-90.

The parts of arithmetic liked most are shown in Table 7. Thought-problems, fractions, and all the processes, but especially the fundamental processes, were liked most.

TABLE 8

ASPECTS OF ARITHMETIC DISLIKED BY 289 UNIVERSITY
OF CALIFORNIA STUDENTS

Aspect	Number of Students Indicating Dislike	Aspect	Number of Students Indicating Dislike
Word problems	110	Interest problems	18
Long addition problems	37	Decimals	11
Long and difficult division problems	36	Rules, mechanical, cut and dried processes	9
Percentage	27	Memorizing facts	5
Fractions	26	Measurement	4
Drill	24	Total	330
Long multiplication problems.	23		

Responses of students seemed more specific for the phase of the scale which deals with dislike of arithmetic (see Table 8). Word problems were disliked by 110 students, or 38 per cent of the total group. There were 96 students who disliked long problems in addition, division, and multiplication. Fractions, percentage, and drill were mentioned frequently. Many students who liked arithmetic as a subject expressed dislike for word problems and for long, involved problems.

Main Findings and Conclusions

The main findings of this study show that attitudes toward arithmetic may be measured objectively and that significant data may be obtained which will be helpful in the education of prospective elementary-school teachers. Several important conclusions may be made:

1. The techniques for measuring attitudes developed by Thurstone can successfully be applied to subjects taught in the elementary school. The process is laborious, but it will yield desirable results.

2. The experimental scale discussed in this article gives significant information about attitudes toward arithmetic held by students, the intensity of feeling, and general information necessary for more adequate guidance of prospective teachers.

3. Feelings toward arithmetic are developed in all grades. The most crucial spots are in Grades III through VI and in the junior high school.

4. Recognition of the importance of arithmetic, real enjoyment when

problems can be worked with understanding, and pleasure in the challenge presented by an arithmetic problem are the most accepted favorable attitudes reported by students in this study. Students liked arithmetic because it was practical, provided a challenge, was definite and logical, and provided satisfaction in working problems and because they were successful in it.

5. Unfavorable attitudes of significance are: not feeling secure in the subject, being afraid of word problems, and fear of the subject in general. Lack of understanding, teachers who punished students or used inadequate methods, difficulty in working arithmetic, and insecurity were the chief factors causing dislike for arithmetic.

6. Students liked some aspects of arithmetic and disliked others. One group liked thought-problems, fractions, and the fundamental processes. Another substantial group disliked thought-problems, long problems of any type, percentage, and drill.

7. A sizable number of students, slightly over 32 per cent, rated their feelings as neutral or opposed to arithmetic on an over-all rating device.

This study has stimulated other studies that are now in progress: a study of in-service uses of the scale with experienced teachers; a study of attitudes of elementary-school and junior high school pupils; and a follow-up study of the development of attitudes in schools with differing philosophies of education.

PART IV: EVALUATION OF AN OVER-ALL PROGRAM

HOW EFFECTIVE IS THE MEANING METHOD?

G. H. Miller

How effective is the meaning method in teaching arithmetic? The answer to this perplexing question still remains uncertain. It is apparent that despite the great amount of literature written on the benefits to be derived from the use of the meaning method by the students, little research has been initiated to justify the great emphasis upon this approach. Most

[From "How Effective is the Meaning Method?" *The Arithmetic Teacher*, IV (March, 1957), pp. 45-9. Reprinted by permission of *The Arithmetic Teacher*.]

theorists on methods of teaching arithmetic appear to be united in stressing the meaning method. However, are their recommendations on the instruction of arithmetic based upon experimental evidence or are they mere postulation?

The Los Angeles Study has recently been completed to investigate more thoroughly the effectiveness of the meaning method. Before considering the experiment, a discussion of the similarities and differences of the rule method and the meaning method is necessary.

The Rule Method versus the Meaning Method

Although learning in arithmetic can be facilitated in many ways, two predominant methods are used currently. The first, *the rule method,* is a technique in which an instructor solves a problem and describes the specific rules to be learned to obtain the solution to the problem. For instance, to show the class how to add $\begin{array}{r}67\\24\end{array}$, the instructor explains that the 7 and the 4 are added to get a total of 11. The 1 is put underneath the 4 and the other 1 is "carried." Then the 6 and the 2 are added to the 1 which was carried for a total of 9. The 9 is placed in front of the 1 giving the final answer of 91. A sufficient number of problems is explained to the students to cover other types of addition. A similar procedure is followed for computation of all other types of arithmetic problems. Thus the student is shown how to compute any specific problem by using the designated rule or rules necessary to obtain the correct solution.

In the second, *the meaning method,* the instructor explains a problem by reference to concrete examples, making use of definitions and principles of arithmetic. For example, the decimal system is explained as a number system based on ten, with the digits—zero, one, two, three, four, five, six, seven, eight, and nine. The students are told the function of the place value of each number, so that a logical basis exists for the size relationships of a group of digits despite its complexity. Thus, the number 962 is not explained as a group of meaningless and unrelated digits, but as a group of digits in which each has its own particular significance. The 9 represents nine hundred, the 6 represents six tens and the 2 represents two units.

In the previous problem given above, the carrying of the 1 is not explained as a rule to be memorized, but as a specific example based upon the definition of number and principles of place value. When the 7 and 4 are added to obtain 11 units, the 1 in the units column remains in the final answer of the problem. The 1 in the tens column, however, is not considered as one single unit but as a 1 in the tens column representing ten units. Thus the 1 ten is added to the 6 tens and the 2 tens to obtain a total of 9 tens. The final answer is explained as 9 tens and 1 unit or 91. Additional problems are explained in a similar manner. Students are continually encouraged to make useful generalizations from the basic concepts and principles to gain insight into arithmetical operations. Thus the instructor provides the students with a sound basis of definitions and principles of arithmetic to enable them to comprehend the processes that they utilize in the computation of arithmetic problems.

The two methods differ in several respects: the former places emphasis upon the *rules* for learning arithmetic, the latter upon *meaning* and *understanding*. The rule method is concerned with the procedure for working the problem. It presents in a brief interval of time the necessary elements to compute the desired problem. The meaning method, on the other hand, offers the student an integration of the concepts and principles of arithmetic as well as the computation of the problem. Explanations of "why" the processes work are given to the student. Rules are explained, not in isolated segments, but as conclusions based upon arithmetical definitions and principles.

The rule method has its foundations in connectionism or stimulus-response psychology. The meaning method, which is a newer approach that has gained wide acceptance, is based on the principles of gestalt psychology.

In the evaluation of the meaning method made by theorists in arithmetic learning, the usual procedure has been to compare the meaning method with the rule method. Brownell and Chazel [1] were among the first to investigate the problem with an experiment that demonstrated the ineffectiveness of premature drill in the elementary level. Thiele [2] and later Swenson [3] made experiments based on learning the 100 addition facts which showed significant differences in ability to make generalizations in arithmetic problems by those students who were instructed by the meaning method. The "discovery" method was compared with the "traditional" approach in an investigation by McConnell [4] which used the addition

---

[1] William A. Brownell and Charlotte B. Chazel, "The Effects of Premature Drill in Third Grade Arithmetic," *Journal of Educational Research*, XXIX (September, 1935), 17-28.

[2] C. L. Thiele, "The Contribution of Generalization to the Learning of the Addition Facts," Contribution to Education No. 763 (New York: Bureau of Publications, Teachers College, Columbia University, 1938).

[3] Esther J. Swenson, "Organization and Generalization as Factors in Learning Transfer and Retroactive Inhibition," *Learning Theory in School Situations*, University of Minnesota Studies in Education No. 2 (Minneapolis: University of Minnesota Press, 1949).

[4] Raymond T. McConnell, "Discovering versus Authoritative Identification in the Learning of Children," *Studies in the Psychology of Learning II*, Studies in Education, Volume 9, No. 5, Iowa City, 1942.

facts as the criterion of learning. He found that the discovery method was superior for generalization but was inferior for speed. In a recent experiment by Brownell and Moser [5] the decomposition (meaning) method was compared with other rule methods in learning the subtraction facts. Significant differences were found for the decomposition method by rational means. Division was the arithmetic process studied by Anderson [6] who found that the meaning method was effective in transfer of training in this process. An experiment by Howard [7] checked short and long range retention for the meaning and rule methods in the area of fractions. He found that the rule method was superior during the semester but that the meaning method was significantly superior after the period of retention.

This summary of the research on the meaning and rule methods shows that very little research has been done to check on the effectiveness of the meaning method for these specific problems: (1) the areas of arithmetic such as the basic or fundamental process, fractions, decimals and percentage; (2) certain degrees of arithmetic complexity such as definition, simple size relationships and complex analysis; and (3) the retention of the material after the initial experiment has been completed. Several questions arise from these problems. Is it possible that the meaning method is more valuable for one area of arithmetic than another? And if so, what are these areas of maximum effectiveness? Is the meaning method superior for learning in the simple or complex analysis of problems in arithmetic? What is the effect of learning after the experiment has been completed? Do the students only make tentative gains or are these advances in learning of a permanent nature? Obtaining the answers to these questions was the impetus behind the Los Angeles Study.

The Experiment

At the beginning of the semester incoming B7 students in five junior high schools in the Los Angeles City School District were given two tests: The California Arithmetic Test and the Meaning Test. The first was selected since it was a well known standardized test involving computation in arithmetic. The second test was devised for this experiment

[5] William A. Brownell and Harold E. Moser, "Meaningful versus Mechanical Learning: A Study in Grade II Subtraction," Duke University Research Studies in Education, No. 6 (Durham, N. C.: Duke University Press, 1941).

[6] G. Lester Anderson, "Quantitative Thinking as Developed under Connectionist and Field Theories of Learning," *Learning Theory in School Situations*, University of Minnesota Studies in Education, No. 2 (Minneapolis: University of Minnesota Press, 1949), 40-73.

[7] Charles F. Howard, "Three Methods of Teaching Arithmetic," *California Journal of Educational Research*, I (January, 1950), 3-7.

to measure the degree of understanding of arithmetic. These tests were given at the beginning of the semester, the end of the semester and after the summer vacation. The test results were used to examine the difference in gains between the test scores during the semester and after the period of retention.

This experiment differs from others as it tested all areas of arithmetic. Previous investigations only considered one area of arithmetic or one segment of arithmetic such as the 100 addition or 100 subtraction facts. Therefore, the composite scores for all learning during the semester and after the period of retention as well as the scores for the areas of arithmetic were obtained.

In order to establish the method of instruction used by each teacher, the experimenter made six to eight observations in the classrooms of eighteen instructors during the semester. These classes represented a cross-section of the population of Los Angeles. Data concerning their lectures and method of instruction were obtained by observation and recorded. No attempt was made to suggest any procedure of instruction. This feature was different from other experiments in which the method to be taught was specified or implied. In this way normal classroom techniques could be observed without any alteration of the actual instruction. This procedure could lead to more accurate classification.

After the data was collected it was analyzed and the instructors were rated for meaning and rule content in five different categories: (1) lectures in class; (2) type of classwork; (3) type of text; (4) kind of tests, and (5) an independent evaluation by means of a supervisor's rating. An instructor was rated as high in each category if he emphasized the meaning method. He was rated as low if he emphasized the rules without making them meaningful. He was given a medium rating if he used a combination of both methods. The results were compiled and placed along a continuum. Eight instructors were selected at the two extremes: four for the meaning method and four for the rule method. These instructors were the most representative for each method.

The students whose data were included in this experiment were those taught by the eight instructors. This group of over six hundred students from a total of fifteen classes served as the reservoir from which individuals were matched on the basis of Otis I.Q.'s and scores of the Meaning Test (matching was done on the basis of a maximum of a two point difference in test score). In cases of duplication the results of the California Arithmetic Test were used to equate the pairs. A total of one hundred and eighty matched pairs was involved in the tests during the semester, and a total of ninety-five pairs was involved for the test outcomes after the summer vacation.

In this experiment not only were the total test scores for both groups compared but also certain finer subdivisions were studied such as areas of arithmetic, degrees of complexity of arithmetic and I.Q. levels. These subdivisions are as follows:

1. AREAS OF ARITHMETIC
    a) California Arithmetic Test—basic processes (addition, subtraction, multiplication, and division), fractions, decimals, percentage, mixed problems (decimals and fractions) and measurement
    b) Meaning Test—basic processes, number systems, decimals, fractions, percentage and measurement
2. DEGREES OF ARITHMETIC COMPLEXITY (for the Meaning Test only)
    a) 1st degree—definition
    b) 2nd degree—simple size relationships
    c) 3rd degree—complex analysis
3. I.Q. LEVELS
    a) Low (70-89)
    b) Average (90-109)
    c) High (110-140)

Findings of the Study

1. The Meaning Test showed a near significant difference (10 per cent level) in favor of the meaning method at the end of the retention period.

2. The California Arithmetic Test produced a near significant gain (10 per cent level) in favor of the meaning method at the end of the semester and a significant difference (5 per cent level) at the end of the retention period.

3. The Meaning Test showed a significant difference in favor of the rule group in the area of measurement at the end of the semester.

4. The California Arithmetic Test indicated significant differences in favor of the meaning method for the areas of mixed problems and decimals at the end of the semester and for the area of fractions after the vacation. A significant difference in favor of the rule group was noted in the area of measurement at the end of the semester.

5. The Meaning Test revealed significant differences in favor of the meaning method for the highest degree of arithmetic complexity (complex analysis) for the period of retention.

6. The Meaning Test showed significant differences in favor of the rule method for the Low I.Q. group for the end of the semester only. However, statistical analysis showed that this difference may have been the result of a bilingual handicap which entered after the experiment had

begun. Recent research [8] shows that students with a bilingual handicap do significantly poorer in scholastic endeavors than those students without this deficiency. The imbalance in the ratio of bilingual students in the meaning and rule sections of the Low I.Q. group was brought about by the failure of one instructor to administer a test at the proper time. This caused a larger percentage of bilingual students to be found in the Low I.Q. group taught by the meaning method. Prior to this time the students in both sections of the Low I.Q. group were approximately equal in ratio. The study also showed that the average and high I.Q. groups produced significant differences favoring the meaning method for the period of retention.

7. The California Arithmetic Test showed significant differences in favor of the rule group for the Low I.Q. group during the semester. However, this difference again may be attributed to the bilingual factor suggested above. The High and Average I.Q. groups produced significant gains favoring the meaning method for both the period during the semester and for the period of retention.

Conclusions

1. The meaning method was more effective for the area of computation of fractions. The areas of decimals and percentage showed gains favoring the meaning method but only during the semester. The rule method was superior for the area of measurement but only during the semester.

2. The meaning method was more effective in establishing retention in the processes of computation as well as for the understanding of the principles of arithmetic.

3. The meaning method was more effective for the comprehension of complex analysis in arithmetic indicating a potential superiority for difficult concepts.

4. The meaning method was more effective for the Average and High I.Q. groups. The rule method seemed to be more effective for the Low I.Q. groups but the results are open to doubt due to a bilingual factor.

Recommendations

1. Continued research is necessary to establish the effectiveness of the meaning method in all areas of arithmetic. Repetition of experiments is necessary to validate the conclusions of the studies in areas of arithmetic.

---

[8] Charles Brown, "Acculturation and School Achievement," Unpublished Dissertation, University of Southern California, 1956.

2. Better design of experiments is necessary to examine the role of the meaning method for the comprehension of complex processes. Further verification of this trend could lead to important implications for arithmetic learning.

3. A complete investigation should be made to check the value of the meaning method and its effect on increased retention. Such a study could provide evidence for a greater mastery of arithmetic by the students through better teaching techniques.

BIBLIOGRAPHY

Billig, Albert L. "Student Attitude as a Factor in the Mastery of Commercial Arithmetic," *The Mathematics Teacher*, XXXVII (April, 1944), 170-73.

Brueckner, Leo J. "Development of Readiness Tests in Arithmetic," *Journal of Educational Research*, XXXIV (September, 1940), 15-20.

————. "Diagnosis in Arithmetic," *Educational Diagnosis*, National Society for the Study of Education, Thirty-fourth Yearbook (1935). Chicago: University of Chicago Press, 269-302.

————, and Foster E. Grossnickle. *Making Arithmetic Meaningful*. New York: Holt, Winston & Rinehart, Inc., 1953.

————, Foster E. Grossnickle, and John Reckzeh. *Developing Mathematical Understandings in the Upper Grades*. New York: Holt, Winston & Rinehart, Inc., 1957, 458-501.

Burch, Robert L. *An Evaluation of Analytic Testing in Arithmetic Problem Solving*, Doctoral Dissertation. Durham, N. C.: Duke University, 1949.

Clark, John R., and Laura K. Eads. *Guiding Arithmetic Learning*. Yonkers-on-Hudson, N. Y.: World Book Company, 1954, 242-70.

Dutton, Wilbur H. "Attitudes of Junior High School Pupils Toward Arithmetic," *School Review*, LXIV (January, 1956), 18-22.

————. "Attitudes of Prospective Teachers Toward Arithmetic," *Elementary School Journal*, LII (October, 1951), 84-90.

Dyer, Henry S. "On Making Testers of Teachers," *Education Research*, XLI (April, 1960), 111-15.

————, Robert Kalin, and Frederic M. Lord. "Problems in Mathematical Education." Princeton, N. J.: Educational Testing Service, 1956.

Eads, Laura K. "Ten Years of Meaningful Arithmetic in New York City," *Arithmetic Teacher*, II (December, 1955), 142-47.

Flournoy, Frances. "The Effectiveness of Instruction in Mental Arithmetic," *Elementary School Journal*, LV (November, 1954), 148-53.

Glennon, Vincent J., and students. "Developing Meaningful Practices in Arithmetic." Syracuse: Central New York School Study Council, Syracuse University, 1951.

Grossnickle, Foster E. "How the Method of Scoring a Test in Division Affects the Score," *Elementary School Journal*, XL (January, 1940), 366-70.

Grossnickle, Foster E. "Some Factors Affecting a Test Score in Division of Decimals," *Journal of Educational Research,* XXXVII (January, 1944), 338-42.

————, and Leo J. Brueckner. *Discovering Meanings in Arithmetic.* New York: Holt, Rinehart & Winston, Inc., 1959, 352-71.

Gunderson, Agnes G. "Number Concepts Held by Seven-Year-Olds," *Mathematics Teacher,* XXXIII (January, 1940), 18-24.

————, and Ethel Gunderson. "Fraction Concepts Held by Young Children," *The Arithmetic Teacher,* IV (October, 1957), 168-73.

Haggard, Ernest A. "Socialization, Personality, and Academic Achievement in Gifted Children," *The School Review,* LXV (December, 1957), 388-414.

Hartung, Maurice L. "A Forward Look at Evaluation," *The Mathematics Teacher,* XLII (January, 1949), 29-33.

Hamza, Mukhtar. "Retardation in Mathematics Amongst Grammar School Pupils," *British Journal of Educational Psychology,* XXII (November, 1952), 189-95.

Koenker, R. H. "Measuring the Meanings of Arithmetic," *The Arithmetic Teacher,* VII (February, 1960), 93-96.

Lynn, Richard. "Temperamental Characteristics Related to Disparity of Attainment in Reading and Arithmetic," *British Journal of Educational Psychology,* XXVII (February, 1957), 62-67.

MacLatchy, Josephine H. "The Pre-school Child's Familiarity with Measurement," *Education,* LXXI (April, 1951), 479-82.

Marks, John L., C. Richard Purdy, and Lucien B. Kinney. *Teaching Arithmetic for Understanding.* New York: McGraw-Hill Book Company, Inc., 1958, 342-72.

Morton, Robert Lee. *Teaching Children Arithmetic.* Morristown, N. J.: Silver Burdett Company, 1953, 519-46.

National Society for the Study of Education. *The Teaching of Arithmetic,* Fiftieth Yearbook. Chicago: The University of Chicago Press, 1951, Part I, 186-202.

Norton, M. S. "Helping Pupils Help Themselves Through Self-Evaluation," *The Arithmetic Teacher,* VII (April, 1960), 203-4.

Orleans, Jacob S. "The Understanding of Arithmetic Processes and Concepts Possessed by Teachers of Arithmetic," Publication No. 12. New York: College of the City of New York, Division of Teacher Education, Office of Research and Evaluation, 1952.

Poffenberger, Thomas, and Donald A. Norton. "Factors Determining Attitudes Toward Arithmetic and Mathematics," *Arithmetic Teacher,* III (April, 1956), 113-16.

Plank, Emma, and Robert Plank. "Emotional Components in Arithmetical Learning as Seen Through Autobiographies," Psychoanalytic Study of the Child, Vol. 9. Edited by Anna Freud and others. New York: International University Press, 1954, 274-93.

Rappaport, David. "Testing for Meanings in Arithmetic," *The Arithmetic Teacher,* VI (April, 1959), 140-43.

Souder, Hugh C. "Construction and Evaluation of Certain Readiness Tests in Common Fractions," *Journal of Educational Research*, XXXVII (October, 1943), 127-34.

Spitzer, Herbert F. *The Teaching of Arithmetic* (2nd ed.). Boston: Houghton Mifflin Company, 1954, 346-70.

Stokes, C. Newton. *Teaching the Meanings of Arithmetic*. New York: Appleton-Century-Crofts, Inc., 1951, 254-79.

Storm, W. B. "Arithmetic Meanings that Should be Tested," *Arithmetic 1948*. Supplementary Educational Monographs, No. 66. Chicago: University of Chicago Press, 1948, 26-31.

Valentine, Hugh B. "Some Results of Remedial Education in a Child Guidance Center," *British Journal of Educational Psychology*, XXI (June, 1951), 145-49.

Wilson, Guy Mitchell. "Types of Tests in Arithmetic," *Education*, LXXX (April, 1960), 493-94.

IX USING INSTRUCTIONAL MATERIALS EFFECTIVELY

Ron Welch, Indiana University
Ralph Ward, Brookline, Massachusetts

INTRODUCTION

A meaningful program in mathematics in the elementary
school depends, in large measure, upon the identification,
selection, use, and evaluation of appropriate instructional
materials. This important role of materials of instruction in
mathematics is widely accepted by modern elementary

352

school educators. Such ideas should be studied carefully, as they are often presented as conclusions based upon study of the learning processes or as a basis for the development of educational methodology and curriculum.

There is still some vagueness about the philosophical and psychological bases of the effectiveness of instructional materials in learning mathematics. In the development of educational methodology and curriculum, however, there seems to be mounting agreement among elementary education authorities that a rich instructional materials program in mathematics is being verified in experience. This seems to be evidenced by the fact that the elementary mathematics curriculum has been and is being expanded to include more varied learning activities and materials. Further, the varieties of identifiable learning experiences dependent upon instructional materials are increasing.

The teacher of a generation ago would have had little difficulty in identifying the few instructional materials used in teaching mathematics. Today's teacher finds an ever-expanding number and variety of such materials available. This is especially true if today's teachers define instructional materials in mathematics as "anything which contributes to the learning process." [1] For purposes of identifying instructional materials for teaching mathematics, the teacher may turn to the Fiftieth Yearbook, Part II, of the National Society for the Study of Education [2] and the Sixteenth Yearbook of the National Council of Teachers of Mathematics [3] as excellent sources. In addition, almost every professional book devoted to the teaching of mathematics in the elementary school includes descriptions of the kinds of materials which can be used to facilitate learning.

If the issues concerned with the role of instructional materials in teaching mathematics in the elementary school centered just about the identification of these materials, the

---

[1] Foster E. Grossnickle, Charlotte Junge, and William Metzner, "Instructional Materials for Teaching Arithmetic," *The Teaching of Arithmetic*, Fiftieth Yearbook of the N.S.S.E. (Chicago: The University of Chicago Press, 1951), Part I, 155.

[2] *Ibid.*, pp. 161-85.

[3] Irene Sauble, "Enrichment of the Arithmetic Course: Utilizing Supplementary Materials and Devices," *Arithmetic in General Education*, Sixteenth Yearbook of the N.C.T.M. (New York: Bureau of Publications, Teachers College, Columbia University, 1941), 157-95.

educator's job would be greatly simplified. Actually, the selection, use, and evaluation of these materials raise what seem to be more significant questions that need to be explored. These include the following:

What do we know about how children learn mathematics and the selection and use of instructional materials? Not all authorities are in complete agreement as to the most appropriate kinds of instructional materials that should be used to facilitate understandings in mathematics. There is some belief that certain materials destroy the nature of the number system or distort the mathematical principles being illustrated.

There seems to be agreement, however, that learning mathematics in the elementary school consists of an orderly series of experiences. Yet, the complete picture of this "orderly series of experiences" is still somewhat vague. Should the teacher move from concrete to semi-concrete to abstract experiences in his teaching? Do some instructional materials become "crutches" which tend to handicap the learner? It has been maintained by some authorities that the use of certain instructional materials detract from the mathematical principles involved in the learning experiences with numbers. A few writers still maintain the desirability for students to think abstractly without the use of concrete instructional materials.

What do we know about the types of instructional materials which best facilitate learning? The educator needs to be concerned with two facets of this question: Evaluation of the materials themselves and evaluation of their effectiveness in promoting learning. The use of color and other physical characteristics of instructional materials needs to be explored. What is the relationship between the choice of concepts to be taught and the effectiveness of the instructional materials used?

We are on the threshold of the development of powerful teaching aids. We must study and guide this development. We must ready ourselves to receive and use their potential. The rest of this discussion, therefore, is devoted to selected articles and excerpts from articles and books whereby the reader may have an opportunity to sample the thinking related to the issues concerned with the effective use of instructional materials in mathematics.

PART I: INSTRUCTIONAL MATERIALS AND THE DEVELOPMENT OF MATHEMATICAL CONCEPTS

THE FORMATION OF CONCEPTS

Henry Van Engen

The Attainment of Concepts

The development of concepts is basic to growth in learning capacity. In general this growth in learning capacity is a growth in conceptual development. For this reason it is important to make a study of how concepts are formed and to make an application of this knowledge to the methods employed in the classroom. Any such study must of necessity consider the activities of abstracting and generalizing, since these activities are inevitably a part of the total process of concept formation.

When a pupil observes common sensory or perceptual qualities in a number of different situations, or objects, he is abstracting that quality from the total situation. The concept of "green" is acquired by seeing green in connection with many different objects and colors and then focusing the attention on the one element in common—namely, green. Green then eventually is thought of as a "thing" in itself, something separate and apart from everything else. The concept of a number may be acquired in much the same way. The child may attach the number five, for example, to a particular group such as the five fingers of the hand. Later he observes that "five" applies to other groups of objects as well. Eventually the child abstracts a "fiveness" which is common to those groups which can be put into one-to-one correspondence with the fingers of his hand. It is well known that there are primitive tribes which have not made this abstraction. They apply different number names to different groups equal in number but differing in the kind of objects which make up the group.

Abstraction plays an important role in the classification of objects. A common property is fixed upon as the criterion for including an object in a given group. Each item is then examined to see if it should be included

[From "The Formation of Concepts," *The Learning of Mathematics, Its Theory and Practices,* The National Council of Teachers of Mathematics, Twenty-first Yearbook (1953), pp. 82-95. Reprinted by permission of the author and the National Council of Teachers of Mathematics.]

in the group. For example: If numbers are to be classified as prime or not prime each number is examined to see if it is divisible by a number other than itself and one. If it fails to pass this test it is classified as a prime number, otherwise it is not a prime. Here a certain type of divisibility was the abstraction which determined how each number was to be classified.

Generalization is another process used in conceptual learning. Generalization signifies that the detail which has been abstracted from a group of objects, or situations, is used to respond similarly to a whole class of related objects or situations. Thus, a student who understands the Pythagorean theorem has abstracted a property common to all squares constructed on the hypotenuse and the legs of a right triangle. This property can be used, however, to respond similarly to a whole class of other situations. If similar polygons are constructed on the hypotenuse and the legs of a right triangle the same abstraction can be applied to the polygons as was applied to the squares in the Pythagorean theorem. On the other hand, this "Pythagorean property" can be generalized to a much larger class of objects. Any figure, curvilinear or otherwise, constructed on the hypotenuse of a right triangle will have its area equal to the sum of the areas of the similar figures constructed on the two legs of the triangle. Thus a pupil discovers that an abstraction which he has learned by considering a rather limited case (the squares) also covers innumerable other cases.

How are these two processes of generalization and abstraction used in explaining the formation of concepts? Two theories are commonly recognized. The one emphasizes the passive role of the individual and abstraction, while the other emphasizes the active role of the individual and generalization. The theory emphasizing the passive role of the individual and abstraction can best be stated by quoting directly from Hull's [1] classical experiment on concept formation.

> A young child finds himself in a certain situation, reacts to it by approach say, and hears it called "dog." After an indeterminate intervening period he finds himself in a somewhat different situation and hears that called "dog." Later he finds himself in a somewhat different situation still, and hears that called "dog" also. Thus the process continues. The "dog" experiences appear at irregular intervals. The appearances are thus unanticipated. They appear with no obvious label as to their essential nature. This precipitates at each new appearance a more or less acute *problem* as to the proper reaction . . . ; the intervals between the "dog" experiences are filled with all sorts of other absorbing experiences which are contributing to the for-

---

[1] C. L. Hull, "Quantitative Aspects of the Evolution of Concepts," *Psychological Monographs*, XXVIII (1920), 1-85.

mation of other concepts. At length the time arrives when the child has a "meaning" for the word dog. Upon examination this "meaning" is found to be actually a characteristic more or less common to all dogs and not common to cats, dolls, and teddy-bears. But to the child the process of arriving at this meaning or concept has been largely unconscious. . . . Such in brief is our standard or normal-type of concept evolution.

The active role of the individual and generalization is emphasized in the theory of concept formation which stresses that the concept originates as a hypothesis which is tested by applying it to members, or supposed members, of a class of objects or situations.

While these two theories stress different features in the concept formation process, actually it seems better to unite the two to form an eclectic theory of concept formation. This course is indicated because it is difficult to distinguish between generalization and abstraction in the actual behavior of an individual. Heidbreder's [2] experiments have shown that in conceptual learning both processes operate at the adult level. However, there is reason to believe that for the child the sequence of perception-abstraction-generalization is more nearly a true statement of affairs than it is for the adult.

Heidbreder [3] in studying concept formation has achieved a number of very significant results showing the order in which adults attain certain types of concepts. According to Heidbreder those concepts were attained first in which the abstractions could be made by reacting to drawings of pictured objects of things such as trees, faces, and buildings. Next in difficulty she found that abstractions could be made by reacting to drawings of forms—"something less than a thing but not altogether un-thing-like." Such forms as circles, squares and triangles were used in her experiments in this instance. Most difficult of all the concepts studied were those in which the abstractions had to be attained by reacting to facts about collections of objects (numerical quantities of). This latter type of response seems to be more remote from the perception of concrete objects than is the response to such things as visual forms and spatial forms.

What explanation does Heidbreder give for this order of things-form-number concept attainment? Using her own words, "One answer immediately suggests itself: manipulability, relevance to direct motor reaction." The concept "circle" is attained significantly later than the concept "plate" because a circle is beyond the manipulability stage even though it is as perceptible as the plate. The plate can be manipulated with the hands, it

---

[2] E. Heidbreder, "The Attainment of Concepts—A Psychological Interpretation," *Transactions of the New York Academy of Science,* July 28, 1945.

[3] E. Heidbreder, "The Attainment of Concepts: I. Terminology and Methodology," *Journal of General Psychology,* XXXV (1946), 173-89.

can be felt, seen and weighed. The circle drawn on the board cannot be manipulated. Its form can be traced in the air but even this cannot offset the advantage of manipulability from the standpoint of the attainment of the concept. The ease of attaining a concept seems to be more highly correlated with manipulability than with perceptibility. In Heidbreder's own words:

> Dominance in cognitive reactions seems to be correlated, not with maximal openness to inspection, nor with maximal "givenness" in perceptual experience, but with *maximal relevance to action, specifically to manipulation,* that kind of motor reaction which human beings characteristically employ [italics added].

Reactions to the world of concrete objects are the foundation stones from which the structure of abstract ideas arises. These reactions are refined, reorganized and integrated so that they become even more useful and even more powerful than the original response. The part of the reorganization and the refinement of responses in conceptual learning is nicely described by McConnell.[4] Further consideration cannot be given to this problem at this time.

This concept of the part that actions, or manipulations, play in the development of concepts of the first order is of utmost importance to the teacher. Children and adolescents use manipulatory experiences to develop primitive concepts, and those concepts which are more nearly related to the action world of the child are the ones that are more easily developed. From this it would seem that any effort to improve the instruction in mathematics must take into consideration this rather commonly accepted point of view regarding the attainment of concepts. The weakness of mathematical instruction as commonly practiced in our schools is more readily observable in respect to the lack of adequate activities for conceptual development than in almost any other respect. Books, paper, pencils, blackboards, and the drill exercises which usually accompany these instructional tools, are not sufficient except, possibly, for that relatively small percentage of pupils who are symbolically minded. Today's schoolrooms are barren of those small inexpensive objects which provide those opportunities for perceptual and manipulatory experiences from which the average child can abstract and generalize in order to take the first steps in formulating a concept. This barrenness is further accentuated by the lack of pictures, movies and filmstrips which can be used to picture

---

[4] T. R. McConnell, "Recent Trends in Learning Theory: Their Applications and the Psychology of Arithmetic," *Arithmetic in General Education,* National Council of Teachers of Mathematics Sixteenth Yearbook (1941), (New York: Bureau of Publications, Teachers College, Columbia University), 268-89.

the concept-forming actions as a second stage in the learning of abstract symbolism. This action-picture-symbol sequence in concept formation is frequently ignored in its entirety and the symbol introduced immediately. No other method can so thoroughly block conceptual learning, especially for the average and the slow-learning pupil.

The present day emphasis on multi-sensory aids has a secure foundation in the point of view expressed by Heidbreder, Smoke and other psychologists of the operationalists' school of thought. The manipulatory activities that result when blocks, buttons, and models are widely used in instructional procedures provide the essential elements from which concepts are more readily developed. However, this emphasis on multi-sensory aids does place a responsibility on the teacher of mathematics which must be given careful thought. Many of the manipulatory activities now "going the rounds" in the world of mathematics instruction do not include those manipulatory activities which develop the concept, or concepts, for which they were developed. As textbooks, workbooks, and tests need careful evaluation, so also do visual aids. As one example of a visual aid which does not aid the child in developing the desired concept the following may be cited as a horrible example.

Sometimes one finds that the first-graders are being taught "what subtraction means" by the following picture device.

$$OOOOO - OO = OOO$$

Now any teacher knows (and the child knows this even better than the teacher, seemingly) that one cannot actually perform the operation pictured above. It is impossible to take two marbles from five marbles as illustrated. Laying five marbles on the table and giving two of them away will easily establish this fact. Now the child also knows this because he has performed the feat of giving two of his five marbles to Johnny many times. As a result the "learning aid" illustrated above can only block the real meaning of subtraction for the child in the first grade. It blocks learning because it does not picture the real life actions that indicate to the child what the word "subtraction" means.

Number-Concept Formation in Children

Previous sections of this chapter have already commented on the fact that the difference between the processes whereby adults form concepts and the processes whereby children form concepts are likely to be one of degree rather than of kind. Therefore, the action-manipulatory point of view set forth by Heidbreder as quoted in the last section of this chapter are fully as appropriate for the processes of concept formation in the child as they are in the adult. In fact, there is reason to believe that they are even more characteristic of the child's conceptual processes than they are of the learning processes of the adult. It will be the purpose of this section to support the point of view that actions and manipulations are dominant in the formation of the child's concepts.

There can be no doubt that too little thought has been given to the part that actions play in the intellectual development of the child. Attention has already been called by Van Engen [5] to the role of actions in the intellectual development of the child when this development is considered from a philosophic and semantic point of view. However, the psychological foundations of the "action basis" for learning must also be given serious consideration. This is forcefully brought to mind by the phrase "human action system" which Gesell [6] used in his study of the growth aspects of the mind. For Gesell, "action system" denotes "the total organism as a going concern, particularly its behavior capacities, propensities, and patterns."

To those teachers who have thought of learning in terms of "specific habits," "drill" and "teaching by telling" it comes as somewhat of a shock to learn that probably all mental life has at its roots the actions or manipulations performed in a learning situation. Gesell [7] makes this point as follows:

> It is probable that all mental life has a motor basis and a motor origin. The non-mystical mind must always *take hold*. Even in the rarefied realms of conceptual reasoning we speak of intellectual grasp and of symbolic apprehension. Thinking might be defined as a *comprehension* and *manipulation* of meanings. Accordingly, thought has its beginnings in infancy. We have already noted the germ of mathematics which lies in the one-by-one behavior pattern of the year-old infant. Counting is based on serial motor manipulations.

The principle of action is tightly interwoven into Gesell's description of the growth processes of the child (mental, physical and emotional). For example, he says:

---

[5] H. Van Engen, "Analysis of Meaning in Arithmetic," *Elementary School Journal,* XLIX (February, 1949), 395-400, (March, 1949), 26-30.

[6] Arnold Gesell, *Infant Development: The Embryology of Early Human Behavior* (New York: Harper & Brothers, 1952).

[7] *Ibid.,* p. 58.

This principle [of motor priority] is so fundamental that virtually all behavior ontogenetically has a motor origin and aspect. Vision, for example, has a motor as well as a sensory basis; likewise speech, mental imagery, and conceptual thought. Even emotions trace to motor attitudes and tensions.[8]

These quotations taken from the latest of Gesell's publications furnish much food for thought for those interested in the contributions of classroom experiences to the growth of mathematical concepts. But before considering these implications in some detail it will be profitable to consider the point of view of others who have given this problem considerable thought.

The next source from which quotations will be taken is not strictly a study on concept formation. It is rather a study on the development of reasoning in the child; yet thinking is merely the mental manipulation of symbols which represent concepts. The close relationship existing between the mental manipulation of symbols and the overt manipulation of objects is apparent upon reading Piaget's [9] classical studies on reasoning and judgment in the child in the light of the discussion found in the previous sections of this chapter. Although later studies have failed to corroborate Piaget's studies in all details, it is nevertheless a pioneering effort which set the stage for many investigations and can be relied on for its basic point of view.

Piaget emphasizes the close connection between manual operations, or actions, and the thought processes of the child. In fact he holds that the child thinks by picturing, mentally, the manual operations that took place in a given situation. Thus, Piaget [10] says:

So that everything we have said in this work is to show that the thought of the child is less conscious than ours has *ipso facto* led us to the conclusion that childish thought is devoid of logical necessity and genuine implication; *it is nearer to action than ours, and consists simply of mentally pictured manual operations,* which, like the vagaries of movement, follow each other without any necessary succession. This will explain later on why childish reasoning is neither deductive nor inductive; it consists in mental experiments which are non-reversible, i.e., which are not entirely logical. . . [italics added].

These movements and operations are a preparation for conscious reasoning in so far as they reproduce and prepare anew the *manual operations of which thought is a continuation* [italics added].

---

[8] *Ibid.,* p. 65.

[9] Jean Piaget, *Judgment and Reasoning in the Child* (New York: Harcourt, Brace and Co., 1928).

[10] *Ibid.,* pp. 145-46.

This is strong language; it has many important teaching implications. Can it be supported? Werner [11] says:

> The child's concepts always have a concrete content. Image and concept are an indivisible unity. The conceiving and the describing of a thing are not distinctly separated activities. As is true of primitive man, the child's need of adjustment to adult language creates conceptual forms which arise out of concrete perception, which are indeed both perception and conception, which appear to be metaphors and yet really are not. . . . To conceive and define things in terms of concrete activity is in complete accordance with the world-of-action characteristic of the child.

Here again one finds the action and the place of action in the development of the concepts of the child. Are number concepts developed this way? Consider the following quotations also taken from Werner.[12]

> Frequently we find that abstract counting is supplanted by an optical, or even motor configuration and ordering of groups among primitive peoples and, indeed, among the *naïve* of our own culture.
>
> The formation of a "number system" in its proper sense is bound up with two developmental facts: First, with the increasing abstraction; the number concept becomes more and more released from the concrete configuration and the qualities of the objects. Second, with the development of a scheme for the number order in particular.

In view of the importance of the topic and in view of the importance of the contribution to the field it may be well to quote Heidbreder's [13] findings and her interpretation of these findings from a source not previously quoted.

> Definitions referring to concepts of number were especially instructive. . . .
>
> There are thus indications that in attaining concepts of numbers, some subjects reacted first chiefly to pictured objects, next chiefly to spatial arrangements, and eventually chiefly to numerical quantities, thus traversing in arriving at these, the last concepts attained, the entire course of events indicated by the experimental data considered as a whole.
>
> Taken together, the quantitative data and the definitions are interpreted as indicating that in successive stages of an experiment, the subject's reactions were critically determined by successively less thing-like aspects of the drawings as reaction determined by more thing-like aspects proved inadequate.

---

[11] Heinz Werner, *Comparative Psychology of Mental Development* (New York: Harper & Brothers, 1940), 271-72.

[12] *Ibid.*, p. 294.

[13] E. Heidbreder, "The Attainment of Concepts: III. The Process," *Journal of Psychology*, XXIV (1947), 93-138.

While Heidbreder's experiments dealt with the attainment of number concepts in adults its significance for the development of the child's concept of numbers cannot be overlooked. The response to a spatial arrangement prior to the response to the numericalness of a situation is particularly instructive. It would seem to indicate that configurations play a fundamental role in the development of number concepts.

Judd [14] points out that

Number ideas are, in fact, more than images; they depend on the presence of reactions. A child does not learn numbers by having them impressed on his organs of sense. There is no such thing as a number sense. Number is acquired only when there is a positive reaction. One must respond in a definite way to each item of experience which is to be counted. The definite positive response which one makes to each object counted is reduced to an inner reaction in the course of educational development, but it continues to be a reaction.

From these quotations one can conclude that the perceptual, manipulatory activities are of utmost importance in the development of number concepts as well as concepts in general. On this basis one can again conclude that in this respect instructional practices in the elementary school are in general very weak. The usual blackboard-chalk-paper-pencil methods for instructing the child in arithmetic are entirely inadequate. Making marks in a workbook is not a functional activity in the *first* stages of concept development. Neither is continual drill on abstract combinations of symbols functional. These quotations show, clearly, that the manipulation of objects is essential in the *first* stages of number concept development—especially in children. Abstract definitional approaches should be abandoned by the elementary teacher and secondary teacher for an approach which emphasizes the organic awareness of a concept before it is characterized by a definition or designated by a symbol.

The effect of this hypothesis pertaining to conceptual learning is nicely brought out by present-day practices in teaching children to count. Too prevalent is the idea that the first stage in counting is the memorization of a sequence of number names. Nothing could be more erroneous. The part that "number configurations" play in the development of the ability to count has not been thoroughly investigated but there can be no doubt that a configurational awareness of number should precede the sheer memorization of number names.

---

[14] Charles Hubbard Judd, *Psychological Analysis of the Fundamentals of Arithmetic* (Chicago: University of Chicago, 1927), 49.

Implications for the Teaching of Mathematics

What is known about concept formation and the implications for mathematics teachers can probably be best, and most economically, set forth in a few statements which, in part, summarize what has been discussed in earlier sections and, in part, a brief statement of the results of experimental evidence not previously discussed. When new results are included in the following statements a reference to the bibliography will be given.

1. Mathematics teachers have not made enough use of what Heidbreder calls the "thing-like" aspects of conceptual learning. The initial experiences with a new concept should conform to the "world-of-action" characteristic of the pupils' conceptual learning processes. The ease with which concepts are acquired depends to a great extent on the "relevance to direct motor reaction."

2. There seems to be evidence that the more intelligent the pupils, the more they are able to deal with language symbols, and that they rely more and more on such symbols as the problems become complex.[15] The fact is not surprising but it has particular significance for the teacher of the slow learner. These pupils are weak in the use of symbols and yet the instructional tools placed in the hands of the pupil deal almost exclusively with language symbols. Concrete-action learning equipment is needed in any attempt to solve the problem of the slow learner. The slow learner needs the manipulating experiences which develop concepts. He also needs picture sequences to encourage him to become independent of the concrete learning aids.

3. Verbal instructions increase the variability of response.[16] Teachers should be conscious of the fact that pupils interpret the meaning of words in terms of their own experiences and that these experiences are not the same as those of the teacher. Hence, visual aids will help to "unclog" communication lines, avoid misunderstanding and decrease the variability of response.

4. "A combination of abstract presentation and concrete examples yields a distinctly greater functional efficiency than either method alone."[17]

5. "During the evolution of concepts, mildly attracting attention to the common element 'in situ' considerably increases the efficiency of the (learning) process."[18]

---

[15] P. H. Ewert, and J. F. Lambert, "The Effects of Verbal Instructions Upon the Formation of a Concept," *Journal of General Psychology*, VI (1932), 400-413.

[16] *Ibid.*

[17] C. L. Hull, "Quantitative Aspects of the Evolution of Concepts," *Psychological Monographs*, XXVIII (1920), 1-85.

[18] *Ibid.*

6. "A set to learn meanings as well as names yields a much higher rate of learning and degree of retention than a set to learn names only." [19]

7. Concepts logically learned are learned more quickly and are remembered longer than are concepts illogically learned.[20] Commenting on this fact Stroud [21] says:

> Material high in associative value is for that reason comparatively easy to learn and for the same reason easily recalled, relearned or recognized afterward. Logical material, material capable of meaningful organization or reduction to some kind of system, comes within the operations of transfer of training, operations that facilitate recall as well as learning.

8. A given situation will favor one concept over another and the ease of attainment of the concept will depend on how readily discernible the essential features of the concept are to perception.[22]

Teachers might well keep this generalization in mind in evaluating the visual aids used in their classes. Too many visual aids in use today do not highlight the essential features of the concept they are supposed to teach. In many cases the essential features are too imbedded in the total situation. In still others it is merely a visual aid, there is no relevance to the development of the concept.

A simple example may make this clear. Teachers frequently provide counting experiences in which the actions essential for establishing the cardinal concept of number are not readily accessible to perception. This inaccessibility to perception frequently causes the pupil to confuse the ordinal and cardinal concept. If teachers ask the pupils to count six children in a row the predominant features in this situation are essentially ordinal not cardinal. However, in counting six blocks which can be put into familiar number configurations successively, each group is grasped as the child says, "One, two, three, four, five, six." All the actions here present facilitate the development of the cardinal concept, and the eye is aided in seeing the total group and not each successive member of the group as an individual.

9. Negative instances are not necessary for the development of adequate concepts but may be included as checks.[23]

---

[19] H. B. Reed, "Factors Influencing the Learning and Retention of Concepts," *Journal of Experimental Psychology*, XXXVI (February-June, 1946), 71-87, 166-79, 252-61.

[20] *Ibid.*

[21] J. B. Stroud, *Psychology in Education* (New York: Longmans, Green and Co., 1946), 538.

[22] W. Edgar Vinacke, "The Investigation of Concept Formation," *Psychological Bulletin*, XLVIII (January, 1951), 1-31.

[23] K. L. Smoke, "Negative Instances in Concept Learning," *Journal of Experimental Psychology*, XVI (1933), 583-88.

In teaching the concept of adjacent angles in geometry the teacher may include drawings of angles which have a common side but not a common vertex. This is a negative instance inasmuch as it does not fit the definition of adjacent angles. However, research has shown that the inclusion of negative instances does not materially affect the development of the concept.

10. Conceptual development is a growth process. It takes time to develop concepts. Hence the teacher should not expect the pupil to develop a mature concept in a few days. Concepts are developed by reviewing various instances in which they may occur under varying conditions and with varied meanings. Furthermore, concepts are not established readily by definitions unless the pupil is mathematically mature.

11. There are such things as nonverbalizable generalizations. Hendrix [24] and Smoke [25] have discussed the existence of nonverbal generalizations. Hence the pupil who says, "I know what it is but I cannot say it," may be telling the truth. Furthermore developing the awareness of a generalization prior to verbalization facilitates learning.

12. The background of experience of the pupil is an important factor in the development of concepts. This is amply illustrated by the pupil who has done some art work and knows the term "perspective" as it applies to representing three-dimensional objects on two-dimensional paper. This student when confronted with the term "perspective" as used in college geometry is often confused. He is looking for the third dimension and there is no third dimension.

The child who has had many and varied experiences with money encounters much less difficulty with the "arithmetic of money" in the primary grades than the child whose experiences have been limited. Similarly the child who has been given many varied experiences with number ideas will have less difficulty with the abstractions presented at a later date.

From this point of view it would seem that it is the teacher's duty to give the children many varied experiences with the concrete objects and the manipulations and actions which are essential to the development of concepts. Such activities are essential to good instruction in mathematics.

13. Conceptual thinking is not necessarily harder than concrete thinking but it is easier to manipulate the concept of Sam Jones than it is of Mr. A or of *a*. Murphy [26] makes this point very nicely as follows:

---

[24] Gertrude Hendrix, "A New Clue To Transfer of Training," *Elementary School Journal.*

[25] K. L. Smoke, "The Experimental Approach to Concept Learning," *Psychological Review,* XLII (1935), 274-79.

[26] Gardner Murphy, *General Psychology* (New York: Harper & Brothers, 1933), 391.

The abstraction "man" or "Mr. A" is actually handled less efficiently in logical relations than is Mr. Edward Jones or Mr. Harold Smith. The results of experiments in reasoning in which the same rational processes must be carried through first with concrete and then with abstract materials show gross differences. Reasoning depends not on the formal ability to take the necessary logical steps, since the connections required to solve the task are the same in the two cases. But sometimes, in thinking in terms of abstract things like x's and y's, or Mr. A and Mr. B, one is unable to control the concepts and handle them in pure form. One is trying to do two things at once—concrete and abstract. In the concrete tasks one manipulates spatial relations in pictorial or other form which keeps them in the realm of immediate experience rather than abstraction.

Algebra teachers should keep this in mind. The beginning algebra student has learned to think in terms of individual numbers such as 3.14, but he may have difficulty in thinking about an abstract symbol which represents that number, such as π. In particular, symbol x represents a class of numbers which may cause considerable difficulty.

TEACHING CHILDREN ARITHMETIC

Robert L. Morton

Proceed from Concrete and Semiconcrete to Abstract

A child's earliest number experiences are phases of larger experiences in which concrete materials are present. The child, before entering primary school, is likely to learn the number words to twenty or thereabouts and learn to count many of the objects which are a part of his environment.

The program for developing a better understanding of numbers—whole numbers and fractions—and for teaching the various processes with numbers must be founded upon experiences with concrete things. In learning the addition facts, the pupil learns to put groups together; in learning what fractions are, he learns in terms of parts of things; and in many other respects, he gets his early experiences with concrete materials.

Arithmetic is basically abstract. It is necessary that the pupil move from putting groups together to adding abstract numbers. This transition from the concrete to the abstract is usually best made by going through the

[From *Teaching Children Arithmetic* (New York: Silver Burdett Company, 1953), pp. 52-54. By permission of the author and Silver Burdett Company.]

intermediate step in which the semiconcrete kind of experience is provided. Diagrams, drawings, and the like are semiconcrete materials. Sometimes a stage part way between the concrete and the semiconcrete—a picture stage—is helpful.

For example, to learn what the fraction ¼ means, the pupil should first have the experience of dividing actual objects—such as apples, candy bars, or pieces of paper, into fourths. Then he should see pictures of such well-known objects divided into fourths. He may see a rectangle or a circle divided into fourths and one of the fourths shaded, as a semiconcrete representation. Finally, he arrives at the abstract stage where the symbol ¼ has meaning for him.

A good course provides for a skillful organization of learning materials so that the best possible use is made of concrete and semiconcrete materials as a means of developing concepts and making clear the meaning of processes. At the same time, the good course will provide for as rapid progress from the concrete to the abstract as is consistent with successful learning. The teacher should always be alert for opportunities to use concrete and semiconcrete experiences as a means for making abstract number experiences meaningful. The wise teacher will be equally alert to the misuse of these so-called manipulative materials. Such materials must always be a means to an end—the understanding of the abstract. Until we have scientific studies which evaluate the use of these materials, which we do not have as yet, the teacher should permit their use as long as it is reasonably certain that they aid the pupil to discover meaning. The test of their value lies in whether the pupil gives evidence of making a transition from the concrete aids to the abstraction whose truth they demonstrated.

Since, in general, it is only the simplest essentials about number and number processes that can be discovered through manipulative materials, it is necessary that the pupil be encouraged to think abstractly as quickly as he can successfully do so.

The shift from the concrete or semiconcrete to the abstract is not made all at once and finally. Rather, there will be many references back to the concrete or semiconcrete as the pupil's grasp of the abstract increases. These references should gradually become less frequent. Finally, the pupil should be able to do his thinking as well as his working of examples solely in terms of abstract numbers.

EQUIPPING A CLASSROOM FOR LEARNING

Esther J. Swenson

Concrete aids in the teaching of arithmetic are especially helpful in guiding the learning of young children. The topic has been so well treated elsewhere [1] that extensive treatment at this point is unnecessary. A few suggestions concerning the use of concrete aids in the teaching of place value and the decimal system may suffice.

Money—so interesting to most children and adults alike and so neat a concrete aid in the teaching of the decimal idea and place value—is not used as much nor as well as it could be in most primary-grade classrooms. If objections to the use of real money arise, toy money can be purchased or made at small expense.

A teacher planned a simple series of experiences with first-semester first-graders which provided a setting for developing meaningful reading and writing of the number symbols and also gave the children a start on the decimal idea and place value. One Monday morning when the children came to school, there was a penny fastened to a card on the bulletin board with Scotch tape. Underneath it was a large figure "1." The next day there were two pennies and the symbol had changed to "2." So it went; every day one more penny and always a new symbol, the cardinal number for the group of pennies on display.

By the second Thursday, the group of pennies had grown to 9. All along, the children were curious and interested, delighted to discover how the group grew each night, and soon predicting how many pennies there would be the next day. On the second Friday, there were 10 pennies and

[From "Arithmetic for Pre-School and Primary Grade Children," *The Teaching of Arithmetic*, Fiftieth Yearbook (1951) of the N.S.S.E. (Chicago: The University of Chicago Press), Part II, pp. 71-73. Reprinted by permission of the author and the National Society for the Study of Education.]

---

[1] Irene Sauble. "The Enrichment of the Arithmetic Course: Utilizing Supplementary Materials and Devices," *Arithmetic in General Education*, National Council of Teachers of Mathematics Sixteenth Yearbook (1941), (New York: Bureau of Publications, Teachers College, Columbia University), 151-95.

Foster E. Grossnickle. "The Use of Multisensory Aids in Developing Arithmetical Meanings," *Arithmetic*, Supplementary Educational Monographs (Chicago: University of Chicago Press, 1948), 1-14.

the number "10." To the teacher, this was a crucial point. She could have had the children read the number and let it go at that. But she went on, asking if anyone could tell her some other piece of money that was worth the same as 10 pennies. Several children knew that would be a dime, and the teacher was prepared to produce one as soon as it was mentioned. She pointed out that the 1 in the 10 stood for 1 dime instead of 1 penny as on the first day. The germ of the decimal idea and of place value had been planted for at least some of the first-graders.

Dimes and pennies are helpful learning aids in such situations as these: for sums over 10 (e.g., $5 + 8 = 13$ demonstrated as a group of 5 and a group of 8 changed to a group of 10 and a group of 3); for bringing out generalizations related to 10 (e.g., when 9 is added to another number, the sum is 1 less than when 10 is added to that number); or in carrying in addition or changing (borrowing) in subtraction. If in adding two-place money numbers (e.g., 14 cents + 28 cents) toy coins are available, the children can actually change 10 of the pennies in the sum of the pennies' place for 1 dime and carry it to the dimes' place. In changing in subtraction (e.g., 24 cents − 18 cents) one of the 2 dimes can actually be changed for 10 pennies and these pennies grouped with the 4 original pennies, from which group 8 pennies can then be subtracted.

Carrying and changing should also be demonstrated and clarified for nonmoney numbers. Objects which come in tens or can easily be grouped and fastened in tens are readily available (wooden "sucker" sticks, 2 packages of gum, wooden blocks, individual breakfast-food cartons). The abacus has the added advantage that its individual wires typify the *places* in the decimal system. Simple directions for constructing ten blocks and an inexpensive abacus are given by Spitzer.

In using the abacus when adding involves carrying, one *must* change 10 ones for 1 ten because there are only 10 ones on the ones' wire.

"CONDITIONING" FOR THE USE OF ABSTRACT NUMBERS

Gertrude Hildreth

Success in handling number computation in standard algorism form is dependent upon understanding the meanings behind abstract numbers. In moving from number work with concrete objects and representational

[From "Principles of Learning Applied to Arithmetic," *The Arithmetic Teacher*, I (October, 1954), pp. 1-5. Reprinted by permission of the author and *The Arithmetic Teacher*.]

material to dealing with abstract numbers alone, either in print and writing or in "mental" computation, a conditioning process takes place. The meanings formed through work with a number of objects or their representations become shifted through association to the abstract number symbols. The steps in this conditioning process may be illustrated as follows:

Step 1. *a)* Real objects and represent-   Number meanings, number
             ative materials, concrete ——→ terms, computation, and so-
             experiences   lution of problems

Step 2. ⎰ *b)* Graphic symbols   ⎱   Number meanings, number
         ⎱ *a)* Real objects and repre- ⎰ ——→ terms, computation, and solu-
             sentative materials   tion of problems

Step 3. *b)* Graphic symbols alone in   Number meanings, number
             computation; complete ——→ terms, computation, and so-
             abstraction   lution of problems

By way of illustration of Step 2, suppose the problem is, "I bought *x* costing 12 cents and *y* costing 25 cents, and gave the clerk a fifty cent piece. How much money did I have left over (get back)?"

The child first acts out this problem or he sees it solved at the grocery counter. He hears the numbers used and sees them printed on the sales slip. He knows they stand for the number of cents each of the two objects costs. In the final Step 3, the pupil can now compute for solving the problem: $50 - (12 + 25) = 13$ without handling the money or seeing the objects.

Just how to make the transition from concrete to abstract, and to determine the psychological time to accomplish it are questions for every teacher to consider. The error made in former years was to omit the first and second steps pretty largely and to begin drill with the third step. Dealing with abstract symbols is difficult for children whose experiences at the age of entering school have been entirely in the realm of concrete manipulation of objects or pictorial representation of experiences. Learning arithmetic has been made difficult for children by starting off with Step 3 instead of carefully building up to Step 3 through Steps 1 and 2, for example, in work with fractions. We must be careful not to go to the other extreme and delay the conditioning process too long, so that children are too slow in advancing to Step 3. Another mistake would be to fail to return to Step 2 after moving on to Step 3 when this would clear up difficulties in problem solving.

Grade III is about the right level to begin to make the shift from work with representative material to abstract number symbols, with these precautions: the transition should not be made too abruptly; some children are ready to switch over ahead of others. From this point on computation with abstract symbols can be rapidly learned, and must be thoroughly drilled during the remaining elementary school years.

Even after the pupil has learned to use number symbols alone in solving problems, go back to the use of manipulative and visual materials as needed. In the case of fractions this means bringing on the fruit, the measuring cups, the foot rulers, the fractions disks and "pies" cut up in equal-sized parts. When any new process is introduced demonstrate the new meanings with manipulative and visual materials, e.g., place value in decimals.

PART II: TYPES OF INSTRUCTIONAL MATERIALS WHICH FACILITATE LEARNING

THE ROLE OF THE CLASSROOM

Foster E. Grossnickle and Leo J. Brueckner

The instructional materials needed in an arithmetic classroom depend on the nature of the learning activities that are to be carried on. If the function of the classroom is to provide a place where the pupils are to work examples in an intensive drill program and to solve isolated verbal problems, the necessary equipment consists of paper, pencil, and a textbook or workbook. The classroom, then, is a place for learning nothing more than how to perform computations. If on the other hand the classroom is to become a learning laboratory where the children will experiment with numbers and measures, discover meanings and procedures, and experience directed learning activities, then adequate equipment and materials must be provided for meeting these needs.

Kinds of Materials Needed

Three kinds of materials are needed to teach arithmetic effectively in the elementary school. These may be classified as *exploratory, visual,* and *symbolic. Exploratory* materials are those that the child can touch, move

[From *Discovering Meanings in Arithmetic* (New York: Holt, Rinehart & Winston, Inc., 1959), pp. 63-4. Reprinted by permission of the author and Holt, Rinehart & Winston, Inc.]

about, or manipulate, such as an abacus, or fractional cutouts. When the child uses fractional cutouts to discover a principle which he could not understand in a purely verbal discussion, these cutouts are used for exploratory purposes. If on the other hand he merely moves the cutouts about in a perfunctory manner to represent fractions, they become manipulative material only and do not serve exploratory purposes. Pictures, charts, films, slides, and posters are representative of *visual* materials. A page of explanations of some topic in a textbook or workbook, a list of verbal problems, or a set of examples are representative of *symbolic* materials.

THE CLASSROOM—A LEARNING LABORATORY

Peter L. Spencer and Marguerite Brydegaard

The classroom for mathematics should be a learning-laboratory. This does not imply that equipment or fancy gadgets in a room or things that children build make the classroom a "learning-laboratory." Rather, a classroom becomes a learning-laboratory when it produces mental and physical activity that results in experimentation; this in turn should lead to formulation of procedures and to generalizations based upon reliable and sufficient information. The materials for the laboratory are within the reach of every teacher. The materials consist, for the most part, of things that children and teachers bring into the classroom for the lessons under consideration. Cups, glasses, bottles, cans, jars, boxes, labels, cartons, string, measuring sticks, and innumerable other things to use in experiments with measuring should be part of every mathematics classroom.

The force behind the scenes for a laboratory for learning is the classroom teacher. The teacher who senses the procedures for making the classroom a laboratory for learning is invaluable, and no material equipment can replace him. That teacher will find some of the better commercial materials helpful, but he will not be lost without them. He is the type of teacher who can teach without textbooks. On the other hand, the teacher who doesn't sense how to stimulate his learners to experiment and to formulate procedures and generalizations is not likely to do a very different job of teaching just because he has gadgets and equipment in his room.

[From *Building Mathematical Concepts in the Elementary School* (New York: Holt, Rinehart & Winston, Inc., 1952), p. 5. Reprinted by permission of the authors and Holt, Rinehart & Winston, Inc.]

THE FUNCTION OF CHARTS
IN THE ARITHMETIC PROGRAM

Catharine M. Williams

Many teachers do an effective job of using concrete manipulative materials to help children with initial stages of the formation of arithmetic concepts. All too frequently, however, the teachers shift so rapidly from these concrete, visual experiences to abstract verbal symbols that children are unable to breach the gap. Children need intermediary helps paced to their emerging insights. Charts are one type of visual aid which can be developed to help children along the road from need for concrete materials to ability to operate with abstractions.

Usually children should participate in the development of the chart. This participation fosters the habit of organizing one's own ideas and of resourcefully working out one's own self-helps. Then, too, participation in developing a chart serves as insurance against introduction of material in chart form before the children are ready for the organized presentation. Because the pupils understand a chart which they have helped to work out, it becomes the meaningful reference which they need temporarily.

One of the common mistakes in the teaching of arithmetic is that charts (this includes all types of tables) which appear in arithmetic texts are introduced before experience has made them meaningful. Not even the most simple of organizational charts should be introduced until after concepts have been developed through rich first-hand experiences. This seems obvious when we remember that the sense, the meaning of any logically organized form is a development process which evolves as experience provides new insights. Since the meaning of any logical organization is an outgrowth of one's own experiences, children should not be denied opportunities to build up their own organization. After children have worked out their organization, they have basic understanding and are ready critically to study the mathematician's mature organization. Only then will they be able to appreciate his refined terms and short-cuts and/or his inclusion of information which they may have overlooked or lacked.

[From "The Function of Charts in the Arithmetic Program," *The Arithmetic Teacher*, II (October, 1955), p. 72. Reprinted by permission of the author and *The Arithmetic Teacher*.]

DEVICES OF STRUCTURAL ARITHMETIC

Catherine Stern

The approach in Structural Arithmetic, then, is based on measuring. We represent the numbers by blocks that measure 1 unit, 2 units, 3 units, and so on. With these devices the child can discover all existent number relations by himself. He finds out not only by measuring what block combinations give 10; even carrying and borrowing, multiplying and dividing can be discovered with our materials. Moreover, they are as well adapted for use with groups as for individual instruction. If I seem to emphasize the work with individual children, it is only for the sake of clarity.

The use of blocks in the teaching of arithmetic is by no means new. They have been used in many methods from the time of Pestalozzi on, notably in the Tillich number kit, the Spear, the Montessori, and the Badanes systems of teaching. In all these methods, however, even though the two addends are given concrete form, their sum has to be found by counting the units one by one, and the interrelationship between numbers is hardly to be seen.

Thorndike [1] points out that the child has to understand the series meaning of a number, its collection meaning, its ratio meaning, and its relational meaning. The series meaning of a number is the ordinal concept; the child must be sure at what place in the series of numbers a 3 or a 7 stands. This is demonstrated by the "stair" of our blocks in which the child discovers their individual places. The collection meaning is the cardinal aspect; our children measure the blocks and find that the name "three" belongs to a rather short block, that "nine" denotes a long block, and so on. The ratio meaning of numbers is clear also, since the 7-block is 7 times as big as 1, the 6-block contains 6 units, the 8-block equals two 4-blocks, and so on. The relational meaning of numbers becomes apparent as the child fits the blocks into the various devices used in our method.

In the beginning, I experimented with uncolored blocks. In order to distinguish between the larger blocks, the children had to count the units.

[From *Children Discover Arithmetic* (New York: Harper & Brothers, 1949), pp. 18-20. Reprinted by permission of the author and Harper & Brothers.]

---

[1] Edward L. Thorndike, *The Psychology of Arithmetic* (New York: The Macmillan Company, 1924), 3.

But after each block had been given an individual color, the children instantly recognized each block-individual from one to ten. The psychologists were the only ones who were troubled by the colors; the children never were.

When I give the first lecture in a new course, I may remember the girl in the red jumper. As soon as I get to know her personal characteristics, I recognize her even in green. The color helped me to identify her when she was still unknown to me. The association with the red jumper is easily forgotten, since the color is peripheral and not part of her inner nature. In the same way, the yellow color makes the 5-block an individual which the child easily recognizes long before he knows its name. In twenty years of teaching, I have never known a child to exclaim "five" when confronted with yellow objects.

A few weeks ago I tried a crucial experiment. An empty Counting Board was to be filled with single cubes. I threw 4 yellow cubes on the table, asking where they would fit. Marcia (4 years old) formed a row with the yellow cubes, looked at the grooves in the board, and pointed to the 4-groove. "They are 4 and go in here!" In number and color the cubes looked very much like the 5-block; nevertheless, she did not even think of trying the 5-groove.

Once more I tested the colors to see if they misled the children. I had a new set of blocks made with different color-matches. The children were amused but not fooled. Although red is the usual color of our 6-block, they did not try the new red block in the sixth place. They saw that it was the size of a 10, and so they measured all the new blocks in the Number Track and were eager to find their proper names.

COLOR AS AN AID IN TEACHING CONCEPTS

Leland H. Erickson

In this article the writer has suggested that color can be used to a good advantage in helping certain children gain additional insight and meaning in the more abstract or "mathematical" phase of arithmetic instruction. It has been suggested that all children do not respond the same to various methods and devices and that this method will not be equally effective

[From "Color as an Aid in Teaching Concepts," *The Arithmetic Teacher*, V (February, 1958), pp. 10-14. Reprinted by permission of the author and *The Arithmetic Teacher*.]

with all children. In some instances it may be helpful and in other teaching situations it may be of much lesser value. Many teachers can undoubtedly use color more advantageously than has been done in the past in the teaching of arithmetic.

A limited number of specific examples illustrating the uses of color in arithmetic instruction have been included in this article. Many more opportunities for using color will be found as arithmetic is taught in classrooms. It is again stressed that the basic aspects of arithmetic instruction should not be neglected. The use of color should only be additional reenforcement and supplementation. The use of concrete devices, sensory equipment, and experiences in functional problem situations should not be neglected. They should come first. The writer is suggesting that the use of color might open up another avenue of approach in an effort to help some children gain insight and understanding in arithmetic.

BRITISH TEACHERS' REACTIONS TO THE CUISENAIRE-GATTEGNO MATERIALS (THE COLOR ROD APPROACH TO ARITHMETIC)

Charles F. Howard

During the fall of 1956 a study was made of the Cuisenaire-Gattegno color approach to arithmetic as it was used by several teachers in infant and junior schools in the area of London, England. The purpose of the study was to secure the teachers' reactions as to the effectiveness of the approach under everyday classroom conditions.

During the study, twenty-two classes were observed using the materials, and thirty-one teachers using the color approach were interviewed. A number of classroom demonstrations by Dr. Gattegno were also observed.

The materials used in the Cuisenaire-Gattegno approach consisted principally of a large number of rectangular rods, varying in length from one to ten centimeters, and colored so that certain set relationships of number could be demonstrated. The children, individually or in small groups, manipulated these rods in certain ways in order to "discover," or gain insight, into some of the simple but fundamental mathematical concepts that un-

[From "British Teachers' Reactions to the Cuisenaire-Gattegno Materials (The Color Rod Approach to Arithmetic)," *The Arithmetic Teacher*, IV (November, 1957), pp. 191-95. Reprinted by permission of the author and *The Arithmetic Teacher*.]

derlie our number system. Certain charts, involving a game element, were used for practice purposes, and formed part of the materials.

The method of using the materials followed a general procedure that was suggested in the teachers' handbook.[1] The principles underlying the procedure are discussed briefly in Gattegno's article, "New Developments in Arithmetic Teaching in Britain." [2]

As will be noted below, some of the questions the teachers were asked during the interviews were selected to determine whether or not any problems arose in professional or public relations due to their experimenting with the use of color in teaching arithmetic, and the remaining questions were selected to determine the teachers' general impressions regarding the effectiveness of the approach and the materials used. The comparatively small number of cases used in the study, and the difficulties that were involved in obtaining a representative sample did not permit a statistical study of the effectiveness of the procedures. It was thought, nevertheless, that the opinions of the teachers concerned would be of interest to others who might contemplate experimenting with the Cuisenaire-Gattegno materials.

The following seventeen questions were asked of each teacher during the interviews. A comment on the teacher's replies follows each question.

QUESTION 1. *Do the children usually seem to enjoy the color approach to arithmetic?*

To this question, every teacher interviewed answered in the affirmative and without hesitation. Evidently they were quite convinced of the general interest of the children in the procedure. During the classroom observations it was noted that the children manipulated the materials with zest and a high degree of interest. This was noticeable at all age levels and may account, to some extent, for the children's success with the procedure.

QUESTION 2. *Are there some pupils who seem to show very little interest?*

The usual reaction of the teachers to this question was to state promptly that there were some children who showed much less interest than others. Answers to further questions on this point indicated that these were usually the slower pupils, and that the procedure, rather than the materials, should be modified for these pupils. Probably further experiments should be conducted to determine the most effective procedure for working with slow learning children.

---

[1] G. Cuisenaire and C. Gattegno. *Numbers in Colour, A New Method of Teaching Arithmetic in Primary Schools* (2nd ed.; London: William Heinemann Ltd., 1953).

[2] C. Gattegno. "New Developments in Arithmetic Teaching in Britain," *The Arithmetic Teacher*, III (April, 1956), 85-89.

QUESTION 3. *To what factors do you attribute the children's interest in the color approach?*

The six answers received most frequently, in the order of their frequency, were as follows:

1. The children's interest in manipulating objects
2. The color appeal of the material
3. The various challenging situations presented by the materials
4. The children's curiosity
5. The clarification of certain arithmetical processes in the children's minds
6. The play element involved in using the material

The variety of replies indicated that a many-sided appeal seemed to lie in the use of the material. The fifth most frequently given answer, "The clarification of certain arithmetical processes in the children's minds," seemed significant in the light of other studies that have shown that increasing the understanding of arithmetic will strengthen the retention of learning.[3]

QUESTION 4. *What insights into arithmetic do children appear to gain readily from using the material?*

The seven answers received most often, in order of their frequency, were as follows:

1. The children see numbers as wholes
2. A better understanding of fractions
3. A better understanding of division
4. A better understanding of multiplication
5. A better understanding of large numbers
6. The concept of equivalence
7. The concept of volume

The answers showed that the teachers were impressed by the fact that their pupils grasped some of the more difficult concepts of elementary arithmetic more easily than had been expected.

The most frequently given answer, "Children see numbers as wholes," and the sixth most frequently given answer, "The concept of equivalence," may have been prompted by the emphasis given to these aspects of arithmetic by the teachers' handbook on the use of the materials. These answers are significant also in the light of Piaget's conclusions that these concepts

---

[3] Charles F. Howard. "Three Methods of Teaching Arithmetic," *California Journal of Educational Research,* I (January, 1950), 25-29; Russell E. Alkire. "An Experimental Study of the Value of a Meaningful Approach to the Operation of Division with Common Fractions," Master's thesis, Claremont College, Claremont, California, 1949.

are among the most important in the early stages of grasping the meaning of number.[4] The meaning of fractions, and the process of division and multiplication, answers 3 and 4, were probably made more understandable to the children by the nature of the colored rods themselves and by the procedure recommended for their manipulation. The charts, which formed part of the materials, and lent a game element to memorizing the basic multiplication and division facts, possibly strengthened the pupils' use of the multiplication and division process.

The fifth most frequently received answer, "A better understanding of large numbers," was probably prompted by the emphasis given to grasping the meaning of large numbers through "doubling," which was a procedure recommended in the handbook.

"The concept of volume," the seventh most frequently received answer, may have been a by-product of working with the three dimensional material. Piaget reported that the lack of ability to think in terms of three dimensional material was one of the causes of difficulty during early arithmetical learning.[5]

The writer felt that the concept of proportion was also being developed by the children, as he noted during his observations that they often used elementary ideas of proportion when solving their problems by manipulating the materials, and that the nature of the material lent itself to solving problems through the use of proportion.

QUESTION 5. *Where does the use of numerals come into your plan?*

This question was included because the procedure recommended in the handbook permitted young children, in the first stages of using colored rods, to identify the quantities they were manipulating by color names such as "black," "pink," and so on, rather than by numerals. This did not mean that "black" would stand for "seven" or that any color would "stand for" a number. It meant that at first the child could identify the quantities he was manipulating by such statements as, "Two yellow rods are as long as one orange rod."

The answers to the fifth question, "Where does the use of numerals come into your plan?" indicated that the teachers encouraged the children to use numerals quite early and as they found a need for recording their answers. The use of numerals thus increased gradually as the children grasped the meaning, and as more difficult problems were attempted. The attention of the children was at all times directed primarily to the rela-

---

[4] Jean Piaget. *The Child's Conception of Number* (London: Routledge and Kegan Paul, Ltd., 1952), chap. 1.
[5] *Ibid.*

tionships of the quantities themselves rather than to the names of the quantities, i.e. the numerals.

QUESTION 6. *Do the children experience difficulty in transferring their number ideas to social situations involving arithmetic?*

This question was included because the procedure recommended seemed to put the principal emphasis on the understanding of the number system rather than upon the use of numbers in social situations.

The answers indicated that the teachers were unable to estimate the extent to which children's work with the material carried over to social situations. In all the cases interviewed, the children were being given some practice in the social applications of arithmetic in addition to using the materials. Consequently the teachers were unable to estimate the extent to which each type of experience contributed to the total learning. Unless further experimentation indicated otherwise, it is probably desirable for a teacher to continue to emphasize the social applications of arithmetic along with the use of the Cuisenaire-Gattegno material.

QUESTION 7. *Apart from the use of the Cuisenaire-Gattegno material, what other arithmetical experiences do you give your pupils?*

The answers varied considerably among teachers of different grade levels. As was noted above, all teachers included arithmetical experiences other than those furnished by the material. The social uses of arithmetic, particularly those where money calculations were involved, were emphasized for the older pupils. Counting experiences were most frequently mentioned for the younger children.

QUESTION 8. *What amount of time do you give to arithmetic instruction?*

The answers showed that the teachers usually devoted from thirty to forty-five minutes daily to some type of arithmetic instruction. There was no definite proportion of time regularly assigned for the use of the Cuisenaire-Gattegno material, although, with the exception of the practice charts, the material was used more for developing new concepts than for reviews or practice work. The material was often used by the children individually during study periods. The self-correcting aspects of the material made it useful in this respect.

QUESTION 9. *How do you group pupils for instruction?*

The answers showed that, with few exceptions, the teachers had the whole class work together as one group for part of the arithmetic period, and then they had the pupils work in smaller groups, according to their ability, for the remainder of the period. The teachers stated that differences in the pupils' abilities could often be detected quite readily by observing how they manipulated the material in solving their problems during the time they were working in small groups.

QUESTION 10. *Can the pupils work profitably with the materials and without the teacher's direct help for periods of from twenty to thirty minutes?*

The answers were all in the affirmative, although the answers to further questions indicated that the brighter pupils could work alone profitably for longer periods of time than could the slower pupils.

QUESTION 11. *How many pupils can work effectively with one set of colored rods?*

The answers showed that the number was determined by both the age of the pupils and the arithmetical step being studied, but that from two to six pupils usually worked with one box of colored rods and in one group.

QUESTION 12. *How do you evaluate your pupils' progress in arithmetic?*

The teachers of the lower grades usually answered that they evaluated the pupils' work by observing them manipulating the materials, and by examining their written work. The teachers in the upper grades reported that their evaluations were based largely upon the examination of written work.

QUESTION 13. *Have you noted any advantages or disadvantages in using the materials and procedures apart from the mathematical aspect of the work?*

The advantages mentioned by the teachers could be summed up under two points as follows:

1. Some gains in confidence with which pupils attempted new problems were noted. These gains were reported to be more noticeable in the bright pupils.

2. A very favorable opportunity was afforded the teacher for noting and evaluating personality traits of the children, such as persistence, independence, initiative, and so on, as the manipulation of the material afforded a variety of challenging situations of many degrees of difficulty.

No disadvantages were reported by the teachers.

QUESTION 14. *What are the parents' reactions to your use of the colored material in teaching arithmetic?*

Most of the teachers had no evidence of the parents' reactions. No teacher reported unfavorable reactions. Favorable reactions ranged from

"Parents very interested" to "Parents approve when they see the children working."

QUESTION 15. *How do the teachers who have not used the material themselves react to your use of it?*
Many of the teachers had no evidence on this point. Replies ranged from "A neutral attitude" to "Interested."

QUESTION 16. *Is a course needed by teachers in order for them to use the material effectively, or are the procedures explained sufficiently in the teachers' manual?*
The majority of the teachers felt that a course was needed. A minority felt that although a course was not necessary it would be very helpful. It was noted that all the teachers interviewed had had some type of course in the use of the color approach.

QUESTION 17. *Have you any general comments you would like to make about the Cuisenaire-Gattegno approach?*
A wide range of responses, all favorable to the approach, showed that the teachers, without exception, were convinced that the approach held considerable promise. The reply, "Very helpful for bright pupils" was repeated in various ways. Replies to the effect that a teacher should not use the approach until he felt he understood its purpose and was familiar with the procedures were often expressed.

Some general conclusions of the writer, drawn from the results of the interviews and from his observation of classroom activities and demonstrations, were as follows:

1. The Cuisenaire-Gattegno color approach to arithmetic has been used by experienced teachers to their satisfaction. There was general agreement that the approach was valuable and held promise for future development through experimentation.

2. While some benefits were available for slower pupils, the average and brighter pupils seemed to benefit particularly by the teachers' use of the approach.

3. The consensus of opinion of the teachers interviewed was that certain mathematical concepts that are not usually developed easily in children by current approaches to arithmetic were facilitated considerably by the use of the material in the recommended manner.

4. At present the Cuisenaire-Gattegno approach holds considerable promise as a supplement to current methods, and further studies should be made to evaluate its effectiveness and to develop the procedures.

THE USE OF CRUTCHES IN TEACHING ARITHMETIC

John R. Clark

A crutch is a support or aid, for temporary use, to provide security for the user. With the help of an arithmetic crutch the pupil is expected to learn more effectively, to secure better understanding and to acquire increased facility in working with numbers.

We cannot think intelligently about the uses of crutches in arithmetic without awareness of the nature of arithmetic learning. Arithmetic learning is a composite or integration of reasoning, concepts, and techniques (skills). Our chief concern is that the pupil learn to reason, to solve problems, to be resourceful in quantitative thinking. But one cannot reason without the concepts of combining, separating, and comparing. And most problems significant to pupils require numerical answers, calling for the performance of one or more of the fundamental operations.

Many teachers are distressed by the "counting-on-the-finger" crutch. To find the sum of 7 and 4 the "finger counter" looks at one after another of four fingers and thinks eight, nine, ten, eleven. The pupil properly uses the concept of addition as "counting on," but does so immaturely. He has not learned a more mature way of thinking to find the sum, such as:

1. breaking up or separating the four into two and two, making it likely that he can think seven and two more are nine and two more are eleven, or

2. seven and four are as many as ten and one, or

3. four and seven are four and four (eight) and three (eleven).

Thus finger counting indicates inadequate growth or *immaturity in thinking*. Experience in counting by groups, as well as by ones, was not adequately provided. Pupils abandon finger counting as soon as they learn better (more economical) ways of thinking. Practice on the ways of thinking in 1, 2 and 3 helps the pupils learn to recall immediately, without the use of crutches or other intermediate steps in thinking, that the sum of seven and four is eleven.

[From "The Use of Crutches in Teaching Arithmetic," *The Arithmetic Teacher*, I (October, 1954), pp. 6-10. Reprinted by permission of the author and *The Arithmetic Teacher*.]

Levels of Types of Crutches

One further consideration of the nature of learning is essential. Pupils in any age group vary greatly in ability to reason, to get meanings and to manage the techniques of computation. In no third grade (eight-year-old group) will all pupils have reached the same level of maturity in dealing with a system of abstractions such as is arithmetic. To find the number of 4-cent balloons one can buy with 48 cents a pupil might proceed as follows, depending upon the level of arithmetic maturity he may have reached:

Pupil A (immature): Obtain 48 pennies, arrange them in groups of four pennies each, and count the number of groups. If pennies are not available, he may use discs, or a bead frame. In any case the pupil manipulates things (uses crutches).

Pupil B (more mature): Ten balloons would cost 10 × 4 cents or 40 cents. With 8 cents more I could buy 2 balloons; in all, 12 balloons. (No crutch necessary.)

Pupil C (very mature): "I divide 48 cents by 4 cents, this way:

$$\overset{\text{12 times}}{4 \text{ cents} \overline{\smash{\big)}48 \text{ cents.}}}$$

I can get 12 balloons." He is able correctly to use a standard division algorism. He needs neither crutches, nor intermediate "thinking steps."

Obviously Pupil A is not yet ready (arithmetically mature enough) to work on the level of Pupil C. Thus the kind of support or aid or crutch needed is determined by the arithmetic level of maturity of the learner. It is obvious that Pupil C would be bored and retarded if his teacher required him to work on the maturity level of Pupil A. Equally obvious, too, Pupil A should be encouraged to learn to think with symbols, so that he will be able to outgrow or be liberated from his dependence upon things (his crutches).

The teacher selects the crutch which best helps the pupil or the class build a concept or understand a technique. To build the concept of equivalent fractions she finds "fraction-cut-outs" or "pie charts" effective. With their pie-charts the pupils *discover* that 2 fourths will exactly cover half, that 1 third is as large as 2 sixths, that 6 eighths can be exchanged for 3 fourths, etc. (The pupil also uses the charts to *demonstrate* his generalizations.)

During their use of the charts the teacher will be encouraging the pupils to think about equivalence of fractions without the aid of the charts. She guides them to make larger generalizations such as:

"If you double the number of pieces (the numerator) you make the size of the pieces (the denominator) half as large, i.e. $\frac{3}{4} = \frac{6}{8}$.

"If you make the number of pieces half as large you double the size of the pieces, i.e. $\frac{6}{8} = \frac{3}{4}$."

And finally, "A fraction may be converted into an equivalent fraction by multiplying (or dividing) its numerator and denominator by the same number."

All pupils should start with the cut-outs. Some children will soon be able to replace them with one of the generalizations just stated. Others, less mature or with less aptitude, may need to work with the cut-outs for months.

Other illustrations of physical, concrete, manipulative type of crutches are pocket charts, ten-tens frames, abaci, and measuring instruments. We shall not discuss these further, except to point out that they are effective in building concepts of base, place value, combining, separating and comparison. Their selection and use should be determined by the needs of the maturity level of the learner. The teacher has to learn when they are needed, and when they can be discarded. Use them when they support or aid the learner; throw them away when they retard the growth of the learner.

In summary, we like crutches which contribute to understanding. We dislike crutches which are tricky, which do not foster thinking or record thinking. We are as much concerned with learning to dispense with them as we are with having them. We know that a given crutch may be too immature for some pupils in a class and too mature for others. We know that only the teacher is able to guide the learner in his selection and subsequent rejection of a particular crutch. We deplore the fact that many teachers are over-sold, and many under-sold, on crutches.

Our own thinking about crutches was significantly influenced by McConnell's chapter in the Sixteenth Yearbook of the National Council of Teachers of Mathematics, in which he states:

> Repeating the final form of a response from the very beginning may actually encourage the habituation of immature procedures and seriously impede necessary growth.
>
> Intermediate steps such as the use of the "crutch" in subtraction, aid the learner both to understand the process and to compute accurately. With proper guidance, these temporary reactions may be expected to give way to more direct responses in later stages of learning.

Should we use crutches? Yes! Choose crtuches which are appropriate to the arithmetic maturity level of the learner. And equally important, discontinue them when further use limits or arrests growth in arithmetic.

THE USE OF RHYTHM
IN THE TEACHING OF ARITHMETIC

Paul R. Neureiter

... the main theme of the article ... is the use of rhythm in the teaching of arithmetic. The purpose was to establish a solid theoretical basis for the practical suggestions that are to follow. As we examine current practices in arithmetic, we find that the concrete experiences in vogue today are mostly of a visual nature. They require the viewing and possibly manipulating of blocks, dots, toy money, tokens, and the like. The sense of hearing is not utilized as a conveyor of direct number experiences and plays its role only after the symbolic state has been reached. Yet, thinking of music with its strong mathematical elements, one might expect that the acoustic sense, possibly combined with the sense of kinesthesia or muscle sense, would be a very willing and creative reactor to numerical stimulation. That it is so, and that the children would enjoy its being so, we shall try to demonstrate in definite procedures recommended for grades 1 through 5.

Whether we organize an arithmetical rhythm band or not, the simplest way to reach the ear with number experiences is by some kind of percussion. Outlining a rhythmic program for the elementary schools from the angle of music, Grace Fielder says: "According to some authorities, percussion is preferred because it is pure rhythm, uncomplicated by melody and harmony.... Children enjoy experimenting with percussion accompaniment and they should have these experiences." [1] We can clap hands, tap fingers, knock knuckles, rap sticks, strike keys, jingle bells, tingle triangles, rattle castanets, shake tambourines, clash cymbals, sound gongs, beat drums, gourds or tom-toms. If we want to go outside the field of percussion, we can whistle, toot, or honk. Any succession of clearly distinguishable sounds that serves to tally numbers will do, so long as it does not disturb the peace of the school community.

In kindergarten and first grade, both cardinal (one, two, three, etc.)

[From "Strike Up Your Arithmetic Band," *The Arithmetic Teacher*, IV (March, 1957), pp. 64-9. Reprinted by permission of the author and *The Arithmetic Teacher*.]

---

[1] Grace Fielder. *The Rhythmic Program for Elementary Schools* (St. Louis: Mosby Co., 1952), 67.

and ordinal (first, second, etc.) numbers can be studied acoustically. Every cardinal number word has its corresponding sound picture, and this one in turn can be related to a written numeral. As we go beyond the smallest numbers, the need for rhythm and accent will arise; and this means that the first steps toward addition and multiplication are being taken. Accents help to identify groups of strokes; and as these groups are combined, addition is represented. When the groups are equal, they lead to the pattern of multiplication. Jazz rhythm is counting by two's, the waltz furnishes an example of counting by three's, and the drill sergeant's bark, "cadence count," is counting by four's. In order to get the idea of ordinals across, we assign rank numbers to the children and have them make their strokes in the correct sequence; or we let them put the accent on a certain stroke in a succession, the first stroke or the second, and so on.

Subtraction grows out of the demonstration of more or less. Have two children rap out different numbers and let the rest decide, "which is more and which is less?" and "what is the difference between the two counts?" or "how many more are needed to go from the smaller to the larger number?" The basic subtraction situation represented by the take-away idea cannot be shown with sound, however. And that makes a lesson of broader philosophical implications that Johnny Brighteye may catch if it is properly explained to him. Sounds follow each other in time, not in space as marks on paper; and, being irreversible since time flows only in one direction, there is no taking away of sounds that have been produced. An important moral lesson! What has been done cannot be undone. We have to face the responsibilities for our actions.

Multiplication really becomes a study in rhythms. The group to be added repeatedly is like the measure in a piece of music, and you may place the down-beat on the first or last number of the group. The measure corresponds to the multiplicand, and the number of times it is taken makes the multiplier. Unfortunately, because factors are interchangeable by the commutative law of multiplication, we have lost a sense for the nice distinction between multiplicand and multiplier. Yet it is essential to a full understanding of the multiplication pattern. The multiplicand is the concrete grouping, directly perceived by the senses, whereas the multiplier is abstract, always involving a mental operation. With sound signals it is possible to handle the multipliers 1 and 0 meaningfully and do it more convincingly than with visual groups. 1 times 4 is one measure of four beats, and 0 times 4 is no measure at all; so the results should not be in doubt. But when you try to show the same thing with something visual like 0 times 4 marbles, some people will always argue that the marbles are there in plain sight and the result, therefore, cannot be zero.

The demonstration of division, being an inverse operation, runs into the same difficulty as take-away subtraction because of the irreversibility of anything happening in the dimension of time rather than space. We cannot start with the product, which has become the dividend, and work backward to the multiplicand or multiplier, which is now called quotient. A multiplication cannot be undone after it has been entrusted to the flux of time. It is true, the measurement concept of division can be illustrated by a question such as "how many measures of three beats are there in twelve beats?" But the actual sound experience is no different from the one used for multiplication. However, the partition concept of division is demonstrable, not in the form of "divided by a number," but in the form of "a fraction of a number." Have one child strike four times or four measures, and ask the second to strike half as much. The ratio concept of division, too, lends itself perfectly to acoustical representation. We simply strike two different numbers, one being a multiple of the other. Whereas in subtraction we ask, "how much more," we inquire here, "how many times more?" The parallel between the comparison aspects of subtraction and division is close. When we wish to demonstrate the difference between an even and uneven division, we can do it very neatly. An even division is the sound pattern that ends at the end of the measure whereas an uneven division puts in some extra beat or beats. In fact, if the class does arithmetic in a rhythm band, there will be laughter-provoking cases of some children not quitting on time and thereby failing to come out evenly with the others.

Accent the Base Ten

The broad pattern encompassing our decimal system can be concretized in sound. While with manipulative aids we bundle units into tens, tens into hundreds and so forth, we can distinguish the orders of the number system by an appropriate gradation of sound. Let one boy make the "big noise," say with a drum or cymbals, and let one stroke of it signal a bundle of ten. Then we will hear the steady, more delicate beat of the units, and every time a ten is reached, there goes the big bang from the tens' place. We can have an acoustic symbol for every two-digit number; and when the hundred is reached, let there be a sonorous gong announcing the completion of the first century mark. And so we may go on as high as we wish. By this method an appreciation may be created for the real sizes of large numbers in the thousands and millions. The youngsters will be amazed to learn that in order to rap out one billion at the rate of one number per second a person would have to spend over 31 years in uninterrupted tapping, so huge is the billion; and even a million would require over 11 days.

One of the most productive devices in present-day arithmetic teaching is the use of the decades as support points for mental computation. For example, in higher-decade addition, such as 37 plus 8, one may think, first, of completing the 40-decade by taking 3 of the 8 and, then, of adding 5 to 40 to obtain 45. It is of great practical value in more than one way to know instantly how much any number lacks to the next higher decade. With sound it can be easily shown by designating two different types of signals for the original number and the second one it takes to complete the decade. For instance, starting with 7 we need 3 to make a ten. Let the 7 be rapped out with sticks on the desk and the 3 be added with hand claps to complete one ten. With proper modifications this can be carried into the higher decades. The decades should also be used as pegs over which to hang the multiples of the times tables. As the multiples are struck out rhythmically, now and then the big bang of a decade will coincide with a stroke and signalize the completion of a decade. Only in the multiplication of the two's and five's will there be coincidences between the completed multiple and a decade. All the other multiples (below 10 times) come out uneven with the decades.

Psychological Implications

To conclude the subject, we shall look into its psychological implications. Arithmetic learning through rhythmically measured sound opens up a new area of mathematical experience for the children. This means a powerful reenforcement of the other experiences provided in the mathematics classroom. Not only the sense of hearing is involved, but what is even more important, the kinesthetic sense. Through rhythm, numbers enter into the *musculature*. Here is a type of experience that is often deeper than one furnished by the eye. "Rhythm is an attribute of man's nature and the foundation of all art," writes Ann Driver.[2] Greek philosophers defined rhythm as order of movement. It is a feature of human nature common to all races. Primitive music is almost wholly rhythm. The popularity of the dance attests the love of rhythm in the most advanced stage of civilization. There is another peculiar feature in this conveying of number through sound. It is a concrete experience, with all the pleasure and motivation that the concrete always has over the semi-concrete and abstract, and yet it can have the quality of symbols. For instance, in the Morse code the transmitted sounds are symbols for letters. The concrete, semi-concrete and symbolic stages of arithmetic learning coincide.

---

[2] Ann Driver. *Music and Movement* (Oxford University Press, 1938).

As we broaden the base of experience from which quantitative patterns are derived, we are promoting another objective of mathematics instruction, namely, the recognition that the abstract patterns we are studying are truly general. To be able to identify a certain pattern in all kinds of different guises is the mark of the good mathematician; and when we shift from the eye to the ear as our conveyor of mathematical experience, we are certainly becoming aware of the pervasive character of our general patterns.

DO DEVICES HELP?

Vincent J. Glennon

The past six years have witnessed a substantial interest in the role of devices in the teaching of arithmetic. This interest is reflected in the number and variety of studies cited here.

The place of television in arithmetic teaching was investigated in two studies. Himmler [1] studied the use of television in the teaching of reading, arithmetic and French on the fifth grade level. He found almost no observable difference between TV teaching and regular classroom teaching. Also, of the three subjects he found reading to be more teachable via TV than arithmetic or French.

In a different approach Strueve [2] found that television provided a worthwhile means for bringing into the classroom and to the regular teacher the superior teaching of another person. Also, the use of TV teaching, she found, gives the regular teacher more opportunity to help individual children.

Caswell [3] presented a timely, penetrating discussion of the issues involved in teaching by television and offered this caution:

[From *What Does Research Say About Arithmetic* (Washington, D.C.: Association for Supervision and Curriculum Development, 1958), pp. 47-9. Reprinted by permission of the author and the Association for Supervision and Curriculum Development.]

---

[1] Merwin L. Himmler. *An Analysis and Evaluation of a Television Demonstration of the Teaching of Fifth-Grade Reading, Arithmetic, and French.* Doctor's Dissertation. Pittsburgh: The University of Pittsburgh, 1957.

[2] Helen K. Strueve. "Arithmetic via Television: I. A Report of the Pittsburgh Experiment," *The Arithmetic Teacher,* III (October, 1956), 162-64.

[3] Hollis L. Caswell. "The Curriculum Viewpoint on Educational Television," *Educational Leadership,* XV (November, 1957), 107-15.

It will be desirable, in my judgment, as we test the uses to which television may be put, to check persistently against the broader criterion of the kind of curriculum and teaching we wish in our schools and colleges. If some things have to be done for the sake of expediency under the pressure of numbers, let us at least recognize when we compromise with desirable standards of teaching and let us be sure that we are not sold an approach to teaching which will save dollars but will impoverish the educational opportunities of American children and youth.

The use of tachistoscopic presentation of basic facts was studied by two investigators with essentially the same results. Phillips [4] compared two tachistoscopic methods with one workbook method of practice in the learning of certain multiplication and division facts on the fourth grade level. Bebb [5] was concerned with multiplication facts. In each case the tachistoscopic method was novel and interesting but did not bring about any more learning than ordinary practice methods using workbooks.

Schott [6] recognized a place for calculating machines but also offered a caution:

> The research in the use of calculating machines to date is not yet complete enough to be conclusive. There is grave danger that schools will, in their desperation to improve their arithmetic programs, spend large sums of money for these machines without waiting for sound evidence as to the value of such tools of learning.

.   .   .   .

Anderson [7] carried out a controlled study to determine what effect, if any, the use of a kit of 16 visual-tactual devices would have on the learning of a unit involving areas, volumes, and the Pythagorean relationship on the eighth grade level. The teaching group of 541 students comprising 18 subgroups was divided into nine experimental groups using the visual-tactual devices and nine control groups not using the devices. Conclusions were based on data gathered from 105 matched pairs of girls and 99 matched pairs of boys. The experimental groups scored higher than the control groups but the differences were not statistically significant. An

[4] Clarence Phillips. "Background and Mathematical Achievement of Elementary Education Students in Arithmetic for Teachers," *School Science and Mathematics,* LIII (January, 1953), 48-52.

[5] Randall R. Bebb. *Comparison of Tachistoscopic Presentation with a Classroom Method of Teaching the Basic Multiplication Facts.* Doctor's Dissertation. Iowa City: State University of Iowa, 1952.

[6] Andrew F. Schott. "New Tools, Methods for Their Use, and a New Curriculum in Arithmetic," *The Arithmetic Teacher,* IV (November, 1957), 204-9.

[7] George R. Anderson. "Visual-Tactual Devices and Their Efficacy," *The Arithmetic Teacher,* IV (November, 1957), 196-203.

interesting finding was that among the pupils with the lowest mental ages those in the control group scored slightly higher than those in the experimental group. Again, the differences were not statistically significant. Also, the use of the visual-tactual devices had no significant effect on attitude toward arithmetic.

BIBLIOGRAPHY

Association for Childhood Education. "Recommended Equipment and Supplies for Nursery, Kindergarten, Primary and Intermediate Schools." Washington D. C.: The Association, 1949.

Banks, J. Houston. *Learning and Teaching Arithmetic.* Boston: Allyn and Bacon, Inc., 1959.

Bartram, Chester E. "An Analysis and Synthesis of Research Relating to Selected Areas in the Teaching of Arithmetic," *Dissertation Abstracts*, Ph.D. Dissertation, Ohio State University, University Microfilms, Ann Arbor, 1956.

Beck, L. L. "Report on the Use of Calculators," *The Arithmetic Teacher*, VII (February, 1960), 103.

Brownell, William A., and G. Hendricksen. "How Children Learn Information, Concepts and Generalizations," *Learning and Instruction*, National Society for the Study of Education, Forty-ninth Yearbook. Chicago: University of Chicago Press, 1950, Part I, 92-128.

Brueckner, Leo J. *Improving the Arithmetic Program.* New York: Appleton-Century-Crofts, Inc., 1957, 93-4.

Bulletin of the University of the State of New York, *Mathematics for Boys and Girls*, No. 1385. Albany, New York: 1950, 24-5.

Callum, Myles. "You Can Count on the Abacus," *Pageant*, XV (November, 1959).

Carroll, L. Grace. "A Mathematics Classroom Becomes a Laboratory," *Multi-Sensory Aids in the Teaching of Mathematics*, National Council of Teachers of Mathematics, Eighteenth Yearbook (1945). Washington, D. C.: The Council, 16-29.

Clark, Caroline H. "Improvised Aids in Teaching Arithmetic," *Notes for the Arithmetic Teacher 1—10.* New York: World Book Company, 1957, 21, 23.

Clark, J. R., and L. K. Eads. *Guiding Arithmetic Learning.* New York: World Book Company, 1954, 14-5, 21-2.

———. "The Use of Crutches in Teaching Arithmetic," *The Arithmetic Teacher*, I (October, 1954), 6-10.

Dale, Edgar. *Audio-Visual Methods in Teaching* (Rev. ed.). New York: The Dryden Press, 1954.

Deans, Edwina. *Arithmetic: Children Use It!* Washington, D. C.: Association for Childhood Education, 1954.

Drasin, Lillian Packer. "The Forgotten Level: Semi-Concrete Materials—A Valuable Bridge," *The Arithmetic Teacher*, IV (November, 1957), 211-13.

Dunfee, Maxine. "If Arithmetic Is to Be Real," *Journal of Education,* CXXXVI (January, 1954).

Eagle, Edwin. "Don't Let That Inverted Divisor Become Mysterious," *The Arithmetic Teacher,* I (October, 1954), 15-7.

Eidson, William P. "The Role of Instructional Aids in Arithmetic Education," *Dissertation Abstracts,* Doctoral Dissertation, Ohio State University, University Microfilms, Ann Arbor, 1956.

Erickson, Leland H. "Color as an Aid in Teaching Concepts," *The Arithmetic Teacher,* V (February, 1958), 10-4.

Fehr, Howard F., George McMeen, and Max Sobel. "Using Hand-Operated Computing Machines in Learning Arithmetic," *The Arithmetic Teacher,* III (October, 1956), 145-50.

Flewelling, Robert W. "The Abacus as an Arithmetic Teaching Device," *The Arithmetic Teacher,* II (November, 1955), 107-11.

Fox, Marion W. "Manipulative Materials in Intermediate Grades," *The Arithmetic Teacher,* V (April, 1958), 140-42.

Gattegno, C. "New Developments in Arithmetic Teaching in Britain," *The Arithmetic Teacher,* III (April, 1956), 85-9.

Glennon, Vincent J. *What Does Research Say About Arithmetic?* Washington, D. C.: Association for Supervision and Curriculum Development, 1958, 47-9.

Gramlich, Jay J. "Slide Rules for the Upper Elementary Grades," *The Arithmetic Teacher,* V (February, 1958), 29-33.

Grossnickle, F. E., and L. J. Brueckner. *Discovering Meanings in Arithmetic.* New York: Holt, Rinehart & Winston, Inc., 1959, 63-4, 76-9, 367-68.

———, C. Junge, and W. Metzner. "Instructional Materials for Teaching Arithmetic," *The Teaching of Arithmetic,* National Society for the Study of Education, Fiftieth Yearbook (1951). Chicago: The University of Chicago Press, Part II, 155-85.

———. *The Use of Multi-Sensory Aids in Developing Arithmetical Meanings,* Supplementary Educational Monographs. Chicago: University of Chicago Press, 1948.

———, and William Metzner. *The Use of Visual Aids in Teaching Arithmetic.* New York: Rambler Press, 1950.

Hansdoerffer, William H. "Introducing Our Numbering System in the Primary Grades," *The Arithmetic Teacher,* IV (March, 1957), 61-3.

Harding, Lowry W. *Arithmetic for Child Development.* Dubuque: W. C. Brown Company Publishers, 1959, 189-90.

Hartung, Maurice L. "Motivation for Education in Mathematics," *The Learning of Mathematics, Its Theory and Practice,* National Council of Teachers of Mathematics, Twenty-first Yearbook (1953). Washington, D. C.: The Council, 52-5.

Hertz, Pauline. "Manipulative Devices in Lower Grades," *The Arithmetic Teacher,* IV (November, 1957), 214-16.

Hickerson, J. A. *Guiding Children's Arithmetic Experiences.* Englewood Cliffs, N. J.: Prentice-Hall, Inc., 1952, 35-6, 56, 60.

Hildreth, Gertrude. "Principles of Learning Applied to Arithmetic," *The Arithmetic Teacher,* I (October, 1954), 1-5.

Holinger, Dorothy. "Helping the Non-Learner in Grade One," *The Arithmetic Teacher,* V (February, 1958), 15-24.

Howard, Charles F. "British Teachers' Reactions to the Cuisenaire-Gattegno Materials (The Color Rod Approach to Arithmetic)," *The Arithmetic Teacher,* IV (November, 1957), 191-95.

Hudson, Floreine Herron. *A Study of an Enrichment Program in Arithmetic for Children in the Fourth Grade,* Doctoral Dissertation. Auburn: Alabama Polytechnic Institute, 1957.

Koenker, Robert H. "The 'Crutch' in Arithmetic," *The Elementary School Journal,* LVIII (January, 1958), 232-33.

Lansdown, Brenda C. "From Cake to Cancellation," *The Arithmetic Teacher,* IV (April, 1957), 136-37.

Lorenzen, Robert. *The Value of Certain Commercial Aids and Devices in Fourth Grade Arithmetic Instruction,* Doctoral Dissertation. Lawrence: University of Kansas, 1955.

MacRae, Irene. "A Place-Value Game for First Graders," *The Arithmetic Teacher,* I (October, 1954), 18-20.

McSwain, E. T., and Ralph J. Cooke. *Understanding and Teaching Arithmetic in the Elementary School.* New York: Holt, Rinehart & Winston, Inc., 1958.

Marks, L. J., C. R. Purdy, and L. B. Kinney. *Teaching Arithmetic for Understanding.* New York: McGraw-Hill Book Company, 1958, 53-4.

Mayer, Louise A. "The Scarbacus or Scarsdale Abacus," *The Arithmetic Teacher,* II (December, 1955), 159.

Morton, Robert L. *Teaching Children Arithmetic.* Morristown, N. J.: Silver Burdett Company, 1953, 52-4.

Moser, Harold E. "Growth in Number Thinking," *Notes for the Arithmetic Teacher 1—10.* New York: World Book Company, 1957, 24-6.

Motyka, Agnes L. "Learning Aids in Arithmetic," *National Elementary Principal,* XXX (October, 1950), 34-41.

Neureiter, Paul R. "Strike Up Your Arithmetic Band," *The Arithmetic Teacher,* IV (March, 1957), 64-9.

National Society for the Study of Education. "Audio-Visual Materials of Instruction," Forty-eighth Yearbook (1949). Chicago: University of Chicago Press, Part I.

Piaget, Jean. *The Child's Conception of Number.* London: Routledge and Paul, International Library of Psychology, Philosophy and Scientific Method, 1952.

Reddell, Wm. D., and M. Vere DeVault. "In-service Research in Arithmetic Teaching Aids," *The Arithmetic Teacher,* VII (May, 1960), 243-47.

Sauble, Irene. "Enrichment of the Arithmetic Course: Utilizing Supplementary Materials and Devices," *Arithmetic in General Education,* National Council of Teachers of Mathematics, Sixteenth Yearbook (1941). Washington, D.C.: The Council, 157-95.

Schaughency, Mildred D. "Teaching Arithmetic with Calculators," *The Arithmetic Teacher,* II (February, 1955), 21-2.

Schott, Andrew F. "New Tools, Methods for Their Uses, and a New Curriculum in Arithmetic," *The Arithmetic Teacher,* IV (November, 1957), 204-9.

Sifton, Edith. "Multi-Sensory Aids: Some Theory and a Few Practices," *Multi-Sensory Aids in the Teaching of Mathematics,* National Council of Teachers of Mathematics, Eighteenth Yearbook (1945). Washington, D.C.: The Council, 1-15.

Sole, David. "The Use of Materials in the Teaching of Arithmetic," *Dissertation Abstracts,* Doctoral Dissertation, Columbia University, New York, University Microfilms, Ann Arbor, 1957.

Spencer, Peter L., and Marguerite Brydegaard. *Building Mathematical Concepts in the Elementary School.* New York: Holt, Rinehart & Winston, Inc., 1952, 5, 30.

Spitzer, Herbert F. *Practical Classroom Procedures for Enriching Arithmetic.* St. Louis: Webster Publishing Company, 1956.

Stern, Catherine. *Children Discover Arithmetic.* New York: Harper & Brothers, 1949, 3-4, 18-20.

———. "The Concrete Devices of Structural Arithmetic," *The Arithmetic Teacher,* V (April, 1948), 119-30.

Sueltz, Ben A. "Counting Devices and Their Uses," *The Arithmetic Teacher,* I (February, 1954), 25-30.

Swenson, Esther J. "Arithmetic for Pre-School and Primary-Grade Children," *The Teaching of Arithmetic,* National Society for the Study of Education, Fiftieth Yearbook (1951). Chicago: University of Chicago Press, Part II, 72-3.

Syer, Henry W. "Sensory Learning Applied to Mathematics," *The Learning of Mathematics, Its Theory and Practice,* National Council of Teachers of Mathematics, Twenty-first Yearbook (1953). Washington, D.C.: The Council, 99-155.

Thomson, Alice P. "Evaluation by Observation—Grade 3," *The Arithmetic Teacher,* III (April, 1956), 104-8.

Thorndike, Edward L. *The Psychology of Arithmetic.* New York: The Macmillan Company, 1924.

Tuttle, Ruth H. "Counters? Yes, But....," *The Arithmetic Teacher,* V (February, 1958), 25-8.

U.S. Office of Education. "Types of Experiences Children Should Have," *Education Briefs.* Washington, D.C.: United States Office of Education, Federal Security Agency, 1947.

Van Engen, Henry. "The Formation of Concepts," National Council of Teachers of Mathematics, Twenty-first Yearbook (1953). Washington, D.C.: The Council, 69-98.

Van Engen, Henry. "Which Way Arithmetic?" *The Arithmetic Teacher*, II (December, 1955), 131-40.

———. "One, Two, Button My Shoe," *The Arithmetic Teacher*, I (October, 1954), 18-20.

Weaver, Fred. "Materials for Manipulation," *Journal of Education*, CXXXVI (October, 1953), 8-10, 31.

West, R. L., Charles E. Greene, and W. A. Brownell. "The Arithmetic Curriculum," National Society for the Study of Education, Twenty-ninth Yearbook (1930). Chicago: University of Chicago Press, 65-142.

Wheat, Harry Grove. *How to Teach Arithmetic*. Evanston, Illinois: Row, Peterson and Company, 1956, 16-7.

Williams, Catherine M. "The Function of Charts in the Arithmetic Program," *The Arithmetic Teacher*, II (October, 1955), 72-6.

———. "Portable Mathematics Laboratory for In-Service Teacher Education," *Educational Research Bulletin*, XXXIX (April, 1960), 85-91, 103.

———. "Arithmetic Learning in an Experience Curriculum," *Educational Research Bulletin*, XXVIII (September, 1949), 154-62.

Worchester, D. A. "Memory by Visual and by Auditory Presentation," *Journal of Educational Psychology*, XVI (1925), 18-27.

X   UTILIZATION OF THE MATHEMATICS TEXTBOOK AND WORKBOOK

J. Fred Weaver, Boston University

INTRODUCTION

BIBLIOGRAPHY

398

INTRODUCTION

The textbook and the workbook serve important and necessary functions in connection with programs of instruction in elementary-school mathematics. Each has a unique contribution to make toward effective teaching and learning. The textbook and the workbook represent our most commonly used instructional materials in elementary-school mathematics. Unfortunately, however, they also often represent the least well used and most abused of our instructional materials.

Why does this latter condition prevail? Just two of the numerous reasons will be cited here. For one thing, there are honest differences of professional opinion regarding the roles that should be played by textbooks and workbooks in elementary-school mathematics instruction. The readings selected for this chapter were chosen deliberately, in part, to reflect some of these significant differences of opinion. For another thing, teachers often fail to recognize and understand clearly the very important difference between a program of instruction and the materials of instruction in elementary-school mathematics. Pupils' textbooks and workbooks are materials of instruction which often affect or determine the program of instruction to a greater or lesser degree. Trouble is inevitable when anyone uses pupils' textbooks and workbooks as though they were the instructional program rather than in their properly intended way: as instructional materials which, along with other kinds of instructional materials, aid materially in implementing the program of instruction. It is hoped that the readings in this chapter will help to clarify this important distinction.

Special mention should be made here of the selection from *The Elementary School Journal* which constitutes Part I of this chapter. This reading is intended to serve as a broad framework of reference regarding the relation of the textbook, in general, to the elementary-school curriculum as a whole. Subsequent parts of the chapter, which deal with textbooks and workbooks in elementary-school mathematics in particular, should be studied and interpreted in light of the points of view developed in the general background reading in Part I.

There are at least two things from this editor's standpoint that are not covered adequately by the professional literature on textbooks and workbooks. One of these has to do with textbooks and workbooks as instructional materials in the mathematics program for Grades 1 and 2. The other is the very crucial role of the Teacher's Guide or Teacher's Manual or Teacher's Edition of the pupil's textbook or worktext. Some brief comment here regarding each of these seems appropriate.

Generally speaking, we often think of textbooks as being hard-backed publications in which the pupil does no writing. Similarly, we often think of workbooks as being soft-backed publications in which the pupil is expected to write in one way or another. Although there obviously are more fundamental differences in purpose and function between textbooks and workbooks, this distinction is true almost without exception in mathematics textbooks and workbooks for Grades 3-6 (or 3-8). In only a few instances, however, does the same distinction prevail in such instructional materials for Grades 1-2.

From the standpoint of their physical form, most instructional materials of the textbook/workbook variety that are used in connection with the mathematics program in Grades 1-2 are classified as workbooks. But from the standpoint of intent and purpose, instructional materials of this variety often serve the function of a textbook rather than a workbook. For this reason the term worktext currently is used quite frequently as a preferable expression for this kind of instructional material.

It is important for all concerned to recognize and understand the somewhat unique role served by a "true" worktext in connection with the mathematics program for Grades 1-2. In all too many cases the modern worktext unfortunately is confused with the older type of workbook that was little, if any, more than a "drill book." As a consequence the importance and significance of the mathematics worktext in Grades 1-2 often is either underestimated or not sensed at all. The same is true to some extent of separately published mathematics textbooks and companion workbooks for Grades 1-2. Just as the function of the text-book and workbook must be understood clearly if these instructional materials are to be used to best advantage, so must the nature and purpose of the worktext be understood clearly if it is to be used most advantageously. Our professional literature could, with profit, devote more attention to the nature and place of the textbook, the workbook, and the worktext in relation to effective programs of mathematics instruction in Grades 1-2.

Elementary-school mathematics textbooks, workbooks, and worktexts have changed significantly in most instances during the past 25 years. Much more significant changes have occurred in a much shorter time, however, in regard to the Teacher's Manual or Teacher's Guide or Teacher's Edition of the pupils' textbook or worktext. These publications for the teacher have grown from simple "answer books" to truly professional books on the teaching and learning of mathematics at their respective grade levels. Today's manuals or guides do more than offer help for the teacher with her classroom use of the pupil's textbook or worktext or workbook per se. These teacher's editions serve to give her extensive background, suggestion, and guidance in implementing virtually all phases of her program of mathematics instruction.

Unfortunately, however, many teachers fail to use their manuals or guides to the fullest and best advantage. This may be due, at least in part, to the fact that teachers often do not sense the true value of various portions of these publications. Undoubtedly other reasons are also involved. The findings from Folsom's recent significant investigation merit thoughtful consideration in this connection.[1] Teachers clearly need help in using the wealth of material in manuals or guides to greater advantage. This will result in improved use of pupil's textbooks, worktexts, and workbooks, and in an improved mathematics program as a whole.

This editorial introduction should not be concluded without mention of an emerging development in elementary-school mathematics text materials.

---

[1] Mary O'Hearn Folsom, "A Study of Manual Material in the Field of Arithmetic," Unpublished Doctor's Dissertation, Iowa City: State University of Iowa, 1958.

Within the past few years several projects or groups, backed by financial support from organizations such as the Carnegie Corporation and the National Science Foundation, have been engaged in the development of a "modernized" mathematics curriculum at the secondary-school level (Grades 7-12). Outstanding among these are the Commission on Mathematics of the College Entrance Examination Board, the University of Illinois Committee on School Mathematics (UICSM), the School Mathematics Study Group (SMSG), and the University of Maryland Mathematics Project: Junior High School (UMMaP). The last three of these projects or groups—UICSM, SMGS, and UMMaP—have developed textbook materials of one form or another in connection with their work.

More recently similar types of activity have been initiated at the elementary-school level. The University of Illinois Arithmetic Project started its work in the fall of 1958. The School Mathematics Study Group extended the scope of its work downward to the elementary-school grades during 1959-60. Text materials—at least units or booklets, if not full textbooks—undoubtedly will be developed in connection with the activities of these projects or groups. Instructional materials from sources such as these, as well as the familiar text materials from commercial publishers, must be taken into account seriously in the future whenever we consider the nature and role of textbooks, worktexts, workbooks, and the like in the mathematics program of the elementary school.

PART I: TEXTBOOKS AND THE ELEMENTARY-SCHOOL CURRICULUM

PATTERNS OF TEXTBOOK USE—
KEY TO CURRICULUM DEVELOPMENT

Herbert C. Rudman

In one popularly held analysis of curriculum types, curriculums are divided into three categories: those curriculums that are based solely upon organized bodies of knowledge (subject-centered); those based upon, and circumscribed by, the interests of children (child-centered); those based upon the everyday aspects of living (society-centered). If this analysis is valid, it would appear that the overwhelming majority of curriculums in the United States are of the subject-centered variety. One author has estimated that 96 per cent of all curriculums are of this type.[1] Timmerman concluded, after investigating the curriculums of state-approved secondary schools of a southern state, that 74 per cent of these schools selected learning experiences from organized bodies of knowledge. Although his study also pointed out that 48 per cent of these schools were investigating possible alternatives, the significant point here is the high percentage of subject-oriented schools.[2]

And this situation is a national one. This is a disturbing fact. Why are subject-centered curriculums so prevalent? Is our analysis of curriculum types in error? Do administrators and teachers fail to see the significance of curriculums based on experiences other than formal academic subjects? An answer to this enigma lies in the approach we have taken to the description and analysis of existing practices. Our approach is hypothetical; our descriptions and analyses are based upon hypothetical curriculum models.

Researchers attempting to locate these hypothetical curriculum models

[From "Patterns of Textbook Use—Key to Curriculum Development," *The Elementary School Journal*, LVI (April, 1956), pp. 401-6. Reprinted by permission of the author and *The Elementary School Journal*.]

---

[1] Lee J. Cronbach (ed.), *Text Materials in Modern Education* (Champaign, Illinois: University of Illinois Press, 1955), 207.

[2] Gene W. Timmerman, "Differentiated Curriculum Designs, Especially with Reference to Curriculum Practices in the High Schools of South Carolina," Unpublished Doctor's Dissertation, University of South Carolina, 1956.

have had difficulty because these models do not exist in actual practice. Actual practice finds teachers using textbooks in arithmetic, textbooks in social studies, textbooks in a multitude of content areas. Small wonder, then, that investigators searching for hypothetical curriculum models can find only the subject-centered curriculum. The prevalent basic instructional material is the textbook, and the textbook is organized around formal subjects.

Patterns of Textbook Use

Textbooks have been designed to perform one function—supplying a course of study. The textbook is most effective when used for this purpose. In a recent publication of the American Textbook Publishers Institute, the role of the textbook as a course of study is clearly defined:

> Development of a course of study and the selection of textbooks should go hand in hand. It is an unwise and wasteful procedure to attempt to develop a course of study without regard to instructional materials available. One sure way to have a course of study which will actually function in the classroom is to (*a*) define the broad objectives of the program, (*b*) prepare a tentative draft of the course of study, (*c*) select the teaching materials that come closest to meeting the broad objectives in the tentative draft, (*d*) after textbooks are selected, revise the tentative draft in terms of the materials (texts) adapted (parenthetical insertions are those of this author).[3]

Since the textbook is clearly the course of study in the classroom, the text, to be used most efficiently, must be utilized to its fullest extent. This would mean that the textbook is responsible for three essential elements of any curriculum: (1) the content of the curriculum, (2) the skills to be learned, and (3) the sequence in which these skills are to be learned.

The way we use textbooks determines, to a large extent, the actual curriculum of a school and of a classroom unit. It would seem that the way to discuss, to analyze, and to evaluate curriculums would be to make a careful analysis of how textbooks are used. An analysis of the patterns of textbook use yields at least three major emphases: (1) using the textbook as the determiner of content, skills, and the sequence in which skills are to be learned; (2) using the textbook as the determiner of skills to be learned and the sequence in which they are to be learned; (3) using no texts but employing "trade" books and other instructional materials.

---

[3] *Textbooks Are Indispensable!* (New York: American Textbook Publishers Institute, 1956).

PATTERN 1. *The Textbook as a Determiner of Content, Skills, and Sequence*

Children can profit greatly when a teacher uses a textbook as it was designed to be used. The text gives teachers and pupils ample opportunity to use other instructional materials, such as field trips, movies, filmstrips, recordings, and the like, and it encourages pupils and teachers to seek elsewhere further detailed information not to be found in the textbook being used.

A casual observer in a classroom which utilized the text to its fullest extent would be unable to distinguish the learning activities in this classroom from the learning activities in any other classroom using a different basis for the determination of the curriculum being explored. Children might well be engaged in committee work, individual library research, devising skits, painting murals, and a host of other activities which we have come to associate with good learning.

The distinguishing feature here lies in the source of these activities, the content studied, the skills practiced, and the like. The interests of children supplement the content areas to be explored, but it is the textbook itself which determines what the children will study. The use of the textbook in this manner presents the pupils with the kinds of skills that they will practice at this stage of their intellectual development. It also determines the sequence in which these skills will be studied. As an example, the prime reason for having children study percentages in Grade VII rather than in Grade IV is the fact that arithmetic textbooks do not introduce percentages until approximately the seventh-grade level. It is not that youngsters have no interest in the use of percentages before they reach Grade VII; fourth-grade boys are discussing batting averages of baseball players long before they have a clear concept of what these batting averages actually represent.

The use of the textbook as a determiner of content, skills, and sequence has several distinct advantages. If used to its fullest extent, the textbook supplies both teachers and pupils with a complete course of study. It gives both teachers and pupils great leeway in the use of many of the educational inventions of the past several decades, such as committee organization, audio-visual aids, use of resource people. It also presents teachers and pupils with a logical development of skills and gives a total over-all development through the twelve years of public education.

The basic disadvantage of this use of the textbook is that it limits the intellectual development of children by predetermining the content to be studied. It does not take into account the differences in the communities in which children live. It fails to consider the dynamic nature of the world we live in and thus sets the boundaries of children's intellectual horizons and forces them to follow the paths drawn for them by textbook authors.

PATTERN 2. *Using the Textbook as a Determiner of Skills to Be Learned and the Sequence in Which They Will Be Learned*

A second approach to the use of the textbooks, and a modification of the preceding approach, is to use the textbook only to determine the skills to be practiced and the sequence in which they will be practiced. The content itself is derived from the interests of the children, the nature of the community in which they reside, and the demands of the society in which they live. By studying the contents of texts in language, reading, and arithmetic, the teacher can determine the skills called for at a particular grade level. These skills are listed, and the teacher's responsibility is to see that these skills are used during the course of the academic year. The content in which these skills are practiced is determined by the interests held by the children in a particular classroom, by the nature of the community in which they live, and by the demands made upon individuals by the larger community in which they live—the world.

As pointed out by various authors in the 1956-57 issues of the *National Elementary Principal*,[3] the dynamic nature of the world in which we live has posed new problems for mankind and has emphasized certain of the old problems. The concerns of the adult population cannot be totally ignored in developing a set of learning experiences for children, for these concerns affect the nature of the smaller communities in which children reside and these, in turn, have a direct positive relationship to the immediate interests of chidren.

Using the complex of these three factors—total social conditions, the nature of the local community, and children's concerns—the teacher determines the content to be studied at a particular grade level. The complexity of the skills to be practiced, the nature of the skills to be practiced, and the total sequential development of skills are determined by the textbooks. In schools following this pattern, only the teacher uses the textbook. The children use other printed materials—trade books, pamphlets, brochures, and many materials of instruction of a non-verbal nature.

One advantage of this pattern of textbook use is that it gears the curriculum to the needs of the children and to the needs of their community. By retaining the use of the text as determiner of skills, the sequential development of skills through the twelve years of public school will be retained; yet the content which children will study will be related more

---

[3] Harold J. McNally, "What Shall We Teach and How?" *National Elementary Principal*, XXXVI (May, 1957), 6-11. McNally gives a good summarization of the series of articles.

closely to the interests of children and less to the predetermined content of textbook authors. It is conceivable that, within a given community, two schools would have curriculums that would differ greatly, although the skills to be learned and to be practiced would remain constant throughout the school system. It would thus be possible to develop a curriculum that would adhere more closely to the psychological advantages of deriving content from the needs of the pupils and still retain the logical development of skill subjects.

One disadvantage of this type of use of a textbook is the danger that children's interests may become the major basis for determining the curriculum. Since interests are learned, we are interested in those things with which we are most familiar. If we circumscribe the entire curriculum by the familiar, we leave little room for the unfamiliar. Unless, therefore, a balance is maintained between the three sources of content to be studied —interests, the local community, and the total society—the curriculum might well be as limiting as if the content were derived solely from the textbook.

Another disadvantage lies in the demands made upon a teacher. This pattern of textbook use assumes a relatively high order of sophistication on the part of the teacher. It calls for a teacher who is familiar with the nature of the society in which he lives; it calls for a teacher who is aware of the environmental backgrounds of his pupils; and it calls for a teacher who possesses the necessary insights and sensitivities for understanding the needs and the interests of the children in his class.

PATTERN 3. *Using Trade Books [4] and Other Instructional Materials in the Place of Textbooks*

This pattern represents an extreme departure from the use of text materials. The content, the skills to be practiced, and the sequence in which they are to be practiced would be determined solely by the interests of children, the nature of the community, and societal demands.

Although there would be no textbooks, a vast amount of printed material would be used: free and inexpensive materials published by major industries and businesses, chambers of commerce, and trade unions; pamphlets published by various governmental agencies; and trade books. Schools utilizing this pattern would devote the money normally allotted to the purchase of textbooks to the purchase of trade books and other instructional materials.

---

[4] Publishing companies have come to apply the term "trade" books to printed materials of a topical nature, such as books about stars, birds, famous people, and so on. Trade books are available at all reading levels and on a wide variety of topics. They have found their way into public and school libraries and from there to classrooms.

Of necessity, a description of this pattern of use of materials must be couched in normative terms. The available research data give little evidence that many schools are at present engaged in using materials of instruction in this manner. The uniqueness in this approach lies in the fact that there is almost no predetermining of the content, skills, or sequence in which skills and content are to be learned. Patterns 1 and 2 predetermined one or more of these factors for the learner. Pattern 3 does not.

An advantage of this pattern of use of textbooks stems from the psychological concept that children learn most effectively those things which hold the greatest meaning to them. The content to be studied and the various skills to be practiced are determined solely on the basis of the needs and interests of the pupils and upon the environmental demands made upon the children. The sequential development of these skills would be closely related to the demands made upon children. Referring back to the example dealing with the batting averages of famous baseball players, it is quite conceivable that fractions and percentages could be taught much earlier in the elementary school than they are now taught and could be taught with a great deal of meaning. On the other hand, it is equally conceivable that some other concepts, for example, the concepts of profit and loss or of compound interest, could be delayed until they became meaningful to the learner.

Teachers employing this pattern of textbook use would have great opportunities to develop the skills closely associated with the understanding of man's physical and natural environment. The skills associated with social education could be more meaningfully brought into play. All in all, this pattern would give the pupil the greatest opportunity to explore meaningfully his environment and to broaden his intellectual horizons.

This third pattern of textbook use has some serious inherent disadvantages. It takes a secure, confident, skillful teacher to work with boys and girls in this manner. This pattern calls for a widely read teacher, a person who has more than a nodding acquaintance with contemporary affairs. It demands a teacher who can foresee the consequences of the activities undertaken by his pupils. The only guide for the teacher in this situation is his best professional judgment concerning the content to be studied. Unless the teacher has great skill, this situation might be as limiting upon the development of new interests as Pattern 1 would be. Care would need to be exercised to see that children did not study and restudy only those topics which were familiar to them.

Another disadvantage is derived from the present organization of school systems. This pattern demands a high degree of co-ordination between the supervisory staff, the administrative staff, and teachers. As administrators and teachers report the demands made upon them and the time consumed in meeting these demands, it appears that few schools are now organized so that administrators, supervisors, and teachers would be free to implement such a pattern.

Curriculum Change Through the Use of Textbooks

Implied in the normative discussions of curriculum theorists has been the notion that present curricular experiences can be described, analyzed, and evaluated by employing hypothetical curriculum models. These models carry many labels, but all center on one or more of three major themes: subject-centered, child-centered, and society-centered curriculums. Yet, when existing practices are surveyed, it becomes difficult to locate any but the subject-centered curriculum model. Although these curriculum models are convenient vehicles for the normative projections of what theorists would like to see, they are hardly accurate yardsticks by which to measure existing curriculums.

As has been pointed out, the textbook as the basic instructional material is subject-oriented and is designed to be the basic course of study. Since this is the case, a more fruitful approach to analyzing and modifying curriculums lies in modifying the use of the textbook. Although this writer holds value judgments concerning the relative worth of each of the three patterns of textbook use described, these value judgments are subject to scrutiny by research and need not be aired at this point.

Nevertheless the basis for any curriculum modification is a dissatisfaction with existing practice. When change is considered, it is invariably held that there is something better than that which presently exists. This applies with equal validity to textbook use. The important concept central to change in this case, however, is the relationship between a pattern of textbook use and its effect upon the complex of experiences in which the learner is engaged—the curriculum.

Literally thousands of man-hours are expended annually by teachers and administrators who, in good faith, work together in committees to modify or change existing curriculums. But so long as these committees develop curriculums without relating them to the manner in which textbooks will be used, so long will they run the risk of engaging in fruitless endeavor.

In Summary

Pattern 1 is a reflection of the majority of existing curriculums. It determines most of the learning experiences in which children are engaged. Pattern 2 suggests that the textbook is a guide for a sequential development of the twelve-year program, but that it is limited exclusively to that use. Pattern 3 is a modification of Pattern 2, for it implies not only that children will abandon the use of textbooks, but that teachers will do so as well. It implies that the basis for the sequential development of the twelve-year program lies less in an arbitrarily determined organization than it does in the complex of interests, community, and societal demands.

The major purpose of this article has been to trace the relationship that exists between textbook use and curriculum development. Like other analyses, this one is subject to criticism. It may be construed as an over-simplification of a complex problem. Perhaps it is. But the point to under-score is that the key to effective curriculum change lies less in the hypo-thetical logic of curriculum theorists than in the practice of those who must use existing instructional materials.

Practitioners interested in modifying curriculums cannot wait for the publishing companies to provide other types of textbooks—textbooks that are not organized as basic courses of study. They need a blueprint that is geared to the realities of school situations. The textbook and its use supplies a key to a realistic appraisal and modification of existing educational practices.

PART II: THE NATURE, PLACE, AND USE OF TEXTBOOKS

HISTORICAL SKETCH OF THE AMERICAN ARITHMETIC TEXTBOOK

Charles H. Schutter and Richard L. Spreckelmeyer

Early American arithmetics were concisely written and contained diffi-cult and comprehensive material. Still, they considered the background of the child who was to study them, as the following excerpts from a text, written by the famous teacher-author Warren Colburn and used from the 1820's on, will reveal:

[From *Teaching the Third R: A Comparative Study of American and European Textbooks in Arithmetic* (Washington, D.C., Council for Basic Education, 1959), pp. 36-41. Reprinted by permission of the authors and the Council for Basic Education.]

Harry is starting for school; his father's two dogs are frisking and barking before him. . . . A short distance off three other boys are waiting for Harry to come along. . . .

The four boys have nearly reached farmer Brown's house, by the side of which they count one, two, three, four, five pretty trees. . . .
Just beyond the house there are six hens eating. . . .[1]

The Colburn text was in use for well over a half-century, a revised edition being published by the Houghton Mifflin Company in 1884.

Single-volume texts, later expanded to three-volume series, were in vogue during the nineteenth century. These contained surprisingly few pages, and concisely presented a variety of topics. For example, the Chicago edition of *Robinson's Complete Arithmetic*, published in 1874, contained the work of the entire eight grades in one 484-page volume. Some of the topics in this text included foreign money (chiefly English), geometric solids, longitude and time, partial payments, square and cube root, extensive work in ratio and proportion, involution and evolution (exponents and root extraction), and the metric system. Additional topics taught in the 1870's included lumber measure, U.S. currency exchange equivalent for European money, "equation of payments," and "gauging." These and other items make this interesting old arithmetic read like an historical document.

In addition to the topics named, work with the fundamental processes, fractions, denominate numbers, and thought problems was quite difficult when compared with present-day expectations of students in arithmetic. Some problems from texts of this period illustrate this greater difficulty:

How many days will 21 men require to dig a ditch 80 feet long, 3 feet wide, and 8 feet deep, if 7 men can dig a ditch 60 feet long, 8 feet wide, and 6 feet deep, in 12 days? (Answer: $2\frac{2}{3}$ days.)

The hour and minute hand of a clock are together at 12 midnight. When will they be exactly together the third time after this? (Answer: 3 hours, 16 minutes, $21\frac{9}{11}$ seconds later.)

A ship starts at noon and sails west, 9 hours, going 16 minutes and 40 seconds an hour, what time will it be at the place reached? (Answer: 10 minutes before 9.)

Two globes, each 5 inches in diameter, and 2 cubes, each 5 inches in length, were melted into one cube; how long was the side of this cube? (Answer: 7.24+ inches.)

---

[1] Warren Colburn, *Intellectual Arithmetic: Upon the Induction Method of Instruction* (Boston: Houghton Mifflin Company, 1884).

The last of these problems, it might be noted, requires the extraction of a cube root.

By the 1890's, the single-volume text was being replaced by two- or three-volume sets. Content was still concisely presented; an arithmetic for the upper half of the elementary school contained some 250 pages of challenging material. Separate texts for each grade were still rarely found. However, the series *Arithmetic by Grades* [2] (1895) did supply a separate text for each grade. This series thus provides the generally accepted grade placement of the topics taught then. The content of the series follows:

Grade 1: Addition, subtraction, multiplication, division combinations possible in the whole numbers up to and including 20; the fractions $\frac{1}{2}$ and $\frac{1}{5}$; and three-step exercises like $19 - 8 - 9 = ?$ (The author stated that study of the book could be completed in less than one year.)

Grade 2: Addition by carrying and subtraction involving borrowing along with the multiplication and division tables through the 10's. (Its topical content is much like that of texts currently in use in second year programs in Europe.)

Grade 3: The whole numbers to 1,000,000; fractional parts of integers, e.g. $\frac{7}{10}$ of 90 and $\frac{4}{9}$ of 54; multiplication and division by two-digit integers; and various problems dealing with weights and measures.

Grade 4: Extension of the whole numbers; common fractions to twelfths; decimal fractions to thousandths; measurement, and denominate numbers; business transactions; multiplication and division of the common fractions; addition for all numbers. (These topics are comparable to those of current 5th and 6th grade texts of the United States.)

Grade 5: Completion of the processes with decimals; applications to business problems; and several other topics and processes.

Grade 6: Percentage; the metric system; denominate numbers reviewed and extended; mensuration; lumber measure; business transactions and accounts; surface areas; and the English money system.

Grade 7: Continued work in percentage: profit and loss; commission; insurance; taxes; duties on imports; business accounts; geometrical exercises; and ratio and proportion.

Grade 8: Algebra—including linear equations and linear systems such as:

$$\frac{3x}{4} + \frac{x}{4} = 16 \qquad \text{and} \qquad \frac{x}{2} - \frac{y}{4} = 18$$

$$\frac{x}{3} + y = 6$$

---

[2] John T. Prince, *Arithmetic by Grades* (Boston: Ginn & Company, 1895).

respectively; exponents and root extraction (involution and evolution); formulas; exercises in geometry; and miscellaneous problems (from arithmetic).

The author of this series comments that explanations for many processes are provided only in the teachers' manuals "so as not to give too much help to the student."

By 1915, the use of a separate text for each grade level from the third through eighth was well established. The work for grades 1 and 2 was left for the teacher to supply on an informal basis. A second trend, now termed "watering down" of the curriculum, was beginning to emerge under the guise of emphasis on the "practical value" of the subject.

The 1915 edition of *Everyday Arithmetic* [3] was among the first to use considerable work in connection with games, play activities, and other less serious aspects of school life. In the preface, the authors condemned the doctrine of mental discipline while calling for a more "vital kind of teaching..." in reference to practical uses of arithmetic. Hints, often a complete analysis of the problem, accompanied some exercises, as shown in the following example from their fourth grade text:

> After earning $5.50 Robert spent $2.50 for a football and 75 cents for a baseball glove. How much of his money did he have left?
> 1. The problem asks for the amount of money that Robert had left from $5.50 after spending $2.50 for a football and 75 cents for a baseball glove.
> 2. The amount of money left equals the difference between $5.50 and the sum of $2.50 and 75 cents. To find the amount, add $2.50 and 75 cents, and then subtract their sum from $5.50.

Arithmetics of the 1920's continued the policy of lowering standards at the expense of failing to challenge the student's intellect. The *Standard Service Arithmetic* [4] published in 1926 claimed to appeal to the child in his own language, stating in its preface:

> Numerous silent-reading exercises in chatty and informal language... (are intended for child appeal).

Wordiness and extensive use of space were defended:

> While expansive treatment increases bulk, it increases also the rate of progress, and it decreases both the difficulties and the failures.... Every

---

[3] Franklin Hoyt, and Harriet Peet, *Everyday Arithmetic* (Boston: Houghton Mifflin Company, 1915).

[4] F. B. Knight, J. W. Studebaker, and G. M. Ruch, *Standard Service Arithmetic* (Chicago: Scott, Foresman and Company, 1926).

effort was made to present a complete problem with its full social setting, rather than to offer mere verbalized examples.

The extent of the "watering down" in the later grades is easily seen when one considers the content of *Arithmetic by Grades* in comparison with the following comments from a publisher's brochure in 1932 [5]:

> With the completion of the sixth grade, pupils have (learned) all of the fundamental processes with whole numbers, fractions, and decimals. Finding the square root of a number is the only process yet to be taught.
>
> Hence the books for the seventh and eighth grades devote most of their space to informational arithmetic. Some of the units of these grades are: Thrift and Economy; Building, Heating and Lighting Our Homes; Home and Community Problems; Reading the Daily News; Interpreting Statistical Graphs; Geometry in Nature and Design; Practical Applications of Geometry; The Formula; Our Great Industries; Building Up Capital; Investing Capital; Protecting Losses Through Insurance; Civic Enterprises and Taxes; The Use of the Equation; Ratio and Proportion Used in Indirect Measurements; etc.[6]

A significant relaxation of the American arithmetic curriculum took place during the 1930's. The nature of this easing is described in the preface to one of the arithmetics in the *Child Life Arithmetics* published in 1935 [7]:

> . . . authors and publishers alike have placed the demands of childhood in the front rank of preferred claims. This will explain the upward gradation [8] of certain topics; the more gradual development of complex computational processes; the use of relatively small units with their pleasant variety, page unity, and short attention span; the meticulous elimination of unnecessary vocabulary and other linguistic difficulties; the systematic introduction of arithmetical processes in social situations familiar to children; the painstaking attempt to make the necessary technical terms meaningful on their first occurrence; the carefully phrased explanations of new arithmetical processes . . . the wide variety of projects, whose interest appeal is enhanced by hundreds of beautiful illustrations in three and four colors. . . .

---

[5] John C. Stone, "What's New in Arithmetic?" published in connection with *Unit Mastery Arithmetics*, by Stone *et al.*, Benjamin H. Sanborn and Company, 1932.

[6] Most of this work is a *review*, by simple application of previously taught skills. It is a maintenance program. Few additional skills in arithmetic or advanced topics from other branches of mathematics are included.

[7] Clifford Wood, Frederick S. Breed, and James R. Overman, *Child Life Arithmetics* (Chicago: Lyons and Carnahan, 1935).

[8] Upward graduation means, e.g., that a topic formerly studied in the fourth grade is now presented in the fifth or a later grade.

Particular examples of the "... upward gradation of ... major topics ..."
are evidenced by changes listed below.

Division by two-digit numbers was "stepped up" from the third grade to
the fourth grade.

Multiplications and divisions with products or dividends greater than 40
were moved from the third to the fourth grade.

Division problems in which the quotient was a fraction were moved from
the first half to the last half of grade 4.

Multiplication of integers by two- and three-digit multipliers was moved
from the first half of grade 4 to the last half.

Long division was delayed from the fourth to the fifth grade.

Multiplication and division of common fractions (by each other) was delayed from the fifth to the sixth grade.

Percentage was moved from grade 6 to grade 7.

Installment buying was moved from grade 7 to grade 8.

Since the 1930's, changes in textbooks have been minor so far as their
content is concerned. The rates at which cars are supposed to travel, prices
of groceries and hard goods, and social service information have been
revised with the times, and some minor reorganizations have taken place.

Some observations which require little documentation may be cited regarding present-day texts.

An obvious trend concerns the number of pages required to present a
complete course in arithmetic. Early texts presented the topics for several
grades in the number of pages now used for a text for a single grade. This
change may be justified by the realization that, for young students, larger,
well-spaced type aids the development of reading skills. Also, larger numbers of attractive illustrations are included in modern texts than in older
books.

Another change involves the extensive insertion of review exercises
which permeate modern texts.

A change in teaching technique prominent in today's classroom is the
general replacement of oral recitation by written work. This is often accomplished by the use of workbooks which are assigned to pupils for
extra practice. This practice is justifiable when it reinforces recently taught
skills, or develops new ones, but it is often continued to the point of
routine drudgery, especially for the brighter child, who soon becomes
bored and transfers his boredom from the particular problems at hand to
arithmetic and mathematics in general. Later teachers must then apply
extra skill to re-establish his curiosity about and interest in the challenging world of mathematics.

The plan of upward gradation described above seems to have been caused by concern of educators for the slow learner. The detrimental effects of a weakened program upon the brighter (and even the average) child were either not noticed or were ignored. Furthermore the concept of equality of opportunity in a democracy, misinterpreted as identical opportunity, denied the availability of a challenging curriculum to those who were able to progress rapidly. For it was wide acceptance of this fallacious concept which restrained administrators from placing children into sections grouped according to achievement and/or ability. Such plans are certainly feasible, although study is needed to determine methods of identification of children for placement into such groups.

THE RELATION BETWEEN RESEARCH IN ARITHMETIC AND THE CONTENT OF ELEMENTARY ARITHMETIC TEXTBOOKS, 1900-1957

Sister Marie Constance Dooley

The purpose of this study was (1) to note the degree of connection between the recommendations of scholars who carried on scientific investigations in arithmetic and the changes that had been introduced into the content of arithmetic textbooks; (2) to check the recommendations which seemed to have been rejected by authors of textbooks, although presented as substantiated, credible findings based upon scientific investigation; (3) to determine the status of arithmetic research in the curriculum program; and (4) to isolate, if possible, reasons for the gap between recommendations for changes in teaching methods and the application of these recommendations.

The following questions were proposed: (1) Are research recommendations finding their way into textbooks and at what rate? (2) Can reasons be identified to explain the acceptance of some and the non-acceptance of other findings? (3) Are those techniques which have been tried out experimentally and found successful generally recommended? (4) Are

[From "The Relation Between Research in Arithmetic and the Content of Elementary Arithmetic Textbooks, 1900-1957," abstract from the brochure relating to the Sister's final oral examination, February 9, 1959. Reprinted by permission of the author and the University of Southern California.]

any techniques recommended before they have been tried out experimentally? (5) Is there a time pattern which is generally followed?

An over-all review of the available literature on the research studies in elementary arithmetic was made to determine the trends that had developed in content and method since 1900. Two lists were compiled, one with topics which seemed to have been definitely influenced by research recommendations, another containing topics which apparently had not yet been greatly influenced by research. A list of twenty-five topics was compiled from which a national jury of experts chose twelve for this study. A survey was made to locate the research recommendations and critical opinion on each of these twelve topics. This was followed by the examination of 153 series of elementary arithmetic textbooks published in the United States by twenty-nine different publishers between 1900 and 1957.

Conclusions

The effect of research upon the content and methods of arithmetic was found to have been direct and immediate in nine instances.

1. The method of placing the decimal point in the quotient was accepted in 1917, following research recommendations.

2. A slight trend has developed since 1946, when critical opinion reappeared in the literature.

3. Imaginative settings for verbal problems.

4. Elimination of awkward, unrealistic fractions.

5. The use of illustrations as visual aids are applications of research recommendations.

6. The common denominator method is used to introduce the process of division of fractions.

7. Tests are designed to measure concepts.

8. Suggestions for using materials which should contribute to the development of generalizations are being incorporated into textbooks.

9. Authors are cognizant of the fact that the choice between the two usual methods of estimating the true quotient has never been determined by scientific investigation.

In three instances recommendations have been rejected to some degree: (1) The suggested grade placements of long division and of common fractions were not accepted, and modifications were necessary before changes were made in textbooks. (2) Authors have continued to recommend the use of concrete materials in middle and upper grades, even though research data have not been significant. (3) The use of the common denominator method in division of fractions has been limited to introductory use rather than to full development as a method.

Most research in this area has been designed to evaluate practices already in use. Incorporation was found to have been rapid when the recommendations were clear, concise, and exact. Trends took longer to develop when the recommendations were general, intangible, or based upon subjective data. With one exception, the use of concrete materials above the primary grades, recommendations published in yearbooks tended to be applied quickly. Trends were found for all topics in this study.

Implications and Recommendations

This study has shown that authors of textbooks have been aware of and have applied research recommendations, have been selective, and have been influenced by the group approval implied by publication of research in yearbooks. The need for constant re-evaluation has been pointed out and further research recommended, along other lines, to determine the cause of the lag in arithmetic progress.

THE ROLE OF THE TEXTBOOK

Foster E. Grossnickle and Leo J. Brueckner

In most schools, the organization of subject matter is determined by the textbooks. Usually the content is organized on a modified spiral plan. Each grade stresses certain phases of the various branches so as to mark them as the distinctive contribution of a given level of the school. To illustrate, the graded sequence of multiplication of whole numbers given in the Los Angeles course of study for 1957 is as follows:

Grade Three: Concept of adding equal sized groups is developed to find their total, as 2 fives, 2 tens, etc.

Grade Four: All multiplication facts developed and the process of multiplying by one-place numbers.

[From *Discovering Meanings in Arithmetic* (New York: Holt, Rinehart & Winston, Inc., 1959), pp. 49-50, 87. Reprinted by permission of the authors and Holt, Rinehart & Winston, Inc.]

EDITOR'S NOTE: Reference to several other research studies concerned with arithmetic textbooks can be found in sources such as these: Vincent J. Glennon, *What Does Research Say about Arithmetic?* (Rev. ed., ASCD, 1958); and the summaries of research published in *The Arithmetic Teacher* and in the *Review of Educational Research*.

Grade Five: Multiplication by two-place numbers.

Grade Six: Multiplication by three- and four-place numbers.

The course of study obviously calls for a spiral development of this process. With minor variations the textbooks in use follow this same sequence.

Authors of textbooks face the problem of devising an effective way of organizing the content of the subject matter that is usually assigned to the various grades. Practices vary widely in this connection. Some textbooks are organized on an extreme spiral plan, while others are organized in relatively large units of subject matter which have rather long periods of time devoted to them. The following sequence of topics demonstrates the spiral organization of a typical fifth grade textbook:

Chapter 1: A systematic diagnostic review of the subject matter taught in the preceding grades.

Chapter 2: Multiplication by two-place numbers.

Chapter 3: Division by two-place numbers—one figure quotient only. The estimated quotient is the correct quotient in all cases.

Chapter 4: Addition and subtraction of like fractions—no carrying in addition or regrouping in subtraction.

Chapter 5: Division by two-place numbers with up to four figures in the quotient, including zero difficulties.

Chapter 6: Addition and subtraction of like fractions, with carrying in addition and regrouping (borrowing) in subtraction.

Chapter 7: Graphs, drawing to scale; areas.

Chapter 8: Addition and subtraction of halves, fourths, and eighths family.

Chapter 9: Introduction of decimals, including addition and subtraction of tenths and hundredths.

Notice the range of topics covered, the rather extended periods of time that are devoted to each unit of subject matter, and the way in which the treatment of the topics is distributed over the year. In each chapter, there are included systematic sets of mixed practice exercises and groups of verbal problems in which the processes are applied. These maintain skills at a high level. An examination of the content of a group of different textbooks and courses of study will show that the range and sequence of topics varies widely among them at all grade levels. This shows that there is no general agreement as to what the content at the various grade levels should be. The organization and sequence of the subject matter also vary widely, reflecting differences in the judgment of authors as to the optimum arrangement of the materials. It should also be pointed out that a textbook can give only a selection of social applications of general value and interest. The teacher should at all times feel free to supplement the textbook by bringing to the attention of the children local situations in which significant aspects of arithmetic and its application are vital elements.

Textbooks and workbooks contain the most important symbolic materials used in the teaching of arithmetic. A good textbook with its accompanying teachers' manual is an invaluable guide in planning the arithmetic program. It is a source book on methods of teaching arithmetic.

A modern arithmetic textbook is set up as a learner's book. It is well illustrated with functional pictures and illustrations. It contains a carefully arranged systematic step-by-step development of the number processes which are clearly and meaningfully presented. The modern textbook development is geared to the use of exploratory and visual materials. The textbook contains the necessary visualization and simple, adequate explanations of each new step to be learned. Subsequently pupils can refer to them for help when necessary.

The textbook contains an abundance of practice materials to establish and maintain the basic skills in computation and problem solving. The practice materials include exercises to develop skill in reading and interpreting tables, charts, graphs, diagrams, maps, and other kinds of quantitative materials found in general reading and in other areas of the curriculum.

A modern textbook contains many illustrations and problems dealing with everyday social applications of arithmetic that are within the range of interests and needs of most children. It is a source of materials for enriching the work in arithmetic for the more able learners. To assist the teacher in appraising the achievements of the children, the modern textbook provides the necessary testing procedures for evaluating the progress made and for diagnosing and correcting learning difficulties.

TRENDS IN CONSTRUCTION
OF ARITHMETIC TEXTBOOKS

Leo J. Brueckner

An examination of modern arithmetic textbooks reveals the following trends, many of which indicate the desire of authors and publishers to keep textbooks abreast of research and best practices in our schools:

[From *Improving the Arithmetic Program* (New York: Appleton-Century-Crofts, Inc., 1957), p. 101. Reprinted by permission of the author and Appleton-Century-Crofts, Inc.]

1. Contents arranged in light of known facts about their learning difficulty
2. No grade designation for the books to identify them
3. Attractive titles for the books for the different grades
4. Contents provide for two- or three-level program
5. Readiness program for young children
6. Emphasis on meanings and relationships
7. Use of manipulative and visual aids to supplement textbooks
8. Use of functional rather than decorative pictures and illustrations
9. Comprehensive diagnostic testing program
10. Stress on social uses of arithmetic in daily life
11. Consideration of interests of the learners
12. Activities for enriching the work for fast learners
13. Workbooks specifically intended for slow learners
14. Rich, detailed guides for teachers
15. Application of research findings about methods.

THE PLACE OF TEXTBOOKS IN CURRENT PRACTICE

Herbert F. Spitzer

The one most important item on every list of arithmetical instructional materials is the pupil textbook. A textbook for every child has become almost essential equipment for teaching arithmetic in Grades Three through Eight. In fact, many teachers not only rely upon the textbook for determining content and instructional material but also for tests and what little recreational and special motivational material is used in teaching. Such complete dependence on a textbook is not a superior instructional procedure, but it is a very common one. Even the best instructional programs, while not dependent upon a single textbook, make some use of textbooks. Books are probably the cheapest and best source of graded instruction and practice exercises and, of course, books supply a convenient source of material for discussion and study. Having a single convenient (easily handled, stored, used, etc.) piece of instructional equipment with from twenty-five to thirty-five pupils is a point not to be underestimated when a teacher is concerned. For the unskilled teacher, class management is

[From *The Teaching of Arithmetic* (2nd ed.; Boston: Houghton Mifflin Company, 1954), pp. 318-22. Reprinted by permission of the author and the Houghton Mifflin Company.]

easier if a textbook is available than if duplicated exercises, dictated directions and the like are used. Students of arithmetic teaching should therefore give a great deal of attention to the material in pupil books and to ways of using that material.

Weakness of Textbooks and Textbook Instruction

While the preceding paragraph indicated that textbooks are an important piece of instructional equipment, it also suggested that textbooks and textbook instruction possess limitations.

Some of the weaknesses are presented below, not for the purpose of undermining the present important role of textbooks, but in order that the student of arithmetic teaching may devise ways to counteract the possible harm resulting from these weaknesses.

1. Current textbooks because of their very nature use artificial instructional settings. If, for example, an addition situation is being presented, the experience for obvious reasons cannot involve the children in the classroom without at least the addition of new data. In other words, the life situations of the local classroom are not utilized if a textbook is used exclusively.

2. Most current textbooks in beginning new phases of arithmetic emphasize telling and showing as the only means of instruction and rely on the presentation of just the one best method. The sole task of the child is to do as the textbook has shown, a type of learning which is generally considered second-rate, at least, in elementary-school subjects other than arithmetic.

3. Still another weakness of most current textbooks is that the statements of rules and generalizations appear before the pupils have a genuine need for such rules.

4. In general, textbooks do little to develop real learning situations. Consider, for example, the first drill exercises in learning facts and processes. Most books just present them with the suggestion "to do" or "to study." No reason for studying has been provided except that all arithmetic has to be practiced. Even those books which try to develop learning situations are, because of the nature of book presentation, forced to follow a restricted course which hardly allows variation.

5. The majority of textbooks follow a somewhat rigid step-by-step grade placement of topics which results in the presentation of small parts of a topic in widely separated places in a series. For example, in some series, one-figure divisors are presented in one grade, two-figure divisors in the next grade and three-figure divisors in the next grade. Such an arrangement is not conducive to getting across the idea that tens and hun-

dreds are dealt with in much the same manner that ones are. This following of a rigid grade placement of materials also results in the use of examples and problems of much the same relative difficulty, and obviously the level must be determined by what pupils of average or below average quality are able to do. The superior pupil, then, does not find much that is challenging in the textbook material.

6. Since most textbook series fail to develop learning problems, the particular phase of arithmetic presented (actually, the phase to be mastered) is often not clear to the pupils. He may know in general that he is dealing with multiplication, fractions or the like, but will not be able to state just what he is trying to master. Seeing a process in proper context does more to insure its acceptance by the pupils.

7. Partly as a result of the weakness mentioned in the preceding paragraph and partly because many textbooks use a cycle plan of organization, there are no good summary sections in textbooks. For example, after studying multiplication of whole numbers, pupils should find summarization of real value. Learning studies show very clearly that good summaries (1) are a means of identifying and clarifying points not yet understood, and (2) provide an excellent way to retard forgetting. That arithmetic instruction would profit from clarification of hazy points and from better retention of that which has been studied can hardly be questioned.

Suggestions for Improving the Use of Textbooks

One of the best ways to improve the textbook's contribution to instruction is to create situations where the pupils will have a real purpose for turning to the textbook. The following are reasons pupils might have for consulting their books: (a) to see whether or not a procedure developed for multiplying two-figure numbers was the one recommended by the textbook, (b) to find some practice exercises for which a need had been shown, (c) to check the statement of a rule, and (d) to help in the preparation of summary statements about what had been learned in the study of fractions. When pupils have reasons for consulting books, the books are looked on as helpful reference material instead of as a source of seemingly endless exercises which the teacher assigns.

If the teaching procedures recommended in this book are followed, different teaching procedures will be substituted for many of the sections in textbooks where new phases of arithmetic are introduced. This substitution of material for the introductory work in textbooks would not necessarily mean that the book material will have no use. As indicated in (a) of the preceding paragraph, pupils who have developed their own procedure will then have a real purpose for examining the textbook procedure. Pupils under such conditions will probably understand the text presentation much better than they would have if the text material had been used without any introductory material.

It has already been suggested that if the textbook is not the only source of instructional material, there is a better possibility that the text materials will be effective when they are used. This is especially true in the case of problem exercises. The children will consider each set of problems more carefully if it is used only once for a specific purpose, for example, in teaching the reading of problems (no computation). This means many sets of exercises must be available to allow practice of particular skills. An old set of textbooks is an excellent source of such problem exercises and will permit the use of exercises in the regular adopted textbook for other purposes.

Introducing more than one means of solution will make possible variety in using the textbook presentation of the best solution. For example, instead of stopping with the dimes and pennies and short way of adding $28 + 35$, the class should search for and consider other ways of finding the sum. After such other ways have been found, they can be used effectively in "proving" or showing that answers obtained for some textbook problems and examples are correct. Study sheets and different ways of adding displayed on the chalkboard or arithmetic bulletin board may be other sources of the different solutions.

Preparing summaries of what has been learned in the study of certain phases of arithmetic has been previously suggested. Teachers who use this procedure will find it makes for an intensive review study of the textbook. Pupils seldom go back and consider again with a definite purpose any part of an arithmetic book that has once been studied. Therefore, this preparation of summaries should interest teachers as a means of achieving textbook review.

USE OF THE TEXTBOOK IN PRESENTING NEW WORK

Foster E. Grossnickle and Leo J. Brueckner

When a new step is to be introduced, some teachers prefer to develop the step orally at the chalkboard without reference to a treatment of the

[From *Discovering Meanings in Arithmetic* (New York: Holt, Rinehart & Winston, Inc., 1959), pp. 75-76. Reprinted by permission of the author and Holt, Rinehart & Winston, Inc.]

step in the textbook, while others find the plan of using a well-organized textbook development more effective. The weakness of the oral method is that it may lack organization and that some pupils may not understand what is said. Attention may waver, and therefore important points may be missed. Pupils also have no point of reference for subsequent study if difficulty arises later on and review is necessary. These limitations are all obviated when under teacher guidance the children study a carefully worked-out explanation in the textbook, supplemented by meaningful experiences with objective materials and visual aids to give the work meaning and when necessary by additional explanations by the teacher.[1] Since pupil needs are so varied, it is inconceivable that the explanations in a single textbook can meet the needs of all children. The teacher always is an essential element of the learning situation.

MAKING ARITHMETIC MEANINGFUL

Leo J. Brueckner and Foster E. Grossnickle

Modern arithmetic textbooks are so efficiently constructed and contain such a carefully graded development of processes that they are in fact learner's books, to be used not only while learning a new step, but also subsequently when the need for review of a step arises because the procedure has been forgotten. The textbook writer faces the problem of constructing the textbook in such a way that it is in fact a reference book that can be used by the pupil to locate help needed to overcome some deficiency.

The illustrative textbook page unit given below contains the essential elements of a development of the step of addition of mixed numbers involving reduction but no carrying. It provides the basis of the teaching procedures described in the preceding section. An examination of the page will reveal the following elements:

[From *Making Arithmetic Meaningful* (New York: Holt, Rinehart & Winston, Inc., 1953), pp. 134-36. Reprinted by permission of the authors and Holt, Rinehart & Winston, Inc.]

---

[1] Foster E. Grossnickle, "How to Use the Arithmetic Textbook," *NEA Journal*, XLVII, 41-42.

How to Add Mixed Numbers

1. Mrs. Jones had the 1¼ apple pies and the 1¼ cherry pies you see in the picture. How many pies did she have in all?

A   **B**   **C**   **D**

a) How many pies do you see in A? in B?

b) In C you can see 1¼ pies and 1¼ pies put together. How many quarter pies are there in A and B? How many whole pies in A and B?

c) Use C and D to show that 2¾ pies are the same as 2½ pies.

2. We can add these two mixed numbers as shown below.

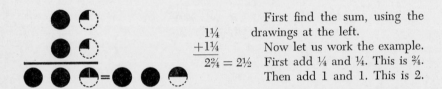

$$\begin{array}{r} 1\frac{1}{4} \\ +1\frac{1}{4} \\ \hline 2\frac{2}{4} = 2\frac{1}{2} \end{array}$$

First find the sum, using the drawings at the left.
Now let us work the example. First add ¼ and ¼. This is ²⁄₄.
Then add 1 and 1. This is 2.

The sum is 2¾. How do we change 2¾ to 2½? Why do we not change 2½?

3. Explain each step in the work in each of these examples:

a) $\begin{array}{r} 3\frac{1}{4} \\ 2\frac{1}{4} \\ \hline 5\frac{2}{4} = 5\frac{1}{2} \end{array}$ *b*) $\begin{array}{r} 2\frac{1}{8} \\ \frac{3}{8} \\ \hline 2\frac{4}{8} = 2\frac{1}{2} \end{array}$ *c*) $\begin{array}{r} 6\frac{1}{6} \\ 3\frac{1}{6} \\ \hline 9\frac{2}{6} = 9\frac{1}{3} \end{array}$ *d*) $\begin{array}{r} \frac{3}{8} \\ 5\frac{3}{8} \\ \hline 5\frac{6}{8} = 5\frac{3}{4} \end{array}$

4. Now copy the examples without the work, close your book, and find the sums. Then compare your work with the work above to see if your answers are correct. Correct any errors you make. If you need help, ask your teacher. If you made no errors, you are ready for the practice below. Find the sums:

5. $\begin{array}{r} 3\frac{1}{4} \\ 5\frac{1}{4} \\ \hline \end{array}$ $\begin{array}{r} 6\frac{3}{8} \\ 2\frac{1}{8} \\ \hline \end{array}$ $\begin{array}{r} 5\frac{1}{6} \\ \frac{1}{6} \\ \hline \end{array}$ $\begin{array}{r} 6\frac{1}{8} \\ 3\frac{5}{8} \\ \hline \end{array}$ $\begin{array}{r} \frac{1}{4} \\ 3\frac{1}{4} \\ \hline \end{array}$ $\begin{array}{r} 8\frac{3}{8} \\ 6\frac{3}{8} \\ \hline \end{array}$

Mixed Practice in Addition

6. $\begin{array}{r} \frac{1}{3} \\ \frac{1}{3} \\ \hline \end{array}$ $\begin{array}{r} \frac{3}{8} \\ \frac{2}{8} \\ \hline \end{array}$ $\begin{array}{r} 4\frac{1}{3} \\ 3\frac{1}{3} \\ \hline \end{array}$ $\begin{array}{r} 7\frac{3}{8} \\ 5\frac{1}{8} \\ \hline \end{array}$ $\begin{array}{r} 5 \\ 4\frac{1}{2} \\ \hline \end{array}$ $\begin{array}{r} \frac{3}{8} \\ 7\frac{3}{8} \\ \hline \end{array}$

1. A problem is given, stating a situation in which there is need for the new step. The teacher may prefer to precede the presentation of the discussion in the textbook by utilizing some situation in the classroom in which the need for the new step has arisen. In that case, the pupils may be able to discover a solution by using manipulative or visual materials. This will prepare them for the development given in the textbook and make it meaningful for them.

2. A picture visualizing the solution is given. Thus the child can see the solution before doing any actual computation. The teacher may supplement this picture by use of concrete objects or other pictures, as may seem necessary, especially for slow learners.

3. An explanation of the procedure follows for study and future reference. Diagnostic tests that are given later on can be keyed back to this page to facilitate ready reference in case help is needed.

4. Several other examples of the step being taught are given next. These are to be studied by the class under teacher direction to assure understanding of the work. The teacher should check carefully at this point for understanding by well-directed questioning.

5. The directions that are given then require the pupils to copy the examples already worked out and to work them with their books closed. Then they are expected to compare their work with the work on the page to discover any errors made. If the work is correct, the teacher can assume that the pupil is ready for practice to develop skill. When there is evidence of lack of understanding, reteaching on a more concrete basis may be needed.

6. Practice on other examples similar to the step taught at the top of the sample page follows.

7. The last section consists of a group of examples containing the new step as well as some of the types of examples previously taught. It provides an excellent form of review as well as a test of ability to work examples involving the new step.

ANOTHER POINT OF VIEW

J. Allen Hickerson

Many elementary schools are moving away from the practice of having books and the library serve as the major source for school problems and for the knowledge necessary for their solution. The trend is in the direction of having the community and its problems the focus of attention and the major source of knowledge. Books are being relegated to the position of supplementing first-hand experiences.

The arithmetic program described in this volume is founded upon the children's and community's everyday problems and concerns. The skillful teacher guides children in broad, challenging, interesting, meaningful, and effective arithmetic experiences by (1) centering attention on the children's everyday experiences, problems, and investigations; (2) utilizing such materials of instruction as those listed above; and (3) providing appropriate computational exercise and practice material.

The skillful teacher does not need a textbook or workbook to organize topics in proper sequence or to supply the explanations for the various techniques of computation.

Textbooks and Workbooks

Some school systems have state-wide adoptions of textbooks. Others have county-wide or city-wide adoptions. There are still other systems that permit the individual school, or even the individual teacher, to make textbook selections.

The newer textbooks and workbooks have many fine features. In general, the topics are related to children's activities and interests and the numbers used for computation are usually not too complex or unreasonable. The sequence of topics is usually planned to give variety to the program and reviews are scattered throughout to help children maintain computational facility. Practice material and tests are also usually included. With many of the newer series profusely illustrated with colorful pictures and graphic charts, these books look very attractive.

It is not necessary that the textbook, no matter what the area, deter-

[From *Guiding Children's Arithmetic Experiences: the Experience-Language Approach to Numbers* (Englewood Cliffs, N.J.: Prentice-Hall, Inc., 1952), pp. 58-60. Reprinted by permission of Prentice-Hall, Inc.]

mine all of the topics to be studied or the sequence of study. So it is with arithmetic. The teacher and children should use the textbook or workbook to supplement the arithmetic program, not to dominate it. In fact, there should be more than one textbook in use. There should be copies of arithmetic books of several series and on different grade levels for reference and comparison.

1. *How can textbooks and workbooks help in the development of children's ability to represent concrete situations with arithmetical symbols?*

The situations and problems described in textbooks can suggest to the teacher the kinds of first-hand situations and problems his own children might have. The teacher might be able to arrange for his children to have similar experiences in school or he might help the children plan to have such experiences out of school.

The book can be used to help children in their own problem solving by dramatizing the situations described and by keeping account of and reporting to the class similar first-hand experiences they have had.

Textbooks and workbooks often contain pictures, drawings, diagrams, and charts that help to clarify quantitative relationships which the children have met in their own first-hand experiences.

2. *How can textbooks and workbooks help in the development of children's ability to compute with meaning and efficiency?*

After the children have experimented with and discovered different techniques and short cuts for a certain type of computation, they can consult different books to see which techniques are recommended by the different textbook authors. When the children are ready to practice a certain computational technique, they can use the appropriate material in books.

The test and review material also can be used when needed.

3. *How can textbooks and workbooks help in the development of children's ability to understand the theory or science of arithmetic?*

Since books develop the reasons for rules, principles, and generalizations of the number system very quickly and briefly, if at all, their method of teaching is more like the deductive than the inductive. Rules of computation, the mathematical meaning of zero, the decimal system of notation, and so forth, as they are explained and propounded in the book, should not be referred to by children until they have discovered and formulated these generalizations themselves. They could refer to the various authors then to see how they formulate the same principles.

It is seen from this brief consideration of the textbook and workbook that their use in the total arithmetic program should be limited. The actual guiding of children's experiences should be performed by the teacher. The children should consult the textbooks only after they have had the first-hand experience themselves, after they have gained an understanding of the computational technique, and after they have gained an understanding of the rule or principle.

PART III: THE NATURE, PLACE, AND USE OF WORKBOOKS

HISTORICAL DEVELOPMENT OF WORKBOOKS

Helen A. Schneider

In looking into the history of arithmetic workbooks, one finds that the developmental background of the workbook has been closely related to the testing movement and to the subsequent attempts to individualize teaching procedure. The trend in this development points to a continued use of schemes of individualization. The workbook was one scheme that was swept in on the tidal wave of individualized learning. The Standard Practice Tests introduced by S. A. Courtis in 1914 and the *Exercise Books* of Frederick Burk were among the earliest forms of these materials to appear. A little later, at the time when the drill theory of teaching arithmetic was at its height, teachers were looking for more and more prepared drill materials. As a result of this demand by teachers, workbooks and other forms of practice materials began to be published in great numbers.

In view of the enormous output of workbooks of all kinds (not only arithmetic workbooks), the amount of critical literature on them is surprisingly small. A list of approximately twenty-eight hundred educational subject headings,[1] published in 1928, does not contain the term "workbook." Although the *Education Index* lists new workbooks as they are published, the first article listed under the heading did not appear until January, 1931.

[From "The Place of Workbooks in the Teaching of Arithmetic," *Arithmetic 1948*, Supplementary Educational Monographs, No. 66. (Chicago: University of Chicago Press, 1948), pp. 54-67. Reprinted by permission of the author and the University of Chicago Press.]

---

[1] *List of Educational Subject Headings.* Prepared by L. Belle Voegelein for the Committee on the Classification of Educational Materials, Commission on Coordination of Research Agencies, the National Education Association (Columbus, Ohio: Ohio State University Press, 1928).

In 1938, Earl P. Andreen, of San Diego, reported a study [2] in which, with the assistance of a group of experts, he drew up a series of thirteen essential features which should be included in arithmetic workbooks for Grades III through VI. Then Andreen applied these criteria to eighteen series of workbooks published before 1938. The result of this analysis showed that many of the workbooks were lacking in provisions for certain features that characterize conditions essential to efficient learning, such as knowledge of the goal of the lesson. One of the greatest weaknesses in the workbooks was found to be in the provision for motivation. In spite of this, Andreen reports that a summary of the findings of studies earlier than this show some agreement only on the point that groups of pupils using workbooks in arithmetic make greater gains in learning than do groups not using workbooks. However, Andreen does not explain the nature of these gains. Were they increased understandings, increased competency in computational skill, or just what? Until we know more specifically what the nature of these gains in learning was, we can scarcely draw valid conclusions from this part of the study.

The findings of Andreen's study indicated, further, that there was a great difference in the character and quality of the workbooks. Only a small percentage of them could be characterized as self-administering materials. Controlled observations of the classroom usage of these materials revealed that a majority of teachers depended on them to such an extent that their own personalities were almost entirely removed from the teaching-learning situation. They were a boon to the teacher to whom oral presentation came hard or to the teacher who had difficulty in holding the interest of his class. They were so easy to put into practice and involved no mastery of new teaching techniques. They were also an effective means of keeping a class busy and reduced teaching to a simple supervisory function.

One can readily see why the workbook came into disrepute. However, in these days of in-service training, of the wide acceptance of the meaning theory, and of the recognized improvement in textbooks, another such study would, or at least should, reveal a somewhat different picture.

Editor's Note. The fact that differences continue to exist in the character and quality of arithmetic workbooks is seen later in this chapter (in material from Brueckner and Grossnickle's *Making Arithmetic Meaningful*). Also of interest in relation to Andreen's study is Durr's recent investigation of "the value of workbooks in promoting learnings concerned with quantitative relationships, arithmetic problem solving, arithmetic vocabulary, and

---

[2] Earl P. Andreen, "A Study of Workbooks in Arithmetic," *Journal of Educational Research*, XXXII (October, 1938), 108-22.

fundamental arithmetical operations" in grades 4-8, from which the following findings were reported: "The students, as a whole, made greater gains in arithmetic vocabulary and fundamental operations after using workbooks. The students who were above average in intelligence and subject matter achievement profited more from using workbooks in the above two areas, while those who were below average made no significantly different gains with or without workbooks. The mean arithmetic achievement gain favored workbooks in grades four and five, but there were no significant differences in grades six through eight.[3]

Most of us will agree, no doubt, that there has been a definite improvement in arithmetic textbooks in the last ten years, and, as most of the authors who write textbooks also write the workbooks, this improvement has been reflected in the workbooks.

Variability in Workbooks

A careful examination of the many available materials on the market today would reveal that workbooks range from excellent to poor. Some workbooks are designed to accompany a given textbook. Some are not keyed to an arithmetic series and can be used with any basal textbook. Others, especially those for the primary grades, supply basic materials without reference to any particular textbook.

The better workbooks are so well organized and prepared that they are practically self-instructing, and their use enables the teacher to adapt instruction to the needs, the rates of learning, and the interests of individual pupils. Such workbooks provide excellent materials for establishing meanings, for they include functional illustrations and full explanations. Through meaningful experiences with number, they direct the pupil toward a known goal. Many of them strive to combine the advantages of the textbook and the workbook by transforming the explanations into demonstrations which lead the pupil into discovering for himself new meaning and new significance in arithmetic. They provide an abundance of balanced, orderly practice material, in addition to the practice in the basic textbook. The better workbooks also provide practice exercises in the interpretation of quantitative materials, vocabulary exercises, reading exercises on steps in problem solving, and a good testing program.

Less desirable workbooks merely include a mass of miscellaneous drill material, poorly organized and arranged, with little or no material to

---

[3] William K. Durr, "The Use of Arithmetic Workbooks in Relation to Mental Abilities and Selected Achievement Levels," *Journal of Educational Research,* LI (April, 1958), 561-71.

establish meanings. It is thus almost impossible to adapt such isolated and meaningless drill items to any arithmetic program.

Practical Aspects of Workbooks

In trying to decide whether or not to use a workbook, the teacher will first have to consider his own arithmetic program. What are the objectives to be achieved? What are the teacher and the children trying to do? What are their purposes? What learning experiences will attain these purposes or ends? What is the best way to arrange or organize these experiences? Finally, what materials will be necessary or helpful? The selection of any workbook should be based on criteria that stress the contributions which such materials could or should make to the guidance and the improvement of learning.

What the teacher conceives the purposes of arithmetic to be and the relation of the teaching materials to the accomplishing of these purposes are the deciding factors. If the teacher's grasp of arithmetic is mechanical and abstract, his instructional methods and materials will stress memorization of the fundamental facts, mechanical computation, and abstract drill. A teacher can share with the pupils only what he interprets arithmetic to be. If, on the other hand, the teacher conceives arithmetic to be a closely knit system of understandable ideas, principles, and processes and believes that the purpose of teaching arithmetic is to produce citizens who can use arithmetic intelligently in the many social situations where quantitative thinking is necessary, his methods and selection of materials will be quite different. He will use many materials and resources of various kinds to achieve these goals. The way in which the teacher organizes these experiences will probably have something to do with what the materials will be. Regardless of the organization of these experiences, however, there are certain specific objectives which the teacher will be trying to achieve.

The workbook can be an invaluable aid to the teacher in achieving these objectives: (1) by providing self-instructing supplementary material designed to develop meanings, to develop skills, to maintain skills and meanings once developed, and to develop ability in problem solving; (2) by helping the teacher adapt the instruction to the needs, the rates of learning, and the interests of individual pupils; and (3) by helping develop in the pupil a sense of personal responsibility.

In order to set up a broad and enriched program of meaningful arithmetic and to provide for individual differences, not only a great variety of materials is needed, but also a range from the simplest to the most challenging. The arithmetic workbook is only one of the materials of in-

struction. There are, or at least should be, many others, all designed for
the same purpose, namely, to assist the teacher and the pupils in achieving
the objectives that they set up.

Goals to Be Reached with Aid of Workbooks

What, then, are some of these goals, and how will the workbook help
to achieve them?

Developing Meanings. One goal might well be the understanding of the
number system and the rationale of the computational processes. Although the initial explanations of the number system will be given by the
teacher or by the teacher with the assistance of the textbook, a great deal
of practice on these meanings is necessary. The better workbooks provide
this practice on the understanding of our number system, with such exercises as this:

> Tell what each 3 means in each of the following numbers: 360; 13,258;
> and 142,633.
>
> In the number 484 the 4 at the left has how many times the value of the
> 4 at the right?
>
> Arrange the following numbers in the order of their value, the smallest
> first: .8; .08; 8; .008; 80.

Practice on the process is introduced with the explanation of what the
particular process means and why it is done that way—why we place the
partial products where we do, etc. In other words, the workbook serves
to redevelop the concepts and processes which are taught in the textbooks.
Because of its format, techniques not easily employed in a textbook, such
as drawing, shading, filling in blanks, and the like, can be used. Many
visual aids are provided in the work with fractions and decimals. For
example, by means of circles, rectangles, pictures, etc., the child is directed
to draw pictures to show why $2\frac{1}{2} = \frac{5}{2}$. The book can show what $\frac{1}{4} \times \frac{1}{2}$
means, and the workbook provides a second meaningful treatment which
helps the less able pupil to grasp ideas that he may have failed to understand in the initial presentation and which helps the average and the more
able pupil to understand more fully what he has begun to learn. Although
the subject matter is not basically different, the workbook often approaches meaning in a new way. It serves to throw new light on familiar
subject matter. Probably we teachers have all had the experience of thinking that we had developed the meaning of a process perfectly, only to
find, when we return to it some time later, that the children remember the
end product only and not the meaning behind the process. This difficulty
occurs because, in developing the process, we practice on the end product

only and not on the meaning. The workbook provides the needed practice on meaning.

Developing Skills. Another goal is efficiency in the performance of the computation itself. Although it is probably better to regard the development of the skills as a means to an end rather than an end in itself, teachers must work on the skills. To develop the skills, authorities agree, some practice is necessary. Practice serves a useful purpose in arithmetic-learning. It helps to fix what has been learned and to maintain the learning at a satisfactory level. The workbook can be very helpful in the accomplishment of this goal.

If practice is necessary, the teacher must have practice material. Here the workbook fills a definite need. Some persons believe that the teacher should prepare his own practice material to fit his situation. However desirable or undesirable this may be, two difficulties stand in the way. First, the great majority of teachers are not qualified to prepare such material. Research, which has been studied and digested by respected authors, is behind the making of systematic, scientific practice material. Those who are selected as authors usually have attained positions of some distinction and have developed favorable reputations as teachers, scholars, and authorities in the field. Brueckner and Grossnickle, in their book, *How To Make Arithmetic Meaningful,* say in regard to this:

> Some of the home made drill materials that the authors have seen used in the classrooms have been prepared hastily with little insight into the learning difficulties involved. In general, prepared materials should be used in preference to those constructed on the spur of the moment by the overworked teacher.[4]

Assuming that the teacher is capable of preparing practice materials, the second difficulty is finding enough time to do it. Never in the history of the profession has there been such a premium on the teacher's time. In these days of democratic school administration, the teacher's time and energy are precious. Many issues that were formerly decided by school boards, administrators, principals, and supervisors are now being resolved democratically by the teachers. The teacher's opinions and suggestions are wanted and needed in practically all areas because he deals directly with the children. Since the teacher today has more responsibility for decisions, more of his time is needed for study in order to make these decisions. The teacher is a curriculum maker, a selector of textbooks, a maker of school policies, and a designer of school buildings. The teacher is making salary schedules; is selecting school furniture; is engaged in an in-

---

[4] Leo J. Brueckner and Foster E. Grossnickle. *How To Make Arithmetic Meaningful* (New York: Holt, Rinehart & Winston, Inc., 1947).

service training program; is reading professional books and periodicals; and is a leader in community activities. He is working on evaluation scales for teachers; is either leading, or is a member of, a child-study group. The teacher is engaged in these and many more such activities over and above the routine duties. Thus the teacher often is compelled to decide between what is desirable and what is practical at the moment. There will always be some instructional materials that the teacher will have to make without making the practice materials also.

Like all prepared materials, the workbook saves the time of the pupil as well as that of the teacher. Time spent copying examples from the blackboard or textbook could be better spent on the practice itself. The greatest saving, however, is of the pupil's eyes. Copying either from the textbook or from the blackboard often involves eyestrain. In addition, the possibility of copying the example incorrectly is eliminated by use of the workbook. However desirable it may be to copy accurately, it is not the goal or the purpose of the practice.

It is not the function of the textbook to be a drill book. Workbooks should be relied on to supply this need. Whenever I come to one of those pages of practice examples in the textbook (for example, a full page of multiplication examples with three-figure multipliers), I never know exactly what to do with it. Shall the children take the time to copy all these examples and work them? Some of the examples are arranged so that paper can be slipped under them and just the work put down, but this plan has disadvantages also. Children will always have to do some copying, even in workbooks—for example, exercises in addition and subtraction of decimals when the examples are put down horizontally and the children must arrange them correctly—but the copying is kept down to a minimum by the use of the workbook.

A Special Word on Skill in Computation. Since workbooks have been so frequently misused, I should like to say a little about using the workbooks in accomplishing the goal of skill in computation. Research has taught us that short, frequent practice periods are the most effective. Hence long, tedious drill assignments are unwise, and short and frequent assignments should be the rule. We also know that drill should be kept well behind meaning. Thus we must be sure that it follows and does not precede understanding.

If the drill is to be effective, the pupil should have a desire to learn the thing practiced. The purpose of the lesson must be evident to the pupil. In other words, the teacher must not only see to it that the children are aware of the purpose of the lesson but also that they have a part in formulating the purpose in the first place. Time spent in doing this through discussion of the lesson or any other means is time well spent.

The teacher must be a skilled discussion leader in guiding the group into understanding the purpose of the lesson. The workbook is the pupil's book. If it is to be really effective, the pupil must understand it, be interested in it, and be able to use it for himself.

When a topic in the workbook is assigned, it is often wise to have the pupils look over the assignment and discuss any questions that may be raised. Such questions as these may be directed to the class by the teacher:

What kind of examples are these?

What does problem 7 mean?

Is there any example that you think might bother you?

What are some of the things you have to be careful about?

What mistake do you think you might make if you are not careful?

Did we come across any examples like this in working on our unit yesterday?

Insofar as possible, practice based on materials in workbooks should grow out of needs derived from meaningful experience or should be readily integrated with such experiences.

After the work has been completed, different methods may be used to check it. Some teachers like to have each child grade his own work; others have the children check each other's work. Some feel that the teacher should do the checking. It makes little difference which method of checking is used as long as the checking is done immediately or at least soon after the lesson. If two or three days elapse, the lesson "gets cold" and the checking is of little value. I have tried all three ways and still use them all, depending on the time available, what the plans for the day are, and what particular thing we are trying to do.

Self-analysis of Errors. Now, in my opinion, comes the most important part of the lesson. If the lesson is to be of any value, each child must analyze his own errors and do something about them. He must know what his errors are and then correct them. I prefer to have the children leave the example in the workbook just as it was originally worked so that I may see it. The pupil can make the correction on a piece of paper. In that way both the child and I can refer to the original work if necessary. More than that, I not only want to see the correction but, in some cases, want to have the pupil tell me what his error was. It would seem that the important thing is that the child know his error and correct it and that it would not make too much difference whether the teacher knew it or not. I have learned from experience, however, that sometimes what a child thinks his error is, really is not his mistake at all even though he will have the problem corrected when I get around to him. If the checking is to be effective, the child must know specifically what the error is and why it is wrong. By having the pupil tell about it, the teacher discovers what the pupil is thinking about the example. Correct answers can often be secured by inferior methods. Children need to be shown and encouraged to use approved procedures.

The teacher, far from being removed from the teaching-learning situation, must be more in evidence than ever. Indeed it sometimes seems that he should be everywhere at once. John's errors will not necessarily be the same as Mary's. The teacher must guide, counsel, and teach individually a whole roomful of Johns and Marys. In such a situation each pupil must be made to realize that learning is an individual matter and that he alone can do the learning. Developing this realization requires the utmost skill in classroom management.

If at all possible, the teacher should see every child in the room who has made an error. Of course the teacher will spend more time with some than with others, depending on the result of the work and on what the child has to say about his work. If it is impossible to see every child (that is, if it takes too much of the class time), the teacher can quickly arrange to see some children later in the day or even the next day (the conference should not be put off longer than one day). If, as the teacher goes from one child to another, he finds that a great many children are missing the same example or making the same error, he can step to the board and explain it to the group as a whole. Teachers gain skill in this technique of pulling the group together for a brief presentation and then releasing them again when each child needs to go his own way. The teacher soon gets to know the group and where corners can be cut to save time. This brief conference with each child is an invaluable aid to the teacher in getting to know the children.

The procedure for analyzing their own errors must be taught to the pupils just as any other procedure or technique is taught. Much time and discussion must be spent with the group at the beginning of the year in training them to do it well and with the minimum expenditure of time. "Why should we correct our mistakes?" "How do we go about correcting them?" Questions such as these could lead the discussion. By just going over his work, a child will waste a great deal of time trying to find his error in a problem in subtraction of fractions if, because of failure to notice the subtraction sign, he has added.

The discussion will probably bring out that the first thing to do in correcting a problem is to see that it is copied correctly, if it is one that has to be copied. If the problem is not to be copied, the first thing is to see that the directions have been followed. Time spent in working out a technique such as this will be time well spent. In my experience, children become very efficient in this and profit a great deal by it. The teacher must be on the alert to spot the child who is making the same error time after time and must call his attention to the mistake. Although the teacher soon gets to know the children, it is frequently unwise to pass up the children who get 100. It pays to stop occasionally and question them on how they thought about this or that problem. Surprisingly enough, sometimes they, too, will need help.

The teacher who does this frequently and systematically soon becomes very skilled at it and, as I said before, learns a great deal about the pupils. In addition, because of intensity of purpose, he soon begins to remember what Mary's error was yesterday and the day before and begins to watch Mary. The instruction becomes not only highly individual but much more effective.

This is a description of a detail in teaching procedure, and there are probably many other and better ways of reaching the objective. Frequently, we only talk about individual instruction and fail to put it into practice. The teacher's job is to help the pupil help himself—a procedure which should eventually make him a more independent worker. Assigning large amounts of drill does not guarantee that effective learning will take place. The fact is that unguided drill actually strengthens inefficient habits and skills, because the pupil repeats the same errors and faulty procedures again and again with no improvement in performance.

If this technique of self-analysis is started fairly early in the grades, by the time the pupil reaches Grade VIII he will have cut his errors down to a minimum and will have become a much more independent worker. As he becomes more and more efficient in this business of self-analysis, he will need the teacher less and less. At best, evaluation is difficult, and one of the important kinds of evaluation is self-evaluation. It is the goal, at least, of all guidance. Then, too, this method provides one of the highest forms of motivation. The child himself can see his progress. The satisfaction and enjoyment to be derived from improved skill in arithmetic are inherently much more valuable sources of motivation than are some of the means supplied by the workbooks, such as progress graphs and record charts. "Nothing succeeds like success," and one of the strongest forms of motivation is the personal satisfaction and joy that a child feels when he succeeds.

Overdrilling or Underdrilling. One of the objections to using workbooks for practice is that the children are frequently overdrilled or even underdrilled. When has John or Mary had enough drill on a process? When he gets a 100? The only way one can ever come to a decision about this is by discussion with the group and by individual conference with the pupil. If the pupil feels that he has mastered a particular phase of the process or is maintaining his skill, it is generally safe to excuse him from further drill.

Although I have no scientific study to support this statement, I feel that the amount of drill needed is probably less for intelligent, interested pupils; that less drill is required also for a simple skill than for a complex skill; and that less drill is required to fix and maintain that which has been learned meaningfully than that which has been learned mechanically and without understanding.

Developing Other Skills. Under the general heading of "skills," skill in computation will not be the only objective of the teacher. He will be striving to develop skill in many other topics, for instance, skill in the use of number relationships. When pupils learn and understand the relationship of common fractions, decimal fractions, and per cent, they must be guided into seeing when and why it is more advantageous to use one in preference to the other two. It is important that they learn to use good judgment in working with these number relationships and that they learn to use the most economical method. Much practice on this is necessary, more than most textbooks provide. The workbook can be depended on to supply practice to develop this understanding of the relationships of common fractions, decimal fractions, and per cent, as well as to develop good judgment in using them.

Another important work-study skill is the reading and interpretation of graphs, charts, and tables. A great deal of practice is necessary if this skill is to be well developed. Again, the workbook is more adaptable than the textbook to supply this practice because of the size of the page. Many more and different kinds of graphs, charts, and tables can be included, and they can be made larger and sometimes more appealing to the children. The practice in quantitative thinking involved is invaluable, for example, rounding off numbers and comparing them in different ways.

Maintenance of Skills. Once the skills and understanding have been developed, they must be maintained. Consequently, the teacher will also have this objective in mind. A good workbook will have several types of exercises to insure the maintenance of the skills and facts. Exercises titled "Do You Remember?" review periodically a single process or type of process. Frequently, at the end of each section of the workbook, a checking-up exercise provides a cumulative review for the pupil, a sampling of the most important skills up to that point, to discover whether he still has any weaknesses which need attention.

Developing Ability in Problem Solving. Since the ultimate aim of arithmetic-teaching is a social one—to develop ability to use arithmetic in solving the problems of life—teachers will be working toward this goal of problem solving. Of course, problem solving should be interpreted much more broadly than "textbook exercises," but the solution of the textbook problems is necessary. Some children are able to develop suitable methods of their own for problem solving and are probably better off left alone. Most children, however, need to be taught the technique for attacking problems.

Such a technique generally consists of a series of steps to be adopted in solving problems. The workbook is a great help here because the child can write out the answer to one step at a time. By giving the child a sample problem, the workbook shows how a logical analysis of the problem should be made. Then he is directed to work out problems in the same way.

This plan is particularly helpful in solving two and three-step problems. One of the reasons for children's difficulty in solving problems is that they cannot visualize the whole situation. They can read the first sentence and understand it, and then the second sentence and understand that; but, by the time they get to the third sentence, they have lost the thought in the first sentence. Writing it out step by step, recording their thinking step by step, gives them the complete picture. The very act of responding physically to each reasoning step is in itself a help. Some teachers have the children illustrate the problem, to get the complete picture, for example, in the problem:

> Mary went to the store with $2.00. She bought two loaves of bread at $.15, a quart of milk for $.21, and a dozen eggs for $.70. How much change did Mary receive?

The children, using stick figures, would sketch Mary going to the store with her purse, and on the purse would be marked $2.00. The next picture would show Mary with the bread, milk, and eggs ready to leave the store, and on her purse this time a question mark. Such simple illustrations, which can be sketched in the workbook, give the children the complete situation.

Adapting Instruction to Individuals. Teachers realize that instruction should be adapted to the individual differences of pupils, but they know, too, that this is easier said than done. Any workable plan for dealing with these differences adequately will necessitate some form of grouping. Groupings will vary, however, according to the purposes of the lesson. Many discussions involving a social or an experience unit on which the group is working may profitably be shared by the entire group of children. The personnel and the size of the group will shift and vary depending on the purpose. At times, some children will be working independently. The workbook can be of help here because it is self-instructing.

The bright child can work ahead with the minimum of help from the teacher. A good workbook redevelops the concepts and processes for the slow child. Although the slow child can understand the relationships that are so quickly grasped by the brighter child, it takes longer for the slow child and he requires many more experiences. The workbook supplies these experiences. The bright child can bridge gaps, but the slow child needs to have his attention directed to each new relationship. Because of this, certain types of material are needed by children who learn slowly but are not especially needed by children who learn readily. The workbook supplies this material. Although the subject material is not basically different, there is no repetition of textbook material because the workbook approaches meaning in a new way.

Again, it serves to throw new light on familiar subject matter. In other words, it provides a second meaningful treatment which helps the less able pupil to grasp ideas that he may have failed to understand. Teachers frequently assign some of this work to the entire group because it helps the average and the more able pupil to understand more fully what the slow child has begun to learn.

When pupils need simpler exercises than those provided in the workbook for the grade, the teacher should feel free to make use of materials found in workbooks for a lower grade level. Workbooks and textbooks with a range of at least three grades should be available for every teacher so that instructional materials adapted to every child's needs and to his level of development can be selected.

Use As Reference Books. Children frequently use a workbook as a reference book. For example, not so long ago, some of the children in one of the small groups working on a unit found that they needed to know how to find the area of a trapezoid. We had not yet discussed that in class. I noticed them referring to their workbooks for a method. I was curious to know why they referred to the workbook instead of to their textbook. When I inquired of one of the group, he said, "Oh, the workbook explains it better." To me the textbook explanation was equally as good, but I did notice that there were more questions and steps leading up to the explanation in the workbook than in the textbook and that the diagrams were considerably larger.

Every year when we begin to study areas of rectangles, triangles, etc., several children in the group get curious about the area of a circle long before we come to it. They frequently say, "How are we going to find the area of a circle?" or "I can't figure out how we are going to find the area of a circle." It is not uncommon to see them studying the workbook diagram and explanation. They frequently refer to their workbooks also when they want to look up some topic that they have previously worked out.

Other Uses. I might mention many other concepts and abilities that the teacher tries to develop and indicate how the workbook can be used to advantage in each, but, since it is used practically in the same way for each goal, this is unnecessary. Few textbooks contain enough material to satisfy the needs of the average pupil in developing concepts and skills. Because of the added emphasis on meaning, much more space than heretofore is being allotted in textbooks to meanings and functional illustrations. Because publishers feel that they must keep their books within a moderate price range, they are unable to increase the number of pages in the book, with the result that much of the practice material is frequently left out. For example, one textbook provides one page of six problems on "Estimating Answers in Solving Problems." I am sure that, after working this page, many children in the average class would still not be able to estimate answers. In another book, I note a total of twelve problems to develop skill in finding the area of a triangle (including examples used in the presentation). This is not enough, I am sure, to do the job.

Developing A Sense of Personal Responsibility. The workbook's contribution to the development of the pupil's sense of responsibility is as important as the others. Having a workbook in which he is able to do his practice for mastery has a psychological effect on a pupil. First, he is able to practice at his own rate of competence. Second, the examples are arranged in such a manner that he must make his computations fit in an orderly pattern. (This is a great help in creating neatness in work —one of the things that the wise teacher discusses frequently with the group. Neatness tends toward accuracy.) Third, there is created within most pupils an inner feeling which deters them from doing as much careless and indifferent work in a workbook as on loose and unbound paper. There is something about the permanent record provided by the workbook that has a tendency to make the pupil more careful. The children should be reminded from time to time that this is a continuous written record of their thinking in arithmetic.

Workbooks should be brought with them when they have individual conferences with the teacher, and at least part of the conference could be spent in discussion on the progress indicated by the workbook. The children will be guided a great deal by what the teacher thinks of the importance of the book. If the teacher thinks it is important, they will think so. If the teacher looks upon it lightly, merely as something for the pupils to do when the teacher is busy, they will not take much pride in the workbook.

Some Things Workbooks Cannot Do

This article would not be complete without listing at least some of the things that the workbook cannot do and is not meant to do. In the first place, the workbook is not a panacea for all ailments. It is a unique kind of self-instructing supplementary arithmetic, adaptable to many techniques that cannot be used in a textbook.

One of the main things the workbook cannot do, and was never meant to do, comes from the very purpose in teaching arithmetic. We teach arithmetic for the help it gives us in adjusting ourselves to the demands of life. It is entirely possible to obtain a high degree of skill in the use of abstract arithmetical processes without making intelligent use of arithmetic in life. The author of any textbook can provide for the application of arithmetical processes to only the important experiences of society in general. But experiences vary with the individual child. Consequently one of the most important sources of material for quantitative thinking must come from the actual experiences of children and from the varied communities in which they live. This requires the teacher to go far beyond the limits of the textbook to use possible interesting applications that no one unfamiliar with the local situation can do. The teacher must also analyze the sorts of problems which her pupils encounter and are able to deal with at various developmental levels. Some of these problems are explicitly quantitative. These real life experiences are so important that they are a "must" in any arithmetic program. Indeed, there are those who feel that the entire program can be organized around them.

The workbook can never take the place of the individual conference with children. When trying to find out how a child is thinking about a particular number situation, the teacher must have him do his thinking aloud. Too frequently, a child can get the right answer by either incorrect or immature methods. For example, if you ask the child this question in a workbook, "to which problem would you get the larger answer $35 \times \frac{3}{8}$ or $35 - \frac{3}{8}$?" a good guess might give the right answer or he might take the time to work it out. If he really understands the example, he can, in an individual conference, give the answer and tell why it is the answer.

The Real Issue

The real issue, then, is not whether to use a workbook or no workbook but what is the desirable method of using the workbook. For over a generation, educational theory, by implication at least, has stigmatized the use of even a basic textbook. In this period a great deal of nonsense has been written and said about the place of the textbook or the workbook in instruction. What we really should condemn is the way in which workbooks are misused, as well as our failure to educate prospective teachers in their proper use. The stigma on the use of a textbook or a workbook is probably a byproduct of our desire to put subject matter in its proper place and of our insistence that the living, moving, personal contact between teacher and pupil is the central factor in good teaching. The workbook, properly used, strengthens these contacts. The effective use of well-constructed workbooks by teachers who understand their functions, as well as their possible limitations, is an important factor in the guidance of learning.

The final criticism, therefore, falls on the use of the workbook. Just as the effectiveness of any policy depends on the person administering it, so the effectiveness of a workbook, or any material of instruction for that matter, depends on the teacher using it. In formulating objectives, the skilled arithmetic teacher will still consistently take into account the interest, abilities, and needs of the pupils. The pupils will co-operate with the teacher in formulating their objectives. The pupils will be aware of their objectives because the teacher has made provisions for developing this awareness. The teacher will combine a functional understanding of children with scholarship in his chosen field in such a fashion as to be able to bring about rapid, permanent, and worth-while learning.

Workbooks should have a place in modern arithmetic-teaching because they have a unique contribution to make to the learning process. However, the advantages likely to accrue to any school system from their use will be in direct proportion to the judgment displayed by administrators and teachers in selecting and using them.

PART IV: BASES FOR SELECTING ELEMENTARY-SCHOOL MATHEMATICS TEXTBOOKS

THE SELECTION OF TEXTBOOKS

Herbert F. Spitzer

The extensive use of textbooks in arithmetic instruction has made a good publisher's market and, as is usually true in such situations, a large number of different books are available. All books on the market have some good features though, of course, some have more than others. What

[From *The Teaching of Arithmetic* (2nd ed.; Boston: Houghton Mifflin Company, 1954), pp. 322-29. Reprinted by permission of the author and the Houghton Mifflin Company.]

is good in books is not, however, a matter of common agreement among teachers, administrators, and others concerned with instruction in arithmetic. There are also parts of every series which some people do not like or which they feel are definitely inferior. To complicate the problem, features which often seem very good to adults (especially those who have not had recent experience teaching children) do not work so well in classroom.

In view of the important role of the textbook in instruction and the considerable variation in the books, selection of a series is a procedure which merits careful study. The choice is difficult enough because of the number and variations in content of the books available. It is made doubly difficult by some of the claims made in advertising materials distributed from the publishing houses and by publishers' representatives.

Perhaps the factor that makes the selection of arithmetic books for a school system most difficult is the lack of knowledge about arithmetic teaching of those whose task it is to choose the books. Far too often, the major information on methods of teaching, issues in arithmetic instruction and so on which the selector of books possesses has been acquired recently from book salesmen, from the examination of a few new books (without reference to old books), and from the reading of a few recent articles and reports. When such conditions exist, it is not strange that books of relatively low merit are sometimes adopted. The fault is not that of book salesmen but of the people who do the selecting, and it points to the need of considering far more than the few features of a book which have good sales appeal.

The first reaction of the inexperienced when confronted with the task of adopting an arithmetic series is to try to formulate some rating scheme that will eliminate bias—"to do the thing scientifically." Unfortunately, no satisfactory non-objective way of rating books has yet been devised. Even such points as a difference in grade placement or of specific teaching procedure cannot be rated objectively unless a decision about the matter has already been made in the course of study or similar guide. In rating such items as initial presentation of a topic, number and quality of problem exercises, tests, and other features of a book, the criteria must be almost entirely dependent upon what the individual or the committee believes. It appears therefore that an unbiased or objective procedure for selecting textbooks is not possible. However, because of the fact that many of the individuals and committee members concerned lack background knowledge for the assignment, some systematic program for study and evaluation of pupil textbooks is highly desirable.

The question "Who shall select the pupil's textbook?" must be answered first. In the past, the superintendent, board of education, supervisor, principal, or other individuals with administrative power chose most of the books. That method of selection is still in use in many smaller school systems, in some county schools, and in a few larger school systems. The common alternative is the committee system. Each year such a system seems to be becoming more popular. This popularity is deserved, for the committee plan has many advantages over the plan of having some administrative officer select the books. The chief advantages lie in the fact that selection is placed in the hands of those who are to use the books, the committee is appointed for this one task so selection is not influenced by previously incurred obligations, and the final decision requiring agreement of members is usually the result of careful study.

The membership of the committee should be made up primarily of classroom teachers for they are in the best position to judge the effectiveness of instructional material. Other members are usually selected from the elementary school principals and supervisors. Whether or not administrative and supervisory staff should be committee members is doubtful. Because of the positions they hold, there is a tendency for them to dominate committees, while committee membership may seriously impair their counseling services to the teacher members of the committee. Since textbook committees so often need much guidance and advice as they go about the task of choosing books, probably the best use of administrative and supervisory staff is to assign to them specific counseling duties. Such duties would not give the administrative staff a vote in the committee.

Regardless of who comprises the committee and its counselors, the membership should be made public. Secret committees are not more effective in the selection of books and their use results in many undesirable practices. Committee membership for most effective work should be small, probably from four to seven members.

A plan of action is described briefly in the steps that follow.

Steps in a Study Plan for the Selection of Textbooks

Study of the Field of Arithmetic. The final choice in the selection of books is heavily weighted by what the individual believes, and what an individual believes about arithmetic is based on what he knows about the field. If his knowledge is sketchy or of doubtful validity, his beliefs cannot be worth much. It is, therefore, highly desirable for the individual or committee selecting textbooks to possess opinions based on the best available information in the field of arithmetic. As the first step in that study, references such as the Fifty-first Yearbook, Part II, of the National Society for the Study of Education and the Fifteenth Yearbook of the National Council of Teachers of Mathematics are suggested. Further study should include consideration of the best professional books on teaching arithmetic and some of the best courses of study.

Limiting the Number of Texts to Be Examined Critically. The number of available textbooks is so large that to consider them all carefully would make the task of selecting a series very time consuming. A procedure for cutting down on the books is very much needed and should be inaugurated early in the program. The selection committee can probably function best if not more than three or four series are examined intensively. The copyright date is frequently used in determining what series shall be inspected. For example, one committee agreed to look at the three series with the latest copyright date and two series published in the preceding ten-year period. The scheme for limiting the number of series should be rather objective, and if possible the entire faculty should approve the plan by referendum. Such a procedure takes some of the pressure off the textbook selection committee.

Insuring Series Rather Than Single Book Evaluation. Classroom teacher members of textbook selection committees especially have a tendency to think only in terms of the grade they teach or in which they have a special interest. The selection then becomes a one-book and not a series proposition. To keep that from happening, the procedure of having a teacher responsible for examining one phase of arithmetic (e.g., addition of whole numbers) in all the books of the various series has been adopted and used successfully by some committees.

Examination Procedures. After the three preliminary steps listed above have been taken, the real task of examination is begun. Most committee members teach full time or have other assignments which make it necessary to limit careful examination of the series of books to ten to fifteen areas. Among the areas most commonly selected for careful study are (1) addition, (2) subtraction, (3) multiplication, and (4) division of whole numbers, (5) study or learning suggestions in the books, (6) practice and review exercises, (7) verbal problems used, (8) the problem-solving program, (9) addition, (10) subtraction, (11) multiplication and (12) division of fractions, (13) tests, (14) pictures, (15) measurement, (16) manuals, and (17) grade placement of content. Committee members working in groups of two or three assume responsibility for each of the areas. Actual study begins with the books. For example, each committee member examines that section of each series which deals with division of fractions and chooses the best and the poorest presentation. Selecting the best is primarily a matter of looking for the material which is most nearly in harmony with one's own ideas on how that phase of arithmetic should be presented and then working out the assignments as a pupil

would. (Neither time nor facilities are usually available to try the procedure in the classroom.) Only those who know classroom situations well
and have that unique faculty of putting themselves in the place of pupil
and teacher can do this try-out procedure easily and effectively, but all
can do it satisfactorily enough by application to warrant its use. In the
final report, the sub-committee responsible for examination of division of
fractions describes to the entire committee what was considered the best
and poorest practice found in the books. Preparing such a report has the
advantage of putting emphasis upon real content and of demanding careful identification of specific good and poor practices.

Using the Representatives of Publishing Companies. The representatives
of publishing companies know their products well, and if given an opportunity, can be of genuine assistance to the textbook selection committee. Whether these representatives should appear before or after the
study suggested in Step Four is debatable. In any case, their appearance
before individual committee members and before the entire committee
is important enough to be scheduled during the day and not left to after-
school hours. To obtain teacher time, a substitute teacher should be provided for committee members on the day or days they are to confer as
individuals with salesmen. It is often very helpful to have the salesmen
appear before the entire textbook selection committee. Such appearances
should probably come after Step Six.

Making a Composite Rating. When all reports from Step Four are in, a
composite rating is needed. This may be obtained by assigning a point
value for best, omitted, and poorest ratings and then finding the total
points for each book.

Making the Final Choice. While the final choice is made by the committee, primarily on the data secured in the intensive study, other factors
may be considered. If no series stands out, the top books may be recon-
sidered, using the same examination procedure suggested in Step Four,
plus the direct comparison of various sections of the books.

Preparing a Final Report. The final report to the superintendent or administrative body responsible should be carefully prepared. A statement
which merely gives the first choice of books is totally inadequate. The
administrative officer should know how the committee went about its
work and why the series chosen was considered superior to the others. It
is recommended that the report be such that when any of the unsuccessful salesmen ask the reasons for their failure, the administrative officer can
find a satisfactory reply in the report.

The student of arithmetic teaching will find that other plans for evaluation of textbooks differ markedly in some respects from the program given

above. Study of these other plans should be of value to committees, especially in connection with Step Four of the proposed plan.[1]

The fact that there is very little in the literature on the procedures used by committees in their study of books calls attention to the importance of preparing a final report. If a number of such reports were available for study, a better plan of work for textbook committees might develop. Under present conditions practically every committee starts from scratch with the result that all spend valuable time either preparing a study plan or doing things inefficiently. The inclusion in a report of reasons for accepting and rejecting books, provided they are sound reasons, should be a means of improving textbooks. Publishers are very sensitive to loss of sales and will alter old books or prepare new ones to meet the demands of the trade.

HOW TO EVALUATE ARITHMETIC TEXTBOOKS

Leo J. Brueckner, Foster E. Grossnickle, and John Reckzeh

Except in a state in which one basic textbook or several designated textbooks in arithmetic are used throughout the state, committees composed of teachers, principals, or other administrative officers usually recommend the adoption of a textbook for a local school district. The basic consideration in evaluating an arithmetic series should be as follows: To what extent does a series of textbooks make possible, or fit into, a complete program in arithmetic? The textbook should be geared to the use of exploratory and visual materials. It should contain the necessary visualization of new steps and adequate explanation of each new process to be learned. The textbook should contain the practice material needed to develop skill with operations. It should also contain an abundance of material dealing with the applications of number operations.

Items that should be considered by the teacher or by committees con-

[From *Developing Mathematical Understandings in the Upper Grades* (New York: Holt, Rinehart & Winston, Inc., 1957), pp. 121-24. Reprinted by permission of the authors and Holt, Rinehart & Winston, Inc.]

---

[1] L. J. Brueckner and F. E. Grossnickle. *How to Make Arithmetic Meaningful* (New York: Holt, Rinehart & Winston, Inc., 1947), pp. 490-93; G. M. Wilson and others. *Teaching the New Arithmetic* (New York: McGraw-Hill Book Co., Inc., 1951), pp. 453-57.

cerned with the evaluation of textbooks are given below. The committee on evaluation may decide to assign a certain number of credits to the items given in order to form a scoreboard.

I. Method of Presentation
   A. Step-by-step development of each operation
   B. Stress placed on the meaning of number and place value and of number operation
   C. Provision for use of exploratory materials to give meanings
   D. Visualization used to extend meanings of processes
   E. Provision for student discovery of relationships and generalization to aid learning and assure retention
   F. Wealth of practice material provided at presentation of new work
   G. Provision of supplementary or optional material available for the teacher
   H. Systematic and frequent planned reviews of all new steps and processes throughout the textbook in order to maintain skills
   I. Diagnostic tests at frequent intervals to locate and correct weak spots
   J. Tests for measuring mastery at the end of blocks of new work
   K. Application of processes in social situations
   L. Provision for different levels of achievement in different processes

II. Grade Placement of Subject Matter
   A. Gradation of topics based on scientific research and on recommendation of yearbooks and leading courses of study
   B. Spiral arrangement of contents at each grade level
   C. Content of difficult topics spaced through several grades and not bunched in one grade
   D. Flexibility of content possible through omission of optional sections as indicated in a guide for the teacher

III. Problems
   A. Problems related to a central theme or topic and not a series of unrelated questions
   B. Miscellaneous problems predominantly of the type that can be solved without use of pencil
   C. Content of problems drawn from various curriculum areas, such as social studies, health, science, and arts
   D. Problems based on information in tables, graphs, charts, and other visual materials to develop ability to interpret them
   E. Emphasis placed on the quantitative thinking involved in formulating and applying relationships and generalizations
   F. Provision for use of community resources to vitalize the learning experience
   G. Use of exploratory materials, dramatization, and visual aids to derive solutions of problems

IV. Provision for Individual Differences
   A. Comprehensive diagnostic program geared to remedial work
   B. Provision of supplementary practice for students requiring more drill
   C. Enrichment exercises and special work for students not needing remedial work
   D. Topics for independent research and reports
   E. Workbook providing special types of aids for slow learners, including exploratory and visual experiences

V. Testing Program and Provision for Related Remedial Measures
   A. Diagnostic review tests at beginning of year's work keyed to self-help remedial work
   B. Developmental diagnostic tests at intervals in the development of each new operation in whole numbers, fractions, decimals, and per cent
   C. Achievement tests covering each block of new work
   D. Cumulative progress tests including all major processes previously taught and keyed to remedial work
   E. Cumulative progress tests in problem solving
   F. Systematic review and test of vocabulary of new concepts introduced

VI. Authorship
   A. Professional contributions to the field of arithmetic
   B. Success previously demonstrated in preparing textbooks and other instructional materials

VII. Physical Features
   A. Durability of books
   B. Quality of paper
   C. Sufficient margins

VIII. Extra Teaching Features
   A. Useful index
   B. Use of pictures that are functional and diagrams of various kinds that are visual aids to teaching

IX. Important Supplementary Considerations
   A. Adequacy of aids given in a teacher's guide accompanying textbook
   B. Supplementary materials for slow learners
   C. Provision by publishers or authors for making available various types of exploratory and visual aids to facilitate learning
   D. Professional books by authors containing a comprehensive presentation of underlying principles and procedures for teaching arithmetic

RATING THE ARITHMETIC TEXTBOOK

Leo J. Brueckner and Foster E. Grossnickle

The modern textbook is a learner's book. It contains a well-graded step-by-step development of the fundamental processes, so clearly and meaningfully presented that the average pupil is able to proceed at his own rate with a minimum of help from the teacher. Ample practice exercises to develop skill are provided. Special attention is given to the meaning of the number system. Numerous groups of problems about interesting social applications of arithmetic parallel the development of number processes. Practice materials are included to develop skill in reading tables, graphs, charts, maps, and other kinds of quantitative materials found in general reading and in the other areas of the curriculum. Special provisions also are made for individual differences, including such materials as diagnostic tests keyed to developmental and practice exercises and starred problems for special investigation and report for the more able pupils.

Items to Be Considered in Evaluating Textbooks

Teachers are often faced with the problem of selecting a textbook. The choice should never be made until after a systematic study of a number of books has been carried out to identify their respective strengths and limitations. The list of items given below suggests some of the important kinds of information that should be considered in making such an evaluation.

It likely will not be feasible to study all of these points for all books during a preliminary overview. Teacher committees should select for study those items in the list that they regard as most important in making an initial sifting. A list of pages and illustrative materials which deal with these items should then be compiled for each book and this information be made the basis of the selection of those textbooks that are to be more fully considered in making the final choice.

As comprehensive an analysis as may be feasible should be made of the two or three books from which there is to be a final selection. If it is desired to give point-ratings to textbooks, the weightings for each item

[From *Making Arithmetic Meaningful* (New York: Holt, Rinehart & Winston, Inc., 1953), pp. 545-50. Reprinted by permission of the authors and Holt, Rinehart & Winston, Inc.]

can be agreed upon by the members of the group. Differences in weightings of items will depend on their significance in the minds of the committee. The basis of a rating may be either a judgment as to the qualitative character of content or an evaluation based on an analysis of quantitative descriptive data. In the former case we ask such questions as: How good is the visualization of meanings? How well is practice organized and distributed? In the latter case we ask: How many items of this kind are there? For example, how many illustrations, or problems, or tests are there in this book?

Items to Consider in Rating a Textbook

1. The point of view of the author
   a) Consideration given to the mathematical and social phases of arithmetic and to its contributions in other curriculum areas
   b) Emphasis on teaching learners the meaning of the number system and about its use in number processes
   c) The use of visualization to assist the learner to discover relationships and to gain insight
   d) The aids to learning that are provided
   e) Recognition of the social utility of the processes taught and of the application of arithmetic
   f) The effort made to enrich the everyday experiences of the learner in which number functions and make these experiences socially significant
   g) The scientific basis of the gradation and organization of the contents
2. The presentation of the review work of previous years at the beginning of the new year
   a) Methods used to locate the needs of individuals
   (Inventory tests on processes are useful here.)
   b) Provision for reviewing the meaning of our number system
   c) Provision for review of essential principles underlying operations
   (Visualization of the principles is highly desirable.)
   d) Diagnostic tests for each operation to locate specific points on which special work should be done
   (Exercises involving analysis of errors in written work should be included.)
   e) Suitable remedial helps and practice exercises keyed to the diagnostic tests which enable the teacher to adapt instruction to the individual needs
   (Special helps on learning basic number facts should be provided. Remedial practice should be self-administering to be most helpful.)
3. Visualization and other aids used in developing processes new to the grade
   a) Use of readiness tests to establish readiness of pupils for new work

   b) Method of showing the need of the new steps in life situations

   c) Provision for manipulative experiences to enable the pupil to discover solutions and basic relationships

   d) Use of charts, diagrams, and graphs to visualize the meaning of the new work and to reveal the thought processes involved in the new work

      (These visual aids will reduce the reading difficulty of explanations.)

   e) Illustrative extra worked-out examples for study and diagnosis

   f) Special helps given on difficult spots

   g) Provision of ample practice on the new step, also including needed supplementary practice for slow learners

   h) Suitable diagnostic tests to locate weak spots

      (To be most effective these tests should be geared to suitable corrective and remedial practice.)

   i) Provision of cumulative mixed practice to maintain skills

   j) The development of generalizations about concepts being learned

4. Consideration of the social applications of arithmetic

   a) Use of social settings in presenting new steps in operations

   b) Social situations in daily life as bases of problem units

   c) Problems intended to make social experiences of children vital and meaningful

   d) Problems based on mathematical relationships and generalizations

   e) Applications of arithmetic in other curriculum areas

      (1) Social studies

      (2) Health, sports, recreation, safety

      (3) Science

      (4) Music and art

      (5) Consumer education

   f) Units of work requiring the interpretation of visual and graphic materials

      (1) Graphs of various kinds found in printed sources

      (2) Maps, scale drawings

      (3) Diagrams, charts, schedules

      (4) Tables, business forms

      (5) Reading of measuring instruments of various kinds

      (6) Arithmetic in pictures, cartoons

   g) Problem-solving helps

      (1) Study of problems illustrating meaning of each process

      (2) Use of illustrations to give meaning to situations on which problems are based

      (3) Visualization of meaning of special types of problems

      (4) Special reading exercises on steps in problem solving

      (5) Estimating answers to problems

      (6) Preparing original problems

      (7) Special vocabulary-building exercises

  h) Use of problems having unfavorable characteristics
   (1) Problems with process to use in solution specified
   (2) Reading difficulty of problems and of processes used in them
   (3) Sets of isolated unrelated problems, essentially disguised drill on processes
   (4) Puzzle types and unreal situations

5. Means provided by the textbook for evaluating pupil progress and for diagnosing their difficulties
  a) Inventory test to be used at start of the year to find out how well the pupils remember the work of preceding years
  b) Process diagnostic tests to locate specific weak spots
   (These tests should be geared to suitable corrective work.)
  c) Readiness tests, geared to suitable developmental work
  d) Developmental diagnostic tests to be administered at intervals in the course of new work, and keyed to helps on hard spots
  e) Block tests on units of new work that have been completed
  f) Exercises testing ability to apply basic generalizations
  g) Progress tests on number processes, cumulative in nature
  h) Tests in problem solving
  i) Cumulative reviews of important principles and concepts
  j) Periodic vocabulary reviews

6. Provision for individual differences
  a) Provisions for adjusting review of the work of previous years to the needs of individual pupils (See section 2 above.)
  b) Readiness tests to determine and correct factors likely to interfere with mastery of subsequent new work
  c) Diagnostic tests on new steps taught, geared to suitable corrective practice
  d) Enrichment of work for the more able pupils
   (1) Starred problems requiring independent study, research, and investigation
   (2) Lists of topics to look up as a means of broadening and enriching interests
   (3) Work with number puzzles, number games, magic squares, etc.
   (4) Dramatizations, excursions suggested
  e) Optional material that may be omitted so as to reduce the work for slow-learning pupils

7. Special features
  a) Character and quality of illustrations
  b) Size of type, appearance of page, readability, margins, paper used
  c) Factors facilitating teaching
   (1) Page unit construction
   (2) Elimination of reading difficulties in all explanations of new processes

(3) Simplification of presentation so that the text may be as self-teaching as possible

(4) Obvious and logical organization of content apparent from the headings of units of work

(5) Large variety of materials adequate in amount for both examples and problems

(6) Completeness of table of contents and index

(7) Number of suggestions of local applications of arithmetic to vitalize the work

(8) Provision for emphasizing new units of work

8. Mechanical features

  a) Attractiveness of the text (cover, design, make-up of pages)

  b) Durability of mechanical structure of text (binding, paper, etc.)

  c) Extent to which the pictures contribute to the text (the number, their color, artistic value, appeal to children, contributions to the understanding of mathematical relations)

  d) Index, table of contents (completeness, usableness)

  e) Provision for emphasis by heavy type, italics, boxing, etc.

  f) Organization as page units

A GUIDE FOR ARITHMETICS

This scoring instrument was designed for country-wide use and has thus been made comprehensive. In specific situations, those using this list may want to eliminate some of the items in accord with the point of view regarding arithmetic in their system.

It is strongly urged that those responsible for making the selection give thorough and objective consideration to the items that are retained on their score card. The task of selecting an arithmetic series that will directly influence the lives of many children is an important responsibility, and each point should be given its deserved consideration.

This rating sheet permits evaluation of each item as *Outstanding, Good,* or *Unsatisfactory.* The spaces provided for further comments allow for important notations that need to be kept in mind. No attempt has been made to assign quantitative values to each of the points. Sensible qualita-

[From "A Guide for Judging Arithmetics," prepared, published, and distributed by Ginn & Company. The Guide was reproduced in *School Science and Mathematics*, LIX (June, 1959), 431-34. Reprinted by permission of Ginn & Company.]

tive judgments regarding the entire analysis will provide a better selection for your program than will a totality of points.

I. Authorship of the Series

1. Have the authors been outstanding leaders in the learning and teaching of arithmetic?
2. Do they understand how children learn and the needs and interests of children?
3. Have they written successful arithmetic materials for children?
Comments regarding authors:

II. Content

1. Is there satisfactory development of concepts, generalizations, and relationships? (Have they been carefully selected? Properly graded? Is presentation meaningful—from concrete to abstract?)
2. Are number-system ideas wisely used? (Is provision made for understanding small and large numbers, for discovery of computational processes, etc.?)
3. Are number-system ideas for the series finally brought together in a summarizing discussion?
4. Is there systematic use of earlier-taught ideas in developing later ones? (E.g., is the relation between factors and their product applied in problems and examples in multiplication and division with fractions, decimals, and per cents?)
5. Is special attention given to such points of difficulty as zeros in quotients?
6. Does the fraction development assure that pupils sense the size of the part when they note the number in the denominator?
7. Are the several meanings of a fraction adequately presented?
8. Is the very meaningful common-denominator method for dividing with fractions taught before the inversion method?
9. Has systematically planned work with money numbers preceded decimal work as such?
10. Have fractions and decimals been so taught that per cent work becomes only a minor variation?
11. Is there thorough teaching of measurement including informal measurement units, approximation, and precision?
12. Have ways of thinking to be used in mental computation been skillfully developed?

13. Is the work with tables, graphs, and scale drawings systematic and practical?

14. Is the introductory work for algebra and geometry well planned?

15. Have business practices been introduced in situations that are understandable to pupils?

Comments regarding content:

III. The Problem-Solving Program

1. Are the meanings of the processes systematically emphasized as the basis for solving problems?

2. Is skill in reading problems developed? (Are pupils taught to recognize tricky words? To write problem questions? To restate problems?)

3. Are sets of problems usually organized around interesting and realistic social situations?

4. Are pictures, diagrams, graphs, and tables functionally used in solving problems?

Comments regarding the problem-solving program:

IV. Method of Presentation

1. Is consistent development through concrete, semi-concrete, and abstract experiences provided in pre-book, book, and post-book suggestions?

2. Are new ideas frequently introduced through motivating social situations?

3. Has provision been made for thorough reteaching at the beginning of each year and also at crucial points during the year?

4. Is there oral guidance toward efficient thought processes?

5. Do presentations move simply and directly in developing the main idea or skill on a given page?

6. In any developmental lesson is there systematic progression from immature to mature methods of solution?

7. Is the practice program satisfactory? (Practice should follow development of understanding and efficient thought procedure. Immediate practice should be sufficient for first fixing of skill. Maintenance program should be well spaced and include practice on meanings as well as on skills. Ample provision should be made at each grade level for extra practice when needed.)

8. Is learning thorough at time of presentation? (Is a major segment of the topic covered? Are a sufficient number of sequential pages used to assure real understanding and skill?)

9. Is the presentation strengthened by frequent use of estimation and mental computation?

10. Is there extensive use of charts and diagrams in the work with whole numbers, fractions, decimals, and per cents?

11. Are pupils taught various checks on work?

12. Does the program provide detailed help in caring for individual differences?

Comments regarding methods of presentation:

V. Testing Program

1. What provision is there for inventory tests?

2. Is there continuous evaluation through self-checking tests, periodic informal tests, and oral work?

3. Is there a complete program of chapter tests (tests of meaning and information, computation tests, problem-solving tests, and diagnostic tests keyed to developmental and practice material)?

4. Are additional tests available in the manual?

Comments regarding testing program:

VI. Other Aids to Learning

1. Are major topics spread over more than one grade level to provide for developmental learning?

2. Is there careful control of vocabulary, of sentence structure, and of paragraph length?

3. Is color used functionally in pictures and diagrams and on the type page?

4. Are variations in type and the page arrangements well planned for ease of use?

5. Is there correlation with the content of other subject areas?

6. Is there well-planned oral developmental work?

7. Are the directions for exercises clear and complete?

8. Is practice made interesting through variations in the text and helpful suggestions in the manual?

9. Do the workbooks help to guide learning and provide ample writing space?

Comments regarding aids to learning:

VII. Other Aids to Teaching

1. Are the ideas to be taught pinpointed? (Are there clue captions, carefully stated lesson objectives, specific background discussions, and so on?)

2. Are text pages made easily teachable? (Are oral and written work clearly designated? Are illustrated examples boxed? Are main points easily located, etc.?)

3. Is the extra practice keyed to specific text pages and shown with answers in the corresponding manual lessons?

4. Do the workbooks help evaluate the completeness of the pupils' understanding, as well as his level of skill?

5. Are there teachers' editions of workbooks with answers?

6. Do the teachers' manuals present a complete program for teaching arithmetic?

   a) A helpful general discussion.

   b) Overviews of the year's work and of the work in each chapter.

   c) Textbook pages reproduced with answers for all the work and not just for problems and abstract examples.

   d) Complete lesson plans including objectives, background discussion, pre-book lessons, book lessons, and sufficient extra suggestions for all pupils, slow learners, and more capable children.

   e) Further helps such as tests, bibliographies, lists of films and film strips, and suggestions for devices and games.

7. Do the texts, workbooks, and manuals have carefully worked-out reference aids, such as indexes, tables of contents, and grade-placement charts?

Comments regarding other aids to teaching:

VIII. Physical Features

1. Is the total effect of the art work, use of color, and general appearance of the page "inviting" to the child?

2. Have the illustrations been carefully made? (Are they abundant? Are they artistic? Are pages open and easy to use, yet complete in their coverage?)

3. Is the paper of acceptable quality? (Has it the proper degree of whiteness without glare? Is it heavy enough to prevent "show-through?")

4. Is the cover attractive and the book well made and durable?

Comments regarding physical features:

**PART V: A NEW PATTERN FOR ELEMENTARY SCHOOL
MATHEMATICS TEXTBOOKS**

ARITHMETIC IN 1970

William A. Brownell

Important as have been the changes in the arithmetic programs in our elementary schools during the last half century, other equally far-reaching changes are in the making. What some of them will be, it takes no gift of prophecy to predict. The directions of these changes, which will affect content, grade placement, and instructional emphasis, are already foreshadowed in current happenings.

.   .   .   .

[Among other things] Practicable means will be found to accommodate effectively differences in learning ability. Attempts to adjust content and methods of teaching to individual differences in learning ability have been none too successful, and published instructional materials have been only moderately helpful.

On the assumption that the children in a given class must be kept together, various practices have been employed. Textbooks have provided special sections marked by some symbol to indicate that they are intended for the more rapid learners, and other sections have been set apart by another symbol for pupils who are slower learners. Usually, these sections are short and are scattered here and there as space permits. In no sense do they add up to real programs for differentiated instruction.

More recently, teachers' manuals have tended to carry the burden, suggesting ways to supplement the text. Usually, these suggestions have been limited to more practice material or additional devices for developing meanings in the case of slower pupils, and to enrichment materials in the case of the more fortunate. The next move will probably be to write the textbook for children of average ability, but to provide two sets

[From "Arithmetic in 1970," *The National Elementary Principal,* XXXIX (October, 1959), pp. 42-44. Reprinted by permission of the author and *The National Elementary Principal.*]

of supporting workbooks—one for those children of superior ability and the other for those of inferior ability.*

IMPROVING TEACHING MATERIALS

Guy T. Buswell

If improvements are made in the program of arithmetic, better teaching materials and better teacher-training are necessary. While outstanding teachers can, and do, use textbooks with flexibility, for many teachers the arithmetic that is taught is the arithmetic of the textbook. Obviously, it is easier to say that teaching materials should be improved than it is to deliver pages of actually improved manuscript.

First, one must recognize the limitations of what may be done in any one textbook when applied to an entire class. For the weak pupils the book is too difficult; for the strong it is too easy. Applied exercises cannot possibly be of equal interest to all pupils. Sufficient explanation to make a concept clear to a slow learner bores the rapid learner. One might study with profit the way teachers of reading have turned to a basic book plus multiple supplementary books. This idea might be of use in arithmetic. If a basic book could be built for average pupils it could include all the facts and understandings essential to the subject. This might then be supplemented by booklets which, for the slow learner, would provide the additional explanations and practice materials that would be needed. For the brighter pupils, supplementary booklets of quite a different nature would be necessary. Rather than more explanation and practice, they would need enriching new topics and processes. For example, a booklet on non-decimal number systems might be prepared in attractive and interesting style. It would be for the intellectually curious pupil and it could afford many opportunities for mathematical imagination. Significant applications could be found, such as the use of different bases in computing machines, the use of modified number systems for automobile licenses in some states, the use of indexing systems in libraries, and many others.

[From "The Content and Organization of Arithmetic," *The Arithmetic Teacher*, VI (March, 1959), p. 81. Reprinted by permission of the author and *The Arithmetic Teacher*.]

---

* (*Editor's Note:* Cf. Brueckner, Grossnickle, and Reckzeh's discussion of "The Mathematics Workbook" in the concluding section of Part 3 of this chapter.)

With travel becoming common, many bright children could be interested in a booklet on foreign money systems and the processes of computing with them. The advantages of a decimal money system might be appreciated better after such a study. A booklet might show the variety of ways in which multiplying and dividing could be done or how answers could be checked. There would be room for a booklet of number puzzles and tricks which would, in turn, contribute to a better understanding of number relations. These illustrations may not be well chosen, but the intent is to find some way to escape from the strait-jacket of uniform textbooks for all types of pupils. Rather than make longer and longer books in an attempt to satisfy all users, there might be advantages in shorter basic books with supplementary booklets for special needs. This would permit more flexible programs, especially for the many small schools where sectioning into special classes is impractical.

BIBLIOGRAPHY

Andreen, Earl P. "A Study of Workbooks in Arithmetic," *Journal of Educational Research,* XXXII (October, 1938), 108-22.

Brueckner, Leo J. *Improving the Arithmetic Program.* New York: Appleton-Century-Crofts, Inc., 1957, 101.

———, and Foster E. Grossnickle. *Making Arithmetic Meaningful.* New York: Holt, Rinehart & Winston, Inc., 1957.

———, ———. *How to Make Arithmetic Meaningful.* New York: Holt, Rinehart & Winston, Inc., 1947.

———, ———, and John Reckzeh. *Developing Mathematical Understandings in the Upper Grades.* New York: Holt, Rinehart & Winston, Inc., 1957.

Brownell, William A. "Arithmetic in 1970," *The National Elementary Principal,* XXXIX (October, 1959), 42-45.

Buswell, G. T. "The Content and Organization of Arithmetic," *The Arithmetic Teacher,* VI (March, 1959), 77-83.

Colburn, Warren. *Intellectual Arithmetic: Upon the Induction Method of Instruction.* Boston: Houghton Mifflin Company, 1884.

Cronbach, Lee J. (ed.). *Text Materials in Modern Education.* Champaign, Ill.: University of Illinois Press, 1955.

Dooley, Sister M. Constance. "The Relationship Between Arithmetic Research and the Content of Arithmetic Textbooks," *The Arithmetic Teacher,* VII (April, 1960), 178-84.

Folsom, Mary O'Hearn. *A Study of Manual Material in the Field of Arithmetic,* Doctoral Dissertation. Iowa City: State University of Iowa, 1958.

———. "Teachers Look at Arithmetic Manuals," *The Arithmetic Teacher,* VII (January, 1960), 13-19.

Ginn & Company. "A Guide for Judging Arithmetics," *School Science and Mathematics,* LIX (June, 1959), 431-34.

Glennon, Vincent J., and C. W. Hunnicutt. *What Does Research Say about Arithmetic?* (rev. ed.). Washington, D.C.: Association for Study of Curriculum Development, 1958.

Grossnickle, Foster E., and Leo J. Brueckner. *Discovering Meanings in Arithmetic.* New York: Holt, Rinehart & Winston, Inc., 1959.

Hickerson, J. Allen. *Guiding Children's Arithmetic Experiences.* Englewood Cliffs, N. J.: Prentice-Hall, Inc., 1952, 59-60.

Hoyt, Franklin, and Harriet Peet. *Everyday Arithmetic.* Boston: Houghton Mifflin Company, 1915.

Knight, F. B., J. W. Studebaker, and G. M. Ruch. *Standard Service Arithmetics.* Chicago: Scott, Foresman & Company, 1926.

McNally, Harold J. "What Shall We Teach and How?" *National Elementary Principal,* XXXVI (May, 1957), 6-11.

Prince, John T. *Arithmetic by Grades.* Boston: Ginn & Company, 1895.

Repp, Florence C. "The Vocabularies of Five Recent Third Grade Arithmetic Textbooks," *The Arithmetic Teacher,* VII (March, 1960), 128-33.

Rudman, Herbert C. "Patterns of Textbook Use—Key to Curriculum Development," *The Elementary School Journal,* LVI (April, 1956), 401-6.

Schneider, Helen A. "The Place of Workbooks in the Teaching of Arithmetic," *Arithmetic 1948* (Chicago: University of Chicago Press, Supplementary Educational Monograph, No. 66, 1948), 54-67.

Schutter, Charles H., and Richard L. Spreckelmeyer. *Teaching the Third R: A Comparative Study of American and European Textbooks in Arithmetic.* Washington, D.C.: Council for Basic Education, 1959, 36-41.

Spitzer, Herbert F. *The Teaching of Arithmetic.* Boston: Houghton Mifflin Company, 1954, 318-29.

Stone, John C. "What's New in Arithmetic?" *Unit Mastery Arithmetic.* New York: Benjamin H. Sanburn and Company, 1932.

Textbooks Are Indispensable. New York: American Textbook Publishers Institute, 1956.

Timmerman, Melvin Eugene. *Differentiated Curriculum Designs, Especially with Reference to Curriculum Practices in the High Schools of South Carolina,* Doctoral Dissertation. University of South Carolina, 1956.

Voegelein, L. Belle. *List of Educational Subject Headings* (Columbus, Ohio: Committee on the Classification of Educational Materials, Commission on Coordination of Research Agencies, the National Education Association, Ohio State University, 1928).

Wilson, G. M., *et al. Teaching the New Arithmetic.* New York: McGraw-Hill Book Co., Inc., 1951, 453-57.

Wood, Clifford, Frederick S. Breed, and James R. Overman. *Child Life Arithmetic.* New York: Lyons & Carnahan, 1935.

XI PLANNING FOR TEACHER COMPETENCE IN MATHEMATICS EDUCATION

Glenn E. Barnett and Udo Jansen, The University of Texas

INTRODUCTION

BIBLIOGRAPHY

INTRODUCTION

Published reports of investigators who have studied the problem indicate that few elementary school teachers are adequately prepared to teach mathematics. With shocking unanimity, writers maintain (1) that teachers in the elementary schools are deficient in knowledge and understanding of mathematics, (2) that they have attitudes about the subject which can only inhibit effective teaching, (3) that they get little, if any, help in mathematics teaching from their pre-service and in-service preparation programs, and (4) that more mathematics in teachers' preparation is an antidote for the problem. The first three are based on a large body of research evidence; the fourth, on empirical interpretation. For each of these, only a representative selec-

466

tion of materials can be presented in the pages which follow. Writings on another area, that of broadly conceived investigation and experimentation in the actual improvement of teaching efficiency, equally important to the teacher-educator, are largely absent both here and in the literature.

The appalling lack of teachers' mastery of mathematics, reported in several of the studies which follow, is frequently attributed to the almost complete lack of mathematics requirements in the teacher certification regulations of the several states. Whatever its cause, Glennon and others have found it to be of major proportions and to have existed over a considerable number of years. But, though the mathematical illiteracy of these teachers is clearly established, no great body of evidence has yet been assembled to prove conclusively either that to require particular mathematics courses has a salutary effect on teachers' competence in this area, or that mastery of mathematics has any great influence on the effectiveness with which it is taught. Both hypotheses receive considerable support on grounds of their face validity; but such studies as those of Glennon and Weaver present conflicting views on the former, and definitive studies on the latter are lacking.

The predominant tone in the literature that teachers are so lacking in mathematics preparation has fathered a multitude of suggestions as to remediation. Authored in large part by those earlier committed to mastery of content, the suggestions might be construed as concluding that bringing the teachers' mastery to reasonable levels would solve the entire problem; but it is probably more in accord with the facts to infer that the influence of the findings to which reference has been made above has led to the belief that the top priority need of teachers is adequate knowledge and understanding of the area to be taught, in this case mathematics.

More recent writings suggest widely based plans for improvements and include such aspects of the teachers' preparation as his understanding of the problems of arithmetic teaching in the school setting. Recent experimentation in teacher education has no doubt produced valuable and provocative research materials regarding these and similar plans and it is hoped that these will shortly be made available on a large scale. It cannot be overemphasized here, however, that there is more need today to discover ways of remedying the situation than to collect and present additional evidence of the elementary school teacher's lack of mastery of mathematics. The situation offers a distinct challenge to those interested in teacher education to engage (1) in experimentation in search of effective ways to improve the teachers' mathematical knowledge and understanding, (2) in clarification of what the teacher should know, (3) in evaluation of the contributions of pre-service and in-service aspects of the teachers' preparation, and, not least of all, (4) in relating certain aspects of preparation to the improved teaching and learning of mathematics in the classroom. The reader will undoubtedly conclude from their near absence in these pages that the paucity of reports in this area is comparable only to the lack of teachers' knowledge of mathematics itself.

THE TEACHER

Henry S. Dyer, Robert Lakin, and Frederick M. Lord

During the early stages of the survey on which this report is based, articles in the newspapers described its purpose. One elementary school teacher, reading about it, wrote in to wish us luck. She said she had always dreaded mathematics and had to be constantly on guard to keep from inducing the same fear of the subject in her pupils.

At least one study supports the presumption that this teacher is not alone in her predicament. It showed that of 211 prospective elementary school teachers, nearly 150 had a long-standing hatred of arithmetic.

This state of affairs may not be unrelated to a lack of ordinary competence with numbers. A random sample of 370 candidates for elementary school positions faced this question on an examination:

The height of a letter in a certain size of print is ¼ inch. If the following are the heights (in inches) of this letter in other sizes of print, which one is the next larger size?

      a) $\frac{5}{16}$ *b)* $\frac{1}{2}$ *c)* $\frac{3}{16}$ *d)* $\frac{3}{8}$ *e)* $\frac{7}{16}$

Half of the 370 candidates picked a wrong answer.

[From *Problems in Mathematical Education* (Princeton: Educational Testing Service, 1956), pp. 12-7. Reprinted by permission of the authors and the Educational Testing Service.]

There have been numerous studies of teacher competence in arithmetic. If they can be believed, it seems pretty clear that many elementary school teachers have a hard time keeping even half a jump ahead of their pupils. Their salvation lies in memorized answers, rather than in any genuine understanding of arithmetical concepts. "Elementary teachers, for the most part," according to one observer who has taught them, "are ignorant of the mathematical basis of arithmetic; high school teachers assigned to teach mathematics fall in this category also."

This ignorance is scarcely surprising, for little knowledge of mathematics is expected, even officially, of prospective school teachers. In the majority of cases an individual with ambition to teach in an elementary school can matriculate at a teachers college without showing any high school mathematics on his record. He can graduate without studying any college mathematics. And in this condition, he can meet the requirements of most states for a certificate to teach arithmetic. The certification requirements for high school math teachers are only a little stiffer: nearly one-third of the states will license them even though they have had no college mathematics at all, and the average requirement for all states is only 10 semester hours.

No doubt many teachers go beyond the certification requirements in preparing for their job. One can suppose, however, that there are plenty of others who yield to human nature and stop at the minimum. In addition to these there is an unknown number on so-called "emergency certificates" who have not yet attained the minimum.

There is one point of view which insists that courses in how to teach, as opposed to courses in straight subject matter, are generally a waste of time, if not worse. Not many candidates for elementary school positions, however, have to "waste" much time taking courses in how to teach arithmetic. Four-fifths of the liberal arts colleges which have departments of education, one-half of the colleges of education, and one-third of the state teachers colleges do not require such a course. Many of these places do require their students to take courses in general teaching methods, but this is a far cry from courses aimed specifically at the strategy and tactics of teaching arithmetic. On the other hand, practically all trainees for high school mathematics teaching get some sort of course on how to present the material, although there is little agreement among the states about the method of presentation.

One writer after looking over the situation says, "Some of the most popular instructional practices (in arithmetic), to say nothing of the inferior ones, are not in quality the equal of methods in other fields in the elementary school, and some lag far behind learning theory." In view of the status of mathematical learning theory, as it has been sketched above, one wonders how the situation could be much different. It is hard to see how sound rules of practice can even be formulated until something more substantial than controversy attends the description of how children are most likely to learn mathematics.

Some people have an affection for the popular cliché that "a good teacher is born, not made." This does not mean that a good mathematics teacher can be devoid of subject matter knowledge or uninitiated in the techniques of imparting it. But it does imply that something more is required for effective teaching, namely, enthusiasm for the job and a sound personality. This seems like good common sense, but what does it involve? What do we really know about the role of personality factors in teaching? Not much. One reason for this is that we have yet to discover sufficiently dependable methods for assessing personality. Another is that the criteria of effective teaching are hard to pin down. If a teacher's personal make-up can not be defined, and if it is impossible to tell with certainty what effect he has on pupils, the task of tracing connections that may exist between what the teacher is and how much the pupils learn is not very easy. A few investigators have tried, but their findings are not very helpful.

With respect to the pupil's actual progress in mathematics, very little, indeed, is known about the relative effects of the teacher's background in subject matter, his training in instructional methods, his personal qualities, or his attitude toward the job. It is even conceivable, in the absence of concrete evidence one way or the other, that the whole difference between successful and unsuccessful mathematics students has nothing to do with the teacher at all, but can be accounted for solely by the pupil's potentiality for intellectual growth and the influences that play upon him outside the school walls.

This is conceivable but not likely. Measured in time alone, the teacher's place in the intellectual environment of his pupils is singularly important. What he knows or does not know, what he does or does not say and do in the classroom can hardly fail to have a considerable influence on what happens in the minds of the pupils. Despite the thinking and research that have been going on for a good many years, however, we still have an imperfect understanding of what a teacher *ought* to know, what he *ought* to say and do if his pupils are to achieve up to their limit in mathematics. This understanding is less likely to come from speculation and argument than it is from some comprehensive and well-controlled research.

In the absence of data, let us accept the assumption that a teacher who has a solid understanding of mathematics himself is more likely than not to develop a similar understanding in his pupils. Where does such an assumption take us? In a vicious circle, apparently—and in reverse—for it has been shown that this "solid understanding" is frequently absent in teachers. Future teachers pass through the elementary schools learning to detest mathematics. They drop it in high school as early as possible. They avoid it in teachers colleges because it is not required. They return to the elementary school to teach a new generation to detest it.

How can the circle be broken? Toughening up requirements for professional certification might help but it would be, at best, only half the solution. Stiffer requirements would exclude a lot of people deficient in mathematical background but they would not produce the numbers so desperately needed to man the rapidly multiplying classrooms of the nation. A much more direct attack on the problem is needed—a kind of Remedial Mathematics for Teachers of Mathematics designed to unravel the teacher's numerical neuroses, to nourish him on the why's and how's of mathematical phenomena, and to liberate him from the confinements of the textbook so that he may enjoy a lively appreciation of the thousands of important uses that mathematics has in the modern world. With that quality and freshness of understanding, he could go back to the classroom and start the circle turning in the right direction—toward a new generation sure-footed in number and delighting in mathematical concepts and the power of abstract reasoning.

This is a pretty picture but far from realistic. Not all the trouble in mathematics can be eliminated by retraining teachers, even if a good retreading process were known. When our observer visited 60 classrooms to verify at first hand what the books and the experts were saying about the deplorable state of mathematics teaching, he found 10 in which the teaching was reasonably effective; in the other 50 the instruction was so confused that learning of any kind seemed to be largely accidental and unillumined by any learning theory whatever. Perhaps our man happened to hit a peculiarly unattractive sample of schools. Maybe he expected too much, or saw too little. Admittedly, this brief glimpse at a few pieces of a very complex jigsaw puzzle cannot be relied upon as a fair representation of the whole picture.

In any case, the teachers themselves could not be censured for the conditions under which they work. Most of them were struggling with classes of 35 to 40 pupils who sometimes spread over two different grade levels and almost always ranged widely from the bright but bored to the dull and bewildered. It takes more than brains, good will, and a sparkling personality to conquer this kind of situation. It takes a fundamental change in the *conditions* of teaching—a change that only the public, acting through its representatives on school boards, can bring about.

PREPARATION OF TEACHERS OF ARITHMETIC

David S. Rappaport

Recent events have alerted the American people to the need for more scientists, mathematicians, engineers, and technicians. At first it was believed that the training of mathematicians was the sole responsibility of the colleges, later it became evident that earlier training in high school was necessary, and now it is generally agreed that interest in mathematics must be developed and furthered while the child is in the elementary school. This places a great responsibility upon the shoulders of the elementary school teacher who must be prepared in other areas of learning as well as in arithmetic. In order to meet this responsibility the modern teacher of arithmetic is required to have a better understanding of the child, of the psychology of learning, and of the subject itself.

How well prepared to teach arithmetic is the elementary school teacher? What are the certification requirements? What arithmetic competencies should the elementary teacher have? What are the teachers' attitudes toward arithmetic? These will be discussed in the present article.

Teachers' Preparation

Weaver has pointed out that, in the past, it has been assumed too often that the teacher did have an adequate understanding of the arithmetic she taught. He found that the teacher's arithmetic background was too often inadequate. He wrote:

> Before students can learn how to teach arithmetic meaningfully, they must have acquired the necessary breadth, depth and maturity of background in the subject-matter of arithmetic so that it may be a functional part of their preparation. Entirely too often this background of understanding and skill is *assumed,* thus becoming an unemphasized aspect of the over-all program of training. . . . All too frequently students are placed in teaching positions in elementary schools without having had any instruction per se since the days of their own elementary or junior high school study. Their point of view and degree of understanding is no broader nor deeper than that of the pupils they teach.[1]

[From "Preparation of Teachers of Arithmetic," *School Science and Mathematics,* LVIII (November, 1958), pp. 636-43. Reprinted by permission of the author and *School Science and Mathematics.*]

---

[1] J. Fred Weaver, "A Crucial Aspect of Meaningful Instruction," *The Mathematics Teacher,* XLIII (March, 1950), 116.

Newsom found that too many teachers were only one step ahead of their good students.[2] Morton reported that 13.6 per cent of the students in his education classes were below the eighth-grade norm in arithmetic and that some were even below the sixth-grade norm.[3]

Glennon conducted the most significant research study in this field. He devised a *Test of Basic Mathematical Understandings* composed of 80 items divided into five sections: Section 1, the decimal system of notation; Section 2, basic understandings of integers and processes; Section 3, basic understandings of fractions and processes; Section 4, basic understandings of decimals and processes; and Section 5, basic understandings of the rationale of computation. These items were limited to the arithmetic taught in the first seven grades of the elementary school. Glennon administered his test to 144 teachers-college freshmen, 172 teachers-college seniors, and to 160 teachers-in-service whose experience ranged from 1 to 34 years. He reported the following findings:

1a. Teachers-college freshmen understand 44 per cent of the basic understandings.

1b. Teachers-college seniors understand 43 per cent.

1c. Teachers-in-service understand 55 per cent.

2a. There is no significant difference in achievement of basic mathematical understandings between teachers-college freshmen and teachers-college seniors. Persons preparing to teach did not grow in achievement during the four years of the program of teacher education.

2b. There is no significant difference between a teachers-college senior who has had a course in the Psychology and Teaching of Arithmetic and the teachers-college senior who has not had such a course.

2c. There is no significant difference in achievements between a teacher-in-service who has done graduate work in Psychology and Teaching of Arithmetic and one who has not done graduate work in that course. Graduate work in Psychology and Teaching of Arithmetic did not contribute to growth in basic mathematical understandings.

2d. Experience in teaching arithmetic is no guarantee that the teacher will grow in the understanding of the subject.[4]

It is of great interest that Glennon's findings remained unchallenged until Weaver made a similar study in 1956: Weaver administered Glen-

---

[2] C. V. Newsom, "Mathematical Background Needed by Teachers of Arithmetic," *The Teaching of Arithmetic*, Fiftieth Yearbook, The National Society for the Study of Education (Chicago: University of Chicago Press, 1951), Part II, 232.

[3] R. L. Morton, *Teaching Arithmetic*, What Research Says to the Teacher, Pamphlet No. 2, Department of Classroom Teachers and American Educational Research Association of the National Education Association, 1953, p. 28.

[4] Vincent J. Glennon, "A Study in Needed Redirection in the Preparation of Teachers of Arithmetic," *The Mathematics Teacher*, XLII (December, 1949), 389-96.

non's test to 92 students in the Fall of 1953, 92 students in the Fall of 1954, 63 students in the Spring of 1955, and 101 students in the Fall of 1955. The average for the 348 students was an understanding of 55.8 per cent. Weaver retested one of the groups at the end of the semester's work in his methods course and found that the students gained an average of 14.2 per cent in basic mathematical understandings. He concluded that a methods course is effective if taught properly.[5]

The evidence appears to show that prospective elementary teachers are not receiving adequate instruction in arithmetic itself. Teachers colleges have the very important task of teaching arithmetic to the prospective elementary school teachers as well as psychology and methods courses. The teacher training program is influenced, of course, by the various certification requirements.

Certification Requirement

Several studies were made at various times to determine what are the certification requirements in different teacher training institutions. As was to be expected, there was, and there still is, a big range in training requirements in arithmetic in different states and institutions. The earlier studies are reported in order to reveal a trend or lack of trend in arithmetic requirements for teachers.

Judd and Morton [6] sent a questionnaire to 142 institutions that were members of the American Association of Teachers Colleges (1932-3). They found that of 104 institutions, 84 required a course in arithmetic for teacher certification while 20 institutions had no such requirement. Six out of 96 institutions had no methods course in teaching arithmetic. Thirty institutions had prerequisites for methods courses in arithmetic while 71 had no prerequisites. Even the term arithmetic course had different meanings, for "69 indicate that it is classified as mathematics, 14 as education, 8 as mathematics and education, 3 as special methods, and 2 as socialized mathematics.

Taylor made the first study of arithmetic requirements in teacher certification in 1928 and then repeated the study in 1935. The following figures taken from his study show the changes that took place between 1928 and 1935:

[5] J. Fred Weaver, "A Crucial Problem in the Preparation of Elementary-School Teachers," *Elementary School Journal,* LVI (February, 1956), 255-61.

[6] R. D. Judd and R. L. Morton, "Current Practices in Teacher-Training Courses in Arithmetic," *The Teaching of Arithmetic,* Tenth Yearbook, National Council of Teachers of Mathematics (New York: Bureau of Publications, Teachers College, Columbia University, 1935), pp. 157-72.

TABLE 1 *

		Per Cent Not Re-quiring Arithmetic	Per Cent Requiring 3 or More Sem-Hrs
Kdg-primary	1928	20.6	37.4
Kdg-primary	1935	29.7	30.6
Int. Grades	1928	10.2	62.6
Int. Grades	1935	28.3	34.8
Gram. Grades & Jr. H. S.	1928	9.9	59.4
Gram. Grades & Jr. H. S.	1935	51.4	28.1
Gen. Elem. Course	1928	45.8	28.9
Gen. Elem. Course	1935	14.8	48.1

* E. H. Taylor, "The Preparation of Teachers of Arithmetic in Teachers Colleges," *The Mathematics Teacher*, XXX (January, 1937), 13.

Table 1 shows that in 1935 fewer schools had a requirement for arithmetic in the teacher training program than in 1928, with the simple exception of their general elementary curriculum. Taylor also found that while the arithmetic that was offered as part of the teacher training program was sometimes classified as arithmetic subject matter, in 53 per cent of the semester hours the arithmetic course was devoted to methods only.[7]

The states also have different certification requirements that range from less than one year of college work to four years of college training. Blyler reported that in 1945:

> Nineteen states require four years of training beyond high school; four states require three years of training of college grade; fourteen states require two years of training beyond high school; nine states require one year of training beyond high school; and two states require less than one year of training beyond high school.[8]

The latest study of the teacher training program for arithmetic teachers was reported by Grossnickle in 1951. He sent a questionnaire to 147 state teachers colleges, members of the American Association of Colleges for Teacher Education. He received 131 returns but was able to use only 129. He found that 65 per cent of the colleges had the same program for all teachers, while 35 per cent had a differentiated program, i.e., kindergarten-primary, intermediate, advanced, and general elementary. He also found that 76 per cent of the colleges had no mathematics requirement for admission to the curriculum preparing teachers of arithmetic, while 24

---

[7] *Ibid.*, p. 13.

[8] Dorothy Blyler, "Certification of Elementary School Teachers in the United States," *Elementary School Journal*, XLV (June, 1945), 571.

per cent required some form of mathematics.[9] This showed that in most teachers colleges many students had not had any mathematics for at least four years. This fact was of great significance in view of the fact that many of these colleges did not require any background mathematics in the curriculum for teachers of arithmetic. Grossnickle reported that the requirement of background mathematics for the different curricula was as follows: 33 per cent for the kindergarten-primary grades, 40 per cent for the intermediate grades, 47 per cent for the advanced grades, and 65 per cent for the general elementary curriculum.[10]

Grossnickle was also concerned with the question of whether the methods of teaching arithmetic was given as a special course or as part of a general methods course. He reported the following:

TABLE 2 *

| Curriculum | Average Number of Semester Hours | Number of Institutions Offering Instruction | | Instruction As Part of General Methods |
| | | Separate Course in Teaching Arithmetic | | |
		Required	Not Required	
Kdg-primary	1.4	27	18	8
Intermediate	1.9	14	6	7
Advanced	1.5	12	5	5
General Elementary	1.5	75	39	34

* *Ibid.*, p. 214.

Grossnickle drew the following conclusions based on the findings in Table 2:

> This means that the average number of semester-hours in both background and professional courses is equivalent to about one course in arithmetic for one semester. A meager offering of this kind is inadequate to equip the teacher to do a satisfactory job in the teaching of arithmetic, especially since most of the colleges have no mathematical requirement for entrance from high school. As long as this situation exists in the training of teachers of arithmetic, the schools of our country are certain to be staffed with teachers who are not adequately trained to teach arithmetic except as a tool subject. When this philosophy is accepted, drill is the chief instrument in the teacher's professional kit.[12]

---

[9] F. E. Grossnickle, "The Training of Teachers of Arithmetic," *The Teaching of Arithmetic*, Fiftieth Yearbook, The National Society for the Study of Education (Chicago: University of Chicago Press, 1951), Part II, 207-8.

[10] *Ibid.*, p. 210.

[12] *Ibid.*, p. 217.

The National Education Association has reported great progress in the number of states that have required college graduation as a minimum for regular elementary-school teaching certificates. However, 13 states still require in 1957 less than a bachelor's degree. Of these states, one requires three years of college training, nine require only two years, two require one year, and one state requires only 12 semester-hours of college training.[13] While the requirement of a bachelor's degree is no guarantee that prospective teachers will be adequately trained in arithmetic, it seems reasonable to conclude that less than a bachelor's degree will almost certainly result in inadequate training in arithmetic.

Needed Arithmetic Competencies

There is general agreement by the writers on teacher training that the background course in arithmetic should deal with the concept and nature of number, the fundamental operations, fractions, decimals, and measurement. As is to be expected, there is some variation among specific programs. Newsom recommends the following program:

1. Evolution of arithmetical concepts and notations
2. Number—one-to-one correspondence
3. Positional notation
4. Properties of integers
5. Four basic arithmetical operations
6. The fractions
   a) Terminology
   b) Rational numbers
   c) Common fractions
   d) Decimal fractions
7. The arithmetic of measurement
   a) The process of measurement
   b) Systems of measurement
   c) Computation with approximate numbers
8. Applications
   a) Evaluation of formulas
   b) Ratio and proportion
   c) Business arithmetic
   d) Statistical concepts
   e) Probability [14]

---

[13] National Education Association, "The Postwar Struggle to Provide Competent Teachers," *Research Bulletin*, XXXV (October, 1957), 123.
[14] *Op. cit.*, p. 249.

Schaaf recommends a slightly different program:

I. Number Concepts and Numeration
   A. Historical Development
   B. Theory of Numeration

II. Nature of Number
   A. Psychological Considerations
   B. Number Systems of Algebra
   C. Logical Foundations of Arithmetic

III. Computation
   A. Historical Development
   B. Analysis of Theory of Computation

IV. Measurement
   A. Direct Measurement
   B. Indirect Measurement
   C. Elements of Statistics

V. Socio-economic Applications
   A. Arithmetic in the Home
   B. Arithmetic in the Market Place
   C. Arithmetic and Finance [15]

In order to develop the necessary competencies, Taylor recommended that every prospective teacher take at least eight semester hours of mathematics, including background mathematics and methods of teaching arithmetic.[16] Grossnickle recommended at least six semester hours in background mathematics and one course in the teaching of arithmetic.[17] Newsom recommended that the course covering his outline of needed background be required of all elementary school teachers.[18] In addition to the required courses in mathematics the above writers recommended that these courses be taught by people experienced in the field of arithmetic.

Attitudes of Prospective Teachers

The teacher's attitude toward his subject is one of the important factors in his success as a teacher. Dutton wrote that he always asks the students in his methods classes what their feelings are concerning arithmetic. He arrived at four significant conclusions:

---

[15] William L. Schaaf, "Arithmetic for Arithmetic Teachers," *School Science and Mathematics*, LIII (October, 1953), 540-42.

[16] E. H. Taylor, "Mathematics for a Four-year Course for Teachers in the Elementary School," *School Science and Mathematics*, XXXVIII (May, 1938), 500.

[17] *Op. cit.*, p. 230.

[18] *Op. cit.*, p. 233.

1. A tremendous outpouring of unfavorable feelings toward arithmetic. The language used is expressive and emotional. Seventy-four per cent of all responses were unfavorable.

2. There were seven responses to the reason why.
   a) Lack of understanding
   b) Teaching dissociated from life
   c) Pages of word problems
   d) Boring drill
   e) Poor teaching
   f) Lack of interest
   g) Fear of making mistakes

3. University students come to methods classes with antagonistic attitudes toward arithmetic.

4. The statements expressed . . . seem to be so highly charged emotionally that they will influence the learning of methods for teaching arithmetic for a large proportion of the class.[19]

The present writer's experiences were similar to Dutton's. Many of his students have informed him that they put off taking the required course in background mathematics for as long a time as possible because they had always disliked or feared mathematics. He feels that he has succeeded in removing most of the dislikes but not the fears.

Conclusions and Recommendations

Elementary school teachers have the very important responsibility of helping the elementary school child develop an understanding of, and an interest in, mathematics. In order to perform this task efficiently they must themselves have a better understanding of the basic concepts of mathematics than was characteristic of teachers in the past, or perhaps even the present. The teacher training institutions must shoulder the responsibility of preparing teachers to meet the educational needs of children in an atomic age. These institutions should help prospective teachers overcome fear of, and present antagonism toward, mathematics. Certification requirements should be modified so that all prospective teachers are required to take adequate courses in background mathematics as well as methods of teaching arithmetic. The task is great but an understanding of the problems involved should lead to a program which will better prepare teachers to teach arithmetic in the elementary schools.

---

[19] Wilbur H. Dutton, "Attitudes of Prospective Teachers Toward Arithmetic," *Elementary School Journal,* LII (October, 1951), 85-87.

A STUDY IN NEEDED REDIRECTION IN THE PREPARATION OF TEACHERS OF ARITHMETIC

Vincent J. Glennon

A few years ago in a city in New England there appeared on the front page of the newspaper the story of an investigation of the death of a hospital patient. This story received more than the usual amount of publicity for such an incident because of the fact that the patient was not in any serious condition immediately prior to his death. To the medical authorities the cause of the death was not readily apparent, and an investigation was carried out. Among other things the investigation revealed that the patient was administered a drug shortly before his death. Further investigation of this particular act brought to light the fact that a nurse had been requested by the medical doctor in charge to prepare a solution using *one-eighth* of a grain of a particular drug. Pursuing the investigation still further, the nurse was asked to *tell* and *show* exactly what she had done in preparing the solution. In describing her behavior the nurse said that she did not know what *one-eighth* was, but she thought that since *four* and *four* made *eight, one-fourth* and *one-fourth* should make *one-eighth*. And she prepared the solution accordingly!

The tragic aspect of this incident is equaled only by the high degree of mathematical illiteracy represented in the incident.

The layman might well ask "How could such an error occur?" "How could it happen that the child having become a nurse made such a grave error?" "How could it happen that she did not have a correct understanding of the fraction 'one-eighth'?" The answer to this latter question is not simple and single, but rather subtle and complex. The whole answer might include such factors as the ability of the learner to acquire the understanding, the quality of the social climate in which the learning occurred, the kinds or types of learning activities in which the students participated, the attitude of the teacher toward the methods of teaching that she was using, the understanding of the teacher of the relative effectiveness of different methods of teaching, the appreciation on the part of the teacher of the type of situation in which learning occurs best, and the degree to which the teacher, herself, had acquired those mathematical

[From "A Study in Needed Redirection in the Preparation of Teachers of Arithmetic," *The Mathematics Teacher*, XLII (December, 1949), pp. 389-96. Reprinted by permission of the author and *The Mathematics Teacher*.]

understandings and meanings which are basic to the computational processes commonly taught in grades one to eight.

This paper is concerned with reporting a study of the last of these factors: the degree to which student teachers and teachers-in-service have acquired the basic mathematical understandings and meanings.

The paucity of *precise* studies in this area of teacher education that have been carried out in the last thirty years is disconcerting indeed. The writer found only one *study* [1] that was related to the problem, and it was written over ten years ago. All other published writings in the area of *teacher education* in *arithmetic* seem to be concerned with our telling each other what we *should be doing* in the redirection of the program.

The Present Study: Its Purpose, Method, Findings and Implications [2]

Purpose. It was the purpose of the study to determine the extent of growth and mastery of certain basic mathematical understandings possessed by three groups of persons: teachers-college freshmen, teachers-college seniors, and teachers-in-service. The total group included 476 persons, of which 144 were freshmen, 172 were seniors, and 160 were teachers-in-service. The college students were enrolled in three teachers colleges. All were preparing to teach on the elementary school level.

The teachers-in-service were teaching in kindergarten through grade eight. The numbers of years in service ranged from one to thirty-four years.

Method. The general type of investigative method used in the study was the normative method; that is, a method through the use of which we obtain an index of prevailing conditions within the groups of persons being studied.

The specific method used in gathering the data was the administering of a *Test of Basic Mathematical Understanding.* The first job, then, was the selection of the instrument to be used in gathering the data. For this the researcher turned to a collection of arithmetic texts that included all tests published since 1915. Each test was carefully examined for the purpose of determining the number and quality of items designed for the purpose of measuring *basic mathematical understandings.* The examina-

---

[1] E. H. Taylor, "Mathematics for a Four-Year Course for Teachers in the Elementary School," *School Science and Mathematics,* May, 1938.

[2] Data included in this paper taken from a larger study: Vincent J. Glennon, "A Study of the Growth and Mastery of Certain Basic Mathematical Understandings on Seven Educational Levels." Unpublished doctor's dissertation. Cambridge: Graduate School of Education, Harvard University, 1948.

tion of the tests revealed no tests that would meet the need of the study.

Reflecting this need for newer instruments, Butler [3] said, ". . . it is certain that in the domain of published tests the specific testing for mastery of mathematical concepts (understandings) has received scant attention."

Brownell [4] had this to say on the same point: "Exceedingly little has been done either informally or systematically to find practicable and valid procedures for evaluating the outcomes (in mathematical understandings)."

It was necessary then to construct an instrument that could be used in the study for gathering the data. Stated negatively, the new instrument must be of such a kind as to eliminate entirely or at least minimize the effect of rote computational facility as a determiner of success. A test of mathematical understandings that involved computation habits, which may have been learned largely through repetition, would be quite invalid, since it would be difficult to determine the degree to which the testee's responses were the result of *understanding* or the result of *rote* memory.

This statement does not carry the implication that tests of computational facility such as those examined do not require understanding for success, or that pupils who do not understand will be as successful as those pupils who do understand. On the contrary, it is quite probable that the pupil with the greatest degree of understanding will be the most successful on the test of computational facility. However, it is true that the test which eliminates or minimizes computational facility will also eliminate or minimize one factor contributing to the nonvalidity of the instrument as a measure of understanding of number relationships. For this reason the instrument was constructed in such manner as to eliminate all direct computation.

Another characteristic of the new instrument is objectivity. To attain this characteristic the test items were built in the form of multiple choice items. This type of item was chosen on the basis of such statements as that of Hawkes, Lindquist and Mann.[5] "The multiple choice type is perhaps the most valuable and the most generally applicable of all types of test exercises." Included among the choices in the test items were typical pupil responses. These were obtained by the administration and analysis of test items of the completion type—that is questions in which the testee was not given any aid or clues in recalling the correct answer.

---

[3] C. H. Butler, "Mastery of Certain Mathematical Concepts by Pupils at the Junior High School Level," *The Mathematics Teacher*, March, 1932, pp. 117-172.

[4] W. A. Brownell, Sixteenth Yearbook National Council of Teachers of Mathematics, *Arithmetic in General Education*, 1940, p. 247.

[5] H. E. Hawkes, E. F. Lindquist, and C. R. Mann, *Construction and Use of Achievement Examinations* (Boston: Houghton Mifflin Company, 1936), p. 138.

Several commonly used validation procedures were considered for their applicability to the problem of constructing this particular instrument. There is time here to but list the procedures: the first validation procedure was concerned with analytical or curricular validity; the second procedure considered was that of determining the statistical validity of the instrument by comparing scores made by testees on the new instrument and a criterion instrument; a third technique commonly used and considered for this study is that which is based on the increase of scores with increasing grade levels. Still another technique commonly used and considered here is that type of validation procedure which makes use of the combined judgments of relatively equally well informed experts in the field covered by the test.

No one of these techniques for determining the validity of an instrument is useful by itself. In the last analysis the best method for determining the validity of any instrument is an observation of the behavior of the testee —keeping in mind the question: Does the test distinguish between the behavior of the person who understands (or has a given ability, or has a given attitude, etc.) and the behavior of the person who does *not* understand?

With this question in mind the researcher worked with several groups of children—two children per group—on the seventh grade level over a period of two months. It was felt that working with two children would make for better rapport between the children and the researcher, since a single child might find it difficult to adjust readily to the new situation.

"Loaded" questions were discovered by the child's ability to select the correct answer without being able to describe or verbalize the understanding involved. Such questions were either revised or eliminated. This procedure was repeated with many groups of children until they identified no new "loaded" questions.

During the procedure the tester also noted evidences of reading difficulties stemming from the wording of items. Whenever the item seemed to cause such difficulty, the children were asked to tell what they thought the item meant, and were asked to state the meaning in their own words. This wording was noted and the items changed to conform with wording that was more meaningful for children. Difficulties in sentence structure, vocabulary burden, and ambiguities were also noted and the items modified or eliminated.

Through this procedure the original test of 136 items was reduced to 90 items. A test of 90 items of this ilk is somewhat too long for use in a single classroom sitting, and the number of items was reduced to 80. The items covered five areas of basic mathematical understandings: (1) The decimal system of notation (15 items), (2) Basic understandings of integers and processes (15 items), (3) Basic understandings of fractions and processes (15 items), (4) Basic understandings of decimals and processes (20 items) and (5) Basic understandings of the rationals of computation (15 items).

A preliminary "run" on the seventh grade level provided insights which aided in arranging the items in order of difficulty within each area; and also provided an estimate of the amount of time needed by seventh graders to work the test. Since the test was of a diagnostic variety, rather than achievement variety, the timing was not needed for the purpose of setting a time limit, but only as a guide for school administration purposes.

The test was administered to the teachers-college freshmen at the beginning of the school year, and to the seniors at the end of the school year. Tests were administered to the teachers-in-service at the end of the year.

Some of the Findings of the Study

The data collected through the administration of the *Test of Basic Mathematical Understandings* was collated by using several common techniques. Time does not permit of a detailed reading of the more specific findings, but some of the more general findings can be considered here.

Hypothesis I. One of the hypotheses investigated was stated this way: There is no significant difference in achievement of basic mathematical understandings between a teachers-college freshman and a teachers-college senior.

Findings I. The mean score of the teachers-college freshman was 35.451 and the mean score of the teachers-college senior was 34.186—a difference of 1.255 points in favor of the freshman. The significance ratio of .826 gives a confidence level of 41 per cent. This confidence level supports the hypothesis that there is no significant difference in achievement of basic mathematical understandings between the two groups studied.

The findings seem to present evidence (for the groups studied) that the persons preparing to teach arithmetic in the elementary grades did not grow in achievement of basic mathematical understandings during the four years in the program of teacher education.

Hypothesis II. A second hypothesis was stated this way: There is no significant difference in achievement of basic mathematical understandings between a teachers-college senior who has taken a course in the Psychology and Teaching of Arithmetic, and a teachers-college senior who has *not* taken a course in the Psychology and Teaching of Arithmetic.

Findings II. Before testing this hypothesis the two groups were compared to determine whether or not there was a significant difference between the two groups in the number of mathematics courses taken in col-

lege and high school. In this sub-hypothesis the significance ratio was
.137, placing the confidence level at approximately the 90 per cent level.
This level supports the sub-hypothesis that there is no significant difference between the two groups in the number of mathematics courses taken
previously in college and high school.

The mean score of teachers-college seniors who had a course in the
Psychology and Teaching of Arithmetic was 33.984. The mean score of
teachers-college seniors who had *no* course in the Psychology and Teaching of Arithmetic was 34.886. A significance ratio of .379 places the confidence level at approximately 70 per cent. This supports the hypothesis
that there is no significant difference in the achievement of basic mathematical understandings between a teachers-college senior who has taken
the course in the Psychology and Teaching of Arithmetic and the teachers-
college senior who has *not* taken such a course.

Within the limitations of the study, the evidence seems to point to the
fact that a course in the Psychology and Teaching of Arithmetic did *not*
bring about any significant growth on the part of the teachers-college
student in the area of basic mathematical understandings. This does not
mean that the student did not benefit from the course in educational outcomes other than an understanding of arithmetic. On the contrary, the
student may have profited considerably in acquiring a fund of knowledge
about methods of teaching the subject. However, it is important to know
what to teach as well as *how* to teach it!

Hypothesis III. There is no significant difference in achievement of basic
mathematical understandings between a teacher-in-service who has done
graduate work in the Psychology and Teaching of Arithmetic and one who
has *not* done graduate work in the Psychology and Teaching of Arithmetic. The two groups represented the same statistical population in terms
of the number of courses in mathematics taken previously in college and
high school.

Findings III. Testing the hypothesis we find that the mean score of the
teacher-in-service who has done graduate work in the Psychology and
Teaching of Arithmetic is 42.765, and the mean score of the teacher-in-
service who has *not* done such graduate work is 44.940. The significance
ratio is .898. The confidence level is approximately 38 per cent and the
hypothesis is supported.

Within the limitations of the study this data indicates that graduate
work in the Psychology and Teaching of Arithmetic did *not* contribute to
growth in basic mathematical understandings.

Another question that was investigated in the study could be stated this
way: What degree of relationship exists, among teachers-in-service in the
elementary grades, between the numbers of years of experience the teacher

has had in teaching arithmetic and her achievement of the basic mathematical understandings?

The correlation coefficient (Pearson) between the two variables is − .055. This is close to zero correlation, and indicates that, for the sample tested, there is almost no relationship between the number of years a person has taught arithmetic and her achievement of basic mathematical understandings.

From the findings we may conclude that the experience of teaching arithmetic is no guarantee that the teacher will grow in her understanding of the subject.

The Table is another commonly used technique for presenting collated data. Two tables are presented here:

TABLE 1

Average Per Cent of Achievement of Basic Mathematical
Understandings for Each Level
Total number of test items—80

Grade Level	Average Raw Score	Per Cent of Total (80)
Teachers-college freshmen	35.451	44.31
Teachers-college senior	34.186	42.73
Teachers-in-service	43.813	54.77

Several conclusions can be drawn from this table:

1. The teachers-college freshman understands about 44 per cent of the basic mathematical understandings tested. These understandings are basic to the computational processes commonly taught in grades one through six!

2. The teachers-college senior understands about 43 per cent of these basic mathematical understandings!

3. The teacher-in-service understands about 55 per cent (slightly more than half) of the understandings that are basic to the computational processes commonly taught in grades one through six!

A few statements that can be drawn from Table 2 are:

1. There were no (zero) items that were easy enough to be answered correctly by all (100 per cent) of the freshmen.

2. There were no (zero) items that were easy enough to be answered correctly by all (100 per cent) of the seniors.

3. There were three (3) items that were answered correctly by all (100 per cent) of the teachers-in-service.

4. About half of the items on the test (43 for freshmen, 39 for seniors)

were so difficult for teachers-college students that less than half of the students were able to answer them correctly!

TABLE 2

NUMBER OF TEST ITEMS ANSWERED CORRECTLY BY
PER CENT OF TESTEES ON EACH GRADE LEVEL

Per Cent of Testees	Number of Items Answered Correctly by Grade Level		
	Freshmen	Seniors	Teachers
100%	0	0	3
90-99	5	6	4
75-89	7	11	13
50-74	25	24	32
Less than 50%	43	39	28
Total number of test items	80	80	80

The conclusions drawn from the data that have been presented thus far have not given us a very sanguine picture. The readers of this article might even be asking themselves—What kind of basic mathematical understandings were used in the test that could derive such a picture? Did we select only the very difficult understandings and omit the simpler understandings? It might be worth our while to look at a few of these understandings.

One of the easiest understandings as determined by the number of persons who selected the correct response is: Changing the order of addends in an addition example does not change the value of the answer.

The understanding that ranked about in the twentieth position in order from easy to difficult was: The third place to the left of the decimal point is the "hundreds" place.

The understanding that ranked about half way in order of difficulty was: Dividing the dividend and divisor by ten does not change the value of the answer (quotient).

The understanding that ranked in about sixtieth position out of eighty items in order of difficulty was: The denominator of a fraction tells us the number of equal parts into which the whole is divided.

One of the most difficult understandings in the test was: A digit in the "units" place represents a value one-tenth as large as the same digit in the "tens" place.

Implications of the Findings

Can we say that these understandings are very difficult understandings in the arithmetic of the first six grades? On the contrary, these understandings include some of the less abstract generalizations basic to the computational processes which are commonly taught in grades one through six.

All in all, the findings reported in this study do not present a very optimistic picture of the achievement of basic mathematical understandings on the part of the student teachers and teachers-in-service that were included in the study.

Recalling again for a moment the story of the nurse related at the beginning, is it not possible that the real reason for her lack of understanding of the fraction "one-eighth" may have been that the teachers who taught her arithmetic as a child did not themselves really *understand* arithmetic? And not understanding the subject they had to teach it as a series of meaningless tricks, the chief learning activity being repetition—*without* insight.

One hesitates to generalize on the findings of a study that involved only 476 persons, and 38,000 responses. Also one hesitates to generalize on the findings of a study, the data for which were gathered through the use of a group test. Far superior to this type of test perhaps would be the study of the behavior of each person individually through conversing with him, and keeping anecdotal records of his performances on the test items. Realizing the hazards of generalizing on limited data, and keeping in mind the limitations of the study, we would nevertheless do well to consider the findings of the study as they impinge on the problem of the training of teachers of arithmetic.

One of the more significant findings of the study reported in this article is that which is concerned with the degree of mastery of the basic mathematical understandings on the part of students in teacher-training institutions. This particular finding shows that, on the part of the students tested, there is no significant difference in achievement of basic mathematical understandings between the students who have taken a course in the Psychology and Teaching of Arithmetic and the students who have *not* taken such a course.

One might attempt to rationalize this finding by saying that the students already knew (understood) all of the arithmetic commonly taught in grades one through six, and therefore could not grow any more. An answer to this is in the finding which states that these students *understood* less than half of the arithmetic commonly taught in these grades.

One aspect of the needed redirection of the training of teachers of arithmetic seems to lie in the professional training offered in the teachers colleges and schools of education. This training, as it is usually set up at the present time, consists of a single course in the methodology of teaching arithmetic as a "tool" subject. Little emphasis is placed on the professional study of arithmetic as a science of numbers—as a system of related ideas—as a series of number relationships.

The findings of this study offer factual support for the recommendation made in the "Guidance Report of the Commission on Postwar Plans." [6] In their report the commission states:

(If you should wish to qualify (for a position in the teaching of arithmetic), the main requirement would be that you *understand* arithmetic. You cannot teach what you do not know.

If you are planning to teach in the elementary school, three things are very important: (1) a good methods course; (2) at least one course that will give you subject-matter background for the mathematics taught in Grades I through VI; (3) at least one course that will give you subject-matter background for teaching the general mathematics of Grades VII and VIII.

Other significant findings of the study reported in this paper are concerned with the degree of mastery of the basic mathematical understandings on the part of teachers-in-service. These findings show that the teachers in the study *understood* about half (55 per cent) of the arithmetic commonly taught in grades one through six, that they did not grow in understanding of the subject-matter of arithmetic by taking a graduate course in the Psychology and Teaching of Arithmetic; and that they did not grow in *understanding* of the subject matter of arithmetic as a result of experience in teaching arithmetic in the grades over a period of one or more years.

These findings seem to suggest several aspects of needed redirection in the program of in-service development of teachers of arithmetic. Curriculum revision of the professional courses must be concerned with emphasizing the subject matter *as well* as with the principles of teaching the subject-matter.

Very few persons in responsible educational positions today would doubt the worthwhileness of the educational values derivable from teaching arithmetic, or any other body of subject-matter, on the basis of meanings and understandings. In spite of the demonstrated values, however, understandings are little emphasized; this is particularly true in the field of arithmetic. Perhaps the reason for the general crass indifference to the teaching of meanings and understanding in arithmetic is due to the fact that arithmetic is still laboring under the handicap of being called a "tool" subject—a subject with no inherent understandings or meanings. Perhaps the reason for the general indifference is due to the application

---

[6] "Guidance Report of the Commission on Postwar Plans," *The Mathematics Teacher,* November, 1947. 324-25.

of a narrow interpretation (or mis-interpretation) of S-R psychology—an interpretation which stressed the need for immediacy of response, an interpretation which put a premium on accuracy, and an interpretation which made drill and repetition the chief learning activities. Whatever the reason —it is certain that the values of teaching for understanding have not been appreciated to the point of modifying the teaching and the curriculum to include the understandings, meanings, principles and generalizations basic to the number system.

Another possible reason for the comparative neglect in the teaching of understandings may be due to the fact that the persons responsible for the development of the curriculum materials did not themselves have a knowledge of the basic mathematical understandings. Findings of the study would tend to support this statement.

Since both carefully controlled research studies and other less-precise methods of rational inquiry have proven the worthwhileness of teaching for understandings, we must accept the responsibility for doing so. We are now in a position to create an "all-out" effort to discover new methods and materials for teaching and evaluating for growth in basic mathematical understandings. Dissemination of information about such methods and materials would do much to bring about on the part of the teacher and the administrator, acting in the role of curriculum makers, an increased awareness of the need for teaching and evaluating for growth in these understandings. Out of this increased awareness would come increased emphasis on understandings in textbooks, courses of study, teaching materials, and evaluation devices.

Understanding—This is the frontier of needed redirection in the training of teachers of arithmetic.

A CRUCIAL ASPECT OF MEANINGFUL ARITHMETIC INSTRUCTION

J. Fred Weaver

Certainly no attempt has been made to illustrate exhaustively the major point of emphasis in this discussion. Rather, a few illustrations have been selected to typify the general nature of the broader, more mature gen-

[From "A Crucial Aspect of Meaningful Arithmetic Instruction," *The Mathematics Teacher* XLIII, pp. 115-16. Reprinted by permission of the author and *The Mathematics Teacher*.]

eralizations and rationalizations which must be familiar to the elementary teacher. If children are to be truly quantitatively literate, arithmetic in the elementary school must be taught meaningfully. And if arithmetic is to be taught most meaningfully, the elementary teacher must have as a functional part of her preparation a depth and maturity of mathematical meaning as typified by the illustrative examples just cited.

Many teachers colleges and schools of education recognize the necessity for meaningful instruction in elementary mathematics as a prerequisite to quantitative literacy. Consequently, the methodology of teaching arithmetic meaningfully is becoming an integral part of the training of future elementary teachers in these professional schools. This trend is reflected in the first list of selected references at the conclusion of this discussion. Here are listed professional books in which the methodological and psychological aspects of "meaning arithmetic" have been given primary consideration, and in which meanings and understandings are emphasized in terms of the level of maturity and experience of the children who are to be taught.

However, there is grave danger of overlooking an important link in the complete chain. Before students can learn how to teach arithmetic meaningfully, they must have acquired the necessary breadth, depth and maturity of background in the subject-matter of arithmetic so that it may be a functional part of their preparation. Entirely too often this background of understanding and skill is *assumed*, thus becoming an unemphasized aspect of the over-all program of training. In the vast majority of cases such an assumption of requisite background is a faulty one to say the least. All too frequently students are placed in teaching positions in elementary schools without having had any instruction in arithmetic per se since the days of their own elementary or junior high school study. Their point of view and degree of understanding is no broader nor deeper than that of the pupils they teach. It is true that these teachers well may have received some training in the methodological and psychological aspects of "meaning arithmetic." However, such courses generally do little to enrich, broaden and deepen the maturity of mathematical understanding of the prospective teacher. These courses rightfully are geared to a consideration of meanings and understandings from the point of view of the elementary school child, and generally not that of the college student.

But if such instruction in method is to serve its intended purpose most effectively, it must be preceded by work in elementary mathematics per se, in which meanings, understandings and applications are taught from the point of view of the maturity- and experience-level of the college student. Teachers colleges and schools of education definitely must include specific training of this nature in the subject-matter of "meaning arithmetic" prior to a consideration of important methodological and psychological aspects of the related teaching process.

A point of view akin to this has been forwarded clearly and positively in the statement and subsequent discussion of Thesis 25 in the Commission's second report.[1]

"Teachers of mathematics in Grades 1-8 should have special course work relating to subject matter as well as to the teaching process. . . ." The present writer re-emphasizes strongly this point of view as expressed by the Commission. In fact, the opinion is ventured that institutions engaged in a program of teacher-training for the elementary school field must incorporate such course work into their total program much more so than they have done in the past if maximum effectiveness of over-all training is to be realized. Furthermore, such course work should be made available to many teachers-in-service as well as to all students-in-training.

Obviously some professional schools have had adequate foresight to recognize the crucial aspect of the factor discussed, and have made *appropriate* work in the subject-matter of arithmetic an integral part of their training program. However, this situation is far from a universal one. In the past, the paucity of satisfactory textbook materials giving adequate coverage to arithmetic per se at the collegiate level is a reflection of the status of such courses in our professional schools. However, the pendulum definitely is swinging in the desired direction.

THE PROBLEM

Joseph Stipanowich

Believing that the better preparation of prospective elementary-school teachers in mathematics subject matter is a prerequisite to an improved program in arithmetic in the elementary school, the writer became interested in developing a college course in background mathematics for such future teachers. Since 1952, he has been attempting to develop an initial

[From "The Mathematical Training of Prospective Elementary-School Teachers," *The Arithmetic Teacher*, IV, pp. 242-48. Reprinted by permission of the author and *The Arithmetic Teacher*.]

---

[1] William David Reeve, "The Second Report of the Commission on Post-war Plans," *The Mathematics Teacher*, XXXVIII (March, 1945), 195-221.

college course of this type which would provide the student with an opportunity to develop a broader and deeper understanding of the mathematics she might be expected to teach.

In the initial phase of the investigation, the lack of unanimity among institutions training teachers in their approach to common curricular problems was noted. Because of the influence some of these practices would exert on the type of course in background mathematics an institution might provide for its future grade teachers, it was decided that some attempt at evaluating them should be made. A jury consisting of 70 carefully selected mathematics-education specialists—affiliated with 66 institutions of higher learning in 32 states—was used to determine which of several practices currently employed in college training programs in mathematics for prospective elementary-school teachers were favored by them.[1] A partial summary of their replies to a questionnaire follows.

Preparation in Mathematics for Admission to Elementary Education Curricula

The Practice. The college entrance requirements in mathematics for students desiring to enroll in the elementary curricula would seem to be a factor that should be considered in determining the kind of initial course in mathematics subject matter that an institution should provide for its prospective elementary-school teachers. Foster Grossnickle found a variety of requirements among the 129 state teachers colleges—all members of the American Association of Colleges for Teacher Education—whose training programs he reported on in 1951.[2] Twenty-four per cent of these colleges had some prerequisite in mathematics for admission to their elementary curricula and less than 6 per cent of them required their prospective students to present credits for at least two years of high-school mathematics before being permitted to enroll in the college's elementary curricula.

The Findings. The selected specialists were asked this question: "How much high-school mathematics do you feel teacher-training institutions should require for entrance of students preparing to teach below grade seven?"[3] Ninety-two per cent of the 70 educators who replied to this in-

---

[1] Dr. H. G. Ayre, Western Illinois University, and Dr. E. H. C. Hildebrandt, Northwestern University, assisted the writer by suggesting names of persons for the jury.

[2] Foster E. Grossnickle, "The Training of Teachers of Arithmetic," *The Teaching of Arithmetic*, Fiftieth Yearbook of the National Society for the Study of Education (Chicago: University of Chicago Press, 1951), Part II, 208.

[3] Throughout the study, by "prospective elementary-school teacher" the writer referred to a student who was preparing to teach below grade seven.

quiry indicated that they favored some requirement of this type. Sixty-eight per cent of them stated that they believed credit for at least two years of high-school mathematics should be required.

The Requirement of a Level of Proficiency in Arithmetic

The Practice. It is known that some institutions of higher learning require all of their prospective elementary-school teachers to meet a certain level of proficiency in arithmetic before permitting them to enroll in the credit course in background mathematics which is required of all of the students in their curriculum. The extent of this practice is unknown, but it seems likely that such a practice would influence the type of required credit course in background mathematics that an institution should provide for its future grade teachers.

The Findings. In evaluating this practice, 66 per cent of the selected specialists indicated they favored requiring a level of proficiency of this type. An additional 6 per cent of the educators did not respond to the inquiry.

The Differentiated Curricula

The Practice. Some institutions of higher learning have but a single training program for all of their pupils who wish to teach below grade nine, while others provide specialized training for different groups of students depending upon the grade level for which they are preparing to teach. In the past few years, several leaders in the field of mathematics education—as well as members of committees of prominence—have spoken in favor of the differentiated curricula. Some of these educators have advocated that a distinction be made in the training programs in mathematics for students who are preparing to teach below grade seven from those who are planning to teach in grades seven and eight. For example, Grossnickle made the following recommendation: "The course of training should be differentiated so as to prepare teachers for the kindergarten and the first six grades in one group and teachers for Grades VII and VIII in another group." [4] Although it may be desirable to have the curricula differentiated for the training of teachers, Grossnickle pointed out that this practice has not been the modal pattern of operation. His 1951 report seems to indicate that about two-thirds of the 129 state teachers colleges whose training programs he studied had but a single general curriculum for students desiring to teach at any level below grade nine.[5]

---

[4] Grossnickle, *op. cit.*, p. 230.
[5] Grossnickle, *op. cit.*, p. 207.

The Findings. The selected specialists were asked if they believed that a different content in background mathematics (not including methodology) should be provided for those planning to teach in grades seven and eight from that provided for those preparing to teach below grade seven. Fifty-seven per cent of these educators indicated they favored such a distinction and 3 per cent gave no response.

Mathematics Subject Matter Requirements in Elementary Curricula

The Practice. Research has revealed that many institutions of higher learning are not requiring a course in mathematics subject matter as a prerequisite to graduation from their elementary curricula. In 1951, W. I. Layton reported on his findings from a study of the catalogs of 85 teacher-training institutions, which were located in 45 states.[6] He found that but 35 (41 per cent) of these colleges had a requirement of one or more courses in mathematics subject matter for students enrolled in their four year elementary curricula.[7] In the same year, after his nation-wide study, Grossnickle reported these findings:

> Two-thirds of the colleges offering a curriculum for kindergarten and primary grades do not require a course in background mathematics. In more than half of the colleges offering curriculums which prepare teachers for the intermediate and advanced grades, a background course in mathematics is missing.[8]

Layton described this "inadequate preparation" as "alarming." Grossnickle expressed the opinion that it was unfortunate that "too many colleges neither offer a background course in mathematics nor require a minimum standard of competency in arithmetic." He also stated that "this unfavorable situation must be corrected before acceptable minimum professional standards can be established for teachers of arithmetic."[9]

The Findings. Each selected specialist was asked to specify the amount of training in mathematics subject matter (not including methodology) that he believed should be required in a four year curriculum for college students preparing to teach below grade seven. The replies to this inquiry

---

[6] W. I. Layton, "Mathematical Training Prescribed by Teachers Colleges in the Preparation of Elementary Teachers," *The Mathematics Teacher,* XLVI (December, 1951), 553.

[7] It should be mentioned that some teacher-training institutions require a course in mathematics that is a combination of subject matter and methods of teaching arithmetic. Layton found 28 of the 85 colleges requiring courses of this nature.

[8] Grossnickle, *op. cit.,* p. 210.

[9] Grossnickle, *op. cit.,* p. 220.

are summarized in Table 1. It reveals that *all of the 65 educators* who responded *indicated that they favored requiring some training in mathematics subject matter for prospective elementary-school teachers.* The median of the amounts of training that they indicated that they believed would be needed to provided students with the *minimum* training in mathematics subject matter needed by prospective elementary-school teachers (exclusive of their training in the methodology of arithmetic) was 3 *semester hours.* The median of the amounts of training which they indicated they believed would be necessary for a *desirable* program in mathematics subject matter for such students was 6 *semester hours.*

Subject Matter and Professionalized Courses

The Practice. The training in mathematics subject matter provided by institutions of higher learning for prospective elementary-school teachers is generally presented in one of two ways—either alone, in a so-called subject matter or content course, or combined with the methodology of the subject, in what the writer will call a professionalized course. In 1951, Layton reported on this practice.[10] He examined 63 courses that were

TABLE 1 *

TRAINING IN MATHEMATICS SUBJECT MATTER RECOMMENDED FOR FUTURE
TEACHERS BY THE SELECTED SPECIALISTS

Teaching Objective	Minimum Program			Desirable Program		
	No. of Replies	Median (S.H.)	Range (S.H.)	No. of Replies	Median (S.H.)	Range (S.H.)
Below grade VII	65	3	1-10	65	6	2-15

* Adapted from J. J. Stipanowich, "The Development and Appraisal of a Course in Basic Mathematics for Prospective Elementary-School Teachers," Table 7, p. 77. Unpublished Doctoral Dissertation, Northwestern University, 1956.

offered to provide prospective elementary-school teachers with training in background mathematics. He found that 35 (56 per cent) of them were subject matter courses and 28 (44 per cent) were professionalized.

The Findings. When asked which of the practices they preferred, the selected specialists seemed to favor the modal practice reported by Layton. Fifty-four per cent of them indicated they favored presenting the mathematics subject matter and methods of teaching it in separate courses. Four per cent stated that they had no preference, and 9 per cent did not express an opinion.

[10] Layton, *op. cit.*, p. 553.

Suggested Modifications in Programs in Mathematics for Prospective Elementary-School Teachers

The Practice. Because it was felt that many of the existing programs were inadequate, the mathematics-education specialists were asked if there were modifications which they believed would improve the "present program in mathematics for students preparing to teach below grade seven" at the institutions with which they were affiliated.

The Findings. The fact that sixty of these seventy educators actually suggested modifications in their own training programs seemed to provide additional evidence that there is a need for improvement in this area of teacher education. Their replies, for the most part, seemed to be concerned with one thing—the lack of training in basic mathematics subject matter. It was found that at 22 of the 62 institutions served by the selected specialists, no course in mathematics subject matter was required in the four year elementary curricula for prospective teachers. As one might expect, then, when these educators were asked to list specific modifications which they believed would lead to an improved program in mathematics education at their own institutions, the need for more training in mathematics subject matter was most frequently mentioned; as a matter of fact, it was mentioned six times as frequently as any other suggested modification. Other suggested modifications which were frequently mentioned were as follows:

1. Change the content of the subject-matter course so that it more nearly meets the needs of prospective elementary-school teachers.
2. Make a greater effort to provide for the individual differences of prospective elementary-school teachers.
3. Provide better qualified instructors to teach the courses in mathematics for prospective elementary-school teachers.
4. Try to secure a more suitable basic text for use in the subject-matter course for prospective elementary-school teachers.

Content for a Subject-Matter Course for Prospective Elementary-School Teachers

The Practice. There are apparently glaring differences in the content considered in mathematics subject-matter courses provided by institutions of higher education for prospective elementary-school teachers. In 1951, Newsom, in discussing an initial course of this type, expressed this opinion: "The content for a course in background mathematics is a matter of genuine disagreement on the part of even those who are acknowledged authorities in the field." [11] To the writer, it seemed that if certain assumptions were made concerning the nature of an initial course for prospective elementary-school teachers, it might be possible to identify topics that a large per cent of a group of selected mathematics-education specialists would agree should be considered in such a course.

The Findings. In an attempt to verify this hypothesis, the selected specialists were asked to follow these directions in completing Part I of the questionnaire:

> In the part which follows, you are to assume (1) that you are choosing content for a required course in mathematics for college students in the four year elementary curriculum who are planning to teach below grade seven; (2) that the course will not be concerned directly with methods of teaching mathematics since this training is provided for in a separate required course; and (3) that there will be no college or high school mathematics courses listed as prerequisites for this course.

Then, using a detailed check-list as a guide, the selected specialists were asked to do the following:

> Place a check in column A before only those topics you would include in your mathematics course if it were to be a three semester-hour course (about four quarter hours) and were the only mathematics content course required of those students for whom you are developing it.

The topics which were checked in this manner by more than 75 per cent of the 68 selected educators who responded to this inquiry are listed in Table 2 (page 500). A study of this table reveals that there were 26 topics which at least 90 per cent of the 68 educators who completed this section of the questionnaire indicated they would include in an initial college course of this type. Too, although the check list included items that dealt with algebra and intuitive geometry, the topics checked by more than 75 per cent of the group are arithmetical.[12]

Recommendations

The information obtained from a study of the replies of the selected specialists is not very reassuring. It provides additional evidence to support the claim that many institutions that train teachers are not providing adequate training in mathematics subject matter for students preparing to

---

[11] Newsom, *op. cit.*, p. 233.

[12] A majority of the selected specialists indicated they would include topics from algebra and intuitive geometry in the training program in mathematics for prospective elementary-school teachers if time permitted.

teach in the elementary school.[13] But where a large per cent of the carefully selected mathematics education-specialists indicated that they were opposed to what research has reported to be a practice—sometimes the modal practice—of teacher-training institutions, it would seem to suggest lines of attack for improving such training programs. Therefore, in keeping with the opinions expressed by at least a majority of the selected specialists, the following recommendations are made:

1. *Admission requirements*—each student desiring to enroll in an elementary-education curriculum at an institution of higher learning should be required to present at least two units (years) credit in high school mathematics as a prerequisite for admission to the training program.

2. *Provision for a course in mathematics subject matter*—each institution of higher learning that prepares teachers should provide training in background mathematics subject matter for all its prospective elementary-school teachers. This training should be provided for in a separate course from that in which the training in the methodology of arithmetic is presented.

3. *Required training in mathematics subject matter*—each institution of higher learning that prepares teachers should require its prospective elementary-school teachers to complete successfully at least a three semester-hour course in mathematics subject matter while in college. As soon as it is practicable, future teachers in this group should be required to complete six semester hours of training of this type.

4. *Type of subject matter*—the initial three semester hour course in mathematics subject matter for prospective elementary-school teachers should be primarily an arithmetic course in which the meanings and understandings of the subject are emphasized. Related topics from the fields of algebra and an intuitive geometry should be selected and integrated with the subject of arithmetic.

5. *Requirements of a level of proficiency*—any student enrolled in an elementary-education curriculum who shows that she has not reached a reasonable level of achievement in arithmetic should be required to complete a remedial course before being permitted to enroll for the credit course in background mathematics subject matter required of all of the students in her curriculum.

---

[13] A selected specialist, employed at a university in the Midwest, expressed the hope that this investigation might furnish her "with ammunition to work on the deplorable situation with respect to the training of elementary teachers" at the institution with which she was affiliated. Another, when asked about the training program in mathematics at the teacher-training institution where he was employed, stated that there was no course in background mathematics provided for their prospective elementary-school teachers and added "I am ashamed of this, but at present our hands are tied."

TABLE 2 *

Topics Chosen for an Initial Course in Basic Mathematics for Prospective Elementary-School Teachers by More Than Three-Fourths of the Selected Specialists

Topics	No. in Favor	Per Cent
Arithmetic		
Growth in Number		
One-to-one correspondence	64	94
Counting	66	97
Place value	67	99
Hindu-Arabic Numerals		
The numerals in a decimal system		
Basic meanings	59	87
Positional notation	62	91
Numbers in Our System		
Whole numbers		
The meaning of whole number	68	100
The number scale	63	93
The meaning of zero	67	99
Odd and even numbers	55	81
Common fractions		
Meanings common fractions may express	68	100
Meanings of related terms	63	93
Decimal fractions		
Basic understandings	65	96
Meanings of related terms	65	96
Denominate Numbers and Measurement		
Basic meanings	63	93
Units of measure	63	93
The English system of measurement	56	82
The approximate nature of measurement		
Rounding, accuracy, and precision	61	90
The Fundamental Operations Using Integers		
The theory behind the processes		
Meanings of the processes	62	91
Meanings of related terms	64	94
Important relationships (division as repeated subtraction, etc.)	59	87
The rationale—the "why"	66	97
Checking the results		
Estimating the answer	63	93
Using the inverse operations	61	90
The Fundamental Operations Using Common Fractions		
The theory behind the processes		
Meanings of the processes	64	94
Meanings of related terms (equivalent fractions, etc.)	62	91
The rationale	64	94
The Fundamental Operations Using Decimal Fractions		
The theory behind the processes		
Similarity to operations with common fractions	65	96
Meanings of related terms	65	96
The rationale	63	93
Per Cent		
Its meanings and related terms	67	98
The three cases of per cent	56	82
Aids to Problem Solving in Arithmetic		
Recognizing essential and insufficient data	53	78
Discovering dependencies within the problem	55	81

* Adapted from J. J. Stipanowich, *op. cit.*, Table 10, pp. 85-87.

6. *A differentiated curriculum*—the training program in mathematics for teachers should be differentiated so that students desiring to teach below grade seven are trained in one group and students preparing to teach in grades seven and eight are trained in another.

ARITHMETIC FOR ARITHMETIC TEACHERS

William L. Schaaf

For one reason or another, an inexcusably large number of prospective and experienced elementary school teachers simply do not know as much arithmetic as they should in order to teach it effectively. We are not particularly concerned here with the reasons for this serious defection, although not the least of the contributing factors is the somewhat annoying overemphasis upon education courses and the considerable disdain with which subject matter courses are regarded in all too many of our teacher education programs today. The present discussion seeks rather to suggest, first, some evidence for the categorical statement that elementary school teachers, by and large, do not really understand arithmetic, and secondly, what colleges and other teacher-education institutions ought to do about it.

Do Teachers Understand Arithmetic?

Some fifteen years ago, describing conditions in New York City, A. E. Robinson [1] observed that "elementary-school teachers have at best only a mechanical knowledge of arithmetic even though they are fairly proficient in their skills in the manipulation of its various mechanical processes. Anything like a clear and versatile knowledge of the fundamental principles of arithmetic and their mathematical significance is all but totally lacking on the part of such teachers." Ten years later, V. J. Glennon [2] gave further evidence of the arithmetic inadequacies of teachers, showing

[From "Arithmetic for Arithmetic Teachers," *School Science and Mathematics,* LIII (October, 1953), pp. 537-43. Reprinted by permission of the author and *School Science and Mathematics.*]

---

[1] A. E. Robinson, *The Professional Education of Elementary Teachers in the Field of Arithmetic,* Teachers College Contribution to Education, No. 672 (New York: Bureau of Publications, Teachers College, Columbia University, 1936).

[2] V. J. Glennon, "A Study in Needed Redirection in the Preparation of Teachers of Arithmetic," *Mathematics Teacher,* XLII (1949), 389-96.

that teachers college students understood only about 44 per cent of certain basic mathematical understandings which he had tested. He observed further that "it is hardly possible for teachers to help children grow in the understandings which they themselves do not possess."

More recently additional testimony has appeared. In 1951, Wilburn and Wingo [3] pointed out:

> In nothing which is taught in the elementary school is it more important that teachers have an adequate understanding of the content itself than in arithmetic. Yet it is probable that elementary-school teachers have less insight into the content of arithmetic than into any other subject. . . .
>
> One thing which is probably needed is for teacher-training institutions to pay more attention to providing prospective elementary-school teachers with a better understanding of arithmetic and the number system. At the present time very few of them appear to do this, so the responsibility must fall on those responsible for the in-service training of teachers. The question of methods of teaching arithmetic is an important one in both pre-service and in-service training, *but the understanding of the subject itself is of at least equal importance.* Teachers will not see the importance of changing their methods of teaching unless they have sufficient understanding of the number system to enable them to see the deficiencies in their methods.

Again, in a study of the achievement of students beginning a course in "Arithmetic for Teachers" at the University of Illinois, C. Phillips [4] concluded:

a) Lack of achievement in mechanical mastery starts with the topic of fractions and continues with decimal fractions and per cent.

b) Problem-solving achievement involving measurement, fractions, and per cent is very low.

c) Achievement in the meaning and understanding of arithmetic is extremely low.

In a recent and somewhat more elaborate study, J. S. Orleans [5] gave a test to 722 subjects, most of whom were either prospective teachers or student teachers, and a different test to a second group of 322 subjects,

---

[3] G. M. Wingo and D. B. Wilburn, "In Service Development of Teachers of Arithmetic," *The Teaching of Arithmetic,* 50th Yearbook of the N.S.S.E. (Chicago: University of Chicago Press, 1951), Part II, 251-68.

[4] Clarence Phillips, "Background and Mathematical Achievement of Elementary Education Students in Arithmetic for Teachers," *School Science and Mathematics,* LIII (January, 1953), 48-52.

[5] Jacob S. Orleans, "The Understanding of Arithmetic Processes and Concepts Possessed by Teachers of Arithmetic," Office of Research and Evaluation, Division of Teacher Education, Publication No. 12 (New York: College of the City of New York, 1952).

about half of whom had taught arithmetic at various grade levels. According to Orleans:

> Data from the two tests . . . suggest on the one hand that many teachers and prospective teachers have difficulty in verbalizing their thoughts when they try to explain arithmetic concepts and processes, and on the other hand that there are few arithmetic concepts and processes that can be readily explained by a large percentage of teachers. . . . It would seem reasonable to conclude that the teaching of arithmetic has become so routinized that whatever understanding is introduced in the learning process is soon lost. Considering the lack of understanding possessed by most teachers, it is doubtful that they can introduce much meaning to the learning process for their pupils.

Orleans suggests that this general lack of understanding of arithmetical processes, concepts, and relationships may result from the practice of teaching a short cut for a process as though it were the process itself. In any event, he is convinced that the findings are not due to the inherent difficulty of arithmetic, but are undoubtedly a function of the way in which the arithmetic has been learned; he reports further that

> . . . many of the teachers . . . commented fully, both in class discussions and in personal conference, on their lack of understanding of the basic processes and concepts and on their inability to use arithmetic meaningfully and with confidence.

What Should Be Done About It?

Obviously the situation revealed by these studies must be corrected. More than a decade ago, R. L. Morton [6] saw the need, and proposed, among other things, that:

   a) The minimum experience in mathematics of college grade for prospective teachers of arithmetic, should be organized in a year's work of 6 to 10 semester-hours.
   b) The college mathematics experience of prospective teachers of arithmetic should be secured through the medium of courses especially organized for this purpose.
   c) The teacher of the college mathematics course which is designed for prospective elementary teachers should be a special selection for this purpose; there are many teachers of college mathematics who will not qualify.
   d) A college course in mathematics designed for the professional preparation of teachers of arithmetic should be organized cooperatively by

---

[6] R. L. Morton, "Mathematics in the Training of Arithmetic Teachers," *Mathematics Teacher*, XXXII (1939), 106-10.

a group composed of educators and mathematicians. Such a course should be planned as a six-semester-hour course with prescribed additions for making it an eight-hour course or a ten-hour course.

Later, the Commission on Postwar Plans of the National Council of Teachers of Mathematics, in its final report, pointed out to prospective teachers that in addition to a good methods course in the teaching of arithmetic, it was equally important to have at least one course giving the subject-matter background for the mathematics taught in Grades I through VI, and at least one additional course dealing with the subject-matter background for the general mathematics usually taught in Grades VII and VIII.

F. L. Wren has also stressed the need for adequate understanding of mathematical backgrounds. In a series of stimulating and provocative questions,[7] he clearly shows the importance of familiarity with the historical development of numerals, numeration, numbers systems, computational procedures, mechanical aids to computation, and the like; familiarity with the *rationale* of arithmetic, i.e., its logical foundations; familiarity with the social importance of arithmetic, its applications to everyday business, social, economic and vocational demands; and, in general, a thorough understanding of the techniques and generalizations of arithmetic, especially those relating to the number concept, to measurement, to statistics, to computation with approximate data, and to problem-solving. Elsewhere Wren [8] frankly insists that:

> Each student preparing to teach in the elementary school has a right to expect that the teacher-training program will provide full opportunity to build up a backlog of information, appreciation, and competency in arithmetic that will enable him to accept this specific responsibility confident that he is prepared to . . . deal with arithmetic with a feeling of security and assurance.

Equally emphatic in demanding that attention be given to subject matter mastery is C. V. Newsom,[9] who feels that

> . . . it is possible and desirable to include in the curriculum for the training of elementary-school teachers a minimum of a three-hour course of background mathematics, in addition to a course on the teaching of arithmetic; moreover, a six-hour course is preferred. All too frequently teachers in the

---

[7] *Op. cit.*

[8] F. L. Wren, "The Professional Preparation of Teachers of Arithmetic," *Arithmetic 1948*, Supplementary Educational Monographs, No. 66 (Chicago: University of Chicago Press, 1948), 80-90.

[9] *Op. cit.*

elementary grades are hardly a jump ahead of their alert students, and many teachers . . . lack confidence before their classes in approaching various arithmetical concepts.

Finally, we cite some recommendations by Grossnickle: [10]

a) Every elementary-school teacher . . . should have a course in background mathematics, preferably six semester hours in length. This course should acquaint the student with the basic principles of the number system, introduce him to both formal and informal geometry, to algebra as a system of generalized number, and to the study of trigonometry as used in indirect measurement.

b) All teachers in the elementary school, except those . . . in specialized fields, should have a course in the teaching of arithmetic in which both social applications and mathematical meanings of the subject are treated. . . . This course should be part of a general methods course.

c) Teachers of arithmetic for Grades VII and VIII should have at least a minor in college mathematics.

d) Students in liberal-arts colleges who wish to become teachers of arithmetic in the elementary school should be required to meet the same standards of preparation as those who are trained in teachers colleges.

A Content Course in Arithmetic

What should be the scope of a course dealing with the subject matter of arithmetic, or elementary mathematics, as fashion decrees it shall be called? How should it be organized? Who should conduct such a course —a member of the mathematics department, or an education staff member. The answers to these and related questions will naturally vary somewhat in accordance with local conditions. But two primary considerations would seem to be (1) the arithmetic knowledge and competence which students bring to the course, and (2) the stated objectives of the course. As for (1), the implications of the data given in the first section of this paper are self-evident; they may be augmented, in a specific situation, by the administration of appropriate tests. As for (2), the determination of the objectives must be governed by professional considerations as well as the realities of pure and applied mathematics. The course content will be carefully chosen to implement the objectives.

The course of study suggested below, while frankly somewhat arbitrary, is based in part on experiences in working with prospective teachers and a consideration of their needs. The résumé is deliberately brief, and is

---

[10] F. E. Grossnickle, "The Training of Teachers of Arithmetic," *The Teaching of Arithmetic,* 50th Yearbook of the N.S.S.E. (Chicago: University of Chicago Press, 1951), Part II, 203-31.

designed more to indicate the scope and spirit of the course rather than to provide a detailed working outline.

Course of Study in Arithmetic

I. NUMBER CONCEPT AND NUMERATION
  A. *Historical Development*
    1. Primitive beginnings; counting
    2. Babylonian and Egyptian notation
    3. Greek notation
    4. Roman notation
    5. Hindu-Arabic system
    6. Modern numeration in Western culture
    7. Numerology
  B. *Theory of Numeration*
    1. Role of notation in thinking
    2. Base of a number system
    3. Principle of positional value
    4. The empty column
    5. Extension of a decimal system
    6. Exponential notation; number giants and pygmies
    7. Other scales of notation

II. NATURE OF NUMBER
  A. *Psychological Considerations*
    1. Abstract quality of number
    2. Nature of a group
    3. Ordinal and cardinal
    4. Concrete numbers
    5. Operations of arithmetic
    6. Laws of operation
    7. Interrelationships among operations
  B. *Number System of Algebra*
    1. Natural numbers
    2. Historical development of "artificial" numbers
    3. Common and decimal fractions
    4. Negative numbers
    5. Irrational numbers
    6. Complex numbers
    7. Relation of arithmetic to algebra
  C. *Logical Foundations of Arithmetic*
    1. Ordered sets
    2. Finite and infinite
    3. Denumerability of the natural numbers
    4. Rational numbers—a denumerable set

     5. Non-denumerability of the irrationals
     6. The linear continuum
     7. Relationship of measurement to number

III. COMPUTATION
  A. *Historical Development*
     1. Early methods; mechanical aids
     2. Medieval methods of reckoning
     3. Modern methods of computation
     4. Computation with approximate data
     5. Exponents and logarithms; slide rule
     6. Early calculating machines
     7. Contemporary electronic computers
  B. *Analysis of Theory of Computation*
     1. Addition; checks, short cuts, etc.
     2. Subtractions; checks, short cuts, etc.
     3. Multiplication; checks, short cuts, etc.
     4. Division; checks, short cuts, etc.
     5. Common fractions
     6. Decimals; repeating decimals
     7. Percentage

IV. MEASUREMENT
  A. *Direct Measurement*
     1. Historical evolution of weights and measures
     2. Modern standards for units of measure
     3. Metric system
     4. Mensuration of plane and solid figures
     5. Precision measurements; instruments
     6. Theory of measurement: error, precision, accuracy
     7. Measurement of time
  B. *Indirect Measurement*
     1. Ratio, proportion, similarity; scale drawings
     2. Elements of trigonometry
     3. Solution of triangles
     4. Surveying instruments
     5. Mathematics and aviation
     6. Mathematics and navigation
     7. Maps and map projections
  C. *Elements of Statistics*
     1. Graphic methods: categorical and historical
     2. Growth curves; logarithmic grids
     3. Frequency distributions
     4. Measures of central tendency
     5. Measures of dispersion
     6. Meaning of correlation
     7. Concepts of probability

V. Socio-economic Applications
  A. *Arithmetic in the Home*
    1. Kitchen arithmetic
    2. Public utilities
    3. Consumer problems
    4. Real estate taxes
    5. Fire insurance
    6. Mortgages; amortization
    7. Home ownership costs
  B. *Arithmetic in the Market Place*
    1. Retail discount; trade discount
    2. Commission and brokerage
    3. Cost and selling price
    4. Margin and profit
    5. Mark-up; determination of selling price
    6. Depreciation methods
    7. Records and accounts; statements
  C. *Arithmetic and Finance*
    1. Simple interest; accurate interest
    2. Bank discount; relationship to interest
    3. Compound interest and present value
    4. Personal credit; instalment buying
    5. Stocks and bonds; investment yield
    6. Annuities; capitalization
    7. Life insurance principles

I should like to close this discussion with a quotation from the pen of the late Simeon Strunsky, celebrated for his column "Topics of the Times" in the *New York Times*. It is a quotation which I have already used elsewhere, but it is as pertinent today as when it was first written half a dozen years ago:

> Beginning with school children in the first grade, if not actually in kindergarten, and continuing through college and the post-graduate seminars, the one subject in the curriculum which needs to be stressed above all others is arithmetic. It is hard to see how modern man can soberly and usefully attack the terribly complicated problems of his world and age without a firm grasp on the principle that four is more than two, that 90 per cent is more than 10 per cent, that fifty-one nations are more than three nations, and that fifty million war casualties are more than ten million casualties.
>
> Sad to say, respect for arithmetic has never stood so low as it does today in this country. People are not content to speak of the three kinds of lies, of which the worst is statistics. They do not stop short at remarking, curtly, that perhaps figures cannot lie but liars can figure. They find that arithmetic is much worse than untrustworthy. They find it a bore. At least this

is the caution always addressed to writers for the press and authors of books designed for the general public. Avoid statistics. The public wants its truth presented in broad summations or in vivid anecdote, usually in a combination of both. People simply will not read figures.

And yet the one problem which has come to transcend every other human interest today, or is described as such on every hand, is a problem in arithmetic. What is this atomic age upon which humanity has entered, if not the age of an awesome arithmetic? The atomic bomb is our first visible sample of the overwhelming arithmetic in Einstein's formula for the equivalence of matter and energy. To get the energy or force locked up in a piece of matter you simply multiply the mass by the square of the speed of light, that is all. You work out an arithmetical sum in which one step consists of multiplying 186,000 miles a second by 186,000 miles a second. The consequences are Hiroshima and Nagasaki and Bikini; otherwise arithmetic is a bore! [11]

TEACHERS OF MATHEMATICS

Probably the greatest number of professional workers who use mathematics are employed as teachers. In the following sections you will find descriptions of the mathematical training needed by different types of teachers.

Mathematics for Teachers in Elementary Schools

There are over a half million teachers in our elementary schools. Not all of them have to teach arithmetic. Some are departmentalized. If you should wish to qualify for such a position, the main requirement would be that you *understand* arithmetic. You cannot teach what you do not know. Here is the arithmetic that you would have to teach in the first six grades.

1. Basic concepts, processes, and vocabulary of arithmetic
2. Our decimal system of numeration, including the concept of decimal fractions
3. Computation, whole numbers and common and decimal fractions
4. Principal units of measurement for everyday use

[From "Guidance Report of the Commission on Post-War Plans," *The Mathematics Teacher*, XL, pp. 324-25. Reprinted by permission of *The Mathematics Teacher*.]

---

[11] Simeon Strunsky. "Topics of the Times," *The New York Times* (September 29, 1946).

5. Solution of problems involving computation and units of measurement

6. Identification of geometric figures

7. Use of simple graphs

8. Estimation and checking of answers to problems

In grades 7 and 8 you would teach general mathematics, which includes informal geometry, arithmetic, measurement, graphic representation, arithmetic in personal and community problems, and first steps in algebra.

Many teachers in our elementary schools do not as yet have four years of training in college. The better school systems employ only college graduates.

If you are planning to teach in the elementary school, three things are very important: (1) a good methods course; (2) at least one course which will give you subject-matter background for the mathematics taught in grades one through six; (3) at least one course that will give you subject matter background for teaching the general mathematics of grades seven and eight. Junior high school teachers of mathematics should have at least a minor in college mathematics. This should include a year of general mathematics in college, a course in statistics, a course in the mathematics of investment, and a professionalized course in the subject matter taught in these grades.

Nearly all the teachers in the elementary school are women. However, the elementary school is a grand field for a young man who is a fine person and a competent worker.

Mathematics for Teachers in High School

To an increasing extent high schools are providing a "double track" in mathematics. The high school student may choose either (1) the traditional college preparatory courses, or (2) a series of general mathematics courses.

The traditional college preparatory courses usually begin with elementary algebra (9th grade), followed by plane geometry, and further algebra. Large high schools also provide additional courses that may include trigonometry, solid geometry, college algebra, analytic geometry, and surveying. Of course small schools cannot provide this mathematical feast. However, more and more schools are providing correspondence courses to supplement their offering.

The courses on the "other track" include such electives as (*a*) general mathematics—now widely offered as an alternative to algebra in the ninth grade; (*b*) shop mathematics, and (*c*) for the later years of the senior high school, consumer mathematics and possibly statistics. Students in commercial courses may elect business arithmetic sometimes as early as the ninth grade.

These general mathematics courses are provided for a large number of pupils in the present-day high school who do not desire the college preparatory work or for whom such courses seem unsuited.

Thus it is obvious that in planning your college courses as a future teacher in a high school you should prepare yourself to teach two kinds of course with very different goals for two different types of high school pupils. It is too bad, but true, that the typical college does not offer too much that is helpful in preparing you for teaching the general mathematics courses that now enroll a majority of the high school pupils in the country.

As a teacher of mathematics in a high school you need not only an aptitude for mathematics, but also those personal qualities necessary for all good teachers. Usually requirements for such jobs include the bachelor's degree, and for large cities, the master's degree with a major in mathematics. It often happens that a teacher must also teach another subject in addition to mathematics.

Positions are open to both men and women who hold teaching certificates. In some states the minimum salary for the beginning high school teacher with four years of college training has been fixed at $2400; and in a few at $2600.

MATHEMATICS IN THE
TRAINING OF ARITHMETIC TEACHERS

Robert L. Morton

I could continue at some length to recite to you the difficulties which teachers of arithmetic experience because they lack a subject matter background to reinforce them as they try to understand and then to teach certain topics in this subject. The need for additional experience in mathematics becomes so obvious to one who works with teachers and prospective teachers that it is very difficult to understand why the matter should be debated at all.

Those who are assembled here probably agree with what I am saying about the need for further experience with mathematics. However, when

[From "Mathematics in the Training of Arithmetic Teachers," *The Mathematics Teacher*, XXXII, pp. 107-10. Reprinted by permission of the author and *The Mathematics Teacher*.]

one undertakes to state what should be included in the teacher's courses in mathematics and how the content should be organized, he is sure to run into opposition. Nevertheless, I should like to make a few observations.

At the beginning, I should like to be able to assume that each of the young persons who present themselves to teacher-training institutions has had at least one year of algebra and one year of geometry in high school. However, this is not the case. I have analyzed the high school records of 2734 persons who received baccalaureate degrees from Ohio University in the six-year period beginning January 1, 1931, and ending December 31, 1936. This was a part of a larger study having to do with the place of mathematics in the college curricula of these Ohio University graduates. I found that 95 per cent of these 2734 graduates received credit for algebra studied in high school; that the number of units of credit earned in this subject ranged from one-half unit to three and one-third units; that the outstanding mode is one unit, earned by 45 per cent of the entire group; that one and one-half units were earned by nearly 38 per cent of the group; and that two and one-half units were earned by nearly 12 per cent of the group. In addition to these, there were a few whose transcripts of secondary credits showed simply "mathematics," "general mathematics," and the like. Including these, and doing a little guessing, we arrive at a figure of 97 per cent who, apparently, have had one unit or more of high school algebra.

The geometry picture is not so bright. Only 86 per cent of these 2734 baccalaureate graduates had had geometry in high school. The typical individual had one year in this subject. My first proposal, then, is that

All students in teacher-training institutions who have not received credit in high school for a minimum of one year each in algebra and geometry should be required to take these subjects in college and should receive college credit for them.

What additional experience in mathematics should prospective teachers of arithmetic receive in college? Here, again, we must speak in terms of a minimum standard, for, obviously, there is no maximum, although there may quite well be an optimum. The program of courses for teacher preparation as it is typically organized includes many courses from many and varied fields, so many indeed that it is futile to expect that room will be made for very many semester-hours of work in mathematics. I should like to see the minimum set at not fewer than 10 semester-hours, for I find it difficult to see how a defensible minimum program can be organized so as to require less time. If the number of hours is very greatly reduced there is not only the probability that vitally important matters will have to be neglected but also the danger that under the pressure of time limitations the teaching will degenerate into mere drill and the learning into rote learning. Others believe that a defensible minimum program can be organized in 8 semester-hours; still others say that 6 will be sufficient. I know of at least one institution in which it was thought that very ample provision was being made for mathematics in the preparation of elementary teachers by setting up a single three-hour course. And, as you well know, there are many such programs in which no provision whatever is made for mathematics. This matter of semester-hours could be discussed at much greater length but I must hasten. I shall terminate the discussion by offering as a second proposal the following:

The minimum experience in mathematics of college grade for prospective teachers of arithmetic should be organized in a year's work of 6 to 10 semester-hours.

What should be the content of such a year's course? I think that you will agree with me that there are a number of items in the usual courses in freshman mathematics, courses in algebra, trigonometry, and plane analytic geometry, which should be included but that in addition to these, room should be found for items from the mathematics of finance, items from both the differential and the integral calculus, and possibly items from astronomy. If you agree, you will conclude at once that the usual introductory college courses in mathematics as they are organized for students in the college of liberal arts or for students whose major interests lie in the fields of science or engineering will not be satisfactory. The prospective elementary school teacher would have to choose between getting the requisite number of hours but failing to include all of the topics or getting all of the topics but finding it necessary to take far more than 10 semester-hours. Hence my third proposal:

The college mathematics experience of prospective teachers of arithmetic should be secured through the medium of courses especially organized for this purpose.

I have no doubt that such a special course would be a very desirable course for others than prospective teachers to take. So far as I have suggested it, there is no reason to believe that it is better adapted to the needs of prospective elementary teachers than to the needs of other young persons who wish to devote only 6 or 8 or 10 semester-hours to the study of mathematics in college. In other words, I am pleading for a special course for prospective elementary teachers not only because such a special course will be better adapted to their needs than will the more or less traditional college courses but also because I believe that in general a brief course in college mathematics should be a special course.

Unfortunately for this point of view, there are in this country many persons in positions of influence who are violently and unalterably opposed to all such special courses in mathematics. Such courses sound to them too much like "general mathematics," a term for which they seem to have conceived a violent dislike. Just recently, I learned of a department of mathematics in a good-sized university which is presided over by a chairman who will have no general mathematics or other special courses and who batters down all opposition with very loud and very fluent, although not particularly eloquent or very logical denunciation. His department offers a 10-hour course in freshman mathematics, of which 3 hours are devoted to algebra, 2 hours to plane trigonometry, and 5 hours to plane analytic geometry. He asserts, again violently, that regardless of whether the student is to work out a major in mathematics for the B.A. degree, or is to use mathematics as a part of his program in engineering, or is to take a little mathematics as part of a liberal education, or is to study mathematics as a part of his background for elementary teaching, he should pursue these particular freshman courses. Members of his own staff disagree with him but quite without avail.

It would seem that in this particular university (and I refer to it because it is more or less typical of a group) a more valuable and more interesting course of 10 semester-hours could be provided for prospective elementary teachers by reducing markedly the amount of time devoted to analytic geometry and introducing material from the mathematics of finance and elementary calculus. Furthermore, such changes in the course should give the student a more comprehensive idea of the varied nature of mathematics and of its wide usefulness in solving problems which are incident to our complex civilization.

The success of such a course in mathematics will depend to no small extent upon the experience and native equipment of the teacher. The mere fact that the teacher has been a competent student of mathematics and has a Ph.D. in the subject from a recognized institution is not enough to qualify him to give this course for prospective elementary teachers, whatever we may say about his qualifications for teaching other groups. In addition to possessing a knowledge of mathematics, he must be willing to break away from a traditional organization and work out an organization designed for a new purpose, he must be interested in collecting a rich assortment of applications in order that the topics of the course may be interesting and meaningful, and he must be cognizant of and sympathetic with the life ambitions of his students. In short, this is my fourth proposal:

The teacher of the college mathematics course which is designed for prospective elementary teachers should be a special selection for this purpose; there are many teachers of college mathematics who will not qualify.

Those who teach mathematics have, for many years, been deploring the apparent decline in interest in this subject. They say that those in administrative positions in the public schools, supported and sometimes stimulated by professors of education, have failed to recognize the worth of this discipline and have gradually permitted it to be supplanted by other subjects, notably those in the field of the social studies and those involving manual activity. The school administrators and the professors of education, on the other hand, claim to have just reason for criticizing the offerings and the methods of the teachers of mathematics. It seems to me that there are many problems dealing with the place of mathematics in the curriculum, with the organization of courses, and with the teaching of this subject which will not be solved until they have been attacked co-operatively by both mathematicians and educators. The specific issue with which we are here concerned—mathematics in the training of arithmetic teachers—will not be disposed of satisfactorily except through the medium of a friendly council in which members of both of these groups participate. Can the mathematician eat the salt of the educator? Can the educator break bread with the mathematician? And so, finally, my fifth proposal:

A college course in mathematics designed for the professional preparation of teachers of arithmetic should be organized co-operatively by a group composed of educators and mathematicians. Such a course should be planned as a six-semester-hour course with prescribed additions for making it an eight-hour course or a ten-hour course.

SPECIAL TRAINING FOR TEACHERS OF ARITHMETIC

John Mayor

Both pre-service and in-service special training can be of value to the teacher of arithmetic. The teacher training institution merely starts the training. If the training program is successful at all it must take into full consideration the training which comes with teaching experience and planned in-service activities. In this discussion of special training for arithmetic teachers I hope there will be found suggestions helpful to all arithmetic teachers. While the most direct interest in the discussion may be for those responsible for college teacher training programs, new associations and new emphases, if not new ideas, should be suggestive to all teachers interested in arithmetic.

[From "Special Training for Teachers of Arithmetic," *School Science and Mathematics*, XLIX, pp. 539-48. Reprinted by permission of the author and *School Science and Mathematics*.]

Furthermore, any consideration of special training for elementary teachers must be based on recognition of the tremendous task confronting the elementary school teacher. Desirable special training in so many areas makes nearly impossible demands on her time. Too, because she is a generalist, general education so important for all teachers is even more important to her. I hope careful analysis of the proposals which follow will show that the many opportunities and responsibilities of the elementary teacher are fully recognized.

Training Goals

As a starting point for examination of arithmetic teacher training programs a statement is given of certain teacher training goals, including some which are quite broad and to which time will permit only brief reference. These are goals for the experienced teacher or graduate student in elementary education. They are desirable goals for any teacher whether or not he earns credits leading to a degree. Formal school courses should make achievement of these goals easier. It is however not my intention here or at any other point to draw a sharp line between training in colleges and training on the job.

While the core professional courses offered for all teachers, and teacher institutes and meetings certainly give much attention to goals 1 and 2, these goals should also be re-emphasized and interpreted in the professional courses in special areas and in-service training programs in special areas. In this paper goal 3 will be taken up last since it serves as a bridge for our change of focus from a graduate program to an undergraduate program.

The teacher training program should help arithmetic teachers:

1. Develop for themselves a philosophy of education which recognizes the importance and responsibility of teaching as a profession; the role of the teacher as school and community leader; the general education responsibility of the school and that the role of arithmetic is determined largely in terms of this general education responsibility; the ideal of frequent search for new ways to serve the school and society.

2. Identify teaching problems and determine relative importance of problems, and to learn methods of seeking solutions of educational problems, particularly as related to arithmetic.

3. Better understand mathematical concepts which have most direct bearing on the arithmetic of the schools, and appreciate the necessity for the teacher of arithmetic to broaden his intellectual interests to include many areas of knowledge and understanding.

4. Become familiar with sources and means of using current profes-

sional literature and the older writings of direct interest to arithmetic teachers, including books, periodicals, and reports of significance, both in pedagogy and subject matter; and to know the historical background in literature and experience for current educational bias and soundness.

5. Acquire some knowledge and understanding of the total mathematics curriculum for grades 1–10 and the possibilities of each year's experience to contribute to a continuous growth in mathematical power.

6. Learn to use a variety of means of enrichment of learning experiences including applications in daily living and to other areas of instruction, visual aids, good procedures of evaluation, and reference to cultural and social significance of mathematics.

Every school administrator and teacher should be familiar with the recommendations on teaching mathematics and science to be found in *Manpower for Research,* a report of the President's Scientific Research Board.[1] The Report lists reasons for current weaknesses in accomplishment in arithmetic and recommends changes in teacher training and teaching procedures which should aid in overcoming those weaknesses. The Report also emphasizes the desirability of a sound philosophy of education. I count the recognition of the great responsibility and great opportunity of the teacher an essential part of such a sound philosophy. Teachers of today through their influence on boys and girls can make a new world tomorrow. What greater role has any man?

That the place of arithmetic is determined largely in terms of the general education responsibility of the school is in no way better emphasized than the wise selection of the title for the Sixteenth Yearbook of the National Council, *Arithmetic in General Education.*[2] Teachers need to be reminded that these general objectives include both social needs and maximum development of the potentialities of the individual. An adequate program in arithmetic cannot be based on social needs alone unless the use of that term includes as social needs development of attitudes, ideals, approaches to problem solving, sometimes known as mathematical modes of thinking.

Teaching Problems

Teachers in my class last summer had little difficulty in identifying problems. The list and frequency of occurrence is of interest. One-third of the teachers of arithmetic when asked to list problems which they would

---

[1] *Manpower for Research,* Vol. IV of Science and the Public Policy, A Report to the President's Scientific Research Board, October 1947, Superintendent of Documents, U.S. Government Printing Office.

[2] *Arithmetic in General Education,* National Council of Teachers of Mathematics Sixteenth Yearbook (1941).

like to study, included individual differences. The next topic in order of
frequency was procedures in teaching problems and problem solving.
Teaching fractions was in third place. Two teachers listed the retarded
child and two listed enrichment for superior students.

Teaching techniques for grades 7 and 8 was listed as a critical problem
by two teachers. Among problems listed by a single teacher were planned
versus incidental arithmetic, problems of supervision, grade levels versus
areas of instruction, place of drill, remedial teaching, use of texts and
workbooks, teaching of division, teaching of borrowing, curriculum for
grade 7, prognostic value for algebra of arithmetic tests, and methods of
teaching arithmetic which cause difficulty in algebra.

An attempt was made to help each student see the relative importance
of his problem in relation to his whole teaching situation. Each individual
was allowed special credit for successful procedures he was able to develop in seeking possible solutions of his problems.

It was observed through group investigation of the implications of the
meaning theory of instruction that acceptance and use of the meaning
theory on all grade levels provided a new hope of solving many problems
in teaching arithmetic. Since this study was seen to relate to so many of
the specific problems listed it became the central core of the course. A
similar situation might emerge in individual teacher study or in-service
groups.

The problem of individual differences has important implications for
the training program. An individual contract plan in arithmetic makes it
much more difficult for the teacher to teach meaning rather than mechanics. Students must be led to discovery of new relationships and generalizations through directed experiences. It is almost impossible for the
teacher to provide these experiences for one or two individuals at a time.
I should not want to see a class in which at no time was the interest of all
focused on the same topic. After exploratory early experiences further
development will be necessary in groups or on an individual basis, but
even for this the groups need to be as variable as possible. Most any
Johnny sometimes gets interested in an idea which may have caught his
fancy and he thereby belongs with the better students for that particular
idea.

Individual differences must be cared for in terms of the progress and
depth that individuals may achieve with a particular topic. Short division
can be taught when students are ready to discover it which for some of
course is never.

One aid in providing for individual differences would be identification
of minimum understandings and skills with which different individuals
and groups may be permitted to leave a topic and go to the next. State

and city curriculum committees could make their classroom materials of greater value if they indicated possible minimums on which both group and individual instruction could be based for any grade or level.

Professional Literature

All teachers need to become familiar with professional literature in their own area of interest. For the upper grades *School Science and Mathematics* and *The Mathematics Teacher* can be recommended. *The Elementary School Journal* should of course be available in the school library and if every teacher of arithmetic could read or have access to a half dozen of the articles in the valuable summary of writings on arithmetic that appears in each November issue, better practices in arithmetic would result.

The 100 selected references to be found in the *Sixteenth Yearbook* [3] would provide an excellent bibliography from which any teacher could choose good professional reading. The *Tenth* and *Sixteenth Yearbooks* of the National Council should have been studied by all teachers of arithmetic. Furthermore, these references require discussion if the teacher is to get the most from them. Although the date of the *Tenth Yearbook* [4] is 1935 it still could provide a source of valuable discussion material for any teacher group.

In addition to the professional literature there is a large body of semi-popular writing on elementary concepts which could be recommended for elementary teachers.

Continuous Growth in Mathematical Power

Arithmetic power and competence are achieved by continuous growth and development of the individual from kindergarten counting games to the algebra and geometry of the high school. The teacher needs to know the means of guiding development of both basic skills and concepts through the experiences of each year.

Place value is a concept which gives meaning to experiences at many levels. From the earliest numeration beyond the number 10 to polynomials in algebra, there is frequent reference to this device man has found so useful in reaching his present state of engineering ingenuity and businss efficiency.

Place value is a unifying idea in counting, in the rearrangements which we call addition and subtraction, in the repeated additions and subtrac-

---

[3] *Ibid.*
[4] *Teaching Arithmetic,* Tenth Yearbook, 1935.

tions which we call multiplication and division. In roots and powers and short forms of computation and in checking, reference to place value will show relationships with earlier and more familiar concepts.

Many courses of study do a fair job of identifying the skills to be learned at each level. The contributions of the previous grade and the following ones to skills are not too difficult to recognize. Much less has been done in listing meanings which should be taught at the various levels and which should be developed through the experiences of more than one year's work. A list of meanings to be taught, which will be valuable both for use in teaching and in teacher training, is to be found in *Arithmetic 1948*.[5] W. B. Storm has listed 54 understandings that can be learned in arithmetic through division. The list has been prepared in co-operation with the Committee of Seven, and was discussed at the Arithmetic Conference at the University of Chicago last summer. It is not intended to be a complete list, and some might not express the meanings in the same form. Nevertheless such a list of meanings takes its rightful place with the lists of skills previously considered the core of instruction in arithmetic. We have all been concerned with the 81 addition facts and the 810 higher-decade combinations of which 176 are used in carrying in multiplication. When our arithmetic course of study is described in terms of skills, the teaching is apt to be mechanical and the product merely a temporary tool. Teachers would be much more likely to teach meanings if they are given assistance in identifying the meanings. Teachers in groups or as committees in schools or systems, or even in courses, would find it a profitable experience to try to list meanings they will teach.

One of Storm's understandings which is important to all levels is "understanding the significance of checking." Attention must be given to checking and its significance in the training program. More important still for those learning arithmetic is the recognition of the reasonableness of a result. This practice should be cultivated in all situations no matter in what way the result may be obtained and in what social situation it may arise.

One of our gravest faults in the mathematics curriculum has been the large gap which has existed between the program of the elementary and secondary schools. That is being corrected by an extension of the general mathematics of grades 7 and 8 to grade 9. All of us have been too satisfied to teach concepts and skills outlined for our particular grade to the complete neglect of the kind of experiences that have come before or will come after. In mathematics we have actually done a better job of anticipating

---

[5] *Arithmetic 1948*, Compiled and edited by G. T. Buswell (Chicago: The University of Chicago Press, 1948).

the needs of the next course than of relating experiences to the immediately preceding one. If high school teachers knew the problems and goals of arithmetic teaching they could do a much better job and do it more efficiently. The *Manpower for Research* [6] report emphasizes the importance of the 12-year perspective.

In many city and state curriculum committees elementary and secondary teachers are getting together to work on common problems. This co-operative work and the widespread acceptance of the meaning theory are the most promising trends of today in mathematics. Schools and teacher training institutions must plan programs which guarantee that teachers of arithmetic become familiar with the goals in arithmetic of the grades which precede theirs and at least two which follow. If the institution which started the training of your teachers failed in this respect then it is all the more important that your school make provision to remedy the deficiency.

Important Teaching Aids and Procedures

At the recent Wisconsin Education Association meeting two speakers made a real contribution for teachers in their presentations of two important uses of arithmetic. These were arithmetic needs in retailing and in industry. Both presentations were made with references to the special training programs necessarily maintained for prospective workers in these areas. The speaker for retailing called attention to the fact that everyday computations with fractions and decimals are not as simple as we sometimes are led to believe when she made reference to the cost of $4\frac{3}{4}$ yards at $1.95 per yard; or $10.95 plus luxury tax of 20 per cent, plus sales tax of 2 per cent. Direct references to community uses of arithmetic should be made in all teacher training programs.

Teachers in training should have opportunity to see and discuss all recent arithmetic films and film strips and older productions of particular merit. Experienced teachers' questions last summer about a new arithmetic film revealed the desirability, as nothing else had, of study of the meaning theory even for those who have taught. Films provoke good discussion in teacher training groups, even those films which are merely suggestive of procedures that the teacher could better use herself than show by film.

Films are only one of many visual aids useful in arithmetic. Teacher or even student prepared visual materials are always of great value. The preparation of such aids by teacher training groups not only serves to provide the teacher with materials which may be of later use but even more

---

[6] *Op. cit.*

this work requires original planning and concrete experience in preparation for direction of meaningful teaching.

Evaluation in its broadest sense has come to be recognized as an important component of all good teaching. Professional courses for all teachers will certainly include instruction in this area. Measurement of understanding rather than mechanics is a real problem in arithmetic instruction and attention must be given to it in the teacher training programs at all levels.

In the Wisconsin curriculum conferences this fall there was considerable interest in units for use in arithmetic which cross over subject matter lines. The current acceptance of science as a part of the elementary school curriculum opens a new area for correlation with arithmetic. Much study needs to be given to possibilities of correlation of arithmetic and science particularly in the upper grades. This would be a very appropriate topic for special investigation by the Central Association. At some future date the Elementary Mathematics section could profitably devote an entire program to this problem.

Special Training in Mathematics

Point 3 of the goals for teachers includes the desirability for the teacher of arithmetic to broaden his intellectual interests to include many areas of knowledge. This, as has been observed, is not special training for arithmetic teaching and yet it may be more critical in this area than any other of the elementary school curriculum. The breadth of intellectual pursuits which have a direct interest for the teacher of arithmetic can scarcely be exaggerated. In undergraduate training, the new programs of integrated liberal studies, given such impetus by the Harvard Report,[7] make it more possible for the elementary teacher to have broad cultural experiences and to develop interests which should enrich many later teaching situations. In one respect these programs are an attempt on the college level to get away from sharp subject matter divisions. They are an important step forward as far as general education for elementary teachers is concerned.

Such programs cannot carry mathematics instruction in a satisfactory manner, except as a separate course, any more than incidental learning can provide an adequate arithmetic program. Colleges and universities are also considering modifications of the traditional first year mathematics courses to make more certain their contribution to general education. Courses like the Type I and Type II general mathematics for the Junior

---

[7] *General Education in a Free Society*, Report of the Harvard University Committee (Cambridge: The Harvard University Press, 1945).

College, described in the Fifteenth Yearbook of the National Council, *The Place of Mathematics in Secondary Education,*[8] could make real contributions to the professional as well as the general education of arithmetic teachers. In one the emphasis is on broad concepts and certain general mathematical procedures and their applications. In the other the core is social uses, particularly statistics and part of what is commonly taught as mathematics of investment. A course of the latter type has been offered at Southern Illinois University for a number of years. Its original intent was for arithmetic teachers. It actually turned out to be a popular course for many other groups as well.

In a four-year course for elementary teachers I would strongly recommend the inclusion, at least on an elective basis, of a year's sequence of special training for teachers of arithmetic, if possible for four hours a semester. At least one semester of this sequence should be taught by members of the mathematics department and be described as a mathematics course. Teachers of the course should be selected on the basis of their special interest in and sense of the value of teacher education on both the elementary and secondary levels. If at least one semester of this course can count toward general education requirements, so much the better. A course in mathematics planned for general education, like those just described, might be made the first semester of this sequence. It could be much more desirable, however, if a course could be planned and offered especially for elementary teachers.

A selection of topics for such a course planned for elementary teachers might be made from the following list: the number system, including historical background; use of symbols in problem solving; tables and graphs; elementary topics in statistics; ideas of approximate computation; logarithms; recreational arithmetic; compound interest; annuities and elementary topics in life insurance; trigonometric ratios in indirect measurement. This list is not unlike that recommended in General Mathematics, Type I, in the Fifteenth Yearbook.[9] A systematic development of algebra would not be necessary but algebraic principles would naturally be used in a study of the topics listed. Frequent references to historical background and significance should be included.

When teachers study techniques for teaching meaning in arithmetic they discover that too limited understanding of basic mathematical ideas is a major handicap in an attempt to understand relationships and logical developments in elementary number situations. Undergraduate students in training are usually much more deficient in this respect than experi-

---

[8] *The Place of Mathematics in Secondary Education,* Fifteenth Yearbook, 1940.
[9] *Ibid.*

enced teachers, and some course in mathematics of the kind just described is of even greater importance in the undergraduate training program. It does not seem impossible to me that in large systems individual deficiencies in basic mathematics might be made up with the assistance of a competent teacher of mathematics in the system. Such a program should of course be one based on ideas new to those taking the course and one of complete emphasis on meanings—not remedial work on skills, old or new.

Remedial work with meaning, if necessary to bring all prospective teachers up to a defined minimum level of achievement, should be provided before any special training in mathematics. The check list of minimum essentials of the Commission on Post-War Plans [10] might be used as a minimum level of achievement. This list also can serve later as a teacher's guide to some of the principal goals in the total arithmetic program and hence should be known to all teachers of arithmetic.

Even though the prospective teacher may have made a good record in a first semester's college mathematics course of the type discussed above, he may still have little real understanding of some of the basic concepts of elementary arithmetic which he will be called upon as a teacher to teach meaningfully. Direct attention must be given to these concepts in the teacher training program. Books like the recently popular *Elementary Arithmetic* by Buckingham [11] and the older *Arithmetic for Teacher Training Classes* by E. H. Taylor,[12] one of the pioneers in the move to teach arithmetic to prospective teachers of arithmetic, can be very useful as guides or texts in this study. It is my recommendation that this material be studied in close association with the work on methods of the second semester of the sequence for arithmetic teachers and that it also be brought into the first semester's work as it is related to the topics under consideration.

The second semester's course should be devoted to problems in teaching arithmetic with very special emphasis on teaching meaning. This course can be taught so much more efficiently and effectively if students have had some recent experiences in elementary but basic mathematical concepts. In this course there probably should be two basic texts, one of which is a methods text and the other a text on the meanings of arithmetic. Viewpoints and teaching aids discussed in the preceding sections are also important for the undergraduate student and should be brought into the course as time and previous experience of the students permit.

---

[10] "The Second Report of the Commission on Post-War Plans," *The Mathematics Teacher*, XXXVIII (May, 1945), 195-221.

[11] B. R. Buckingham, *Elementary Arithmetic* (New York: Ginn & Company, 1947).

[12] E. H. Taylor, *Arithmetic for Teacher Training Classes* (New York: Holt, Rinehart & Winston, Inc., 1926).

Through the year's sequence the prospective arithmetic teacher must obtain clear understanding of the basic mathematical concepts so that he will be able to lead children to think meaningfully and independently in situations involving number. Too often children merely cultivate the habit of dependence upon rules set down by others for them. Children see number and form and some order in the world around them. So far as possible their classroom experiences should be similar to their out-of-school contacts with number. But this is not always easy in the process of leading children to see relationships and seek generalizations. The teacher must be able to introduce situations which will create for the student the need to see meaning and relations.

All teachers in training need to re-emphasize in their own thinking two aspects of teacher responsibility. One is to provide for the present and anticipated (as nearly as is possible) future needs of their students. The second responsibility is to provide the student an introduction to goals, ideas, ideals, relationships, and possibilities that he would not easily find in his everyday experiences present or future.

MILWAUKEE'S IN-SERVICE ARITHMETIC EDUCATION PROGRAM

Lillian C. Paukner

As a part of the in-service education program in the Milwaukee Public Schools, designed to encourage professional study and instructional improvement, a course in the teaching of arithmetic will be offered to intermediate grade teachers. Emphasis will be placed on the sequential program for these grades, teaching techniques, provisions for individual differences, use of manipulative materials, and the evaluation of pupil growth. This will be a workshop type of course giving teachers opportunities to share successful practices in the teaching of arithmetic and the laboratory experience of trying out these practices in their own classrooms.

Participation in such courses as this carry credit for salary classification purposes. "All salary schedules are established in divisions so that mem-

[From "Milwaukee's In-Service Arithmetic Education Program," *The Arithmetic Teacher*, IV (November, 1957), pp. 222-23. Reprinted by permission of the author and *The Arithmetic Teacher*.]

bers of the staff may qualify by degree status or by earned units of preparation." Credit allowances are given for travel, work experience, authorship, and professional committee service as well as courses earned in accredited schools. An outstanding feature of the program is the freedom of choice each individual has in planning his program of professional activities.

Enrichment Activities for the Gifted Child

The Mathematics Committee at the elementary school level has considered the problem of providing enrichment activities for the gifted or very bright children. This committee has defined enrichment activities as being those activities that:

1. Extend basic understandings and processes in mathematics
2. Give the pupil added power to handle more difficult aspects of what the class is doing
3. Give opportunities for exploration in the particular area of study
4. Give opportunities to relate mathematics to other areas of study—science, astronomy
5. Apply mathematics to everyday living activities over and above regular class work.

To assist the teacher in finding activities which will interest the gifted pupil and challenge his thinking, the Committee has summarized suggestions from its thinking and from literature in the field of mathematics. The suggestions are as follows:

Experiment or Exploration

1. Short cut methods in computation
2. Discovery of mathematical processes
3. Mathematics implications in science—astronomy, expansion, etc.

Research Projects and Reports

1. History of the number system
2. Comparative studies—sizes of buildings, bridges, countries, rivers, etc.
3. History of measures
4. Measurement systems of the world
5. Budgets and their construction

Construction Projects

1. Mobiles to illustrate plane figures, solids, etc.
2. Scale models of community, buildings, rooms, etc.
3. Blueprint reading in the construction of models
4. Geometric objects to show cubic measure

Measurement Projects

1. Laying out garden plots, play fields, etc.
2. Gas and electric meters
3. Measurements in the home

Mathematical Puzzles and Games

1. Magic squares
2. Crossword puzzles involving mathematical terms and vocabulary
3. Puzzle problems

Drawings

1. Geometric designs
2. Graphs to illustrate statistical information

Field Trips

1. Places where mathematics is important—banks, weather bureau, etc.
2. Mathematics implications in other field trips (gifted children alerted to look for them)

Scrapbooks

1. Pictures, news items that illustrate use of number

Language Activities

1. Books related to mathematics—example, "The Wonderful World of Mathematics"
2. Dramatizations of the social applications of mathematics
3. Panels and debates on current issues and problems

SUPERVISORS HELP TEACHERS IN ARITHMETIC

Irvin H. Brune

Originally a supervisor was one who looked from above, a critical overseer, a strict authority. Presently, however, a supervisor is one who helps, a farseeing planner, a wise leader. Numerous supervisors have brought this new look to their responsibilities.

Such a transformation came not as an accident. The authoritarian way of life got a lengthy tryout in American schools. And it was found want-

[From "Supervisors Help Teachers in Arithmetic," *Education*, LXXVIII (December, 1957), pp. 228-34. Reprinted by permission of Bobbs-Merrill Company, Inc., Indianapolis, Indiana.]

ing. As educators looked at themselves and their work, they came to realize that lock-step methods bore little fruit, whether applied to children in a classroom or to teachers in a school system.

Accordingly, today's supervisor is a helper, not a taskmaster; a friend, not a fiend. The following sections will suggest how supervisors assist teachers in arithmetic, whether the teachers grope somewhat as beginners or gasp somewhat as veterans. Although not every help listed appears in a majority of schools, more and more teachers find such helps effective.

Supervisors Help Teachers to Procure Time

Within a welter of differences among teachers, one striking likeness appears, namely, teachers all lack time. This holds particularly for elementary teachers, the ones society commissions to help children learn priceless fundamentals.

Most of the ways whereby supervisors help teachers in arithmetic provide a saving of time. When supervisors were overseers rather than planners, they often overlooked the importance of time. Standardized tests, for example, while good enough in themselves, defeat their purpose if the administration robs teachers of the time needed for planning and teaching. Granted that an occasional evaluation provides direction, it does not follow that numerous testing multiply the good. Indeed, an overdone program of measures steals the very time teachers need to reteach, and redirect learning.

Closely allied to the overuse of standardized tests are overdone records and reports. For teachers to record all grades thirteen times every term, as was revealed in a study made in one school system, certainly represents an abuse. Clerical duties apparently mount insidiously. Temptations ironically lurk in innovations. If the new way, though plausible, adds another chore without replacing an outmoded procedure, teachers soon bear needless burdens of busywork. Supervisors can help teachers tremendously by pruning such routine ruthlessly.

Supervisors also can help teachers keep distractions to a minimum. Many time-stealing nuisances in teachers' lives begin laudably. The catch is that they soon surge out of bounds. A few minutes to help Worthy Cause A soon becomes hours because Worthy Causes B, C, D . . . also clamor for time and attention. A few minutes that should go to arithmetic, but are diverted for holding a pep meeting, for practicing a dance, or for rehearsing pupils' baton twirling, actually become a shameful diversion of time. As another example, an easily rationalized campaign to acquaint parents with what schools are doing readily converts to chaos. Any ranking school officer who freely invites parents to "visit our school at any time whatsoever" at the same time courts immeasurable harm. Surely better ways to "sell the public" exist than to herd parents (and sometimes their preschool children with them) indiscriminately into classrooms already filled to overflowing.

Besides helping teachers (and administrators who sanction interruptions) greatly reduce losses due to distractions, supervisors help teachers to make wise use of the school day. Life in a contemporary school grows increasingly complex; unless time is budgeted, first things, i.e., the Three R's, will not come first. This is not to urge that every school necessarily allot more time to, say, arithmetic. Rather it seeks to use arithmetic time, whatever be its amount, effectively, and above all to respect that time. If, as a later section suggests, meaningless drill wastes time in arithmetic, then, of course, one can not reasonably seek more time for such drill. The point to reiterate here is that teachers need time to plan lessons and to prepare materials, and supervisors can help them procure that time. Although such assistance no doubt furthers *any* learning activity, the very nature of arithmetic, as considered in the next section, stipulates regular and adequate time. This risks stressing the obvious; supervisors help tremendously when they work with teachers to keep arithmetic time strictly for arithmetic.

Supervisors Help Teachers to Emphasize Big Ideas

What is arithmetic? How do pupils learn arithmetic? All interested in public education need continually to ask themselves these questions. For on the answers thereto depend their philosophies and their procedures.

As regards the first question, arithmetic is a way of thinking. It enables people to handle problems involving numbers and quantities. It provides people with facts and information about sizes, orders, relations. It affords a system, whereby people keep track of ones, tens, hundreds, and so on.

With respect to the second question, pupils learn arithmetic by solving problems. Teachers set up situations, ask questions, provide problems. From the outset pupils handle sets of objects, compare sizes of sets, put sets together, take sets apart. Gradually pupils learn to order sets with respect to size, and to substitute an order of names of sizes for the sets themselves. Pupils use this order of number names when they count. Via counting, pupils can solve any problem in arithmetic.

But counting grows tedious. Memorized answers to various simple sums, differences, products, and quotients expedite the work. Symbols, particularly those wherein the positions of digits signify numerical values, facilitate thinking and record its results.

So pupils progress from things to symbols. All the while, however, they compare, count, assemble, and disassemble quantities involved in situations which are, to them, genuine problems. Indeed, they embark, on seas to some extent unknown to them, to make discoveries for themselves.

The implications for supervisors abound. First of all, teachers themselves must understand arithmetic. Seldom, to be sure, did teachers neglect the details of arithmetic in their own schooling. They know arithmetic facts. They retain, or can readily refurbish, the rules. But not infrequently they possess the threads, rather than the fabric. So supervisors often help them regard arithmetic as a system, a discipline designed to help people process problems by comparing, counting, combining, and removing quantities. Such ideas (and they pervade all arithmetic) matter more than number facts which pupils memorize and number operations which pupils imitate.

Supervisors help by emphasizing big ideas in arithmetic. They encourage teachers to attend extension classes, educational conferences, and summer schools that weigh such ideas. Preschool workshops highlight major concepts in arithmetic, and invite people to see the system, rather than the skills.

Ever mindful of that precious ingredient in teachers' lives, *time,* supervisors work within the schedule rather than beyond it. One particularly effective way to help teachers emphasize major concepts comes into play when the supervisor himself teaches preview, overview, or review lessons during the regular arithmetic period. Such demonstration lessons stress major concepts. They inevitably provide variety, which benefits the pupils, and they afford regular teachers opportunities to observe their pupils' reactions from a different viewpoint. No quantity of bulletins, directives, and conference notes can entirely displace the benefits that result from supervisor-taught demonstration lessons. An ounce of example, supervisors find, really outweighs a pound of precept.

Supervisors Help Teachers to Employ Learning Aids

Stemming from sizeable gains in knowledge as to how pupils learn arithmetic, learning aids merit careful consideration. Pupils learn best by solving more-or-less-puzzling situations that intrigue them. When the individual learner hears, sees, feels, and thinks simultaneously, he learns more than he would via a single avenue of stimulation. Moreover, what he handles conduces more to his learning than what he merely hears.

Accordingly, supervisors help teachers to acquire and employ many types of learning aids. Films and filmstrips, if selected carefully and used sparingly, add interest and variety. Demonstration devices, such as a fraction board or a wall pocket, enable the whole group to follow a development. Information, neatly tabulated on a chalkboard, provides the setting for a class discussion.

But, since learning is individual even though a social situation may enhance it, supervisors see beyond the benefits of demonstration devices. Individual learning aids, that is to say, outperform the contraptions which merely enhance teaching of the tell-and-show sort. Materials that pupils themselves use to contrive an answer to a quantitative question avail abundantly. The pupil *feels* and sees and thinks. He *handles* the objects that represent the problem and illustrates its solution. Numerous experiences with such materials prepare the pupil to manage other symbols, such as words, numerals, marks, and signs, that represent ideas in arithmetic. So more and more supervisors see materials including sticks to group and count, square inches to arrange and enumerate, and graphs to construct and compare, as tremendous helps. Obviously, the commonplace controversy, perpetuated, on the one hand, by administrators who aver that they "don't buy materials because teachers don't ask for them," and, on the other hand, by teachers who assert that they "don't ask for materials because administrators won't buy them," should cease. Indeed, many forward-looking supervisors encourage teachers to ask for arithmetic materials, and exhort administrators to buy them.

Supervisors Help Teachers Develop Pupil Readiness

People, pets, and playthings appeal to children. Marks, signs, and symbols, on the other hand, seem less natural. As pupils work in arithmetic they learn to deal with symbols that represent objects, actions, and ideas. Above all else, arithmetic applies to a set of ideas—concepts of size, order, and operations of combining and separating groups.

The transition from things to symbols seldom occurs without effort. But adults, including teachers, all too easily overlook this fact. Accordingly, the supervisor helps by reminding teachers occasionally that symbols, and what they represent; principles, and what they signify in the total structure; and shortcuts and what they expedite, assume meaning only gradually. Pupils learn arithmetic, this is to say, by enlarging understandings.

From numbers used for counting, for example, pupils go to enlarged concepts. Whereas $3 + 4 = 7$ and $7 - 4 = 3$ still involve only the numbers previously used to count objects, the situation $7 - 7$ does not. A new number, zero, becomes necessary. And effective teaching employs experiences emphasizing the new group, the empty set, the none-left idea. Seldom is arithmetic difficult, provided that the pupils are ready.

Readiness involves preparedness and willingness. Each of these, happily, complements the other. Interest, based on understanding arithmetic, facilitates pupils' further understandings. Success in the subject, more-over, enhances willingness to achieve further successes.

Teachers under pressures of time sometimes forget these matters. Su-pervisors, by alleviating such pressures as suggested earlier in the present article, can do much to shift teachers' questionable concerns with cover-ing pages to more significant concerns with grasping ideas.

Supervisors Help Teachers Provide for Individual Differences

Learning arithmetic, though nurtured in a class, proceeds individually. Each pupil learns at his own rate. To challenge the able and simultane-ously not to frustrate the slow is the problem. What can supervisors do about it? What should the supervisor suggest?

Answers could range all the way from tutoring individual pupils to guiding the class as a whole each step of the way. Each approach has its advocates; to date no one plan rates as a panacea. Those who clamor for subgroups in arithmetic often overlook the matter of time; how does one schedule subgroups in reading, arithmetic, and yet other subjects? At the other extreme, should fast learners be slowed to boredom and slow learn-ers be incited to bewilderment?

Some supervisors have compromised rather successfully by recommend-ing a sort of uniformity plus diversity. Since arithmetic deals with big ideas, all pupils should work with those ideas. Everybody, for example, should learn to count. All pupils profit by at least some of many various activities that prepare pupils for work in counting. Recognizing sets of things, comparing sets, composing sets, matching sets, arranging subsets, ordering sets—these are helpful activities. Fast learners explore them all, even those designed as too deep for slow learners, and probably invent some of their own. But all pupils learn to count in the allotted time. Some, of course, will go haltingly one by one; others may be going by twos, by fives, or possibly even by nines!

Helping teachers to meet individual differences among pupils merits a separate article, or possibly a book. Classes containing no more than twenty-five pupils working on minimum essentials with plenty of challeng-ing extra materials available for gifted children seem to be one good answer. Just as the pupils present a great variety of abilities, however, so the supervisor should encourage a variety of ways to reach all the chil-dren. Good teaching is not a series of set steps. Especially do some super-visors help teachers and pupils by providing enrichment materials.

In no case should pupils skip any of the major concepts in arithmetic. Rather they should probe those ideas more thoroughly. While slow learners seek a single solution to a problem of moderate difficulty, fast learners should seek two, or three, or six solutions. While the plodders cope with $\frac{1}{2} + \frac{3}{8} + \frac{1}{4}$, the able tackle $1 + \frac{1}{2} + \frac{1}{3} + \frac{1}{4} + \frac{1}{5} \ldots$ to any limit they desire. Besides this, pupils compose and exchange problems. Stated simply, the plan some supervisors rightfully recommend provides open doors —ways that lead to considerable understanding for all, and enrichment for at least a few.

Supervisors Help Teachers Regarding Drill

To contrast arithmetic teaching today with its pedagogy twenty years ago is to describe a mild revolution. Far-reaching changes came because our knowledge of how people learn arithmetic progressed. The former pedagogy, for example, treated arithmetic as bits—facts, principles, rules— to be memorized. The present procedure, however, handles arithmetic as a system of ideas, a way of thinking. Whereas most teachers formerly gave little, if any, thought to pupils' understanding arithmetic, most teachers nowadays consider understanding as paramount.

But, though significant, the revolution lacks completeness. Teachers still evaluate textbooks according to the quantity of drill material they contain. Teachers' insistence that teaching materials enhance understanding lags.

Here lies a fertile ground for supervisors. Just what should one recommend concerning drill?

Drill indubitably has a place. It is not, however, the be-all. Many supervisors urge that pupils experience an idea in numerous ways, so that they understand the idea thoroughly, before they memorize symbols representing the idea. This holds for $A = lw$, as well as for $8 \times 7 = 56$. For a child to memorize that "the average of n numbers equals their sum over n" avails but little if he doesn't know what the statement means. Arithmetic teems with examples wherein rote learning amounts practically to no learning.

If a pupil has had sufficient experiences, however, with length, width, perimeter, rectangle to compose something resembling $p = 2(1 + w)$ in meaning, then he may well memorize his rule. This interesting sequel, however, usually comes to light: after he composes the statement himself, the pupil usually knows it by heart without any drill.

Of course once pupils understand, say, the multiplication facts, they should memorize them. When pupils first approach a simple problem such as What is the cost of 7 three-cent stamps? they readily realize that, while some are counting or adding, the ones who *know* that 7 threes are 21 have the best way of all.

But the counting and the adding matter too. They bring out meanings pupils otherwise would miss. On the other hand, to tell and show pupils shortcuts prematurely usually defeats the very objective it should enhance; instead of saving time, it loses time. Drilling the esoteric keeps pupils busy—and ignorant. *Merely memorizing meaningless marks makes mathematics miserable material.*

Supervisors Help Teachers ... A Summary

Insight is the principal thing. Therefore supervisors seek to foster insight. They help teachers because, from their vantage point, supervisors see the momentous as well as the minute. Whether a pupil understands arithmetic as a system is momentous. So, too, is his attitude. Does he experiment with numbers? Or is he afraid? Or bored? Whether a pupil mouths rules is minute. Does he comprehend what he says? Or is it Choctaw? Or half true?

Teachers know all this. From their training and experience they know that insight pays. Yet all too frequently they believe that their role is to obey orders, push someone's pet theory, practice a method prescribed from on high.

But supervisors nowadays look at things differently. They doubt that there is one best method for teaching arithmetic. Or, if there were, they know, too, that the variety provided by interspersed applications of less-than-best procedures also brings benefits. Accordingly, they eschew rigid schedules of topics and strict how-to's.

Above all, supervisors help teachers obtain and maintain time. The well-conceived slogan, "r r r +", by no means suggests that the "+" displaces any of the 3 R's. And supervisors count it as elementary that time is the essence. Without time to explore it, arithmetic necessarily makes no lasting impressions.

Supervisors help teachers underline big ideas. Arithmetic systematizes people's thoughts about quantitative situations. Pupils answer questions of How much and How many? via numbers, measures, operations. They learn to put quantities together and take them apart. Properly to stress major concepts in arithmetic, supervisors teach demonstration lessons highlighting estimating, approximating, solving, and proving. Teachers need occasionally to note their pupils' responses as seen from such a vantage point.

Supervisors help teachers use learning materials. Teachers agree that there are many effective ways to teach arithmetic. Yet the utility of objects that help pupils transfer their thinking from the world of real things to the realm of abstractions looms large. None disputes this utility. Indeed the supervisor seldom renders greater service than when he provides learning aids for children. And *shows* teachers how to use these aids effectively!

Supervisors help teachers foster readiness, which blends attitude with aptitude. If nothing succeeds like success, arithmetic certainly illustrates the point. Pupils who understand arithmetic like it. Their liking it, in turn, enables them to increase their understandings.

Supervisors help teachers provide for differences among pupils. All citizens need to size up situations; all need to estimate outcomes; all need to recognize quantitative reasonableness. While the entire class works with details leading to such number sense, the ablest pupils also investigate further, but related, details; they solve standard problems in numerous ways; they solve harder problems. In a word, teachers *open* new doors. The supervisor aids immeasurably by contributing items to the collection of situations every effective teacher builds.

Supervisors help teachers maintain a sane attitude toward drill. To know basic facts by heart befits all citizens; drill makes this possible. But to drill on arithmetical items, before they are clear, wastes time. For what does it profit a man to know *how* to divide if he doesn't know *when* to divide?

New occasions teach new duties. Steady growth in our knowledge of how pupils learn arithmetic has definitely altered supervisors' responsibilities. No longer do supervisors purvey standard drill sheets, standard study schedules, standard unit tests, and standard ways to teach. Rather they help teachers provide experiences, situations, materials, problems. In solving for themselves the precisely appropriate problems teachers provide for them, pupils learn best.

What do teachers need? Patience, understanding, and time—these three —and the greatest is time; at least supervisors can *do* something about time. Granted that supervisors invariably prefer teachers who manifest patience and understanding, the necessary further step is to provide the obvious, but often overlooked, prime ingredient, *time*. The net effect really amounts to this: *They let their teachers teach!*

BIBLIOGRAPHY

Bean, J. E. "Arithmetical Understandings of Elementary-School Teachers," *Elementary School Journal*, LIX (May, 1959), 447-50.

Boyer, Lee Emerson. "Preparation of Elementary Arithmetic Teachers," *Emerging Practices in Mathematics Education*, National Council of Teachers of Mathematics, Twenty-second Yearbook (1954). Washington, D.C.: The Council, 172-80.

Breslich, E. R. "Some Proposals Regarding the Preparation for Teaching High School Mathematics," *Mathematics Teacher*, XXXIX (May, 1946), 200-5.

Brown, Kenneth. "In-service Education for Teachers of Mathematics, Institutes-Workshops-Conferences," *Emerging Practices in Mathematics Education*,

National Council of Teachers of Mathematics, Twenty-second Yearbook (1954). Washington, D.C.; The Council, 238-43.

Brune, I. H. "Supervisors Help Teachers in Arithmetic," *Education,* LXXVIII (December, 1957), 228-34.

Burger, J. M. "Academic Backgrounds of Kansas Mathematics Teachers," *School Science and Mathematics,* LX (February, 1960), 139-42.

Burnett, R. Will, and Lillian Gragg. "Teacher Education in Science and Mathematics," *Review of Educational Research Bulletin,* XVIII (October, 1948), 364-67.

Buswell, G. T. "Content and Organization of Arithmetic," *Arithmetic Teacher,* VI (March, 1959), 77-83.

Blyler, Dorothea. "Certification of Elementary School Teachers in the United States," *Elementary School Journal,* XLV (June, 1945), 578-89.

Dutton, Wilbur H. "Attitudes of Prospective Teachers Toward Arithmetic," *Elementary School Journal,* LII (October, 1951), 84-90.

Eads, Laura K. "Developmental Mathematics in New York City," *Emerging Practices in Mathematics Education,* National Council of Teachers of Mathematics, Twenty-second Yearbook (1954). Washington, D.C.: The Council, 232-37.

Fehr, Howard F. "Present Research in the Teaching of Arithmetic," *Teachers College Record,* LII (October, 1950), 11-23.

Fulkerson, Elbert. "How Well Do 158 Prospective Elementary Teachers Know Arithmetic?" *The Arithmetic Teacher,* VII (March, 1960), 141-46.

Glennon, V. J. *A Study of the Growth and Mastery of Certain Basic Mathematical Understandings on Seven Education Levels,* Doctoral Dissertation. Cambridge, Mass.: Harvard University Graduate School of Education, 1948.

Grime, Herschel E. "A Plan for the In-service Training of Teachers in the Elementary Schools," *School Science and Mathematics,* XLVIII (October, 1948), 517-21.

Grossnickle, F. E. "Training of Teachers of Arithmetic," *The Teaching of Arithmetic,* National Society for Study of Education, Fiftieth Yearbook (1950). Washington, D.C.: The Council, 203-31.

"Guidance Report of the Commission on Post-War Plans," *Mathematics Teacher,* XL (November, 1947), 315-39.

Ireland, D. B. "Birmingham, Michigan, Conducts In-service Training Program in Arithmetic," *American School Board Journal,* CXV (July, 1947), 45.

Judd, Romie D., and Robert Lee Morton. "Current Practices in Teacher-Training Courses in Arithmetic," *Teaching of Arithmetic,* National Council of Teachers of Mathematics, Tenth Yearbook (1935). Washington, D.C.: The Council, 157-72.

Layton, W. I. "Certification of Teachers of Mathematics," *The Mathematics Teacher,* XLII (December, 1949), 377-80.

Layton, W. I. "Mathematical Training Prescribed by Teachers Colleges in the Preparation of Elementary Teachers," *The Mathematics Teacher,* XLVI (December, 1951), 551-56.

Mayor, John R. "Special Training for Teachers of Arithmetic," *School Science and Mathematics,* XLIX (October, 1949), 539-48.

———. "Teachers and Scientists Form New Partnership," *Nation's Schools,* LXV (February, 1960), 99.

Morton, R. L. "Mathematics in the Training of Arithmetic Teachers," *Mathematics Teacher,* XXXII (March, 1939), 106-10.

Mueller, Francis J. "Arithmetic Preparation for Elementary Teachers," *Education,* LXXIX (January, 1959), 299-302.

———, and Harold Moser. "Background Mathematics for Teachers of Arithmetic," *Emerging Practices in Mathematics Education,* National Council of Teachers of Mathematics, Twenty-second Yearbook (1954). Washington, D.C.: The Council, 180-88.

Newsom, C. V. "Mathematical Background Needed by Teachers of Arithmetic," *The Teaching of Arithmetic,* National Society for Study of Education, Fiftieth Yearbook (1950). Chicago: University of Chicago Press, Part II, 232-50.

Orleans, Jacob S., and Edwin Wandt. "The Understanding of Arithmetic Possessed by Teachers," *Elementary School Journal,* LIII (May, 1953), 501-7.

Paukner, Lillian C. "Milwaukee's In-service Arithmetic Education Program," *Arithmetic Teacher,* IV (November, 1957), 222-23.

Phillips, Clarence. "Background and Mathematical Achievement of Elementary Education Students in Arithmetic for Teachers," *School Science and Mathematics,* LIII (January, 1953), 48-52.

———. "A Combined Content-Methods Course for Elementary Mathematics Teachers," *The Arithmetic Teacher,* VII (March, 1960), 138-40.

Rappaport, D. "Preparation of Teachers of Arithmetic," *School Science and Mathematics,* LVIII (November, 1958), 636-43.

Reeve, W. D., and Homer Howard. "Student Teaching in Mathematics," *Mathematics Teacher,* XL (March, 1947), 99-132.

Robinson, Arthur E. *The Professional Education of Elementary Teachers in the Field of Arithmetic,* Contributions to Education, No. 672. New York: Teachers College, Columbia University, 1936.

Rhoads, Margaret V. *The Training of Elementary School Arithmetic Teachers,* Education Department Project Report. New York: Columbia University, 1950.

Roudebush, Elizabeth J. "Professional Classes of the Seattle Public Schools," *Emerging Practices in Mathematics Education,* National Council of Teachers of Mathematics, Twenty-second Yearbook (1954). Washington, D.C.: The Council, 252-55.

Schaaf, W. L. "Arithmetic for Arithmetic Teachers," *School Science and Mathematics,* LIII (October, 1953), 537-43.

Stipanowich, J. "The Mathematical Training of Prospective Elementary-School Teachers," *Arithmetic Teacher*, IV (December, 1957), 240-48.

Sueltz, B. "Arithmetic in Teacher Training," *Mathematics Teacher*, XXV (February, 1932), 95-108.

Taylor, E. H. "Mathematics for a Four-Year Course for Teachers in the Elementary School," *School Science and Mathematics*, XXXVIII (May, 1938), 499-503.

————. "The Preparation of Teachers of Arithmetic in Teachers Colleges," *The Mathematics Teacher*, XXX (January, 1937), 10-14.

Waggoner, W. "Improving the Mathematical Competency of Teachers in Training," *Arithmetic Teacher*, V (March, 1958), 84-86.

Weaver, J. F. "A Crucial Aspect of Meaningful Arithmetic Instruction," *Mathematics Teacher*, XLIII (March, 1950), 112-17.

————. "A Crucial Problem in the Preparation of Elementary-School Teachers," *Elementary School Journal*, LVI (February, 1956), 255-61.

————. "Teacher Education in Arithmetic," *Review of Educational Research Bulletin*, XXI (October, 1951), 317-20.

Wilburn, D. Banks, and G. Max Wingo. "In-service Development of Teachers of Arithmetic," *The Teaching of Arithmetic*, National Society for Study of Education, Fiftieth Yearbook (1950). Chicago: University of Chicago Press, Part II, 251-68.

Williams, Catharine Melissa. "Portable Mathematics Laboratory for In-service Teacher Education," *Education Research Bulletin*, XXXIX (April, 1960), 85-91, 103.

Wren, F. Lynwood. "The Professional Preparation of Teachers of Arithmetic," *Arithmetic 1948*, Supplementary Education Monographs No. 66. Chicago: University of Chicago Press, 1948.

————. "Questions for the Teacher of Arithmetic," *Arithmetic in General Education*, National Council of Teachers of Mathematics, Sixteenth Yearbook (1941). Washington, D.C.: The Council, 290-303.

Yorke, Gertrude C., "The Preparation Needed by Teachers of Arithmetic," *Education*, LXIX (February, 1949), 373-75.

Young, Kenneth G. "Science and Mathematics in the General Education of Teachers," *The Education of Teachers as Viewed by the Profession*, National Education Commission on Teacher Education and Professional Standards, National Education Association (1948).

INDEX

INDEX OF SUBJECTS

547